PHOTOGRAPHY
ITS MATERIALS AND PROCESSES

by

C. B. NEBLETTE, F.R.P.S., F.P.S.A.

Counselor and Administrative Head
Department of Photographic Technology
Rochester Institute of Technology

FIFTH EDITION—THIRD PRINTING

D. VAN NOSTRAND COMPANY, INC.

PRINCETON, NEW JERSEY

TORONTO   LONDON

NEW YORK

D. VAN NOSTRAND COMPANY, INC.

120 Alexander St., Princeton, New Jersey
257 Fourth Avenue, New York 3, New York
25 Hollinger Rd., Toronto 16, Canada
Macmillan & Co., Ltd., St. Martin's St., London, W.C. 2, England

*All correspondence should be addressed to the
principal office of the company at Princeton, N. J.*

Library of Congress Card No. 52–5744

———

First Edition, 1927
Recopyright, 1954

———

Three Editions
Nineteen Reprintings
1927–1951

———

Fifth Edition, 1952
Reprinted September 1953;
August 1955

PRINTED IN THE UNITED STATES OF AMERICA
BY LANCASTER PRESS, INC., LANCASTER, PA.

CONTRIBUTORS

J. M. Calhoun

H. C. Colton

W. T. Hanson

G. H. Keyes

Charles Reid

M. L. Sandell

Alfred Schwarz

Silas Thronson

Hollis Todd

J. L. Tupper

Earl Van Lare

Lloyd E. Varden

William West

W. T. Williams

PREFACE

The number of colleges, universities, and technical institutions with courses in photography has increased considerably in recent years and with the increase has come a greater diversity in objectives and course content. For a long time, the objective, in most cases, was to give instruction in the practice of photography as applied to the student's major course of study, although in few instances photography was considered primarily as a branch of chemistry or physics. There now seems to be a growing realization of the need of an understanding of photographic technology even in a course whose objective is essentially practical picture taking. This edition, therefore, concerns itself with the materials and the processes of photography and less with its practice than previous editions.

In the preparation of this edition I have had the help of several members of the faculty of the Department of Photographic Technology. The first chapter was written by Hollis N. Todd, Chapter 6 by Silas N. Thronson, and five chapters on color photography by H. C. Colton.

Chapter 2 was written by Charles Reid, Chapter 8 by G. B. Keyes, Earl Van Lare and William West, Chapter 9 by J. M. Calhoun, chapters 10, 12, and 14 by W. T. Hanson, Jr., and Chapter 18 by J. L. Tupper, all of the Eastman Kodak Company.

Chapter 4 was written by Alfred Schwarz of the Ilex Optical Company, chapters 16 and 19 by Lloyd E. Varden of Pavelle Color Inc., and Chapter 22 by W. T. Williams of the Weston Electrical Instrument Corporation.

My thanks are due to all of these and also to M. L. Sandell who contributed the section on electronic flash lamps, S. C. Slifkin of the Ozalid Corporation who revised the section on diazo materials and to Allen Murray, Bausch & Lomb Optical Company, and Fritz Wentzel for a number of suggestion and corrections to chapters 3 and 7, respectively. My thanks are due also to my secretary, Mrs. Edith M. Sturge, who typed the manuscript and assisted with the proofs and to the Kodak Research Laboratories for a number of the illustrations.

Rochester, N. Y.
September, 1951

NOTE ON REFERENCE MATERIAL

Photostatic copies of articles and papers referred to in this book may be obtained, in most cases, at nominal cost from the Franklin Institute, Benjamin Franklin Parkway at 20th Street, Philadelphia 3, Pa.; the New York Public Library; The Library of Congress; the Department of Photographic Technology, Rochester Institute of Technology, and, by special arrangement, from the library, Kodak Research Laboratories, Rochester 4, New York.

CONTENTS

Chapter 1

LIGHT SOURCES FOR PHOTOGRAPHY

Introduction. Light is that form of radiant energy which is capable of affecting our sense of sight. Its exact nature has been a subject of much conjecture and experiment among physicists and philosophers for many centuries. One can conceive of energy as being transferred in two ways only: one, by the passage of a body from one place to another (bullets, for example); the other, by the passage of a wave motion (as in water waves). The ancients regarded a beam of light as a stream of in-

and the experimental verification by Hertz, of the electromagnetic theory of radiation, including light.

Electromagnetic Theory of Radiation. According to Maxwell's theory, light and similar forms of radiation are presumed to be transmitted as waves through a hypothetical all-pervading ether, such waves being characterized by moving electrical and magnetic forces.

The first determination of the velocity of electromagnetic waves was made by

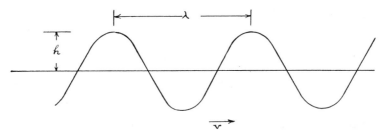

Fig. 1.1. Simple form of wave motion.

finitesimally small particles traveling in all directions from the light source. Such a *corpuscular* theory of light was accepted by most physicists until Thomas Young, in 1800, showed by experimentation and by mathematical reasoning that light energy must be of an undulatory or *wave* nature if such phenomena as diffraction and interference are to be explained in a rational manner. The work of such scientists as Foucault in measuring the velocity of light in different media, and Fraunhofer in establishing the wave length of various lines in the solar spectrum, culminated in the mathematical development by Maxwell,

Roemer in 1675. His value (obtained from a study of the apparent time of eclipse of a satellite of Jupiter as seen from various positions of the earth) was 3.0×10^{10} centimeters per second, a figure in remarkably close agreement with the latest values obtained by Michelson in terrestrial experiments (2.997776×10^{10} centimeters per second). This value is for radiation in a vacuum; in other media the velocity varies with the nature of the medium and the wave length of the radiation. In glass, for example, light has a velocity about two-thirds as great as in a vacuum.

If electromagnetic radiations are regarded as a wave motion, there must be associated with any given radiation a specific wave length. Fig. 1.1 represents diagrammatically a simple form of wave motion—a sinusoidal motion of a medium forming a transverse wave. The distance between corresponding positions of two adjacent waves represents one wave length (λ). If V is the velocity of the wave, and

The numbers given in the tabulation are somewhat arbitrary, inasmuch as the various kinds of radiation merge gradually into one another with considerable overlapping.

The tremendous extent of the electromagnetic spectrum is illustrated in Fig. 1.2. The characteristic difference between the various radiations is their wave length. For light, the part of the electromagnetic

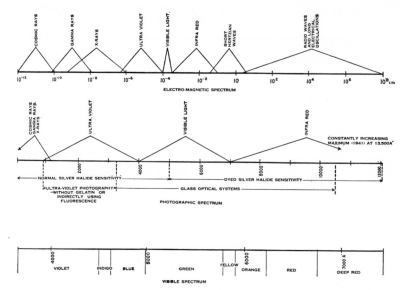

FIG. 1.2.   The electromagnetic spectrum.

T the time for one wave to pass a fixed point, then $\lambda = VT$. The quantity T is usually referred to as the *period* while its reciprocal is known as the *frequency* (f), the latter being the number of waves passing a given point in unit time. Expressing λ as a function of f, we have $\lambda = V/f$.

The various types of electromagnetic waves are shown in the following table:

spectrum is very small, and the waves very short; the frequency of green light, for example, is 6×10^{14} or six hundred thousand billion vibrations per second. Radiation of a single wave length is called *monochromatic*; of a complex nature *heterochromatic*. Because of the extreme shortness of the wave lengths of light, the customary units of inches or centimeters

Type of Radiation	Wave-length Range (cm.)	Manner of Detection
Radio	3×10^6 to 0.4	Electrical receivers
Infrared	0.4 to 8×10^{-5}	Bolometer; photographic emulsion
Visible	8×10^{-5} to 4×10^{-5}	Eye; photographic emulsion, photoelectric cell
Ultraviolet	4×10^{-5} to 10^{-7}	Fluorescence; silver halides, photoelectric cell
X-rays	10^{-7} to 10^{-9}	Ionization; silver halides
Gamma rays	10^{-9} to 10^{-10}	Ionization; silver halides
Cosmic rays	from 10^{-10}	Ionization; silver halides

are usually replaced by more convenient units, as follows:

Micron (μ) = 1/10,000 cm. (10^{-4} cm.)

Millimicron $(m\mu)$
$$= 1/10,000,000 \text{ cm. } (10^{-7} \text{ cm.})$$

Angstrom (Å)
$$= 1/100,000,000 \text{ cm. } (10^{-8} \text{ cm.})$$

Radiation from about 400 to 700 $m\mu$ is visible.

Discontinuity of Radiation. At the turn of the last century, new experimental facts were discovered which could not be explained on the basis of the electromagnetic theory.

When an object is heated to incandescence, the quantity of energy radiated constantly increases, and the character of the radiation is altered. The wave length at which the radiation is a maximum is shifted toward the shorter wave lengths with any increase of the temperature of the radiating source. The total radiation emitted by a perfect *blackbody* [1] varies as the fourth power of the temperature (Stefan-Boltzmann Law) and the wave length of maximum radiation is given by Wien's Law $(\lambda_{\max.} = CT)$. The curves in Fig. 1.3 were obtained experimentally, but a theoretical equation which agrees with observations was derived by Planck on the assumption that radiation is discontinuous, being emitted in definite, indivisible units or packets of energy called *quanta.* Another example of experimental evidence that is difficult to explain by the wave theory is the photoelectric effect. Hertz observed that a spark passes more readily between electrodes when they are illuminated, and other observers discovered that plates of certain metals emit electrons when exposed

---

[1] A blackbody is one that would absorb all radiation falling upon it; it also would radiate more energy than any other body at the same temperature.

to light. These observations resulted in a wider acceptance of the quantum theory which is the simplest explanation of the observed facts.

Radiation, including light, is now regarded as being composed of bundles of energy which have definite wave properties. Perhaps the nature of light may be best expressed as being undulatory and/or corpuscular, depending entirely on the physical phenomena which are to be explained.

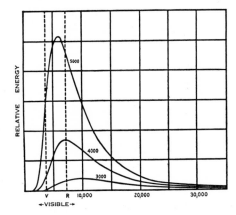

FIG. 1.3. Spectral energy curves.

The wave theory is usually employed when explaining diffraction and interference; the quantum theory is a more satisfactory explanation for the photoelectric and photochemical effects.

Intensity of Light. The intensity of a source is expressed in *candles or candlepower.* This term comes to us from the days when candles were the only reliable source of artificial light. The difficulty of obtaining standardized, constant sources using actual candles has led to the use of carefully calibrated incandescent electric lamps as standards.

The *foot-candle* is a unit of illumination, indicating the rate at which light falls on a surface; one foot-candle may be thought of as the intensity of light on a surface all parts of which are one foot from a source whose intensity is one candle. The intensity of illumination on a surface is directly proportional to the intensity of the source, and inversely proportional to the square of the distance of the surface from the source.

Spectral Energy and Color Temperature. It has been shown that the energy appearing at any wave length is dependent upon the temperature to which the body is heated. The curves are strictly correct only for a theoretical blackbody, but are satisfactory approximations for many actual objects, including for example the tungsten filaments of incandescent lamps. In fact, any object which is not strongly colored (i.e., a gray body) is likely to give, at any temperature, a curve of distribution of emitted energy having a shape substantially the same as that from a blackbody, differing only in that less energy is produced at all wave lengths.

The foregoing statements apply only to incandescent solids, liquids, and, in part, to highly compressed gases. Gases at nearly normal or reduced pressures do not produce continuous radiation, but instead radiation at (usually) widely separated points in the spectrum, with little or no energy being emitted at intermediate wave lengths. Temperature has little effect upon the wave length (or wave-length range) of the radiation produced which is determined primarily by the nature of the substance emitting the radiation. For example, incandescent sodium vapor gives substantially monochromatic radiation at one point in the spectrum (yellow) regardless of the temperature to which it is heated.

For solids and liquids, the fact that the temperature is the controlling factor in the *spectral energy distribution* enables the color of the light produced to be indicated by a number called the *color temperature*. When it is said that the color temperature

of a certain lamp is 3200°K, it should be understood that the lamp is producing radiation having the same visual effect (color-sensation) as a blackbody would have at the given temperature. Such terminology may be used even when the radiation is not caused by heat at all (as in radiation from the sky, where the color temperature may be as high as 25,000°K).[2]

It should be emphasized that the use of color temperature to specify the radiation from a source is reasonably accurate only when applied to bodies giving continuous radiation like that from a blackbody. It has, strictly speaking, no meaning applied to vapor sources (a mercury arc, for example), nor can it be used without qualification for a source like a fluorescent tube where part of the light is emitted by a solid, and part by a vapor. Where, as is often the case, color temperature is measured with a meter making use of a visual response, two sources may seem to the eye to have the same color, and yet their spectral energy distributions may be greatly different producing greatly different photographic results. The eye, for example, is insensitive to ultraviolet radiation to which photographic emulsions have their greatest response; the ultraviolet content of daylight may change without a noticeable change in the visible light.

Visual Measurement of Color Temperature. Two instruments have been devised to enable the color photographer to measure color temperature. In one of these,[3] two images of the subject are seen, one through a monochromatic filter, the other through a dichroic (two color) filter. These two fields are made to match by revolving a wedge which controls the transmissions of the two

---

[2] K is the symbol for Kelvin or absolute temperature, found by adding 273° to the centigrade temperature value.

[3] Lowry and Weaver, *J. Soc. Mot. Pict. Eng.* **32**, 298 (1939).

filters. The wedge is calibrated in color temperature so that, when the transmissions of the two filters have been equalized, the effective color temperature of the source is indicated on the dial of the instrument.[3] The other type makes use of a series of blue-red filters arranged on the periphery of a disc in such a way that three adjacent filters are visible at one time. A color temperature number is obtained when the central visible filter seems to the eye to be intermediate in color between a definitely reddish filter on one side and a definitely bluish filter on the other.[4]

Both of the meters discussed above are subject to error in their use, requiring considerable experience before usable readings may be obtained; it must be recognized that individual differences in color perception are important.

Photoelectric Color Temperature Meters. Visual errors in the measurement of color temperature are avoided by the use of photoelectric cells. One type of such an instrument compares the readings of two similar cells: one of these receives light through a red filter, the other through a blue filter (see *Functional Photography*, Feb., 1950). An attachment is available for some photoelectric exposure meters which similarly compares the readings of the meter through red and blue filters successively (see *American Cinematographer*, March, 1950). Still another photoelectric color temperature meter measures samples of the light in three spectral regions, instead of in two only (see *American Cinematographer*, Sept., 1950).

Light Sources. The chief sources of light are bodies or gases heated to the point of incandescence. The light of the sun, for example, is due to masses of hot gas under high pressure. In the tungsten lamp, a filament of tungsten is heated to the point of incandescence by the resistance offered to the passage of an electric current. In flashlamps, aluminum or magnesium is heated to the point of incandescence in an atmosphere of oxygen. In the carbon arc lamp light is produced from the resistance offered to the passage of an electric current across the air gap between the carbon electrodes which renders the latter incandescent. In gaseous conductor lamps, such as those employing argon, neon, mercury or sodium, light is produced from the conduction of an electric current through a gas. The fluorescent lamp makes use of another means of producing light; i.e., by fluorescence. The inside of the tube of a mercury lamp is coated with a phosphor which absorbs the radiation emitted by the mercury lamp and reradiates energy at other wave lengths. In the gaseous discharge lamp, a gas is rendered incandescent momentarily by the passage of a high voltage electric current.

Daylight. Daylight is a mixture of direct sunlight and reflected light from the sky and from nearby objects; the relative proportions of the two kinds of light depend on the location of the subject, the altitude of the sun, and particularly on the atmospheric conditions. With no clouds, skylight accounts for about 20% of the total illumination. Thin clouds reduce direct sunlight to about one-third of the intensity found with a cloudless sky, whereas skylight is reduced only slightly. With a totally overcast sky, sunlight is reduced to about 25%, and skylight to about 50% of their values when there are no clouds.[5]

The spectrum of the sun is substantially continuous, with the negligible exception of the dark Fraunhofer lines representing partial absorption of some wave lengths by the atmosphere of the sun. Energy in the near ultraviolet is relatively intense, de-

---

[4] Harrison and Harrison, Hollywood, Calif.

[5] Elvegard and Sjostedt, *Phot. J.* **86B**, 91 (1946).

TABLE 1.1.   AVERAGE COLOR-TEMPERATURES OF DAYLIGHT FOR VARIOUS SEASONS AND
WEATHER CONDITIONS
(LIGHT RECEIVED ON A HORIZONTAL PLANE)

	April and May	June and July	Sept. and Oct.	Nov., Dec. and Feb.
Direct sunlight alone, 9 a.m. to 3 p.m.	5800° K.	5800° K.	5450° K.	*5500° K.
Direct sunlight before 9 and after 3	5400	5600	4900	*5000
Sunlight plus light from clear sky				
9 a.m. to 3 p.m.	6500	6500	6100	*6200
Before 9, after 3	6100	6200	5900	*5700
Sunlight plus light from a hazy or slightly overcast sky	5900	5800	5900	5700
Sunlight plus light from 25% to 75% overcast sky	6450	6700	6250	....
Totally overcast skylight	6700	6950	6750	....
Light from hazy or smoky sky	7500	8150	*8400	7700
Light from clear blue sky				
9 a.m. to 3 p.m.	26,000	14,000	12,000	*12,000
Before 9, after 3	27,000	....	....	12,000

* One observation.

spite some absorption by carbon dioxide in the air. Molecular and dust particles in the air scatter the shorter wave lengths of direct sunlight; this accounts for the redness of the sun, especially when near the horizon. Skylight is blue by re-reflection of the shorter, blue rays. When the sky is hazy or overcast, the larger particles present scatter all wave lengths to approximately the same degree, and sunlight and skylight have about the same quality. Table 1.1 shows some of the variations found in the color temperature of natural light under various conditions:[6]

By international agreement, 5400°K has been accepted as a standard representing the color temperature of average, direct summer sunlight in the latitude of Washington, D. C., while 6200°K is a widely accepted standard for average daylight.

[6] Trans. *Ill. Eng. Soc.* **25**, 154 (1930).

Note: that daylight color temperatures obtained by visual methods do not necessarily enable a prediction of photographic effect to be made, since the proportion of ultraviolet radiation present cannot be estimated visually, but profoundly affects the response of an emulsion.

Sources. The maximum illumination available from the sun at a latitude of 42° is about 10,000 foot-candles. It is considered a very dreary day if the illumination falls to 1000 foot-candles; this compares with ordinary levels of illumination of less than 10 foot-candles in a room lighted with artificial sources. The eye easily compensates for wide changes in illumination, hence the difficulty of estimating exposures without the aid of a meter.

In the absence of clouds, the illumination from the sun depends upon its altitude, this being determined by the latitude, the time of day, and the date, as follows:

$$\sin h = \sin \phi \sin \delta + \cos \phi \cos \delta \cos 15\, t,$$

where h is the altitude of the sun, ϕ is the latitude, δ is the declination of the sun and t is the difference in time from true noon. Then the illumination on a horizontal surface from the whole unclouded sky is given by $H = 0.211 \sqrt{\sin h}$, H being the illumination in relative measures. The illumination from the direct sun can be calculated from the formula $S = 1.6 \sin h \, 10^{-0.1M}$, where M

stands for the thickness of the atmosphere through which the sunlight passes.[7]

The following graph shows the results of measurements of the intensity of daylight for various times of the year and for various hours before or after noon at one place on the Earth's surface.[8]

Artificial Light Sources. For the present discussion, these include (1) incandescent tungsten lamps, (2) flashlamps, (3) carbon arc lamps, (4) mercury arc lamps, (5) fluorescent lamps, and (6) gaseous discharge lamps.

Incandescent Tungsten Lamps. The incandescent tungsten lamp consists essentially of a drawn filament of tungsten in a glass globe containing argon and nitrogen. The energy required to force an electric current through the filament raises its temperature to incandescence. The operating temperature in the modern, high-efficiency lamp is in the neighborhood of 5500° F. The filament is consumed but slowly, despite this high temperature, because it is surrounded by inert gases which do not combine chemically with it and serve to retard evaporation.

The following tabulation[9] gives some significant operating characteristics of ordinary tungsten bulbs:

CHARACTERISTICS OF TUNGSTEN FILAMENT LAMPS

Watts Input	Color Temp.	Lumens per Watt	Fraction of Radiant Energy in Visible Range (400–760 mμ)
50	2670	10.0	0.090
100	2740	12.9	0.099
200	2810	15.1	0.109
500	2920	18.1	0.120
1,000	2980	20.0	0.133
30,000	3300	31.0	0.182

It should be noted that the efficiency (lumens per watt) increases as the wattage increases, due primarily to the higher operating temperature. Even the largest lamp, however, gives less than 20% of the total radiated energy as visible light; by far the largest amount of energy appears as relatively useless infrared.

The color temperatures given in the table are approximate only; as the lamp is used, the reduction in size of the filament and the deposit of evaporated tungsten on the bulb combine to lower both the intensity and the color temperature. Fig. 1.5 shows graphically the reduction in color temperature for a typical incandescent bulb as it is used.

The color temperature of a given lamp is determined by the voltage at which the lamp is operated, as shown in Fig. 1.6. Fluctuations of 3 to 5 volts are not uncommon in buildings with the usual wir-

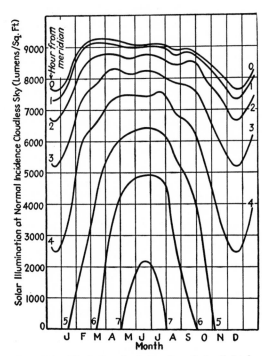

FIG. 1.4. Variation in intensity of daylight by hour and month (Henny and Dudley, p. 274).

⁷ Elvegard and Sjostedt, *op. cit.*

⁸ Henney and Dudley, *Handbook of Photography,* p. 274, McGraw-Hill Book Co., New York.

⁹ *J. Opt. Soc. Amer.* **17**, 329 (1928).

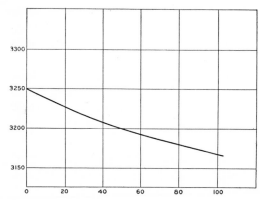

FIG. 1.5. Change in color temperature of a tungsten lamp with use.

ing arrangements, these variations being caused by changes in the load on the supply lines. If a lamp is operated on a long extension cord, the lamp will be operating at somewhat less than its rated voltage by reason of the loss in the cord. These factors are ordinarily not important with black-and-white photographic materials, although exposure is affected to some degree.

Color photography requires the use of voltmeters on studio and enlarging lamps so that the voltage applied can be accurately known, and voltage regulating devices to keep the voltage within the required limits. Transformers can be obtained which will automatically keep

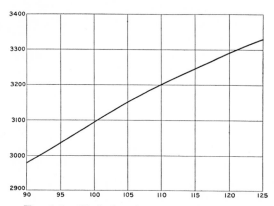

FIG. 1.6. Variation in color temperature of tungsten lamp with voltage.

voltage constant to within less than 1%; manually operated variable transformers, although less convenient, are otherwise entirely satisfactory and less expensive.

Photoflood Lamps. The Photoflood lamp is a tungsten filament lamp in which the filament is operated at a voltage much higher than normal. This raises the temperature of the filament increasing both the luminous intensity and color temperature but reduces the life of the lamp to from 2–10 hours as compared with 200 to 1000 hours for other tungsten lamps.

Flashlamps. Flashlamps may be divided into two types. The first, and more common, type consists of a glass bulb containing (1) aluminum or aluminum-magnesium in the form of (a) wire, (b) shredded foil, or (c), in a few cases, leaf foil; (2) oxygen at a pressure equivalent to about 300 mm. of mercury; and (3) a small filament covered with a primer and connected to the terminals of the lamp. When the current is applied, the filament is heated, the primer ignited, and, in the atmosphere of oxygen, the aluminum is consumed within the fraction of a second producing a light of high intensity. The second type, known as the Speed Midget (SM) lamp, contains neither foil nor wire filling; a heavy coating of primer carried on the filament and lead-in wires burns in oxygen to produce light. Combustion is more rapid in this lamp, requiring about 5 milliseconds after the filament is energized as compared with 20 milliseconds for the foil and wire lamps.

The following characteristics of a flashlamp are required to describe fully its photographic usefulness as a light source.

1. Spectral distribution of the emitted radiation.

2. The total light produced (approximately the product of the average luminous flux and the time).

3. The maximum rate of emission.

4. The relationship between the intensity of the flash and time; especially (a) the time required to begin to produce light, (b) the time for the lamp to reach its maximum rate of light emission, and (c) the time during which the lamp produces light above some minimum intensity.

It is now known that most, if not all, of the light produced by a flashlamp comes from the incandescence of the vaporized aluminum or the combination of aluminum and magnesium. The spectrum of the flash is characterized by bright lines, the temperature inside the bulb is above the boiling point of aluminum, and the residue from the flash is composed of spherical particles, characteristic of those from condensed vapor.[10] Listed color temperatures, therefore, are approximate only (between 3450° and 3800°).

It was originally supposed that the color temperature varied as the burning aluminum rose to its maximum intensity, but it is now known that the average color temperature is nearly constant, since various parts of the wire or foil are in different stages of combustion.[11] It is, therefore, unnecessary, even in precise work with color sensitive materials, to use open flash, or to use any particular part of the flash to get correct color response. The color temperature of different samples of photoflash lamps is, however, variable; color temperatures as high as 4700° have been measured for aluminum-foil lamps.[12] Such lamps are entirely satisfactory for use with both orthochromatic and panchromatic emulsions.

Flashlamps are supplied coated with a blue lacquer for use with color films bal-

[10] *J. Opt. Soc. Amer.*, August 1947.

[11] *Op. cit.*

[12] W. Leo, *Z. angew. Phot.* **4**, 28–32 (April 1942).

anced for exposure to daylight; clear lamps may be used with a suitable compensating filter for color films balanced for tungsten light.

Time-Intensity Relationships. The total light emission is governed by the mass of aluminum burned during the flash; the rate of emission by the size of the wire or thickness of foil with which the lamp is filled. Fig. 1.7 is a graph showing the

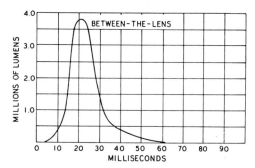

FIG. 1.7. Time-intensity curve of a flashlamp for use with inter-lens shutters.

time-intensity relationships for a typical bulb intended for use with between-the-lens shutters. It should be observed that:

1. The lamp requires about 10 milliseconds (0.01 second) to begin to emit light. This is the time required for the aluminum to begin to burn.

2. The lamp reaches its maximum rate of emission in 20 milliseconds.

3. The lamp completes its operation in 60 milliseconds.

4. The maximum rate of light emission is 2,250,000 lumens.

5. The period over which the emission exceeds one million lumens is approximately 12 milliseconds.

Fig. 1.8 is for a lamp intended for use with focal-plane shutters. Compared with the lamp discussed previously:

1. The time for the beginning of light emission is the same.

2. The time for the complete operation of the lamp is considerably greater.

3. The lamp reaches a high rate of emission at 20 milliseconds and thereafter builds up its intensity steadily for approximately 40 milliseconds.

4. The maximum rate of emission is less than the lamp intended for between-in-the-lens shutters.

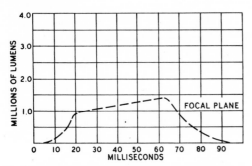

FIG. 1.8.   Time-intensity curve of a flashlamp for use with focal plane shutters.

This focal plane lamp contains two sizes of wire, or shredded foil: the finer begins to burn quickly and is quickly exhausted; the coarser wire which burns more slowly maintains the intensity for a relatively long period of time. The slightly rising plateau of the curve is designed to compensate for the acceleration of the focal plane shutter.

A similar time-light curve for the Speed Midget (SM) lamp is shown in Fig. 1.9.

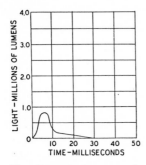

FIG. 1.9.   Time-intensity curve of the S M lamp.

The Carbon Arc Lamp. The simplest arc lamp consists of two carbon electrodes so arranged that they can be made to touch and, when sufficiently heated by a current of electricity, separated so as to leave a small air gap. In order to keep the current within limits a resistance is placed in series with the electrodes.

The resistance to the passage of an electric current across the gap between the two electrodes raises the temperature to the vaporization point producing an intense light. Most of the light comes from the incandescent electrodes producing a continuous spectrum; some light, however, is produced by the vapor as bright lines. Much of the latter energy is in the short wave-length range, which makes the arc lamp useful in photomechanical processes, in blueprinting, and other processes in which blue sensitive materials of comparatively low sensitivity are employed.

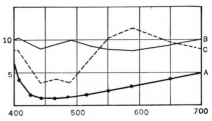

FIG. 1.10.   Spectral energy curves of the carbon arc.

Most carbon arc lamps today use carbon rods with the center filled with a mixture of inorganic salts whose vapors increase the total amount of light emitted and modify the spectral distribution of the light. The complexity of the line arrangement in the spectrum makes cored carbons produce what is practically equivalent to a continuous distribution of energy. Fig. 1.10 gives curves of spectral energy for typical carbon arcs.

Except in the special fields mentioned in a preceding paragraph, the carbon arc lamp has been almost completely replaced by tungsten and other sources which are clearer, more constant, require less attention, emit no fumes, and in general are better adapted to the requirements of general flood lighting.

Gaseous Conductor Lamps. Lamps of this type consist of a tubular bulb with an electrode in each end, the tube being filled with gaseous sodium, neon, mercury or another suitable element. When a current of suitable voltage is applied, the flow of current produces an arc, and light is produced as a result of electronic displacements within the atomic structure of the gas. The mercury vapor, or Cooper-Hewitt lamp, was the first to be introduced commercially and, until recently, the only one whose characteristics rendered it suitable for general photography. The spectrum is confined to four bright lines in the violet, blue, green, and yellow; the visual appearance being strongly bluish (Fig. 1.11).

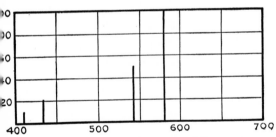

Fig. 1.11.   Spectral energy of the mercury vapor lamp.

Lamps of this type, therefore, are not suitable for use with color-sensitive materials in the photography of colored objects.

They are useful, however, for projection printing, blueprinting, exposing rotogravure and other pigment papers, and the copying of black and white originals in photoengraving and other photomechanical reproduction processes.

Among the advantages are the low current consumption, high degree of diffusion, and low operating temperature. A disadvantage for many purposes is that the lamps require some time to start. This makes them unsuitable for use where the light must be switched on and off as in a contact printer. A recent development [13] in mercury arcs makes use of a relatively small quartz bulb with massive tungsten electrodes placed close together. Cadmium is added to the mercury, and the pressure inside the bulb is relatively high. This provides a small, bright (160,000 c/cm.^{2}) source with long life and high efficiency (45–55 lumens/watt) and the numerous cadmium spectral lines fill in the gaps in the mercury spectrum.

Fluorescent Lamps. Fluorescent lamps may be regarded as a development of the mercury-vapor lamp. The vapor pressure and voltage are adjusted so that the discharge produces little visible light, but has a high emission of energy in the ultraviolet. The inside of the bulb is then coated with certain *phosphors* which are capable of absorbing energy of short wave length and re-radiating this energy in a longer wave-length range. The nature of the energy finally emitted can be controlled by an appropriate choice of coatings: e.g., calcium tungstate emits radiation over the range from 310 to 700 mμ, with peak emission at 4400; cadmium borate gives energy from 520 to 750 mμ with the peak at about 600. Many colors are therefore available; but, in every such lamp, an appreciable part of the radiation is from the visible lines in the mercury spectrum. For example, a 40-watt lamp gives approximately 8.2 watts visible light, of which 0.9 watts represents visible mercury radiation, more than 10% of the total. It is for this reason (the discontinuity of the spectral energy emitted) that any assigned color temperature is based on visual equivalence only

[13] *Amer. Cinemat.* (March 1948).

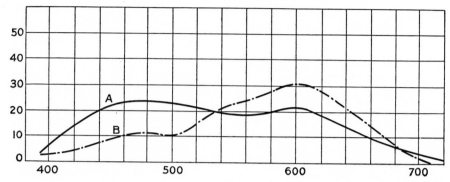

Fig. 1.12.   Spectral energy curves of the fluorescent lamps useful in Photography.

and cannot be strictly applied to photography without danger of serious error.

The lamp mentioned above gives 58 lumens/watt and is therefore one of the most efficient and inexpensively operated lamps available.   Fluorescent sources provide soft, well-diffused light desirable for general illumination without sharply defined shadows.   Conditions of operation have an important bearing on the efficiency of the lamps.   Cooling the bulb from its normal temperature of 100°–120° F. (as outdoors, or by drafts) lowers the output appreciably.   Baffles used with some lamps may cause local cooling, resulting in deposition of liquid mercury and loss of light.   Frequent starting is the most important factor in reducing the life of the tubes because the tungsten filament deteriorates.   As the end of the lamp's life is approached, starting is noticeably slower, and eventually the lamp flickers instead of glowing continuously; simultaneously black deposits appear on the tube coatings, especially near the ends.   It is economical to replace the tubes before they begin to flicker, since light output is low, and the flickering lamps damage the electrical starting apparatus.   There is a hardly noticeable stroboscopic effect due to the alternations in the current supply, most annoying with low-frequency (especially 25-cycle) currents.   The lamps continue to glow

for an appreciable time after they are turned off, making them hardly suitable for general illumination in a darkroom; they may be used in enlargers, in spite of the time lag in starting, if the design is such that the lamps may be on continuously. Since they develop little heat, the danger of damaging the negative is practically nonexistent.

ELECTRONIC FLASH PHOTOGRAPHY

The use of gaseous-discharge tubes for photographic lighting has considerably increased in recent years.   The spectral quality and softness of the light make it an excellent source for exposing black-and-white negatives.   The color temperature (about 7000° Kelvin) approximates that of daylight, making color photography possible with a minimum of correction.   In addition, the extremely short duration of the flash produces sharp pictures without fear of subject or camera motion and subsequent loss of the negative.   The flash may be repeated many thousands of times, and the amount of current used is very small, thereby making the use of such tubes economical, although the initial capital investment for the equipment is considerably higher than the more conventional light sources.

The principle is that of building up energy in a capacitor over a period of time

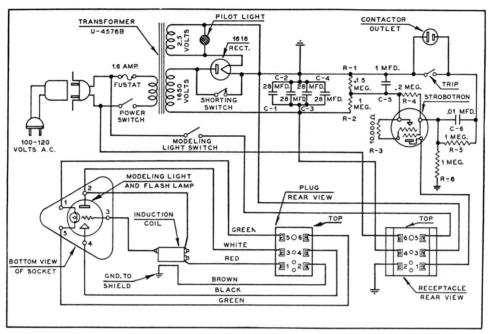

Fig. 1.13. Typical electronic flash circuit.

and suddenly discharging it through a gas-filled tube. The high voltage necessary is obtained by passing ordinary house lighting current through a high-ratio transformer. This voltage is then rectified to direct current with which the capacitors are charged. In battery operation, the direct current is converted to alternating current through the use of a vibrator converter, after which it is stepped up and then rectified as before. Voltages may vary considerably among different manufacturers, although the range from 2000 to 4000 volts is most frequently encountered. The capacitance ranges from 25 microfarads for the small, battery-operated portable models to several hundred microfarads for the large studio color outfits. A typical circuit for an average size studio unit is shown in Fig. 1.13.[14]

14 No representation is made herein as to the patent situation concerning flashtube circuits, and prospective users should make their own investigations of patents in connection with any circuits shown or discussed.

Characteristics of Electronic Flashtubes. The conventional form of flashtube is a long slender glass or quartz tube commonly wound into a helix to present a more concentrated light source. It is filled with an inert gas, generally xenon, at partial pressure. Electrodes are attached at either end and a third, called the "starting band," is in external contact with the helix. Some models incorporate a tungsten-filament lamp within the helix in order to obtain a preview of the lighting to be expected. A protective glass envelope, which may be slightly frosted for better diffusion of the light, encloses the whole assembly. Another type of flashtube has the lower end of the helix open and uses only two electrodes.

Methods of Initiating the Flash. There are two methods currently employed for firing the flashtube. In the Edgerton circuit, the voltage of the capacitor is across the flashtube at all times that the power is

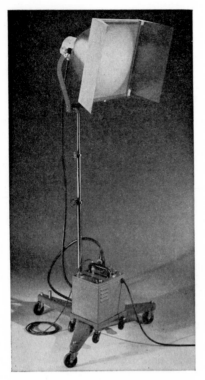

FIG. 1.14. Kodatron studio speed lamp,
Model 2.

on, but the tube does not flash because the internal gas pressure is so adjusted as to give a "stand-off" value greater than the voltage applied. To initiate the flash, the internal resistance of the tube must be momentarily reduced to permit the stored energy of the capacitor to discharge through it.

A cold-cathode, arc-relay tube, capable of carrying high peak current, discharges the energy stored in a 1-microfarad capacitor, charged to about 300 volts, into the primary of a small high-ratio transformer or ignition coil. The secondary is connected to the starting band of the tube. The resulting pulse of 10 to 15 kilovolts creates a high electrostatic field around the coil of the tube, lowering by ionization the resistance of the internal gas, and the tube

fires, producing a brilliant flash of very short duration.

This whole cycle takes place in an incredibly short time. Cathode-ray oscillograms of the current and luminous flux show that after the trip circuit is closed the light is "on" in from thirty to fifty millionths of a second.[15] However, for the many applications of high-speed photography in science and industry, not only is such instantaneous response essential, but it makes synchronization of shutters for general photography both simple and accurate. It is only necessary that contact be made at the instant the shutter blades are wide open. Negligible current is required to initiate the arc in the strobotron, as the arc-relay tube is called, because the starting is controlled by potentials on the grids. As a result, no arcing takes place at the shutter contacts, and there is no shock hazard.

Speedlights not employing a strobotron-type (Edgerton) triggering circuit are usually fired by means of a relay. When this relay is energized by the synchronizer circuit, it closes the main power circuit between the capacitor and the flashtube. The sudden application of high voltage across the tube produces the flash. The use of a relay, however, introduces certain disadvantages, since the points have a tendency to stick and there is need for frequent adjustment. Moreover, the mechanical delay introduced by the pickup time of the relay makes for erratic synchronization at higher speeds, although this is not important for portraiture or general photog-

---

[15] In the large, high-voltage, high-capacity units used for color photography, an inductance is introduced into the circuit to limit the peak current and to reduce the noise resulting from the flash. This practice increases the time interval between the closing of the circuit and the peak intensity of the flash, but not sufficiently to alter the synchronizing characteristics of the equipment.

raphy where slow shutter speeds can be tolerated.

Because the tube in this type of circuit is fired without benefit of a high-voltage trip surge, the internal gas pressure must be reduced to a point at which the gas becomes conductive to the voltage of the capacitor. This results in somewhat less light for a given charge. The flashtubes used with this kind of circuit have only two electrodes, since there is no need for a starting band to apply the trip surge.

There is a third, although infrequently used, method for firing a flashtube which essentially combines the two methods described above. An inductance is connected in series with the capacitance between the two terminals of the lamp, and the mid-connection between the inductance and the capacitance is connected to the starting electrode. This system applies a surge of about double the voltage to the starting electrode.

Calculation of Energy Input. The energy discharged into any flashtube may be closely approximated by the formula:

$$J = \frac{CE^2}{2},$$

where J is the energy in watt-seconds, C the capacitance in microfarads, and E the voltage in kilovolts. For example, the first Kodatron Speed-lamp marketed by the Eastman Kodak Company in August, 1940, had a capaciy of 112 microfarads and operated at a potential of 2000 volts. The total energy discharged into the tube would be calculated as follows:

$$J = \frac{112 \times (2)^2}{2} = \frac{112 \times 4}{2}$$

$$= 224 \text{ watt-seconds.}$$

Actually, not all of the energy reaches the tube, as there is a small residual voltage on the capacitor, and some energy is consumed in ohmic losses in the conductors that interconnect the tube and the capacitor. These losses, of course, are usually negligible. It can be seen from the above that for a given capacitance the energy input to the tube varies as the square of the voltage. However, this is not necessarily an indication of the light output, because the efficiency of the tube increases with the voltage applied. For this reason, the intensity of the flash at higher inputs may reach a value approaching the cube of the applied voltage. Despite this increase in efficiency, it should be remembered that loading a tube beyond that recommended by the manufacturer will considerably shorten its life.

The flash duration is the product of the resistance in ohms of the flashtube and the rating of the capacitor in farads. As an example, the General Electric Flashtube FT–220, which is used on a number of battery-operated outfits, has a resistance of about 6 ohms when operated at 2000 volts through a range of 10 to 100 microfarads. Assuming a capacitance of 30 microfarads, the flash duration becomes:

Duration $= 6 \times 30 \times 10^{-6}$
$$= 0.00018 \text{ second.}$$

This is equal to 0.18 millisecond or 180 microseconds. The result is only an approximation, as this formula usually produces a duration somewhat too short, since the tube resistance is large during the initial part of the discharge.

Reference to the time-light curves (Fig. 1.15) will show the effect on flash duration of increasing the capacitance at a given voltage, using the FT–214 and FT–403 Flashtubes. At the high loadings for which the FT–503 is rated, it is necessary to include one-half millihenry inductance in series with each 100 microfarads of capacitance in the operating circuit in order to limit the peak discharge current

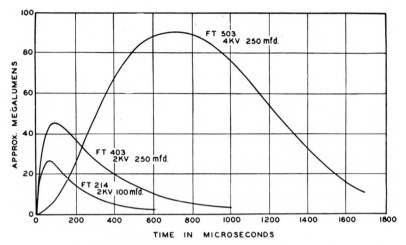

Fig. 1.15. Characteristic time-light curves for an electronic flash lamp. (*General Electric Co.*)

and reduce the noise. The curve for the FT–503 Flashtube shows the effect on flash duration when the recommended amount of inductance is used in the circuit.

For a given input, the output of a flashtube is constant within a very small percentage throughout its life. There is not the same loss of efficiency that occurs with tungsten lamps in which the filament evaporates and condenses on the inside of the lamp, darkening it and decreasing its output. The spectral distribution is dependent upon electronic molecular excitation and is, therefore, independent of voltage changes and of tube life. For these reasons, it has been proposed that a flashtube operating under specified conditions be used as a standard light source.

Determination of Exposure. Exposure guide numbers are convenient for determining exposure for a given set of conditions, since it is only necessary to divide them by the lamp-to-subject distance in feet in order to obtain the correct f-number to use. In the same manner, dividing the exposure guide number by the f-number will give the distance in feet at which the lamp must be placed from the subject. This

system is particularly advantageous with electronic flash because shutter speed does not have to be considered, the flash duration always being much shorter than the open period of the fastest shutter. A satisfactory exposure guide number can be obtained by using the following formula:

$$df = K\sqrt{nJM},$$

where d is the lamp-to-subject distance in feet, f is the f-number of the lens, K is a constant obtained from the square root of the American Standard Exposure Index of the film, n is the efficiency factor (about 35) based on output in lumens per watt, J is the energy in watt-seconds $CE^2/2$, and M is the per unit increase of apparent beam candle power resulting from the use of a reflector instead of a bare lamp. The value for M may vary through a wide range, depending upon the efficiency and angle of the reflector.

Assuming a value for K of 0.5, for J of 224 watt-seconds, and a reflector factor (M) of 10, this equation becomes:

$$df = 0.5\sqrt{35 \times 224 \times 10} = 140.$$

Dividing this number by the lamp-to-subject distance will give the desired f-number for the proposed conditions.

The following table gives the value for K corresponding to a number of exposure indexes. Other approximate values for K may be obtained from the square root of the American Standard Exposure Indexes multiplied by .0354, which is an arbitrary figure obtained experimentally.

Exposure Index	K Well-Exposed Negative
250	0.56
200	0.50
125	0.40
100	0.35
50	0.25

Using the values for K given above will result in a normal distribution of densities along the characteristic curve so that excessive overdevelopment will not be required. In an emergency, however, the values for K may be doubled, but a thin negative will result without overdevelop-

ment. A satisfactory compromise between these extremes may be obtained from the guide number chart shown in Fig. 1.16.

As an example, the dotted lines on the chart show one determination of exposure. The unit to be used is designed to place 2100 volts across the tube, and this is spotted by placing the point of a pencil at the proper point on the voltage scale. The capacitance for the equipment being used is 33 microfarads, so the pencil is moved vertically upward from the voltage scale until the 33-microfarad line is reached. (Since there is no line for 33, its position must be estimated as just past the 30-microfarad line.) Moving the pencil horizontally across the paper, the watt-seconds scale is passed and it is found that the rating of the unit is approximately 72 watt-seconds. The pencil continues to move horizontally until it reaches a film speed range of from 40 to 64, since a medium speed film with an American Standard in-

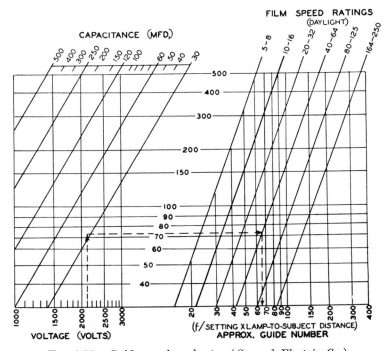

Fig. 1.16. Guide number chart. (*General Electric Co.*)

Fig. 1.17.   Light meter.   (*General Radio Co.*)

dex of 40 to 64 is being used. From this point, the pencil line should be dropped vertically to the guide number scale, and a guide number of about 65 read.

It is obvious that any such means of computing exposure results only in an approximation. When exposure is critical, as in the case of color photography or when a number of lights are used at various distances, some other means of calculating exposure should be used. Ordinary exposure meters of the photoelectric type cannot be used, since they are designed for measuring the intensity of a continuous light source. The General Radio Company manufactures a meter especially for use with electronic flash. The general Radio Light Meter (Fig. 1.17) gives a reading of the integrated incident light on a phototube. Light entering the aperture on the front of the meter, after being attenuated by a pair of adjustable crossed polaroid discs, strikes the phototube and produces current proportional to light. This current is integrated against time in a capacitor giving a voltage proportional to the exposure or quantity of light received. Readings

may be converted to *f*-numbers for use with films of different speeds by reference to the tables supplied with the meter.

Use of Color Films. As was mentioned before, electronic flash is well suited for exposing color films without the necessity for heavy filter correction.

The Ansco Corporation recommends the use of Ansco Color Film, Tungsten Type, with an Ansco Color Conversion Filter No. 12 over the camera lens. This film is much higher in speed and produces better color rendition than their daylight type of film. However, if their daylight type film is used, a combination of Ansco Color Conversion Filters Nos. 23 and 44 should be used over the lens.

The Eastman Kodak Company recommends the use of Kodachrome Film, Daylight Type, and Ektachrome Film, Daylight Type, with electronic flash. Naturally, their Type B color films which are balanced for tungsten illumination are not recommended for use with this type of light source because the higher color correction required results in a substantial loss of effective film speed. Since Kodachrome Sheet Film has been suspended, only miniature sizes of Kodachrome Roll Film are now available and for Kodachrome a Wratten No. 81C filter is recommended. In the case of Ektachrome Roll Film, Daylight Type, a CC–10Y filter is recommended, whereas for Ektachrome Sheet Film, Daylight Type, filter recommendations are made on a supplementary data sheet which is packed with this product. It is also well to point out that these filter recommendations may be changed from time to time and it should therefore be standard practice to consult the packaged film instruction sheets each time a new box of film is opened to be sure that the correct filter recommendations are being followed.

Conventional electronic flash equipment is often, though erroneously, referred to as a strobe or stroboscopic light. Stroboscopic photography is a specialized type in that a rapidly intermittent or occulting flash is used. This equipment usually employs a relatively low capacity, and some times high voltages, so that charging can be done very quickly. The intermittency effect is obtained either by electronic means within the unit or by means of an external circuit-interrupting device. The technique is that of illuminating a subject in action in a dark or semi-darkened room while the camera shutter is open. The result is a series of still pictures, often overlapping, on a single film. Because of the relatively long charging time necessary between flashes of conventional electronic equipment, it is not possible to interrupt the light rapidly enough to produce a stroboscopic light.

Chapter 2

PHOTOGRAPHIC OPTICS

The Pinhole. Photography in its simplest form is found in the use of the pinhole camera, which consists of a box with a pinhole in one end and a place for film at the other. To begin with, it is necessary only to remember that light travels in straight lines to see that in Fig. 2.1. light from A will pass through the pinhole and arrive at A', and similarly light from B will arrive at B'. In this way an image of the extent of the image is limited mainly by the cross section of the camera box. Finally, exposures may be made simply by uncovering the pinhole so a shutter is unnecessary.

The shortcomings are: First although all objects in the field of view are in focus, none is very sharp. The sharpness of the image depends upon the size of the pinhole. If it is too small the light passing through

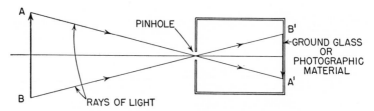

FIG. 2.1.   Path of light in the pinhole camera.

the object AB is formed at $A'B'$ when light from the object passes through the small aperture. From Fig. 2.1 it will be noted that the image $A'B'$ is upside down. This inversion is common to all simple camera systems, either with or without a lens. Many cameras have been provided with a mirror to erect the image in the finder, but the image remains reversed left for right.

The pinhole camera has some very real advantages over a camera with a lens and some serious limitations. The advantages follow. First, no focusing is required, for objects at all distances are about equally in focus. Second, the size of the image of the object is limited only by the length of the camera. Third, the image is always the same shape as the object, which is not always true when lenses are used. Fourth, it is diffracted (scattered) as shown in Fig. 2.2a. If, on the other hand, as in Fig. 2.2b, the pinhole is too large, the image becomes less sharp, as the bundle of light is too great in cross section. So it will be seen that there is a best size. The best diameter is found to be dependent upon the distance f from the pinhole to the film and is equal to about $0.03\sqrt{f}$. However, even in this case, the image on the ground glass is not very sharp. Secondly, although the size of the image formed by the pinhole is limited only by the length of the camera, the brightness of the image—which is low at best—decreases rapidly with the scale of the image. If the length of the camera is doubled, the size of the image is doubled also, but its brightness is reduced to one-quarter. Except for still objects, the ex-

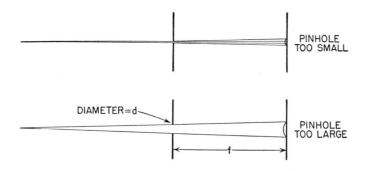

OPTIMUM SIZE — DIAMETER = 0.03√f̄

FIG. 2.2.   Effect of the size of the pinhole on the sharpness of the image; (a) pinhole too small; (b) pinhole too large.

posure time is usually too long to be practicable. For example, with reasonably fast film an exposure of about 5 seconds is required in bright sunlight. Next, although theoretically there is no limit to the extent of the pinhole image, except the cross section of the camera, actually the illumination provided by the pinhole decreases steadily from the center of the picture to the edge. The illumination at any point in the image area depends upon the size of the angle θ of Fig. 2.3. Even with a pinhole in very thin material, the brightness of the image

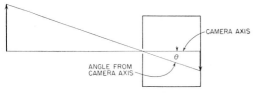

FIG. 2.3.   Effect of angular distance from the axis on the illumination of the pinhole image.

when $\theta = 45°$ is only about 25% of its value in the center and decreases rapidly at still greater angles. This decrease in illumination away from the center places a practical limit on the picture area.

Refraction of Light. As already mentioned, light travels in straight lines. If a ray of light in air strikes the flat surface of a sheet of glass at an angle, as in Fig.

2.4, it is divided into two parts, one of which enters the glass but with a change in direction, while the other is reflected back into air. The angle of the reflected ray to the surface, r, is equal to the angle of incidence i. This is the law of reflection.

The change in direction of that part of the light which enters the glass is due to

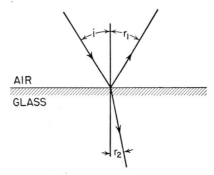

FIG. 2.4.   Reflection and refraction at a glass surface.

the difference in the speed of light in air and in glass. The ratio of the speeds of light in the two media is called the *index of refraction.*

$$n = \frac{\text{Speed of light in air}}{\text{Speed of light in glass}}. \quad (1)$$

This index, n, is related to the angle i at which light strikes a surface and to the angle r_2 at which it passes into the second material, as follows:

$$n = \frac{\sin i}{\sin r_2}. \qquad (2)$$

This is a very useful formula, for, if the value of n is known, the angle through which a ray of light will be bent as it passes from one medium to the next can be predicted.

Types of Simple Lenses. There are two different types of simple lenses: *positive* lenses and *negative* lenses. Fig. 2.5 illus-

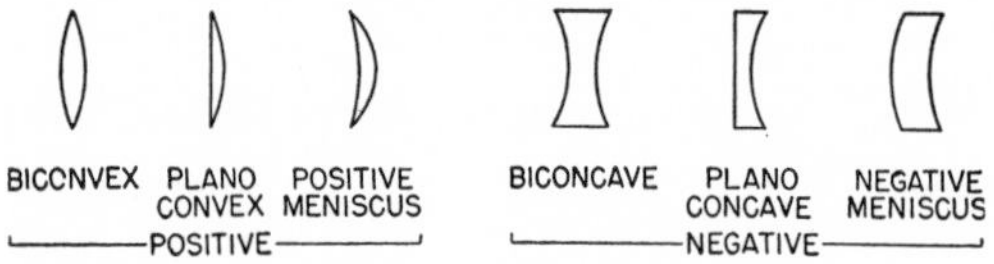

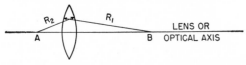

FIG. 2.5. Types of simple lenses.

trates the forms each type may have. These are also known respectively as *collective* and *dispersive* lenses, because the positive lens collects the light and forms an image of the source, whereas the negative lens spreads out the light.

Positive Lenses. The radius of each spherical surface of the lens is called its

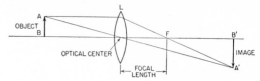

FIG. 2.6. Radii of curvature of lens surface.

radius of curvature. In Fig. 2.6 these are designated R_1 and R_2. The line joining the centers A and B of these two spherical surfaces is known as the lens axis, or optical axis. There is another property of a lens which must be mentioned here. With the pinhole the size of the image is limited only by the length of the camera; however, when an image of a distant object is formed by a lens, the image has a fixed size and position with respect to the lens. The property of the lens which determines the image

size is called its focal length. In a simple lens, as shown in Fig. 2.7, the image of a very distant object (usually said to be at

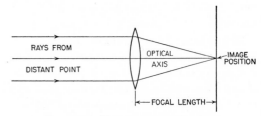

FIG. 2.7. Focal length of a lens.

infinity) is formed at a distance from the lens about equal to its focal length.

The relation between the index of refraction of the glass, the radii of curvature of the lens, and the focal length of the lens may be represented as:

$$\frac{1}{f} = (n - 1) \left(\frac{1}{R_1} + \frac{1}{R_2} \right), \qquad (3)$$

where n is the index of refraction of the glass in the lens; R_1, R_2 are the radii of curvature of the lens surfaces; and f is the focal length of the lens.

In Fig. 2.8 an object AB at B is imaged by a lens L as $A'B'$ at B'. The lines drawn in the figure represent rays of light coming from A. By drawing these particular rays from A, the position of its image A' can be determined. The first ray drawn is the one which passes through the optical center C of the lens toward the image. The second

FIG. 2.8. Position of the image formed by a lens.

ray travels parallel to the axis. This ray is bent as it traverses the lens and passes through the focal point of the lens. The meeting point of these two rays is the position of the image. It will be noticed that the image is inverted.

This image is said to be a real image, as light really passes through the image points, and if the light falls on a piece of paper placed at $A'B'$, the image is actually visible.

The Simple Photographic Lens. In inexpensive box cameras, there is just a simple lens made of one piece of glass. When this lens is of the right shape and is placed in the camera properly, the image it produces at small apertures is quite satisfactory for the average snapshot.

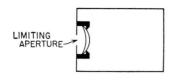

FIG. 2.9.   Single lens.

The single lens usually has the shape shown in Fig. 2.9, known as meniscus. A positive meniscus, as shown, has been found to give a better image than a biconvex lens. In front of it there is a circular aperture which limits the size of the opening in the lens. Not only does this *diaphragm* control the aperture of the lens, but its position is used to control the shape of the image surface and also to insure that straight lines in the object shall be as straight as possible in the image. If the latter is not the case, the lens is said to have *distortion* which sometimes is bad enough to be seen easily, as shown in Fig. 2.10 in rather exaggerated cases. If the diaphragm is placed behind the lens, the

result is termed *pincushion* distortion; in front of the lens, it is called *barrel* distortion.

Even in rather inexpensive cameras, apertures of different sizes, frequently known as stops, are provided to control the amount of light passing through the lens and thus regulate the exposure independently of the shutter speed. Since the lens transmits far more light than a pinhole, the time of exposure is much less.

But now, both the size and the position of the image are determined by the focal length of the lens, and the image of all distant objects is found at a fixed distance from the lens. The extent of the picture, or *field of view*, as illustrated in Fig. 2.11, is limited by the ability of the lens to form a clear image only over a confined area, or *field*, as it is usually called. In fact, with simple lenses, the clarity of the image decreases steadily with the distance from the picture center.

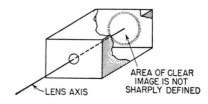

FIG. 2.11.   Field of a simple photographic lens.

For a simple lens, it has been found that the best image is not formed on a flat surface but on a saucer-shaped surface with the concave side toward the lens. In some inexpensive cameras where the lens is in front of the diaphragm, the picture area has been increased somewhat by curving the film to approximate the saucer shape, as in Fig. 2.12.

Single lenses of this type must be used at a rather small aperture, otherwise the image will not be sufficiently sharp. This small aperture may require exposures which are too long for moving objects, or when making pictures in the shade or in dull

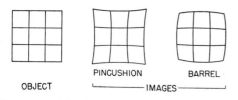

FIG. 2.10.   Linear distortion produced by single lens; (a) *barrel* distortion; (b) *pincushion* distortion.

light. Under such conditions, lenses with a larger aperture are required. Furthermore, with single lenses, the sharpness of the image, particularly away from the center, leaves much to be desired. To improve

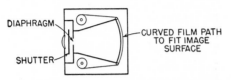

Fig. 2.12. Camera with curved film surface to increase the field of the lens.

the definition and at the same time increase the aperture, it is necessary to discard the single lens for more complex types.

Aberrations. First, however, it is necessary to discuss the behavior of light a little further. Up to the present the word light has been used to describe light of all colors indiscriminately. It has also been assumed that all the light from a point in the object can be brought to a focus at the corresponding point in the image. This assumption has been correct to a sufficient degree.

If, however, the image from a simple single lens is examined more closely, several things may be noted. First, the light which passes through the edge of the lens is brought to a focus closer to the lens than the light which passes through the central zones of the lens, as shown in Fig. 2.13. Second, if the image formed by the lens is examined as the color of light is changed from blue to red, it will be found that the blue light is brought to a focus closer to the lens than the red, as shown in Fig. 2.14. Thus, with a single lens, the focal length

and size of image vary with the wave length. The first of these defects, or *aberrations*, of a simple lens, is known as spherical aberration. The second is termed longitudinal chromatic aberration, or merely "chromatic aberration," and is a result of the variation with color of the refractive index of the glass. This difference is often referred to as a difference between the visual and chemical focus. The eye is most sensitive to yellow-green and, therefore, the visual image is formed by light of that color. Photographic emulsions have their maximum sensitivity in the blue-violet, so that

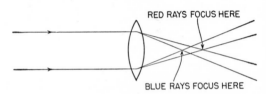

Fig. 2.14. Difference in focal point for different colors.

the photographic exposure is made principally by that region of the spectrum. Thus with simple lenses which are not corrected for longitudinal chromatic aberration, the sharpest photographic image is not obtained with the film at the visual focus.

It has been mentioned previously that a ray of light is bent, when it travels from one material to another, by an amount controlled by the indices of refraction of the materials. But a complication arises, since this bending is different for different colors; i.e., the index of refraction changes from color to color. It is this fact which causes the change in position of the image shown

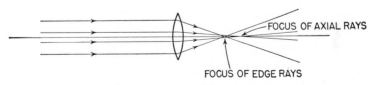

Fig. 2.13. Spherical aberration.

in Fig. 2.15, for the index of refraction is greater for blue light than for red, as in-

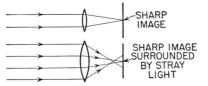

FIG. 2.15. Longitudinal chromatic aberration.

dicated in Table 1. In order to correct the color errors in lenses, different kinds of glass are required.

TABLE 2.1. CHANGE OF REFRACTIVE INDEX WITH COLOR

Color	Index of Refraction
Red	1.5720
Yellow	1.5755
Green	1.5812
Blue	1.5917

Optical Glass and Achromatic Lenses.

So far the word "glass" has been used indiscriminately; there are, however, many kinds of optical glass. These do not differ in quality, because all optical glass is superior glass, highly transparent, without streaks or stria, and of very uniform quality, but in refractive index and the variation in refractive index with wave length or dispersion (Fig. 2.16).

With a simple positive lens the focal length is shorter for blue light than for red

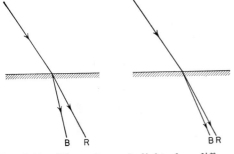

FIG. 2.16. Dispersion of light by different glasses.

TABLE 2.2. SOME TYPICAL OPTICAL GLASSES

Name	Index of Refraction	V*
Borosilicate Crown	1.51100	63.5
White Optical Crown	1.52300	58.6
Dense Barium Crown	1.61088	57.2
EK 11 (Nonsilica)	1.69677	56.1
Extra Light Flint	1.52301	50.5
Barium Flint	1.60530	43.6
EK 45 (Nonsilica)	1.80367	41.8
Dense Flint	1.61700	36.6
Extra Dense Flint	1.64900	33.8

* This quantity is inversely proportional to the dispersive power of the glass.

because all glasses have a higher index of refraction for blue light than for red. With a negative lens, however, the opposite is true and the focal length is shorter for red than for blue. Therefore, chromatic aberration may be corrected for two colors

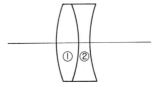

① CROWN GLASS n=1.573 v=57.4
② FLINT GLASS n=1.649 v=33.8

FIG. 2.17. Chromatic correction for two colors with a lens of two different glasses.

by making a compound lens of two separate lenses, one positive and the other negative, provided they are of the proper strength and the correct indices of refraction. Usually the adjacent surfaces of the two glasses are given the same curvature which enables them to be cemented together. This makes the two lenses a single unit physically, eliminating the reflection losses which would be present if the lenses were separated by air (Fig. 2.17).

Both spherical and chromatic aberration affect the definition of the image on or near the lens axis, i.e., in the central region of the picture. There are five other aberrations which must be considered, although they affect chiefly the sharpness of points away from the axis, i.e., toward the margins of the image. These aberrations are (1) astigmatism, (2) coma, (3) distortion, (4) lateral color or chromatic difference of magnification, and (5) curvature of field.

Astigmatism. This is the lens aberration which, when it occurs in the human eye, causes one to see vertical lines better than horizontal, or vice versa. With a lens the vertical lines are in focus (sharp) at one point, whereas the horizontal lines are out of focus (unsharp). If the focal plane is shifted the horizontal lines can be brought into focus but then the vertical lines are not sharp. In other words, either vertical or horizontal lines can be focused sharply, but both cannot be in focus simultaneously (Fig. 2.18). Although not easy to recognize in an ordinary snapshot, astigmatism may affect the definition of points away from the axis. A wire screen photographed against a well illuminated surface forms a convenient subject when testing for astigmatism. If astigmatism is present the image of the horizontal lines near the margin of the picture will be sharp at one point of focus while the vertical lines are out-of-focus. The reverse is true for a slightly different plane of focus.

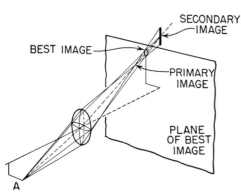

FIG. 2.18. Astigmatism.

In practice, astigmatism is lessened by the use of compound lenses having glasses of properly selected indices and a combination of spherical surfaces with the proper relation to each other. A lens corrected for astigmatism is known as an *anastigmat*, i.e., not astigmatic. Even in anastigmat lenses there is almost always some residual astigmatism, because it is only removed completely at one point in the field.

Coma. Coma is a very objectionable aberration if present to an appreciable extent, because the images of points off the

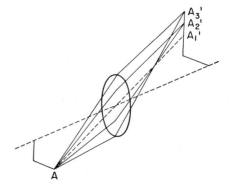

FIG. 2.19. Coma.

axis are smeared. It arises when oblique rays of light on passing through the lens are brought to a focus in approximately the same plane, but fall at different distances from the axis instead of being superimposed (Fig. 2.19). Like astigmatism it is limited to points off the axis and becomes rapidly worse as the distance from the axis increases. The elimination of coma from a compound lens is accomplished by using positive and negative lenses each of which suffer from coma but in the opposite sense. It is difficult to correct for coma in all the circular zones of the lens. A lens which is corrected for coma and spherical aberration is termed an *aplanat*.

SALT, "Graphic and Simple Method of Demonstrating Some Aberrations of Lenses," *Brit. J. Phot.* **76**, 308 (1929).

Lateral Chromatic Aberration. Lateral chromatic aberration is described more accurately as chromatic difference of magnification: in other words, since the focal length and, hence, the size of image vary

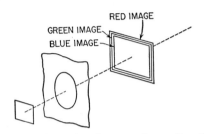

Fig. 2.20. Lateral color or chromatic difference of magnification.

with the wave length, the images formed by the different colors are not the same size. In color photography, this results in color fringes; in black and white photography it is not as noticeable, but the definition is affected by the overlapping images, especially at the edges of the picture area.

Curvature of Field. Curvature of field and distortion differ from astigmatism, coma, and lateral chromatic aberration, in that the first two are not concerned with the sharpness of the image of a point but with the location of the image point. With a simple lens, the image of a flat object, as for example a map, is curved, usually concave to the lens, as shown in Fig. 2.21.

Therefore, if the central portion is focused sharply on the flat surface of a film or plate, the marginal portions of the image will be somewhat out of focus. If the focus is changed to make the outer portions sharp, the center will not be sharp. This lack of flatness is known as *curvature of field*. Curvature can be reduced by using a combination of lenses of the proper curvatures and indices of refraction and by separating the elements of the lens and placing a diaphragm between them. The effect of the position of the diaphragm on the curvature of field with a single lens has been mentioned previously.

Focal Length of Complex Lenses. When a lens is relatively thin in proportion to its focal length (thin lens), it may, for many purposes, be regarded as a plane. Thus

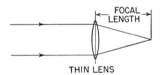

Fig. 2.22. Focal length of thin lens.

the focal length of the single lens in Fig. 2.22 may be determined by measuring the distance from the center plane of the lens to the point at which parallel rays of light from the left are brought to a focus. With more complex lenses, however, the thick-

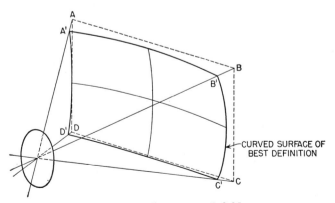

Fig. 2.21. Curvature of field.

ness of the lens system as a whole is much greater and we must consider it as two planes, which are known as the principal surfaces. The intersections of these planes with the lens axis are called nodal points.

Nodal points, illustrated in Fig. 2.23, are frequently separated slightly, and occasionally by a considerable distance. In working with thick lenses the object distance must be measured from the first or front nodal point, and the image distances from the second or rear nodal point. The focal length of a lens is the distance from the rear nodal point to the image plane for a distant object. The positions of these nodal points on the lens axis are not obvious, but

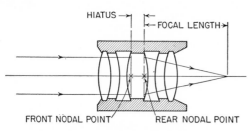

Fig. 2.23. Focal length and nodal points in a thick lens.

can be determined when required. The distance between them is called the *hiatus*.

One further word about nodal points. The lens designer can control their positions to suit his needs. Actually, in some lens designs these planes are crossed; i.e., the positions of the first and second nodal points are interchanged. In this case the hiatus is negative.

There are several special cases where a consideration of the positions of the nodal points may be of interest. Lenses of long focal length require a camera with a long bellows extension or, on small cameras, may be mounted in extension tubes. In this case they may be heavy and hard to support. This situation is much improved by the use of a lens with the nodal points designed to be ahead of the lens, as in Fig.

2.24. Such a lens is called a telephoto lens. The design of a telephoto lens frequently sacrifices quality in some respect in order to obtain the desirable short distance be-

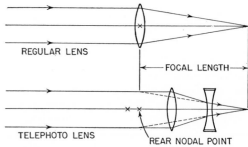

Fig. 2.24. Comparison between a normal and a telephoto lens.

tween the lens and the image plane. Modern telephoto lenses are much improved over earlier types, particularly if only a moderate telephoto effect is produced.

Another example of the manipulation of the nodal points is to be found where it is necessary to have an unusually long distance between the lens and the image plane. The wide-angle attachments for motion picture lenses are an illustration of this.

The Control of Lens Aperture. The amount of light transmitted by a lens is controlled by an aperture or *diaphragm*. In inexpensive cameras with single lenses, the diaphragm is either a single opening, or a series of openings in a sliding metal plate in front of the lens. In other cameras an *iris* diaphragm formed of blades of metal attached to a ring which, depending upon the direction of rotation, enlarges or reduces the diameter of the opening continuously.

A number of different systems have been employed in marking lens apertures. Some are purely arbitrary, as, for example, 1, 2, 3, 4. Another is the now obsolete Uniform System. Most lenses, however, are now marked according to the F/system. The F/number is the ratio of the focal length of the lens to the apparent diameter of the

TABLE 2.3.   COMPARISON OF SYSTEMS FOR MARKING LENS APERTURES

Uniform System				1	2	4	8	16	32	64
F-Number		1.4	2.0	2.8	4.0	5.6	8.0	11.0	16	22	32
Relative Light to Image	1024	512	256	128	64	32	16	8	4	2	1

TABLE 2.4.   STANDARD SERIES OF LENS MARKINGS TO INDICATE RELATIVE APERTURES

European Series of F-numbers	1.5	2.5	3.5	4.5	6.3	9	12.5	18		
American Series of F-numbers	1.4	2.0	2.8	4.0	5.6	8	11	16	22	32 etc.

lens opening as seen from the front of the lens. Since the focal length determines the image size, it is evident that the F/number expresses the relationship between the aperture of the lens and the size of the image. Therefore, if losses due to the absorption or reflection of light within the lens are disregarded, all lenses of the same F/number require the same exposure under like conditions regardless of the focal length. Thus

$$F \text{ number} = \frac{f}{d}, \qquad (4)$$

where f is the focal length of the lens, and d is the apparent diameter of the lens opening as seen from the front of the lens.

There are some disadvantages of this system, for it will be noticed that as the size of the number F (F-number) becomes smaller, the aperture increases; thus an $f/2$ lens is faster than an $f/4$ lens. Then, too, the amount of light that enters the lens changes with the *square* of the F-number rather than directly. Thus an $f/2$ lens is *four* times as fast as an $f/4$. This will be understood if it is recalled that the area of the circular aperture of the lens is proportional to the square of its diameter.

By general agreement, a series of F/numbers has been chosen in which the exposure changes by a factor of two. The series of F/numbers generally used in Europe, however, is different from that in use in English-speaking countries.

Commercial photographic lenses have been made with a maximum aperture of $f/0.85$. Such lenses are used to record the images formed on x-ray screens.

Focusing the Lens. It will be recalled that no focusing is required for a pinhole camera. The image is almost equally good over a very wide range of positions of the film. For the simple lens, with its relatively small opening, although the lens had to be placed at a fixed distance from the film, images of objects over a wide

DAILY, "Lens-Calibrating System," *J. Soc. Mot. Pict. Eng.* 46, 343 (1946).

GARDNER, "Compensation of the Aperture Ratio Markings of a Photographic Lens for Absorption, Reflection and Vignetting Losses," *J. Soc. Mot. Pict. Eng.* 49, 96 (1947).

TOWNSLEY, "An Instrument for Photometric Calibration of Lens Iris Scales," *J. Soc. Mot. Pict. Eng.* 49, 111 (1947).

BAEK, "A Simplified Method for Precision Calibration of Effective f/Stops," *J. Soc. Mot. Pict. Eng.* 49, 122 (1947).

BERLANT, "System of Lens Stop Calibration," *J. Soc. Mot. Pict. Eng.* 46, 17 (1946).

MURRAY, "Photometric Calibration of Lens Aperture," *J. Soc. Mot. Pict. Eng.* 47, 142 (1946).

TUPPER AND REID, "Lens Aperture Marking Systems," *P.S.A. Journal* 16, 776 (1951).

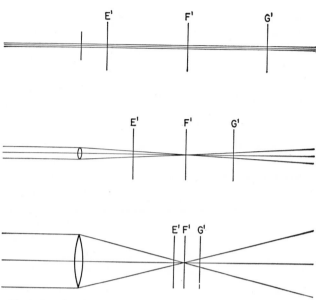

Fig. 2.25.   Variation in the region of sharp focus as the speed of the system
is increased.

range of distances appear sharp unless the object is too close to the camera.

By referring to Fig. 2.25 it will be seen that if the beam of light passing into the camera is very narrow, the size of a spot made by it will not be critically dependent upon where the film is placed. With the pinhole, almost anywhere will do. With the simple lens, the best place for the film is at F' (Fig. 2.25), where the rays come to a focus, but the size of the image of the spot is not much greater if the film is placed at either E' or G'. With a wide-aperture lens, the position of the film becomes more critical, for it will be seen that as soon as the film is moved appreciably from the focus of the lens, the image of a point becomes a blob of light and forms what is frequently called a disc or *circle of confusion.*[1] It is, therefore, important to have the lens at the right distance from the film; to do this, the lens must be focused

---

[1] This term is sometimes used by designers to denote the size of the smallest image of a point that a lens will form.

by moving part or all of the lens with respect to the film. The greater the angle of the cone of light from the lens, i.e., the greater the relative aperture of the lens, the more critically this adjustment of the lens must be made.

The Lens Law. It may now be of interest to inquire into the law that governs the position of the image formed, with respect to the lens and to the object. The law is a very simple one and may be stated conveniently in more than one form, but the usual one is

$$\frac{1}{u} + \frac{1}{v} = \frac{1}{f}, \qquad (5)$$

where u is the distance of the object from the lens, v is the distance of the image behind the lens, and f is the focal length. In cases where the nodal points of the system are widely separated, it is necessary to measure u and v from them.

It is not the intention to become involved in mathematics at this point, but some of the results of the law can be stated. First, if the object distance is very great, the image distance becomes equal to the focal length of the lens. Again, as the object approaches the lens, the image recedes from the lens, slowly at first and then with increasing rapidity as the object comes closer. Thus, in Fig. 2.26, if there is a series of objects, *A*, *B*, and *C*, in front of a lens, the images will be arranged behind the lens at *A'*, *B'* and *C'*, with the image of the more distant object closest to the lens.

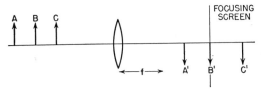

Fɪɢ. 2.26. Position of object and image.

If a ground-glass focusing screen is placed at the position of the image of *B*, only its image *B'* will look sharp, and *A'* and *C'* will look fuzzy. The same thing will happen when a film is placed at *B'*; only sharp pictures of *B* will be obtained.

In the usual hand camera, the selection of which object shall be in sharp focus on the film is made by moving the lens in accordance with a focusing scale, calibrated when the camera is manufactured. If the lens is set, for example, at a mark labeled 6 feet, an object at a distance of 6 feet will be reproduced clearly on the film. If the position of the lens for very distant objects (infinity) can be found experimentally, the positions of the other marks on the focus scale with respect to it can be calculated from the equation

$$\Delta v = \frac{f^2}{u - f}, \qquad (6)$$

where *u* and *f* are, respectively, object distance from the lens and focal length. For example, a camera has a 6-inch lens. It is desired to find out how much the lens should be moved forward from its position for an infinitely distant object when it is focused on an object 4 feet away. This distance is

$$\Delta v = \frac{6 \times 6}{(4 \times 12) - 6} = \frac{6}{7} \text{ inches.} \qquad (7)$$

(Note that *u* and *f* must be in the same units.)

The equation used is just another, and at the moment more convenient, form of the lens law just stated, and Δv is the distance the lens must be moved out from its infinity position. The formula can be used directly only when the entire lens is moved for focusing. The calculation of the scale for lenses focused by moving only the front element is similar to this, but the focal length of the moving element must be used and some allowance made for aberrations. Front-element focusing is often more convenient and less costly than moving the lens as a whole and is used for these reasons.

It is to be noted that the focus scale is dependent only on the focal length of the lens in question, so the same scale will do for all lenses of the same focal length, regardless of aperture.

Objects and Images Not in the Plane of Best Focus: Circles of Confusion. Only images in the plane of best focus have been treated so far, but it is also necessary to study the images which are not in best focus on the film. In Fig. 2.27 the lens is focused so that the rays of light from a point *A* on the object form a sharp image on the film. From a closer position, *B*, the rays cross behind the film plane, and hence instead of forming a point on the film plane, they produce a disc. This disc, the circle of confusion, is usually described in terms of its diameter. The image will seem sharp as long as this circle appears to the eye as a point. The diameter of the circle of confusion that can be accepted varies with the application. However, in general it must be remembered that the tolerable size of the circle of confusion de-

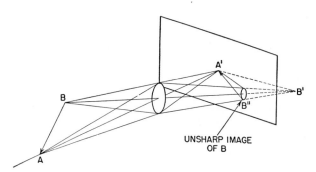

FIG. 2.27.   The unsharp image on the film.

pends upon the acuity of vision of the eye and upon the conditions under which the final photographic product is viewed, whether it be contact print, enlargement, or projected image. The permissible diameter of this disc must be small enough so that under specified viewing conditions it is impossible to distinguish it from a point.

Under good viewing conditions the average eye can distinguish two points as such, if they are far enough apart so that lines drawn from them to the eye make an angle of about 1½ minutes. This is quite a small angle and is equal to the angle between the lines drawn from two objects 3 feet apart 1.3 miles away, as indicated by the exaggerated angle shown in Fig. 2.28. To a very good first approximation at least, the permissible diameter of the circle of confusion is independent of the lens unless the latter is extremely poor.

Depth of Field and Depth of Focus. In almost all scenes, there are objects not only in the plane on which the camera is focused but also in front of it and behind it. In the last section it was pointed out that the images of objects not in the plane of best focus are recorded on the film as more or less fuzzy. Examination of the image on a ground glass will show that the out-of-focus effect increases gradually as the object concerned becomes more and more removed from the plane of focus. The effect is associated with a continuous increase in the circle of confusion just described.

It is, therefore, necessary to specify just how great the diameter of the out-of-focus image point can be allowed to become for the purposes in hand. In other words, a permissible diameter for the circle of confusion must be selected.

The *depth of field* of a lens is the range of object distances within which the images formed by the lens on the film have acceptable sharpness as defined by the selected circle of confusion. The distance on the image side of the lens corresponding to this range of object distances is called *depth of focus* (Fig. 2.29).

The magnitude of the depth of field available in a given situation depends upon four things: the relative aperture of the lens; the focal length of the lens; the distance of the object on which the lens is focused; and last, but by no means least, how critically the final photographic product is to be examined. Upon the last factor the se-

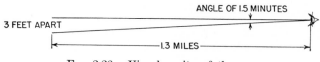

FIG. 2.28.   Visual acuity of the eye.

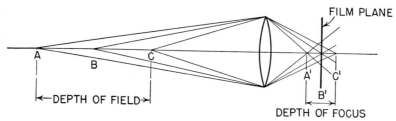

FIG. 2.29. Depth of field and depth of focus.

lection of the permissible circle of confusion depends.

The depth of field of a lens can be calculated if the above factors are known, and many modern cameras are provided with a depth-of-field scale to furnish the photographer with this information. The actual numerical selection of the diameter of the circle of confusion and the calculation of the depth of field will be discussed later.

Perspective and Image Size. At this point a new term, *perspective,* must be introduced. For the most part, when a finished picture is viewed, it is expected to appear as natural as possible. When the objects in a photographic print have the same relative size, shape, and position as they have when viewed directly, the objects are said to have correct perspective, and the viewing position is the center of perspective.

What determines the perspective in a picture? Once the position from which to take the picture has been decided, the relative size of the images which will appear on the negative have also been decided. This fact cannot be emphasized too strongly. From here on, the only influence of focal length is on the size of the image, not the relative sizes of the different parts of the image on the negative. Whether the lens covers a wide field or not determines how much of the scene is included but has no effect on the perspective.

It has been implicitly assumed in the foregoing paragraph that the picture resulting from any photographic exposure is to be viewed from the right place, i.e., from the center of perspective. Where is the center of perspective?

If the eye can be imagined at the camera lens in Fig. 2.30 looking toward the object, it will be seen just as it is viewed by the camera lens. If the eye is now turned toward the image, except for the fact that the image is inverted, the eye will see the parts of the image in the same relative positions as they were arranged in the object. Since a contact print is the same size as the negative, to be viewed cor-

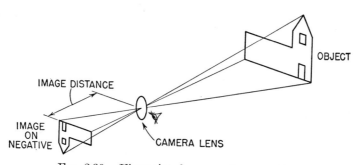

FIG. 2.30. Viewpoint for correct perspective.

rectly, it must be observed from a distance equal to that from lens to negative. This is usually about equal to the focal length of the lens. The perspective is then said to be correct. This distance is seldom critical, and viewing distances increased by 50%, or even more, are quite customary and not usually objectionable except when a very wide field is included by the camera.

It may be noted here that a great many camera lenses in the amateur field are only 4 or 5 inches in focal length. It is, therefore, not possible for the average person to view the resulting pictures from the position which gives correct perspective without some aid. However, since most prints from these lenses are contact prints, people have become accustomed to the abnormal perspective. In the contact prints referred to, the magnification of objects near the lens will be found to be too great.

However, to attain proper perspective, two common methods are in use. The first is by means of an appropriate magnifier; the second is by enlargement of the image either in the form of an enlarged print or by projecting the picture on a screen with a slide projector.

In addition to the increased visibility of detail in an enlargement, perhaps the most important reason why enlarged pictures and projected pictures appear so much improved over small prints is the fact that the enlarged picture can be viewed from its center of perspective.

Interchangeable Lenses. In selecting a lens the following must be considered in relation to the purpose for which it is to be used: (1) the focal length, (2) the angular field, or picture size, the lens is to

cover, (3) the relative aperture, (4) the requirements as regards definition, and (5) the scale of reproduction, i.e., the ratio of the size of the image to that of the object.

Although many cameras, large and small, have been designed to work with a series of lenses of different focal lengths, the following paragraphs are especially concerned with the miniature camera. After a brief statement of the advantages and disadvantages associated with them, the topics with which the photographer must be concerned when using the lens will be discussed.

Miniature cameras give picture sizes so small that the images must be enlarged to be viewed, whereas most other cameras produce pictures large enough for direct viewing when contact prints are made.

One of the principal advantages of the miniature camera other than the lower cost of film, portability, and convenience is that, for a corresponding relative aperture, the depth of field is much greater with short focus lenses than with the long focal length lenses which must be used on larger cameras. More specifically, suppose a lens of long focal length and one of short focal length are used from the same position, and the negatives are subsequently enlarged to the same size; the picture made with the lens of shorter focal length will have the greater depth of field. To obtain the same depth of field in finished prints of the same size, from two lenses of different focal lengths, it is necessary to stop down the two lenses so that the effective diameter of the lens opening is the same in each case. Furthermore, for the miniature camera, it is possible to provide an extended series of lenses varying in focal length from as little as 1 inch, to 10 inches, without the longer lenses becoming monstrosities. On a 4 × 5-inch camera, the comparable range of focal lengths would run from about 3 inches to 30 inches.

WALLIS, "Perspective in Photography," *Amer. Phot.*, September 24 (1945).

RENWICK, "Perspective in Photography," *Brit. J. Phot.* **75**, 750 (1928).

ASTER, "Perspective in Photography," *Photo-Technique,* January 22 (1940).

Even a reasonably-low-aperture 30-inch lens is extremely large and heavy.

Small size is not attained without disadvantages. First, it is necessary to have as fine-grained film as possible, which is accompanied by some sacrifice in speed. Second, every blemish on the film is magnified when the necessary enlargement is made. Third, image sharpness is generally proportionally worse when short-focal-length lenses are used. This means that from a large negative it is easier to get good definition of the object focused upon. These are some of the points to keep in mind when miniature cameras are to be considered for use.

Field of View. The cameras which have been mentioned up to the present are equipped with a single lens and encompass a fixed angle of view, as shown in Fig. 2.31,

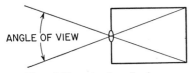

ANGLE OF VIEW

FIG. 2.31. Angle of view.

limited by the size of the camera. Many cameras, however, may be equipped with lenses of different focal lengths. By their use two different effects may be produced. First, as the lenses for miniature cameras vary in focal length from almost 1 inch (25 mm.) to 10 inches or even longer occasionally, it is possible, from a given camera position, to change the size of the image on the film by a factor of ten merely by changing the lens. Secondly, as the image becomes larger, the area included in

the picture becomes less. In other words, the angular field covered by the lens becomes smaller as the focal length of the lens increases.

In Fig. 2.32, the angle θ is the field angle of the lens. This is the angle used by the lens designer. Frequently the photographer uses the whole angle shown as β. When field angle is mentioned, it should be definitely stated which one is meant. The angle may be calculated from the relation between the diagonal of the negative and the focal length of the lens. For a given picture size, the longer the focal length, the narrower the field angle.

The maximum angle of field with any lens depends upon the relationship between its focal length and the diameter of the circle over which satisfactory definition is obtained. A lens made to cover a field large in proportion to its focal length is termed a *wide-field* or *wide-angle* lens.

Viewing the Print. In general, it is desirable to view the final picture from its center of perspective so that the view may appear to have the proportions of the original. It has been explained that unless some enlargement of the camera image is produced, this viewing distance should be equal to the focal length of the taking lens. Therefore, if in turn lenses of several focal lengths are used on the camera, each picture will require a different degree of enlargement to provide correct viewing. If prints are to be viewed at 12 inches, the degree of magnification required will be $12/f$, where f is the focal length of the taking lens in inches. But it is frequently not intended to produce the best perspec-

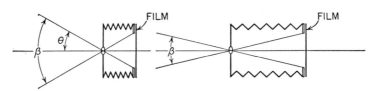

FILM   FILM

FIG. 2.32. Relation between angle of view and focal length.

tive. An image of a bird at some distance is taken with a lens of long focal length in order to examine the bird more closely; the picture of the interior of a room is made with a lens of short focal length with the intention that, although it may appear odd in shape, a large proportion of the interior will be included in the picture.

Choice of the Permissible Circle of Confusion. On page 32 it was stated that the acuity of the normal eye is 1½ minutes of arc. Therefore, if two points subtend an angle less than this at the eye, they appear as one. It may be assumed that, unless the circle has a diameter which subtends an angle as great as 1½ minutes, it cannot be distinguished from a point. If it is agreed that 12 inches is a satisfactory distance for viewing pictures, the out-of-focus circle must not exceed 1/200 of an inch in diameter on the print. Therefore, if a print is to be made by contact, the circle of confusion must also be less than 1/200 of an inch on the negative.

If the picture is to be viewed from its center of perspective, this viewpoint must lie at least 12 inches from the print. In the case that the negative is made with a 2-inch lens, it must be enlarged to 6 times its size if the center of perspective is to be 12 inches from the enlargement. The relation may be stated more generally,

Degree of Enlargement

$$= \frac{\text{Final Viewing Distance}}{\text{Focal Length of Camera Lens}}. \quad (8)$$

If the negative is to be enlarged as indicated above and is still to be viewed from a distance of 12 inches, then the allowable circle of confusion in the negative, which limits acceptable definition and hence the depth of field, must be decreased accordingly. For example, since a miniature negative taken with a standard

2-inch lens needs to be enlarged 6 times if it is to be viewed correctly, the permissible circle of confusion in the negative should be 1/6 of 1/200 of an inch, or 1/1200 of an inch. In practice the figure used is somewhat larger than this, 1/500 of an inch, as usually the degree of magnification is lower than 6. A figure frequently used is 1/1000 of the focal length, and experience seems to indicate that this figure is small enough. This corresponds to a visual resolution of 3 minutes of arc. It should be recalled that the choice of the size of the circle of confusion is somewhat arbitrary and depends upon the particular application.

A further word is necessary in regard to the choice of a circle of confusion for motion pictures and 2 × 2-inch slides. Here, in spite of changes in the focal length of the camera lens, all the pictures are likely to be viewed from the same distance. Therefore, the criterion for sharpness is usually held at 1/1000 of the focal length of the standard lens. For 8-mm. work this figure is 0.0005 of an inch, for 16-mm. work 0.001 of an inch; and for 2 × 2-inch slides it becomes 0.002 of an inch, regardless of the focal length of the camera lens.

Hyperfocal Distance and the Calculation of Depth of Field. After a specific value has been selected for the diameter of the circle of confusion, it is possible to compute the depth of field which corresponds to it for any focal length and object distance. For each set of conditions there is a distance, called the hyperfocal distance, which it is convenient to use in making such calculations. The hyperfocal distance may be defined as the nearest distance at which the lens can be focused so that all images out to infinity are adequately sharp. In terms of the selected circle of confusion a, the focal length f, and the F-number, the hyperfocal distance H is given by the equation

$$H = \frac{f^2}{a[F]}. \qquad (9)$$

The near limit u_N and the far limit u_F, of the depth of field when a lens of focal length f is focused on an object at a distance u, may be computed from the following formulas:

$$u_N = Hu/[H + (u - f)], \qquad (10)$$

$$u_F = Hu/[H - (u - f)]. \qquad (11)$$

In these formulas it is essential to have all distances in the same units.

The above expressions may be simplified if the object focused upon is always at a great distance from the lens in comparison with the focal length of the lens in use. The relations then become

$$u_N = Hu/H + u \quad \text{and} \quad u_F = Hu/H - u.$$

For a miniature camera with a 2-inch $f/1.9$ lens, it is usual to use a circle of confusion of 1/500 of an inch. The hyperfocal distance

$$H = \frac{4}{\dfrac{1}{500} \times 1.9} = 1050 \text{ inches} = 88 \text{ feet.}$$

Then for an object distance of 6 feet

$$u_N = \frac{88 \times 6}{88 + 6} = \frac{528}{94} = 5.63 \text{ feet,}$$

and

$$u_F = \frac{88 \times 6}{88 - 6} = \frac{528}{82} = 6.45 \text{ feet.}$$

It will be noted that there is a total depth of field of less than 1 foot, and it becomes even less with shorter object distances. Is it possible to guess the distance from camera lens to object within 6 inches at 6 feet? Some people may be able to do so, but many cannot.

There are two alternatives; one is to measure the distance with a tape and set the focusing scale of the lens to the proper figure. This is a good method, perhaps the best, if there are appropriate distance markings on the scale, and if the subject is one which is not disturbed by the process. The second method is to use a *range finder*, either a separate one or one fastened to the camera.

Range Finders. In Fig. 2.33, two rays of light may be seen coming from a distant object. If it is at a sufficient distance, these

NACHOD, "Depth of Field Chart," *Amer. Phot.* **39**, September 39 (1945).

PYLE, "A Depth of Field Scale," *Photo-Technique,* September 58 (1941).

BAILEY, "Focal Length and Depth of Field," *Amer. Phot.* **41**, November 8 (1947).

HASELGROVE, "A Nomogram for Solving Depth of Field Problems," *Brit. J. Phot.* **92**, 10 (1945).

DeBois, "Depth of Field in Photography," *Amer. Ann. of Phot.* **47**, 242 (1933).

ERIKSEN, "Depth of Field and Definition," *Amer. Ann. of Phot.* **54**, 192 (1940).

BROWN, "Theory and Practice of Depth of Focus," *Brit. J. Phot.* **69**, 492, 507, 521, 534 (1922).

SOUTHWORTH, "Numerical Expression for the Depth of Focus," *Brit. J. Phot.* **76**, 483–486 (1929).

COLLINS, "Depth of Focus and Its Graphical Representation," *Brit. J. Phot.* **67**, 659, 676 (1920).

LEE, "Chart for Finding the Depth of Focus," *Phot. J.* **62**, 229 (1922); *Brit. J. Phot.* **69**, 135 (1922).

BROWN, "A Simple Depth Chart," *Brit. J. Phot.* **70**, 775 (1923).

JONES, "Depth of Field Determination," *Phot. Tech.* **1** (October 1939), p. 17.

JACROUX, *Photo-Revue* **49**, 289 (1937).

LIESEGANG, "Depth of Field Calculations," *Phot. Tech.* **1** (October 1939), p. 48.

GORDON, "Depth of Focus in a Nutshell," *Amer. Phot.* **31**, 112, 114 (1937).

GAGE, "Focusing Scales and a Graphical Method of Handling Depth of Focus," *Amer. Ann. of Phot.* **52**, 181 (1938).

WHEELER, "Chart for Lens Calculation," *Photo-Technique* **2**, 29 (February 1940).

rays will both come from the same direction. One ray is reflected at right angles on mirror A, and then to a second mirror, B, which reflects it into the eye. The second ray goes directly through a half-silvered

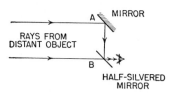

FIG. 2.33. Path of light from a distant object in a simple range finder.

mirror to the eye. Thus, although there are two images of the object, in this case they are exactly superimposed so that they appear as one. When the object point moves closer, as in Fig. 2.34, the two rays

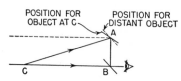

FIG. 2.34. Path of light from an object nearby in a simple range finder.

no longer come from the same direction, and the two images are no longer superimposed but are seen separately. It is now possible, by rotating the mirror A, to bring the two images together again so that they are superimposed. The amount by which the mirror A must be rotated, i.e., this convergence, depends upon the distance of the object; and the relation between the rotation and the distance is known. Therefore, the distance can be found in terms of the amount of rotation of the mirror A required to bring the two images together, or into *coincidence*, as it is frequently termed.

This is the range finder in a simple arrangement, and it is used in this form on some cameras. There are no lenses involved, so the image is the same size as it is

when viewed without the finder; hence, the range finder is said to have unit magnification. The distance between mirrors A and B is called the base of the range finder. For an object at some particular distance, the angle between rays 1 and 2 will be greater when this base is long, and hence the sensitiveness of the range finder is increased by increasing the base. The length of the base in a camera range finder is limited by the size and construction of the camera, but of course it should be made as great as possible.

There are many variations of the basic range finder. The movable mirror can be replaced by any device which can be made to change the angle at which ray 2 strikes mirror B.

It will be noted that the distance of an object from the eye is slightly greater as seen through mirrors A and B than as seen through the half-silvered mirror B directly. For distant objects this small difference is of no consequence; but for close objects it means that the two images are different in size, and in many instances this fault is objectionable because the setting of the range finder will depend upon the position of the image in the field of view.

It is frequently desirable to magnify the image seen through the range finder. This, in general, limits the amount of the scene visible through the range finder, and therefore a magnified image is seldom found where the camera range finder and view finder are combined in a single image field.

Types of Range Finders. There are two types of range finders used on cameras. In one type, the field of view in the finder is divided into two parts and is referred to as the *split-field* type. The field appears as shown in Fig. 2.35 when the range finder is not set. The image, as seen by reflection from mirrors A and B, Fig. 2.33, is visible only in the upper half of the field shown in

Fig. 2.35; that seen through the other side of the range finder is viewed only in the lower half. The range finder reads the correct distance when the upper and lower halves of the object match. In the other common type, the images from the two sides of the range finder are superimposed over

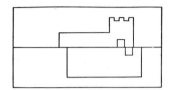

FIG. 2.35. Appearance of image in the split field type of range finder.

at least part of the field, as in Fig. 2.36. In this case the range finder is set correctly when the two images appear as a single image, at which time the combined image appears to have more contrast. Often one of the images is viewed through a colored filter to provide more contrast between the images.

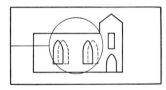

FIG. 2.36. Appearance of the image in a superimposed type of range finder.

When range finders are used on cameras, they are usually connected directly to the lens and are referred to as *coupled* range finders. Thus, when the range finder is set, the lens is at the same time focused properly. There is usually no scale which reads in distance except the usual focusing scale on the lens. Since the motion of the lens is not precisely proportional to that required to set the range finder, a cam is usually provided to transfer the motion of the lens into the proper corresponding motion for the range finder. Sometimes

this cam is on the lens mount, and sometimes it is within the range finder itself.

The sensitivity and accuracy which the range finder must possess are dictated by the maximum size of the opening of the lens which is to be used in conjunction with it. It may be proved also that if a range finder is adequate at one distance from the camera, it will be satisfactory for any and all distances. Thus, for example, at close distances, when the depth of field of a lens is least, the accuracy of the range finder is greatest.

View Finders. In all cameras except those focused on the ground glass it is impossible to see the image which is formed by the camera lens, since the film must be kept dark until the exposure is made. Therefore, some means must be provided for indicating the limits of the scene which the lens will include. This is accomplished by means of an auxiliary lens system which forms an image similar in extent to that formed by the camera lens.

Wire View Finders. The simplest finder system consists of a wire frame of appropriate dimensions mounted on the front of the camera. A small peep sight, which positions the eye, is provided on the body of the camera. The scene to be photographed is viewed through this sight, outlined by a wire frame. Such view finders are in common use, but are often flimsy. They also tend to be rather large, since the wire frame must be far enough from the peep sight to be seen reasonably clearly at the same time as the subject.

Small View Finders. On many of the early cameras, as well as on some of the inexpensive box cameras of today, the finder is merely a small-sized version of the camera itself. A short-focus lens forms an image of the scene to be photographed on a ground glass. Usually such finders are waist-level finders, so it is convenient to have a mirror in the system, as shown in Fig. 2.37, which erects the image.

A slightly modified version of this finder is used on many hand cameras. The ground glass is replaced by a second lens which collects the light toward the photographer's

Fig. 2.37. Ground-glass type of waist level finder.

eye. This type, shown in Fig. 2.38, is termed a brilliant finder and is also generally used at waist level.

In both of the above finders, the focal length of the lens which forms the image is so short that all objects in the field of view appear sharp. Such finders are not useful for focusing.

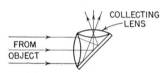

Fig. 2.38. Brilliant type of waist level finder.

Real and Virtual Images. The images which have been discussed so far are termed real images. Such images are formed by light which diverges from a point on the object and, after passing through a lens, converges to a point on the image. If a ground glass is placed at the position of a real image, it will be visible on the glass, and similarly it may be recorded on film. A single convex lens will form a real image of an object if the object distance is greater than the focal length of the lens. The image is inverted and on the opposite side of the lens from the object.

There is also another sort of image, the virtual image. Light forming such an image acts as though it came from an object at a certain position. The most common examples of virtual images are those seen in a plane mirror or through the simple magnifier, which is shown schematically in Fig. 2.39.

It will be noted that the image is on the same side of the lens as the object, is larger than the object, and is right side up. As mentioned above, no light actually comes from the position of the image. If the magnifying glass has a focal length f and the distance of the virtual image $A'B'$ is D, the magnification M for an eye position close to the lens is found to be

$$M = 1 + \frac{D}{f}. \qquad (12)$$

In this case D is commonly considered to be 10 inches, which is the minimum distance for distinct vision. Hence, a 1-inch lens gives a magnification of about 11. A sufficient approximation in most cases is given

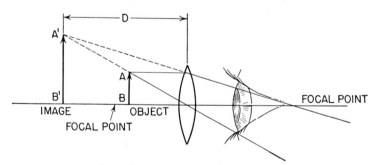

Fig. 2.39. The simple magnifier.

by dividing the distance D by the focal length of the lens.

A negative lens usually forms a virtual image. As seen in Fig. 2.40, the image in this case is still erect like the object, but is smaller. If the object is far away, the virtual image seems to be at the focal point of the negative lens. It will be seen that

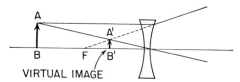

FIG. 2.40. Virtual image formed by a negative lens.

an extended object examined through a negative lens appears less extended. This property of a negative lens is useful in finders.

Eye-Level Finders. It has been stressed already that wire view finders are fre-

quently too large in area and too long between the eye position and the wire frame for convenience, and most waist-level finders are too small. By the use of a negative lens, the larger size of the wire frame can be disposed of, and the same scene can be viewed through a much smaller front aperture. However, this brings the apparent image of the scene quite close to the negative lens, and, therefore, in order to be seen clearly by the average person, the negative lens must be about 10 inches or more from the eye. This is a long distance for small cameras. Hence, a magnifier is used for the eye, which can now be placed closer to the negative lens and is able to see clearly the image formed by it, as indicated in Fig. 2.41.

The Albada Finder. One of the worst defects of the finders we have described is the fact that the negative lens, or the wire frame, not only appears ill-defined but is

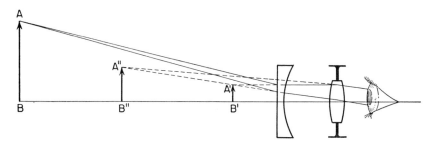

FIG. 2.41. Image formation in optical type of eye-level finder.

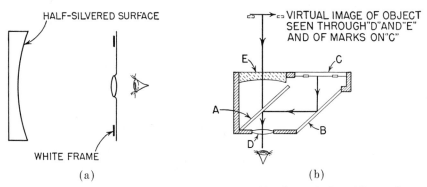

(a) (b)

FIG. 2.42. (a) The Albada finder; (b) Modification of the Albada finder (markfinder).

not in the plane of the scene, so that the boundaries of the scene change with the position of the eye in the eyepiece. This difficulty has been overcome in a finder designed by L. von Albada, by making the side of the negative lens facing the eye partly reflecting and by placing a white frame back near the magnifying lens, as shown in Fig. 2.42(a). If the curves are correct, an image of the white frame will appear to be far out in front of the camera in the plane of the scene, thus outlining the field of view sharply. This construction makes an excellent finder.

A modification of the Albada finder, currently called the "Mark finder," is shown in Fig. 2.42(b). By the insertion of a semi-transparent reflector *A* and a mirror *B,* an outline *C* indicating the limits of the picture area, illuminated through the ground glass, is made to appear in the same plane as the virtual image viewed through the eye lens *D*. Therefore, there is no relative movement between the frame and the image.

Supplementary Lenses. The simple non-focusing cameras will ordinarily not make sharp pictures of objects closer than about 6 feet.

But there is an easy way of accomplishing this, especially if very fine detail is not required. A nearby object may be imaged sharply on the film by the aid of a supplementary lens of the proper strength placed in front of the regular camera lens. The so-called *portrait attachment* is usually a positive meniscus lens with a focal length of about 4½ feet. If the object to be photographed is placed about 4½ feet in front of such a lens, the object will appear to the camera lens to be a long way off, but to be as large as if it were close. Since in simple cameras the taking lens is set to give a sharp image of a distant object, the nearby object will now be sharply imaged on the film.

It is quite common to express the strength of supplementary lenses in diopters. A lens whose focal length is 1 meter or 1000 millimeters is said to have a power of 1 diopter. The relation between focal length and strength in diopters is

$$S = \frac{1000}{f}, \qquad (13)$$

where *S* is strength in diopters, and

f is the focal length of the lens in millimeters.

The portrait attachment is usually ¾ of a diopter and hence

$$\frac{3}{4} = \frac{1000}{f},$$

which makes *f* = 1330 mm. or 4 feet 5 inches.

Stronger supplementary lenses than this, up to 3 diopters or more, may be used for the photography of small objects. In every case, if the camera lens is focused for distant objects, the object to be taken close-up is placed at the focal length of the supplementary lens. This focal length can be determined as shown above. Particularly with stronger lenses, it is desirable to use the camera lens at a reduced aperture, since the use of supplementary lenses disturbs the corrections of the camera lens to some extent.

Negative supplementary lenses can also be used, but only on cameras in which the length between lens and film can be increased considerably, for example, in cameras with long bellows. In this case a larger image is obtained from an object at a given distance than would be obtained with the camera lens.

It will be remembered that the size of an image of any object at a given distance depends upon the focal length of the lens. When simple supplementary lenses are used, they combine with the camera lens to give a new focal length. This focal length, *f_c,* of the combination of a camera lens of focal length f, and a supplementary lens of focal length f_s is

$$f_c = \frac{ff_s}{f + f_s - d}, \qquad (14)$$

where d is the distance between the nodal points of the camera lens and the supplementary lens. This distance can often be neglected in rough calculations; then

$$f_c = \frac{ff_s}{f + f_s}. \qquad (15)$$

When f_s is negative, f_c will prove to be greater than f.

Although it has been assumed that the camera lens is focused for distant objects, i.e., objects at infinity, supplementary lenses are often used with the camera lens focused for closer distances. Elaborate tables are usually available to give the proper object distances under all circumstances.

Optical Problems Related to the Stand Camera. Heretofore, the film plane has always been perpendicular to the optical axis of the lens, which in turn passed through the center of the picture area, as indicated in Fig. 2.43. Furthermore, the

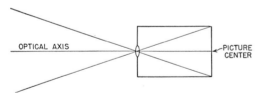

FIG. 2.43. Relation of the optical axis to the center of the picture.

picture area in any camera is usually fixed.

In studio and view cameras, the lens may be moved up, down, and sideways with respect to its normal position. In addition, it may be tilted, and the film itself may be tipped with respect to the lens axis, as in Fig. 2.44.

The distance from lens to film may now be changed by a considerable amount so that an object may be photographed full

size or even larger in some cases. The increased freedom of lens and film movement necessitates a re-examination of the optics involved because, unless thoroughly understood, these may be the source of much confusion, and improper use may defeat the purpose for which they are intended.

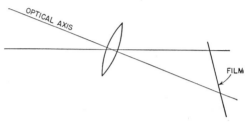

FIG. 2.44. Possible relative position of optical axis and film plane.

The field of view of a lens is circular in character and this may be seen if a lens of relatively short focal length forms an image on a large ground glass. The larger circle, as in Fig. 2.45, is often called the

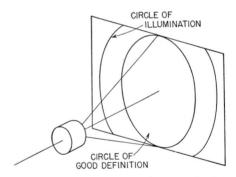

FIG. 2.45. Circles of illumination and of good definition.

circle of illumination. It is limited in size because, since corrected lenses are thick, as shown in Fig. 2.46, light from beyond a certain angle is cut off, or *vignetted*, by the lens mount. The circle of illumination is almost always larger in diameter than the circle of good definition, sometimes considerably larger. The size of the circle of good definition depends upon the design of the lens. In almost all cases the size

of this circle increases as the aperture of
the lens is decreased, until in some cases
the entire circle of illumination is filled
with good definition. It is usual to measure
the size of these circles in terms of the

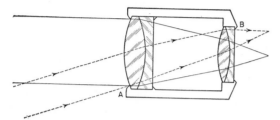

FIG. 2.46.   Vignetting by barrel of lens.

half-angle of the cone formed by the circle
as base with its apex at the center of the
lens, as illustrated in Fig. 2.47. Sometimes
the whole angle is used, and, therefore, it
is good practice to specify just what angle
is meant. It is important to remember that
the cone of light, within which a sharp
image is formed by the lens, acts much as
if it were fastened rigidly to the lens.

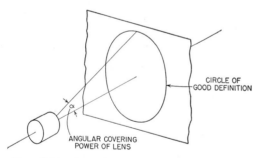

FIG. 2.47.   Angular covering power of lens.

The lens on a studio camera can be moved
further along its axis than is usually possible in ordinary hand cameras. If a study
is made of the lens formula,

$$\frac{1}{u} + \frac{1}{v} = \frac{1}{f},$$

or an experiment is performed with a
camera, it will be discovered that for a very
distant object, the image is at a distance of
one focal length from the lens, as in Fig.

2.48. As the object approaches the lens,
the image recedes from it, necessitating increased camera length or, in the usual
language, more bellows draw. When the
image becomes equal in size to the object,
the distances of both object and image from
the lens will be found to be equal and to
be twice the focal length of the lens. This

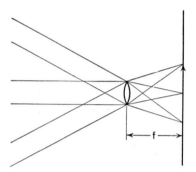

FIG. 2.48.   Position of the image of a distant
object.

distance, 4f, Fig. 2.49, is also the smallest
distance between object and image for a
lens of a specified focal length. The image
is now twice as far from the lens as it was
when a distant object was being photographed. Under these conditions, the lens
will give a good image over a much larger
area, in fact, an area with about twice the
diameter.

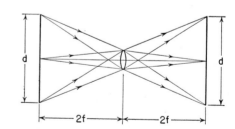

FIG. 2.49.   Position of image with object two
focal lengths from lens.

For this reason a lens with a focal length
much too short to cover a given size film
or plate for distant objects may very easily
cover it when copying to exact size from a
relatively close object. In general, as the

image size approaches the size of the object, the area of good definition increases. Under such circumstances, for critical work it may be necessary to use the lens at a reduced aperture, for the lens corrections change with objects less than 10 or 12 focal lengths away.

Change of Relative Aperture with Image Magnification. There is another effect which accompanies change in image size or magnification. In spite of the fact that the image of any object covers a larger area, the aperture through which the light is admitted remains the same. It should be fairly evident that the image has become less bright and, therefore, the exposure must be increased. There is actually a change in the effective speed of the lens. The regular *F*-aperture of the lens is given by the ratio of the focal length to the apparent diameter of the lens opening. The effective aperture of a lens of diameter *d* forming an image farther from the lens than the focal plane becomes

$$[F]_{\text{eff.}} = \frac{v}{d} \quad \text{or} \quad [F]_{\text{eff.}} = [F] \cdot \frac{v}{f}, \quad (16)$$

where *v* is the new image distance. This speed change is only of consequence when *v* becomes considerably different from *f*. For occasions when *v* is greater than *f* by more than about 15 to 20%, it must be considered. Since the picture area increases with the square of *v*, the percentage increase in exposure will then be twice as great, i.e., from 30 to 40%. When the image size is equal to that of the object, $v = 2f$, the effective aperture has been reduced to half, and the exposure required will be four times as great, since the same amount of light is now spread over four times the area.

Rising Fronts. As the lens is moved up and down (rising front) or is displaced sideways, the image also moves. If the object is far away, the image moves the same amount as the lens and in the same direction; in other words, it moves with the lens. Where the object is only a few focal lengths distant, the image moves more than the lens so that the movement *b* of the image is equal to

$$a \left(\frac{u + v}{v} \right), \quad (17)$$

where *a* is the lens motion, and *u* and *v* are the image and object distances. This relation may be seen from Fig. 2.50.

FIG. 2.50. Relative motion of lens and image.

Tilting Backs. So far it has been assumed that the plane of the film is always at right angles to the optical axis of the lens and that the principal objects are also, in general, perpendicular to this axis, as in Fig. 2.51. In the stand camera, both lens and film may be tilted. Actually, if parallel lines in the object are to be parallel on the film, the film plane must be made parallel to the object plane containing the lines, and both must be perpendicular to the lens axis.

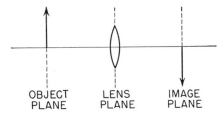

FIG. 2.51. Usual relation of object, lens and image planes.

But there is a much more general relation between image and object plane than this. For any plane on the object side of the lens, there is a corresponding plane on the image side of the lens in which the object is in sharp focus, as in Fig. 2.52. In this case, lines which are straight in the object remain straight in the image, but the shape of the image is no longer the shape of the object. This results from the fact that different parts of the object are

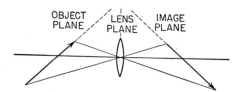

FIG. 2.52. General position of object, lens and image planes.

at different distances from the plane of the lens, which in turn means that different parts of the image are magnified by different amounts. In Fig. 2.53, $A'B' = AB \cdot v_1/u_1$, but $C'D' = CD \cdot v_2/u_2$, and since by inspection u_2 is greater than u_1, and v_2 is less than v_1, v_2/u_2 must be less than v_1/u_1. Therefore, since AB and CD are the same length, $C'D'$ must be less than $A'B'$.

There is a fixed and reasonably simple relationship between the plane of the object, the plane of the sharpest image, and the plane of the lens (i.e., the plane through the optical center of the lens at right angles to the optical axis). This is shown in Fig. 2.54, from which it will be seen that the planes containing the object, lens, and image meet in a line which is at right angles to the plane of the paper.

Under such circumstances it is very important to note where the optical axis of the lens points and to remember that the lens still covers with sharp definition only the same angular field as in normal use. In the above figure it will be evident that object and image are far from being centered about the axis; and, unless the lens used has a wide field of good definition, the image near A' may be poor. This is true in spite of the fact that objects, lens, and image seem to be lined up along the camera axis.

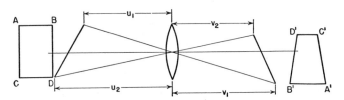

FIG. 2.53. Relation of shape of object and image.

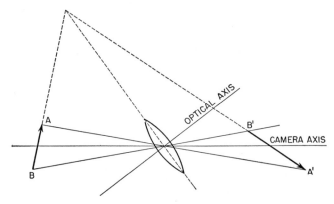

FIG. 2.54. Relation of image and object planes for best image definition.

When tilting backs or lenses are in use, it is well to remember the above relation, for lack of this information may require a lens to be unduly stopped-down in order to obtain good definition over the entire field.

Flare and Ghost Images from Photographic Lenses. It is not sufficient that a good photographic lens be relatively free from the aberrations which have been described. In addition to the usual image-forming light which arrives at the film, there is always some stray light which serves to decrease the contrast of the image. There are several sources of this unwanted light: the lens itself, the lens mount, and the interior of the camera.

As the light from the object passes through the several glass-air surfaces of a lens, some of it, as shown in Fig. 2.55, is reflected back from each surface. Except from the first surface, a fraction of this light is reflected again, and this small fraction travels back toward the film plane.

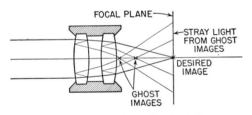

FIG. 2.55. Formation of ghost images.

This light may form an image, called a ghost image, which will not usually be in focus on the film; and, even if it is, the image size will be different from that of the principal image. The number of ghost images formed depends upon the number of glass-air surfaces and grows greater rapidly as the number of interfaces increases, as enumerated in Table 2.5.

Under most conditions the amount of undesired light is not sufficient to do much damage. However, if there is a bright sky and a dark foreground, or if the sun, or other very bright light, is in the field of

TABLE 2.5.   NUMBER OF GHOST IMAGES FORMED
BY A GIVEN NUMBER OF SURFACES

Number of Surfaces	Number of Ghost Images
2	1
4	6
6	15
8	28

the lens, the effects of stray light often become very noticeable. Ghost images may be formed, depending upon the shape of the glass surfaces, i.e., upon the design of the lens and upon the intensity of the source and its surroundings.

In recent years the reflection of light from the lens surfaces has been minimized by the use of anti-reflection layers. By means of a layer, or layers, of transparent material of the proper thickness and index of refraction, the amount of light reflected from a surface can be considerably diminished. As the thickness and index of this layer are usually correct for only one color, different colors are reflected by the coated surface in different amounts, and hence the residual reflected light has a characteristic tint. Very little change in color can be noted in the transmitted light unless there are many surfaces, i.e., six or more. In such cases the color change can be minimized by the proper choice of thickness for the coating or by making the coatings slightly different in thickness for each successive surface.

Although at first low-reflection coatings were fragile, now they are made sufficiently hard to withstand all ordinary cleaning.

In single-layer coatings, the thickness of the layer is one-quarter of a wave length of light, and the index of refraction of the coating material is as nearly as possible the square root of the index of refraction of the glass on which it is coated. No material is available with an index of refraction low enough to fulfill this last condition exactly.

Lens coatings are a remedial measure and do not entirely remove reflections. It is better to have the lens design such that ghost images are not troublesome without coatings, and then to add the coatings to produce optimum results.

But all stray light does not come from the lens surfaces. There are other important sources of flare. Sometimes light is reflected from the edges of the lenses, particularly of the negative elements, which have wide edges. In order to prevent such reflections, the edges are usually covered with a black ink. Further, light scattered from the internal parts of the mount adds to the flare. Good mount design minimizes the contribution from this source.

Finally, light reflected from the inside of the camera body is spread over the film. As a source of flare, this light is often underestimated. Small cameras are likely to be bad in this respect, particularly if the circle of illumination from the lens is large. Initial precautions in the design of the camera plus the blackening of inner parts which have become "shiny" in use, can keep this light to a minimum.

Reflected light from sources other than the lens surfaces does not produce ghost images but contributes to a reduction in the contrast of the image.

For these reasons it is only partially useful to coat a lens to prevent flare. It is necessary, if best results are to be obtained, to consider the lens mount and the interior of the camera on which the lens is to be placed.

Relation Between Relative Aperture and Definition. What has been said about the properties of lenses so far consists of statements regarding the different faults which may occur as a result either of faulty design or because of the simplicity of the lens construction.

When simple lenses are used, it can be assumed that certain aberrations will be present. There will be, for example, some spherical aberration, which will mean some change in focus as the aperture is changed. However, the maximum aperture in simple lenses is usually kept small, and in this way the effect of spherical aberration is minimized.

The camera owner seldom finds it necessary to isolate the different aberrations. His estimate of lens performance is usually based on the definition in the print. If the print has good sharp definition and reasonable brilliance, he will probably consider the lens satisfactory. However, it may be well to inquire into what should be expected of a good lens. All lenses when used at maximum aperture give better definition on the axis than along the margin. The image quality can almost always be improved by decreasing the aperture. In most cases this enhancement of central image quality continues for about two stops below the maximum opening; e.g., an $f/2.0$ lens improves in central definition until about $f/4.0$ is reached. At about this aperture the aberrations cease to be the limiting factor. At smaller apertures, the central definition generally becomes slowly worse, for, when aberrations cease to control the definition, diffraction limits it. The deterioration of image quality at small aper-

McFarlane, "The Practical Aspects of Camera Lens Flare," *P.S.A. Journal* **13**, 344 (1947).

Jacobs, "Fundamentals of Optical Engineering," Chapter VIII, Low Reflectance Lens Coating, McGraw-Hill Book Company, Inc., New York.

Lee, "Surface Treatment of Glass to Reduce its Reflecting Power," *Phot. J.* **84**, 223 (1944).

Smethurst, "Scattered Light, Image Gradation and Surface-Treated Lenses," *Brit. J. Phot.* **88**, 427, 434 (1941).

tures is seldom noticed except in the most critical work, for the quality of definition obtained in the center of a picture is very often better than necessary.

In the corners of the picture area, definition usually continues to improve with decrease of relative aperture even below $f/16$, for oblique aberrations are not eliminated until smaller apertures are reached.

The best aperture at which a lens should be used varies with the lens design and with the application. For the entire central region the critical aperture of most lenses is usually two or three F/numbers below the maximum opening. However, it should be remembered that the choice of aperture is often dictated by the required depth of field.

Chapter 3

PHOTOGRAPHIC OBJECTIVES

Photographic objectives may be classified functionally in accordance with the purpose for which intended, portrait, process, wide angle, etc.; by derivation or by design. Each has its own complications. A functional classification is simple in some cases, difficult in others. Wide-angle lenses, for example, represent a well-defined type, but lenses for portrait or press photography do not. Classification by derivation is of interest principally to the historian. Classification by design with reference to general characteristics and application is the simplest and possibly the most generally useful.

Lenses may be divided into six main types designated as follows:

I. Single lenses.
II. Double lenses, consisting of a single, or compound, element on opposite sides of the diaphragm.

    A. Balanced design, not anastigmatic.
    B. Unbalanced design, not anastigmatic.
    C. Balanced design—anastigmats.
    D. Unbalanced design—anastigmats.

III. Triplets, consisting of three elements which may be single or compound.

    A. Simple, three single lenses.
    B. Balanced design with cemented elements.
    C. Unbalanced design with divided elements.

IV. Quadruplets, or lenses consisting of four simple or compound elements.

    A. Balanced design—single lenses.
    B. Balanced design—outside elements compound.
    C. Balanced design—inside elements compound.
    D. Unbalanced design.

V. Telephoto lenses.

    A. Telephoto combinations.
    B. Telephoto lenses.
    C. Reversed telephoto lenses.

VI. Mirror systems.

Lenses for motion picture photography, projection and special purposes are not included in this chapter.

Single Lenses. *Type IA.* Single, uncorrected lenses are seldom used today even on the cheapest cameras. The meniscus form (Wollaston 1802) may be used either

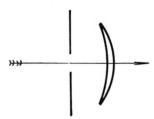

Fig. 3.1. *Type IA.*

behind or in front of the diaphragm. The relative aperture varies from $f/14$ to $f/16$, but the focal length must be relatively long in proportion to the picture area to obtain good marginal definition. Single lenses are not achromatic; therefore they cannot be focused visually and must be used on fixed focus cameras, or those focused by scale.

Type IB. Single achromatic lenses corrected for chromatic aberration at two wave lengths and, to a limited degree, for spherical aberration and coma. Well-designed lenses of this type produce sharper images and cover larger fields than the single lens at apertures of $f/12.5$ to $f/16$.

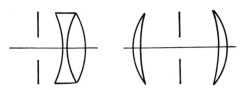

FIG. 3.2. *Type IB.*   FIG. 3.3. *Type IIA, 1.*

Double Lenses Consisting of a Single, or Compound, Element on Opposite Sides of the Diaphragm. *Type IIA, 1.* Double lenses of the type shown are usually termed periscopic after the *Periscop* of Steinheil (1865). With the symmetrical or *balanced*

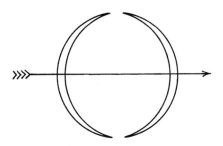

FIG. 3.4. *Type IIA, 2.*

design in which the front and rear elements are identical and equidistant from the diaphragm, there is no distortion and a high degree of correction for lateral chromatic aberration and coma at unit magnification; i.e., when the image and object are the same size. Unbalanced designs, in which the front and rear elements are different, were made at one time to obtain improved correction for general photography where the object distance is much greater than the image distance, but these have long since

disappeared. Achromatic periscopic lenses in which one, or both, of the lenses are replaced by compound elements are now obsolete also. The simple periscopic lens is used on inexpensive folding cameras at apertures ranging from $f/12.5$ to $f/16$.

Type IIA, 2. A form of periscopic lens in which the lenses are very nearly hemispherical was designed by Von Hoegh, about 1900, and introduced by Goerz as an extreme wide angle lens under the trade name *Hypergon*. This lens covers an angle of approximately 150° with good definition at $f/35$. The falling-off in illumination at points away from the axis was overcome by placing a rotating star diaphragm in front of the lens. The Hypergon is no longer made in this form, but the *Topogon* of Carl Zeiss and the *Metrogon* of Bausch and Lomb may be regarded as developments of it with a larger aperture.

Type IIA, 3. This type consists of two single achromatic lenses, symmetrically disposed to a central aperture and was developed independently by Steinheil as the *Aplanat* and by Dallmeyer as the *Rapid*

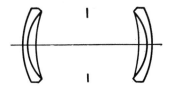

FIG. 3.5. *Type IIA, 3.*

Rectilinear. This was the first symmetrical lens which was definitely superior to the best single lenses and was so successful that it remained in general use until well after the turn of the century. It was finally superseded by triplet-type anastigmats which are cheaper to manufacture and give better results at a larger aperture. The maximum aperture is usually about $f/8$, but some lenses of this type, intended for portrait work and covering a small field, were made to work at $f/6$. The separate elements may be used alone at a smaller diaphragm for their longer focal length. The marginal definition is poor as compared with the later lenses, because correction for astigmatism must be sacrificed to obtain a flat field.

Type IIB. This is the portrait lens designed by Joseph Petzval in 1841, and commonly known as the "Petzval lens."

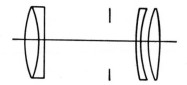

F IG. 3.6. *Type IIB.*

Lenses of this type are made ordinarily with apertures of from $f/4$ to $f/3.5$, but have been made with apertures up to $f/2.2$. The central definition is excellent, but the field is sharply curved and is limited to about 24°. J. H. Dallmeyer, of London, increased the field slightly by reversing the rear elements. Despite the relatively small field, the illumination falls off rapidly away from the axis. These shortcomings limit this design to lenses for portrait photography, projection, and large-aperture motion picture lenses of long focal length.

Type IIC, 1. The first objectives of this type were improved aplantic constructions, such as the *Rectigraphic* of Gundlach

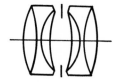

F IG. 3.7. *Type IIC, 1.*

(1890), but the best known is the double anastigmat *Dagor* which was placed on the market by Goerz in 1892. Although one of the earliest anastigmats, lenses of this type with a relative aperture of $f/6.8$ to $f/7.7$ are

still popular with commercial photographers because of their excellent definition, the large field, particularly at small f-values, and the possibility of using the elements separately at $f/12.5$ to $f/16$. The *Super Dagor, f/8*, covers a field of approximately 100°.

The following are similar:

Aerotar................Goerz American Opt. Co.
Amatar................Carl Zeiss
Angulon..............J. Schneider
Collinear.............Voightlander
Double Anastigmat......Hugo Meyer
Holostigmat...........Watson
Makinar..............Plaubel
Maxima...............Ica
Optar (side angle)......Wollensak
Orthar................Plaubel
Orthostigmat..........Steinheil
Raptor (wide angle).....Wollensak
Symmar...............J. Schneider

Double objectives of this type, but with different arrangements of the lenses within the elements, were made by Steinheil as the

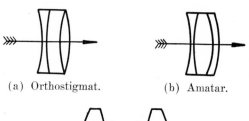

(a) Orthostigmat.   (b) Amatar.

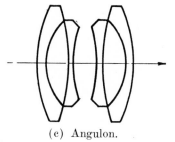

(c) Angulon.

F IG. 3.8.

Orthostigmat, by Voghtlander as the *Collinear*, and by Carl Zeiss as the *Amatar*. The Angulon, $f/6.8$, of Schneider, a wide-angle lens with a field of almost 100°, is this type, the outer members being made larger than the others to increase the marginal illumination.

Type IIC, 2. The first anastigmatic objective of this type was the *Double Protar,* which was calculated by Paul Rudolph and placed on the market by Carl Zeiss in 1893.

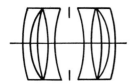

FIG. 3.9. *Type IIC, 2.*

Each half of the Protar is completely corrected for use alone and thus the double lens provides the photographer with three focal lengths. The double lens has an aperture of $f/6.8$ to $f/7.7$ over an angular field of about 70°. The excellent definition of the single elements, the large flat field, and the brilliant image have made these lenses popular for many years among commercial photographers where a large aperture is not required.

Other lenses of similar type are:

Combinable. . . . . .Ross
Bystigmar. . . . . .Beck
Gundlach Convertible. . . .Gundlach
Protar VIIa. . . . . Carl Zeiss
                     Bausch & Lomb
Raptar Ia. . . . . .Wollensak
Velostigmat Ia. . . . . .Wollensak

Type IIC, 3. In these, a thin air space has been introduced to provide the designer with greater freedom in the choice of glass and the configuration of the surfaces of the individual lenses than is possible when all four lenses are cemented together. The

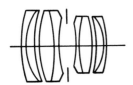

FIG. 3.10. *Type IIC, 3.*

Cooke Convertible, Series XV, with an aperture of $f/6.8$ is of this type.

Type IIC, 4. These have the same general characteristics as the three- and four-glass symmetrical lenses described above. The best-known lens of this construction is

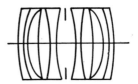

FIG. 3.11. *Type IIC, 4.*

the *Turner-Reich* Anastigmat of Gundlach which has a relative aperture of $f/7.7$. The large flat field enables it to be used as a wide field lens and the halves are well corrected for use alone.

Type IID. In the lenses described previously both front and rear elements are similar and each half is corrected sepa-

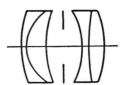

FIG. 3.12. *Type IID.*

rately. The designer has greater freedom, however, if he has only the lens as a whole to correct and is not required to correct each half separately. In the lens shown the errors of one half are balanced against the other half to obtain good correction of the complete lens. The first anastigmat lens based on this principal was calculated by Paul Rudolph and placed on the market by Carl Zeiss in 1890. It was the first well-corrected anastigmat and covers a large flat field, but cannot be made to work at a large aperture. It survives today as a wide angle lens with an angular field of from 90° to 95° at apertures from $f/12.5$ to $f/18$. In some examples, one of the halves is made into a three-glass element to obtain good correction at a larger aperture.

The following objectives are of similar design:

Dasykar......................J. Schneider
Protar, Series IV, V..........Carl Zeiss
                             Bausch and Lomb
Raptar extreme wide angle......Wollensak

Triplets, Lenses Consisting of Three Simple or Compound Elements. *Type IIIA.* The first *anastigmatic* triplet was calculated by H. Dennis Taylor in 1893 and is frequently termed the "Cooke" triplet as Mr. Taylor was then employed by

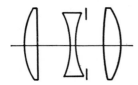

Fig. 3.13. *Type IIIA.*

Thomas Cooke and Sons Ltd., of York (England). This was actually the first anastigmat of large aperture with a flat field. In addition, it was much cheaper to manufacture than the rapid rectilinear and soon displaced it entirely for hand cameras. The triplet, if well made, will cover sharply a field of about 40° at $f/4.5$ and is used for lenses of still larger aperture where the field is smaller. The field covered by the triplet does not increase appreciably with smaller apertures. In this respect it differs from Type IIC which may be used as wide angle lenses at small apertures.

The triplet is an inexpensive design from a manufacturer's standpoint, but as there are only three elements the tolerances are close and many cheap lenses of this type do not produce the results, even near the axis, which may be expected of this design at its best.

The following are of this type:

Alepar...............Angénieux
Alestar..............Angénieux
Anaston..............Eastman Kodak Company
Ansco anastigmat......Ansco
Apotar...............Agfa
Cassar...............Steinheil
Helomar..............Voightlander
Hypar................Goerz
Nettar...............Zeiss Ikon
Novar................Zeiss Ikon
Portric..............Taylor, Taylor and Hobson
Portrillic...........Taylor, Taylor and Hobson
Portronic............Taylor, Taylor and Hobson
Radionar.............J. Schneider
Serenar (100 mm.).....Canon
Trinar...............G. Rodenstock
Triplar..............Steinheil
Trioplan.............Hugo Meyer
Trioptar.............Wollensak
Triotar..............Carl Zeiss
Voigtar..............Voghtlander

Type IIIB, 1. The first lens of this type was calculated by Paul Rudolph and placed on the market by Carl Zeiss of Jena in 1903 as the *Tessar.* This design with its greater flexibility enables the correction of the simple triplet to be improved for a larger field. It can be made to work at

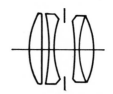

Fig. 3.14. *Type IIIB, 1.*

apertures up to $f/2.7$ and at equal apertures will cover a larger field than the simple triplet. The field increases some on stopping down but not sufficiently to make it a wide field lens.

In some lenses of this type, as in the Carl Zeiss *Tessar, f/2.7,* the positions of the lenses in the rear element are reversed.

The following are of this type:

Alcorar.....................Angénieux
Alfinar.....................Old Delft
Alfinon.....................Old Delft
Anastar.....................Eastman Kodak
Anticoma...................Plaubel
Dominar....................Ica
Ektar.......................Eastman Kodak
Elmar......................E. Leitz
Ensar......................Barnet, Ensign, Ross
Ernon......................Erneman
Glyptar....................Busch
Holostigmat................Voghtlander
Optar......................Wollensak
Paragon....................Ilex
Primotar...................Hugo Meyer
Radar f/4.5................Gundlach
Radar wide angle f/16.......Gundlach
Raptar f/4.5................Wollensak
Serenar f/3.5...............Canon
Serrac.....................Dallmeyer
Skopar.....................Voightlander
Solinar....................Agfa
Tessar.....................Carl Zeiss,
                           Bausch and Lomb
Xenar f/2.8, f/3.5, f/4.5......J. Schneider
Xpres......................Ross

In the *Xpres* f/4.5 of Ross Ltd., and the *Radar* f/4.5 of Gundlach, the rear element consists of three cemented lenses. The three glass element was chosen to provide greater freedom in the use of glass and in calculation.

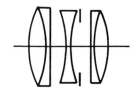

Fig. 3.15.   *Type IIIB, 2.*

Type IIIB, 2. In this development of the simple triplet, the single positive elements are replaced by compound elements. The increase in the number of surfaces and glasses enables the correction to be carried out more thoroughly for an objective with a larger field than the simple triplet. The

first well-known objective of this type was the *Heliar* calculated by Harting for Voightlander in 1900. In the longer focal lengths this is a popular lens among portrait photographers and is made in apertures up to f/2.8 for use on miniature cameras. The *Pentac* f/2.9 of Dallmeyer, the Kodak *Ektar* f/3.5 and f/3.7, and the *Biotessar* f/2.7 of Carl Zeiss are similar. In the latter, the rear element consists of three cemented lenses.

Type IIIB, 3. In this development of the simple triplet, all three elements are compound. The *Hektor* of Leitz is of this type.

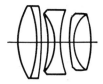

Fig. 3.16.   *Type IIIB, 3.*

Type IIIC, 1. In this construction, the central negative lens of the triplet has been developed into a compound element of three cemented lenses. The best-known objective

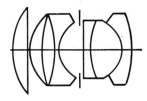

Fig. 3.17.   *Type IIIC, 1.*

of this type is the *Sonnar* of Carl Zeiss, with an aperture of f/1.5 and f/2. The latter covers a field of 25°.

Type IIIC, 2. Dividing one of the two positive lenses of the simple triplet pro-

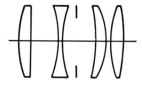

Fig. 3.18.   *Type IIIC, 2.*

vides two extra surfaces for the designer and the possibility of using different glasses to improve the correction. In some objectives of this type the rear lens is divided, in others the front. The *Alportar f/2.5* and *Alogar f/3.5* of Angénieux (France) and the *Tachar* of Astro (Berlin) are of this design.

Type IIIC, 3. To increase further the number of elements at the disposal of the designer, and increase the relative aper-

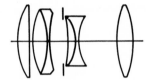

FIG. 3.19. *Type IIIC, 3.*

ture, the single lenses in the design above were replaced by cemented doublets in the *Ernostar f/2* designed by Bertele of the Ernemann-Werke. Although this is a four-glass lens, it is essentially a triplet.

Type IV Quadruplets. Lenses Consisting of Four Simple or Compound Elements. *Type IVA, 1.* This construction was developed in two different ways: (1) from Type IIC by reducing the refractive

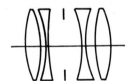

FIG. 3.20. *Type IVA, 1.*

power required of the central lens to zero through appropriate changes in the types of glass used and the powers of the other lenses, and (2) by dividing the central element of the simple triplet (Type IIIA) into two single lenses of lower power.

The first lenses of this type, derived from the three-glass element, were introduced by Goerz in 1899 as the *Celor f/4.5*, and *Syn-*

tor, with a larger field, at *f/6.8*.[1] These are no longer made. Later (1909) Zschokke improved the correction for coma by departing from strict symmetrical design and the Goerz *Dogmar* with a relative aperture of *f/4.5* is still made by the Goerz American Optical Company (New York). The Cooke *Aviar*, although similar in appearance, was developed by Warmisham of Taylor, Taylor and Hobson Ltd. from the triplet. Dividing the single negative lens of the triplet into two of lower individual power increases the number of surfaces and permits the use of shallower curves and different glasses. As a result of this added freedom, it was possible to extend the angular field to about 55° and to improve the correction for coma at an aperture of *f/4.5*.

The following lenses are of this type:

Artar . . . . Goerz American Opt. Co.
Aviar . . . . Taylor, Taylor and Hobson
Celor . . . . C. P. Goerz
Dogmar . . . . Goerz American Opt. Co.
Ektar, *f/7.7* . . . . Eastman Kodak Company
Eurynar . . . . G. Rodenstock
Gotar . . . . Goerz American Opt. Co.
Graf Anastigmat . . . . Graf Opt. Co.
Gundlach Anastigmat,
  Series IV . . . . Gundlach Mfg. Co.
Helioplan . . . . Hugo Meyer
Isoconar . . . . J. Schneider
Raptar Process . . . . Wollensak
Raptar, Series IV . . . . . . Wollensak
Unofocal . . . . Steinheil

Type IVA, 2. Objectives of this type are sometimes referred to as Gauss lenses because each half resembles a telescope objective designed by the German mathematician and astronomer Karl Gauss. This construction is notable for the facility which it affords the designer in obtaining good

─────────────

1 Steinheil introduced (1901) as the *Unofocal* a lens of this design which is interesting in that all four lenses were made of glass of the same refractive index, but different dispersive values, and each lens is approximately the same focal power; a converging lens system being obtained from the separation of the positive and negative lenses.

spherical correction for more than one color and over a large, flat field.

The first photographic lens of this type was a portrait lens designed by Alvan Clark and placed on the market in 1889 by Bausch and Lomb as the Clark lens. It was not successful and was soon withdrawn.

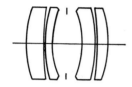

FIG. 3.21. *Type IVA, 2.*

In 1900, Kollmergen designed for Hugo Meyer the *Aristostigmat* $f/6.8$ with a field of about 70°, and since that time lenses of this type have been made for commercial photography, for process work, as well as wide angle by several manufacturers in Germany, England, and the United States.

Aristostigmat......... Hugo Meyer
Cooke Series VIIb wide
   angle............. Taylor, Taylor and Hobson
Eistal (wide angle).... Taylor, Taylor and Hobson
Ektar (wide field $f/6.3$). Eastman Kodak Company
Homocentric......... Ross Ltd.
Omnar.............. E. Busch
Orthar (wide angle $f/6.8$) Plaubel
Process $f/10$..........Bausch and Lomb
Raptar (wide angle $f/6.8$) Wollensak
Wide Angle $f/11$...... Dallmeyer

Type IVA, 3. The construction shown was developed as a wide-angle lens for aerial mapping by Carl Zeiss and introduced as the *Topogon*, with an aperture of $f/6.3$ and an angle of 100°. The aperture

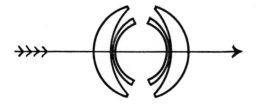

FIG. 3.22. *Type IVA, 3.*

was increased to $f/5.6$ in 1936 by Ross Ltd., who divided one of the outer lenses into two to gain greater freedom. This lens was made for the R.A.F. as the *Wide Angle Survey Lens*. A similar construction was utilized by Bausch and Lomb in the *Metrogon*. The Goerz *Rectagon* and the *Radar High Speed Wide Angle* $f/6.3$, of Gundlach, are similar.

Type IVB, 1. These were developed from the three-glass cemented elements by separating the inner lens from the other two by an air space. The greater freedom which this construction affords the calcu-

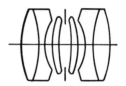

FIG. 3.23. *Type IVB, 1.*

lator makes possible a well-corrected lens of a larger aperture without sacrificing the large angular field which is a characteristic of the three- and four-glass cemented element. The *Euryplan* and *Double-Plasmat* of Hugo Meyer, the latter calculated by Paul Rudolph, are designed for general exterior and interior photography and have relative apertures of $f/6$ and $f/4.5$, respectively. The single elements of these lenses may be used alone, the maximum aperture being $f/11$ and $f/8$, respectively. The following lenses are of this type:

Altimar.................... Bausch and Lomb
Euryplan.................... Hugo Meyer
Korona Convertible.......... Gundlach
Ortho-Angulon.............. J. Schneider
Orthometar................. Carl Zeiss
Plasmat (Double and Process).. Hugo Meyer
Process..................... Ross
Wide Angle Xpres,.......... Ross

The *Orthometer*, $f/4.5$, of Carl Zeiss, the *Altimar*, $f/4$, of Bausch and Lomb, and the *Wide Angle Xpres*, $f/4$, of Ross Ltd., are all designed for aerial photography and cover a field of approximately 60°. These lenses, however, are not symmetrical, and the front and rear elements cannot be used separately.

Type IVB, 2. This design, with the inner lenses reversed, was introduced by Hugo Meyer, from the calculations of Paul Rudolph, as the *Kino-Plasmat* with an angle of approximately 30° at $f/1.5$ and the *Mikro-Plasmat* with an aperture of $f/2.9$.

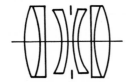

FIG. 3.24. *Type IVB, 2.*

Type IVC. The first anastigmatic objective of this design was calculated by Paul Rudolph and placed on the market in 1896 by Carl Zeiss as the *Planar*, $f/4.5$. Rudolph was unable at the time to obtain the glasses needed for correction of both

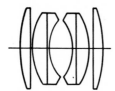

FIG. 3.25. *Type IVC.*

chromatic and spherical aberration with four simple lenses and it was necessary to make the innermost elements compound. The Planar was later replaced by the *Tessar*, except for the *Apo-Planar* which is still made for three-color process photography.

This type of lens was greatly improved by Lee of Taylor, Taylor and Hobson, who departed from exact symmetry to obtain an aperture of $f/2$ for a field of 25°. This lens was introduced as the *Opic*. Still later, he increased the aperture to $f/1.5$ without

greatly changing the design by reducing the field to 20° which is sufficient for motion picture photography.

This construction has been very attractive to designers in their attempt to provide the miniature camera user with lenses of still larger aperture and improved performance and a number of useful designs have already been developed from this basic type.

Alitar $f/1.8$ (on Alpa
    Reflex)............ Angénieux
Amotal (on Bell and
    Howell Foton)...... Taylor, Taylor and Hobson
Baltar............... Bausch and Lomb
Biotar............... Carl Zeiss
Opic................ Taylor, Taylor and Hobson
Planar and Apo-Planar. Carl Zeiss
Septar.............. Dallmeyer
Serenar............. Canon
Summar............. E. Leitz
Super-six $f/1.9$....... Dallmeyer
Supracoma.......... Plaubel
Xenon.............. J. Schneider
Xpres $f/1.9$......... Ross Ltd.

The *Summaron* of Leitz is a wide-angle lens covering a field of 68° at an aperture of $f/3.5$. The outer elements have been made large to increase the marginal illumination. This lens is exceptionally well corrected for spherical aberration and replaces the Elmar $f/3.5$ (Type IIIB, 1) formerly supplied as a wide-field lens for the Leica camera.

Type IVD, 1. Birek, of Leitz, sought to improve the marginal illumination of the field by making the front element com-

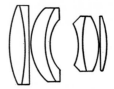

FIG. 3.26. *Type IVD, 1.*

pound. This is the well known Leitz *Summitar* $f/2$ with an angle of 48°. Merté, of Carl Zeiss, with basically the same design but reversed, increased the aperture to $f/$

1.5 for motion picture work with a field of 28°.

Type IVD, 2. In this development the rear meniscus lens has been divided into two. This design was developed first by

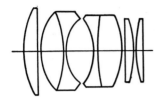

FIG. 3.27. *Type IVD, 2.*

Lee of Taylor, Taylor and Hobson. The *Xenon f/1.5* of Schneider, the *Summarit f/1.5*, and the *Summarex f/1.5* of Leitz are of this type.

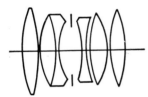

FIG. 3.28. *Type IVD, 3.*

Type IVD, 3. In this construction one of the inner cemented doublets has been divided into two single lenses. In the *Tachon* of Astro, the cemented element in the rear has been split; in the *Xenon f/2* of Schneider the front element has been split.

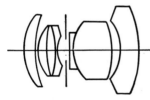

FIG. 3.29. *Type IVD, 4.*

Type IVD, 4. This strongly unbalanced system is the wide angle *Biogon* of Zeiss which covers a field of approximately 60° at *f/2.7*. The large negative lens at the rear serves to flatten the field. This lens, like the *Sonnar*, is for the Contax camera.

TYPE V. TELEPHOTO LENSES

Type V. The word *telephoto* is usually applied to lenses of special design in which the image size, for a given lens-to-image distance, is greater than with conventional lenses.[2] There are, however, what may be called *reversed telephoto* lenses in which the image size is *smaller* than with a conventional lens of the same image-lens distance. Since a lens of this type includes a wider angle than other lenses for the same lens-image distance (commonly termed *back* focus), it may be used as a wide-angle lens on reflex and other cameras where conventional wide-angle lenses cannot be used because of the swinging mirror.

Type VA, 1. The first *telephoto* lenses consisted of a conventional lens and a telephoto attachment in the rear with the distance between the two adjustable to change the size of the image. The diagram shows a telephoto unit made by Dallmeyer, of London, early in the present century. The positive lens in front is the Petzval portrait lens as modified by Dallmeyer and the negative element is a double lens. Lens systems

FIG. 3.30. *Type VA, 1.*

of this kind are heavy and cumbersome and even at a small aperture the definition is poor as compared with other lenses, and there is considerable distortion.

Type VA, 2. A different type of telephoto attachment was introduced in 1902 by Dallmeyer of London as the *Adon*. This is essentially a low power Galilean telescope placed in front of the camera lens.

---

[2] The word telephoto is unfortunately and inaccurately used by many to describe lenses, especially for the miniature camera, which are simply of longer focal length and, therefore, produce larger images (telephoto effects) as compared with the normal camera lens.

The magnification depends upon the separation of the positive and negative elements and as the system is afocal, i.e., has no focal length, the focus of the camera lens is not

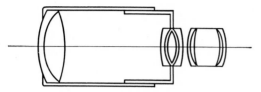

FIG. 3.31. *Type VA, 2.*

changed.[3] If the diameter of the positive element is equal to that of the camera lens *times* the degree of magnification, the aperture of the camera lens also remains unchanged. In the *Adon* of Dallmeyer and the *Telepeconar* of Plaubel, these advantages were not completely realized as it was considered more important to provide for different degrees of magnification by changing the separation between the front and rear elements. The diagram shows the Adon attached to a rapid rectlinear camera lens.

Recent telephoto attachments of this type slip on over the camera lens and increase the image size from 1.5 to 2 times. When used on the lenses for which they are designed, there is no appreciable change in focus or speed.

Lenses of this construction are:

Gruenex telephoto.......... Mansfield Industries
Magnifar.................. Morton Co.
Spiratone Telephoto........ Spiratone
Telemagnar (for Rolleiflex)... Carl Zeiss

Type VB. This includes all *teleobjectives,* i.e., complete telephoto lenses as distinguished from telephoto attachments used with the camera lens, *except* reversed systems where the object is to obtain a smaller rather than a larger image.

---

[3] This principle, in reverse, has been applied to wide-angle attachments which, when used with the camera lens, increase the field without substantially changing the focus or aperture.

Since a telephoto lens system can be corrected for only one degree of magnification, it was necessary to use the older lenses, having variable magnification, at smaller apertures in order to obtain good definition. This limited the use of such lenses to architecture and other subjects which would not show movement. If the advantages of variable magnification are sacrificed, the distance between the front and rear elements may be fixed and the lens can then be corrected as a whole. With a magnification of two to three times, good

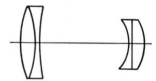

FIG. 3.32. *Type VB, 1.*

definition can be obtained at apertures of $f/5.5$ to $f/3.5$, or even larger, in lenses for motion picture photography. There is some distortion, however, and in general the definition of existing telephoto lenses does not equal that of the best lenses of conventional design.

Type VB, 1. This design is suitable for a magnification of from 1.5 to 2 times at apertures of $f/5.5$ to $f/4.5$. In the *Telic* $f/5.5$ of Taylor, Taylor and Hobson Ltd., and the *Teleros* of Ross Ltd., both having a magnification of three times, the rear element is a cemented three-glass lens.

Other lenses of this construction are:

Altelar (for Alpa reflex) S. O. M.
Alefar (for Alpa reflex). Old Delft
Dallon.............. Dallmeyer
Kilar............... Kilar
Plustrar............ Wray
Radar telephoto....... Gundlach
Raptar telephoto...... Wollensak
Teleoptar........... Wollensak
Telephoto........... Bausch and Lomb
Teleros............. Ross Ltd.
Telic.............. Taylor, Taylor and Hobson

Type VB, 2. The form shown has been adopted by Carl Zeiss for the *Teletessar* which has a magnification of two times at $f/5.5$ and the Cooke *Telic* (2×) of Taylor,

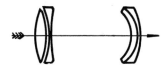

FIG. 3.33. *Type VB, 2.*

Taylor and Hobson Ltd. The *Tele-Xenar* $f/5.5$ of Schneider is similar but in the *Tele-Xenar* $f/4.5$ and $f/3.8$ a separate meniscus lens has been added in the rear.

Type VB, 3. The pincushion distortion of ordinary teleobjectives was removed by Lee of Taylor, Taylor and Hobson Ltd. with the construction shown. This lens was

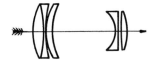

FIG. 3.34. *Type VB, 3.*

intended primarily for aerial mapping. The aperture is $f/5$ and the magnification, 2.5 times.

Type VC. Excluding special purpose lenses for cinematography, the only lens of this type commercially available is the *Retrofocus* of Angénieux near Paris. This

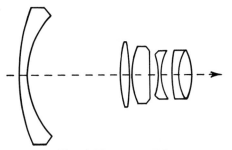

FIG. 3.35. *Type VC.*

provides the user of 24 × 36 mm. reflex cameras, such as the Kine-Exakta, and the Practiflex, with a wide field lens covering an angle of 65° at $f/2.5$. Ordinary wide-

angle lenses cannot be used with these cameras because of the space required for the swinging mirror.

Type VI. Mirror Systems. While mirror systems have been used in astronomy for many years, the *Fotel* of Old Delft (Holland) is the first commercial mirror-type photographic objective. This lens-reflector system is designed for 24 × 36 mm. cameras and, although only 6 inches long, has a

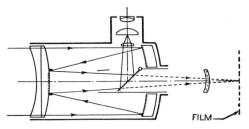

FIG. 3.36. *Type VI.*

focal length of 18 inches and an aperture of $f/5.6$. Light transmitted by the lens system to the left is reflected by the concave mirror at the rear to a mirror on the back surface of the lens system, from which it is reflected through the opening in the rear mirror and the correcting lens to the focal plane. The pivoted mirror directly in front of the opening in the rear mirror is used, in conjunction with the eyepiece directly above, for focusing the image. Before making the exposure, it is released and swings up, as does the mirror of a reflex camera, to close the eyepiece and clear the optical system.

On the Choice of Lenses. It is quite fallacious to judge the quality of a lens by the number of glasses of which it is composed. The larger number of glasses and surfaces do provide the designer with additional means for making the necessary corrections, but the difficulties in manufacturing—particularly in centering—are increased also. Thus the improvement sought by the calculator may be lost in manufacturing There have been, in fact, known cases in which a promising design has been modified, or discarded, because the lenses could not be assembled with sufficient precision.

Nor should too much importance be attached to design. A lens of the "Tessar" type will give better results than a simple triplet only if both are made equally well. A "Tessar" which has not been well made may be distinctly inferior to a triplet of the highest quality. In lenses there is no substitute for skilled, conscientious, precision craftsmanship.

In general, the simpler the design the less the manufacturing difficulties, but there are exceptions. The triplet, for example, is easy to make but must be made and assembled with a high degree of precision because of the limited number of elements. Lenses with a number of cemented surfaces are difficult to center accurately. This is one reason, perhaps, why the performance of most lenses composed of four and five cemented glasses (Types IIC, 2 and IIC, 4) is not greatly superior to those with three glasses.

Formerly, other things being equal, lenses with the minimum number of reflecting surfaces were to be preferred as producing more brilliant images, less subject to flare, but this difference has largely been overcome by the modern practice of coating. Thus, in choosing a large-aperture lens a few years ago there would have been some justification for selecting the design with the smaller number of reflecting surfaces; with modern coated lenses this consideration is far outweighed by other factors.

The field included by the lens, or covering power, as it is often termed, is no guarantee of definition. It is often assumed that if the covering power of the lens is much larger than the picture area, the definition of that part of the field which is actually used must of necessity be superior. This, however, is not the case. A lens designed to cover a given picture field *adequately* may give superior results to a lens which will actually cover a much larger field. For example, a lens of 90 mm. focal length, designed expressly for a 24 × 36 mm. picture area, may be expected to be superior, *for that picture size*, to another lens of the same design and focal length but for a picture area of 60 × 60 mm.

The increased number of glasses which have become available to the lens designer in recent years has made new constructions possible and also, in many cases, an improvement in the old. Thus, the correction of some of the older, well-established designs has been carried still further in recent lenses using the newer glasses. As more and more glasses with a wider range of optical characteristics become available, we may expect continued improvement in some of the older designs as well as new constructions not possible with the present glasses.

Large-Aperture Lenses. It is well to bear in mind, also, that in the present stage of photographic optics the definition of lenses of extremely large aperture cannot equal that of lenses of smaller aperture and that, in general, the lens with the smaller maximum aperture is preferable even when both are used at the same aperture. Thus lenses with an aperture of $f/1.8$, $f/1.5$, etc. must not be expected to produce the same definition as an $f/3.5$ lens, assuming, of course, that both are equally well made and for the same picture area. Large aperture lenses, in a number of cases, are corrected primarily for use at their maximum aperture and the definition is not improved appreciably at smaller apertures. In fact, when focusing with a range finder, the definition may actually be inferior at smaller apertures due to the change in the position of the sharpest focus with the diaphragm used. Large aperture lenses should be regarded as "speed lenses" for use where a large aperture is an absolute necessity, not as universal lenses for general use.

One of the best indications of quality in any lens, and particularly one of large aperture, is the brilliancy of the image by which we mean "image contrast." Lenses of poor quality, whether by design or manufacture, cannot produce images with the maximum contrast in small detail.

Wide-Angle Lenses. Wide-angle, or wide-field, lenses must be corrected for a larger field than other lenses of the same focal length and must be compact in design in order to obtain the maximum illumination at the margins of the image.

Lenses of the *Tessar* construction can be made to cover a field of approximately 68°, and several wide-field lenses for use on miniature cameras are of this type. There is usually some vignetting of the corners with such lenses unless used at $f/4.5$ to $f/6.3$. The so-called Gaussian construction (Type IVD) provides better coverage at larger apertures.

Wide field lenses of longer focal length with maximum apertures of $f/6.3$ to $f/6.8$ are usually four-element lenses of Gaussian design (Type IVB). The field included varies from 70° to 90°. Lenses including the wider field, in most cases, must be used at $f/11$ to $f/16$; the larger aperture being intended for focusing only. In some cases, where the field is smaller, the lens may be used at maximum opening but the best definition is obtained at $f/11$ or smaller.

Extreme wide-angle lenses are either double lenses consisting of two three-glass cemented elements (Type IIC) at apertures of from $f/6.8$ to $f/8$ or unsymmetrical doublets (Type IID) at $f/12.5$ to $f/18$.

Lenses for Color Photography. Lenses for color photography must be well corrected for both longitudinal and lateral color if good definition is to be expected. The requirements, however, are much more critical for three-color printing, and par-

ticularly if enlarged, than for color transparencies for projection or direct viewing. Correction for color is particularly important because it is not removed by the use of smaller apertures. Freedom from flare and good spherical and comatic correction are important factors in color reproduction particularly of fine detail. Coated lenses are advisable, but coating is not a substitute for good correction.

Apochromatic process lenses are to be preferred for color separation negatives where a large aperture is not required and the subject-distance is short, as still-life in the studio, or in making separations from transparencies.

Lenses for Projection Printing. Lenses for projection printing must give critical definition on a flat field for the range of enlargement, or reduction, necessary. Since the image is focused visually, longitudinal chromatic aberration must be exceptionally well corrected and, for color work, the lateral aberrations as well. Enlarging lenses are usually triplets of type IIIA or IIIB and differ from camera lenses of the same design in being corrected for shorter working distances. Apochromatic process lenses are desirable for critical color work.

Camera lenses used for projection printing usually require some stopping down for best results.

Lens Tests. Tests of a lens are not easy to make without a lens bench and special skills which the average photographer does not have. For many purposes, a photograph of the skyline across the diagnoal of the picture is adequate for there is nearly always fine detail to examine in such a picture. A brick wall at a distance of not less than 20 times the focal length of the lens also forms a good test object. To be of practical value, the test negatives should be made at the apertures and with the emulsions commonly used. The use of a high-contrast negative material, for example, will tend to give a fictitious appearance of sharpness because of the increased contrast of the test negative.

A photographic test is a test not only of the lens but of the camera on which it is used. Lack of sharpness in the negative is not always the result of poor lens performance. It is necessary to be sure that the lens is actually in focus. If a ground glass is used for focusing it is important that the film holders are in register so that

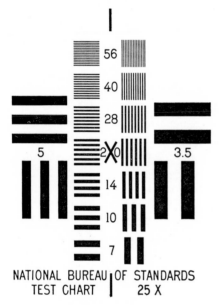

NATIONAL BUREAU OF STANDARDS
TEST CHART   25 X

Fig. 3.37.   Lens Test Chart.   (U. S. Bureau of Standards.)

the film occupies the same position as the ground glass screen. A few thousandths of an inch difference in the two may cause a lens of high quality to produce very inferior results. Likewise photographic tests made with scale-focusing or coupled range-finder cameras do not distinguish between lens performance and errors in focusing.

The usual way of testing a lens is to measure the numerical value of its resolving power. Resolving power is determined by photographing charts similar to that

shown in Fig. 3.37,[4] and finding the number of lines per millimeter which can be distinguished on the photographic test plate. This figure is of significance only for a particular negative material, exposure and development. It is not sufficient to determine the resolving power on the axis for any lens of good repute is satisfactory at this point. It is necessary to determine values for resolving power at several points in the field of the lens. At off-the-axis points the resolving power is not so easily measured, for usually the resolution in two mutually perpendicular directions, radial and tangential, must be measured. The two sets of lines are seldom resolved equally well which increases the difficulty of evaluating the resolving power for points off the axis.

In a print to be viewed at 12 inches, the resolving power must be on the order of 10 lines per millimeter for the image to appear sharp. If the negative is to be enlarged, the resolving power must increase accordingly. Thus, if a miniature negative is to be enlarged six times, the resolution must be approximately 60 lines per millimeter. A well-corrected lens must be used if resolution of this magnitude is to be obtained over its entire field.

A test of the lens alone may be made visually by examining the image of an artificial star on the ground glass at different distances from the axis with a low power magnifier. A test object for the purpose may be made by cutting an opening in the form of a cross in black opaque paper and placing this in a window open to the sky, or it may be placed on ground glass and illuminated by an electric lamp. The image should first be focused sharply in the center and examined carefully with the magnifier. Then the camera should be rotated about the lens as a pivot and the

[4] U. S. Bureau of Standards, Washington, D. C.

image of the test object examined, without refocusing, at different distances from the axis.

Unless one knows what to expect, he is likely to be disappointed with the results of such a test and may be inclined to discard a lens which would be found entirely satisfactory in practice. Any lens is a compromise between many exacting and conflicting requirements. Complete correction for all aberrations cannot be made simultaneously in the present state of photographic optics. One making this test should not expect perfect definition at points away from the axis. Indeed the principal difficulty with a test of this kind, if it is carefully made, is not that it lacks precision but that the interpretation of the result, in terms of photographic performance, requires experience that is beyond that of the average photographer. Only one who has examined hundreds of lenses and knows what to expect is able to determine what may be expected of the lens from the appearance of the image of such a test object.

Chromatic difference of magnification is a serious defect in a lens used for color photography because it results in color fringes in color transparencies and lack of register on three-color negatives. Color fringes can be detected on star images, or a test object which consists of a fine white thread on black velvet may be used. This test object should be well illuminated and placed so that the image of the thread is along one side of the focusing screen. If color fringing is seen when the image is examined with a good magnifier, the lens is not suitable for exacting color photography. Slight color fringing is usually of little concern in color transparencies of landscapes, portraits, and pictorial work in general.

Lenses for enlarging may be tested for color fringing by projecting a negative of a line copy, focusing critically, preferably with a sharp focusing device, and examining lines near the edge of the picture area for evidence of color fringes.

Care of Lenses. Lenses should be protected from falls and sudden jars, from sharp changes in temperature and from excessive heat and moisture. Exposed glass surfaces should be protected when not in use from dust and atmospheric gases by a lens cap or by keeping the camera closed or in a case. Despite these precautions, the outer surface of the lens will require an occasional cleaning. For this the special lens paper obtainable from opticians is recommended. If this is not available, a soft, *clean* linen handkerchief may be used. In either case avoid undue pressure as some varieties of optical glass are quite soft and the polish may be affected. Solvents, such as alcohol, are best avoided, although those sold by opticians for cleaning lenses may be used sparingly. If a lens requires more than simple cleaning of the exposed glass surfaces, it should be returned to the maker for attention.

Chapter 4

PHOTOGRAPHIC LIGHT FILTERS

Photographic Light Filters. Photographic light filters may be divided into four classes: (1) color filters, (2) viewing filters, (3) neutral density filters, and (4) polarizing filters. *Color* filters are used to control the relative tone values in which colors are rendered by the photographic process; i.e., to lighten or darken particular colors or to obtain color-separation records for color photography. *Viewing* filters are designed to show by direct observation the relative values in which colors will be reproduced by a particular type of sensitive material without or with a given filter. *Neutral density* filters are used to reduce the light intensity to prevent overexposure. In professional motion picture photography, for example, the use of neutral density filters on desert scenes, views over water, etc., enables these subjects to be photographed at the same lens aperture as the other scenes in the film so as to avoid any change in depth of field or image characteristics. In amateur cinematography, neutral density filters may be necessary, with certain cameras, to prevent overexposure on strongly illuminated subjects when high-speed negative materials are used. Neutral density filters are used in tricolor cameras to obtain equal exposures on the three negatives. *Polarizing* filters are used primarily to control light reflected from highly polished surfaces, metallic objects, etc., to photograph through glass and to darken the sky in color photography where a color filter cannot be used.

Color Filters. A color filter may be defined as an optically homogeneous (i.e.,

nondiffusing) medium in which the absorption of light (and therefore the transmission) varies with the wave length. The curve in Fig. 4.1 represents the relation

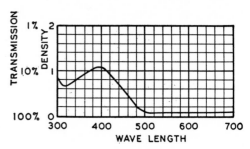

FIG. 4.1. Spectrophotometric curve of a yellow filter (Wratten No. 6, K₁).

between absorption and wave length of a common yellow filter. The portion above represents the transmission in relation to wave length

$$T = \frac{I_0}{I_x}$$

where I_0 is the illumination incident on the filter, and I_x is the intensity of the illumination emerging. For convenience, the value of I_0/I_x is usually multiplied by 100 so that that the transmission is expressed as a percentage. The dark portion represents the relation between absorption and wave length in terms of *density*

$$D = \log \frac{I}{T} \quad \text{or} \quad \log_{10} \frac{I}{I}.$$

Curves of this type are determined by means of measurements made in a spectrophotometer which is an instrument for

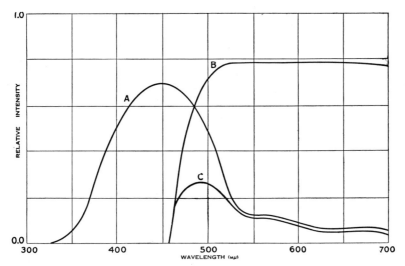

FIG. 4.2. Curves representing (a) the spectral sensitivity of a particular panchromatic emulsion, (b) the transmission curve of a yellow filter, and (c) the distribution of sensitivity with the filter.

making comparisons of light intensity in different parts of the spectrum.[1]

The absorption curve, in which density is plotted as a function of wave length, is more convenient than the transmission curve for calculations of (1) the effect of the dye concentration on the spectral absorption characteristics of the filter, (2) the absorption characteristics of a mixture of two or more dyes, or (3) the result obtained by superimposing filters. Thus to compute the curve for two dyes used together, or if certain corrections are made, two dyed gelatin filters superimposed, it is only necessary to add at each wave length the density values as determined in the spectrophotometer[2] in terms of I_0/I_x.

[1] Barton, A Textbook on Light, Longmans Green and Co., New York, 1939. Jacobs, *Fundamentals of Optical Engineering*, McGraw-Hill Book Co., New York.

[2] Spectrophotometric curves of more than 100 dyed gelatin filters will be found in Wratten Light Filters published by the Eastman Kodak Company, Rochester, N. Y. (1948).

The absorption of filters is frequently represented by wedge spectrograms. While useful for

The effect of a filter on the distribution of sensitivity for a particular photographic material may be found by multiplying, wave length by wave length, the ordinates of the curve representing the spectral response of the emulsion by those of the curve representing the transmission of the filter. In Fig. 4.2, for example, curve A represents the spectral sensitivity of a panchromatic material, B is the transmission curve of a yellow filter plotted on the same basis. By multiplying the ordinates of curve A by those of curve B at corresponding wave length, curve C representing the distribution of sensitivity of the film with the filter is obtained.

Filter Factors. When a filter is used which absorbs some of the radiation to which the photographic material is sensitive, (1) the exposure time, (2) the lens

comparative purposes, wedge spectrograms necessarily represent filter characteristics in terms of some particular light source and photographic material.

Photographic Filter Terminology and Nomenclature. ASA Standard Z52.61–1945.

aperture, or (3) the illumination on the subject must be increased to obtain the same exposure on the negative as when no filter is used. If any two of these are constant, the ratio of the third factor as required with the filter to the same factor without a filter is termed the *filter factor*. Thus, if the illumination on the subject and the lens aperture are constant, the filter factor is the ratio of the *times* of exposure with and without a filter, for the same effective exposure. A filter with a factor of 4 requires, under the same conditions, an increase of four times either in the time of exposure or in the lens aperture.[3]

The filter factor depends upon (1) the absorption characteristics of the filter, (2) the spectral energy distribution of the illumination on the subject, (3) the spectral sensitivity of the emulsion, and (4) processing conditions. If, for example, 75% of the total sensitivity of a blue-sensitive material lies within the blue and violet, then a color filter which absorbs the violet and blue completely, but transmits the remainder of the spectrum freely, will reduce the sensitivity to ¼ of its original value. Thus, to obtain the same effect with a filter, the exposure must be increased four times. On the other hand, if the same filter is used on a panchromatic material which has 50% of its sensitivity in the violet and blue, 25% in the green and 25% in the orange-red, the total sensitivity will

be reduced to but ½ of its original value and the filter factor will be 2×.

Tungsten light contains a relatively greater abundance of long-wave radiation (yellow, orange, and red) and less violet and blue than sunlight. Consequently, a larger proportion of the total effective sensitivity will be to long-wave radiation and a smaller amount to blue and violet than with sunlight. Thus, with tungsten light, the distribution of effective sensitivity for the hypothetical panchromatic material in the preceding paragraph may be blue-violet 30%, green 20%, and orange-red 40%. A yellow filter which absorbed violet and blue only would, in this case, reduce the total sensitivity of the material to only 60% of its original value, and the filter factor would be approximately 1.6.[4]

The variation in the filter factor with the time of development and other processing conditions depends upon the gamma-wave-length characteristics of the sensitive material and is discussed in greater detail in the section which follows.

Determination of the Filter Factor. The filter factor may be computed by integration from curves representing the distribution of sensitivity with wave length with and without the filter[5] or experimentally by sensitometric methods. For example in Fig. 4.3 curve *A* is the *D* log *E* curve of a

---

[3] Since practically all negative materials are subject to reciprocity law failure, the filter factor will depend upon which of the two factors—illumination or time—is increased to compensate for the absorption of the filter. In other words, the filter factor applying when the time of exposure is increased is not the same as when the lens aperture is increased. The difference, however, is small and may be ignored except in the exposure of color separation negative. See Tupper, "Filter Factors in Color Photography," *Phot.-Tech.* **2**, 29 (May 1940).

[4] With tungsten lamps, the filter factor will vary with the kind of lamp, its age, and the voltage at which it is operated. The factor is influenced at times by reflectors and diffusing materials. Filter factors vary also with variations in the spectral energy distribution of sunlight. Thus the factor of a yellow filter in the yellow light of late afternoon will tend to be less than at noon and the factor for a subject illuminated chiefly by reflected skylight will be different from one illuminated by direct sunlight. These variations, however, are seldom sufficient to be of much concern except in the exposure of three color separation negatives.

[5] Jones, *Trans. Soc. Mot. Pict. Eng.* No. 30 (1927), p. 135.

particular emulsion exposed without a filter, whereas curve *B* represents the same emulsion exposed under the same conditions, but with a filter, both strips being developed for the same time and plotted on the same log *E* scale, the exposure values used being those produced in the sensitometer *without* a filter. It will be noted that, although both strips were developed under

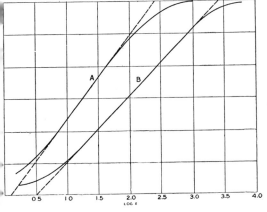

Fig. 4.3. *D* log *E* curves showing the effect of a filter on gamma. Both curves represent identical development conditions.

the same conditions, the gamma of curve A is greater than that of curve B; in other words, on this particular material, the effect of the filter used is to *lower* the gamma for a given time of development. This indicates that the gamma depends upon the spectral energy characteristics of the radiation to which the emulsion is exposed as well as on the time and conditions of development. Since the *D* log *E* curves are not parallel, it is clear that if the filter factor is determined by any of the usual methods (inertia, gradient, etc.), or from the exposures producing a given density, negatives exposed in accordance with the factor thus determined will match in density at only one point. This, however, is usually of minor importance in general photography if the densities which match

are within the density range of the average negative. In determining filter factors for three-color photography, the sensitometric strips should be developed to the same gamma and the filter factors determined from the ratio of the exposures for a common density on the straight line portion of the *D* log *E* curve.

It will be clear from the above that the factor of a filter, on the same emulsion, when used in exposing color separation negatives, will not be the same as for black and white photography, if in this case both negatives are developed alike.[6]

In practice, filter factors may be determined quite accurately without plotting the *D* log *E* curves, simply by comparing visually the densities on the two strips and determining the ratio of the exposures for a pair of steps having the same density. The matching of the densities may be accomplished simply and readily by placing the two strips side by side on an illuminator and sliding one up and down until a step with an equivalent density is found on the other strip. The filter factor is the ratio of the exposures for the two steps.

Filter factors may be determined without a sensitometer by (1) photographing a gray scale, or preferably a step wedge, with and without a filter, but the exposure differences must be known; and (2) by making a series of exposures—preferably by varying the lens aperture so as to avoid variations in shutter speed—of a black and white photograph with and without the filter. After developing, the negatives made without a filter are compared with those exposed with the filter and images selected which have equal densities in the most important parts of the subject. The filter factor is calculated from the ratio of the two exposures.

6 Jones, *Photographic Sensitometry*, Eastman Kodak Co., Rochester, N. Y., 1936. Tupper, *Photo-Technique* **2**, 32 (May 1940).

Factors determined in this way will apply, of course, only to the conditions under which the original negatives were exposed and developed.

Types of Filters. Filters may be divided broadly into two classes: (1) Those which transmit the entire visible spectrum, the transmission varying with the wave length, and (2) those in which the absorption for a part of the spectrum is, for practical purposes, complete. The spectrophotometric curves of two such filters are shown in Fig. 4.4; A is a light yellow filter (Kl) absorbing principally between 300–500 mμ, whereas B is a green transmitting filter with almost total absorption except for wave lengths between 480–610 mμ. Photographic filters of the first class are frequently referred to as "correction" or, at times, as "orthochromatic" filters because they are used to obtain a more nearly correct or orthochromatic reproduction of color. To produce the desired result a filter of this type must have the absorption characteristics necessary for the particular emulsion and light source with which it is used.[7]

Filters of the second class are commonly termed "contrast" or "color separation" filters because they are used to separate, i.e., to increase the contrast between one color and others that may be present. The filter represented by curve B, Fig. 4.4, for example, transmits green and absorbs violet, blue, and red. It will, therefore, reproduce green objects as white, or nearly so, and violet, blue, and red objects much darker—in many many cases as black. Filters of this type find many applications in commercial and technical photography, where it is necessary to emphasize one color

at the expense of others present in order to show the pattern, the structure, or to secure greater contrast between different areas of nearly the same brightness. Colors in the transmission range of a filter are reproduced light; those in the absorption range, dark.

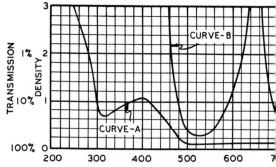

Fig. 4.4. Spectrophotometric curves of a typical (a) Correcting filter (Wratten No. 6, K$_1$) same as No. 1, and (b) A typical contrast filter (Wratten No. 68, B). (*Wratten Light Filters.*)

Graded Filters. A *graded* or *sky* filter is one in which the absorption increases from one side to the other. Usually in filters of this type the density of the filter dye, and therefore the factor, changes more or less uniformly from one side to the other but in some cases a filter of uniform density has been attached to a neutral wedge so that the light transmission is varied from side to side without alteration of the spectral absorption characteristics of the filter. If such a filter is placed well in front of

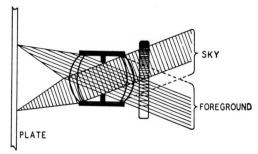

Fig. 4.5. The graded or sky filter. The effect varies with the distance between the filter and the lens.

---

[7] Color compensating filters used in color photography with integral tripack materials, or with tricolor cameras, to compensate for variations in the spectral energy distribution of the light with which the picture must be made, may be regarded as a special variant of this class of filter.

the lens, the action of the filter is restricted to the sky and distant portions of the landscape, the nearer objects being relatively unaffected. Thus it is possible to obtain clouds in the landscape without increasing the exposure. When orthochromatic materials were in general use, this was a decided advantage; with the high-speed panchromatic materials available today there is less need for the sky filter and it is now almost obsolete.

Optical Properties of Light Filters. Light filters are produced in one of three ways:

1. By dyeing thin sheets of gelatin [8] or a thermoplastic with suitable dyes to produce a gelatin film filter which may be used alone or cemented between glass for greater protection.[9]

2. By infusing molten glass or plastic during manufacture with suitable coloring materials.

3. By colored liquids contained in cells of glass or other suitable materials.

The first method is by far the most important. A large number of suitable dyes is available, and filters having almost any desired absorption characteristics may be prepared. The gelatin film is easily damaged, but this is avoided by cementing it between two pieces of glass. Filters produced in this manner are quite satisfactory if the cementing has been done properly

and the glass is flat; the only drawback is that heat, moisture, or excessive strain may cause the cement to soften, or give way, thus producing inequalities in the filter which affect its performance.

The number of colored substances which may be added to molten glass is rather limited and the production of colored glass filters has been hampered: (1) by the difficulty in finding substances having the required spectral absorption and (2) by the difficulty experienced in producing a uniform product. Recently, some success has been attained in the use of low temperature plastics in place of glass. Colored glass filters are rather more durable than those formed by cementing gelatin film between glass, but their absorption characteristics are not as well adapted to the requirements of modern color-sensitive materials.

Liquid filters are now seldom employed, except for laboratory use and then only when other types of similar absorption are unavailable, owing to their bulk, inconvenience, and rapid deterioration.

Gelatin film filters, owing to their thinness, are practically without effect on the definition of the lens.

For ordinary purposes, filters prepared by cementing the gelatin film between carefully selected pieces of optical glass are satisfactory if the cementing is done carefully to avoid strains in the glass. To insure satisfaction, however, only filters of the highest repute should be chosen. Cheap filters are poor economy; as filters, they are frequently ill adapted to the requirements of the sensitive material while the glasses used are neither plane nor parallel and the cementing faulty. With long focus and telephoto lenses and the large aperture lenses used on miniature cameras, it is especially important that only filters of the highest quality be used.

For three-color process work, filters cemented in optical flats and tested to work

---

[8] Synthetic resins have been patented to replace gelatin which is hygroscopic and therefore objectional from the standpoint of stability, but unfortunately most of the dyes used for filters are water-soluble and cannot be dissolved in synthetic resins. Certain of the polyvinyl acetates may be used, however, under certain conditions. See B.P. 537,578 (1938). Matthews and Atkins, assigned to Eastman Kodak Co.

[9] Formulas for the preparation of light filters: Hubl, *Die Photographischen Lichtfilter.* Hodgman, *Brit. J. Phot.* **69**, 6 (1922). Hnatek, *Brit. J. Phot.* **68**, 95 (1921). Gundlach, *Brit. J. Phot.* **77**, 61 (1930). Smith, *Brit. J. Phot.* **68**, 459 (1921).

together must be used if three equal-sized images are to be obtained.

Position of the Light Filter. The light filter may be placed in one of several positions:

1. *Over the light source.* This has the disadvantage in most cases of requiring large filters; on the other hand, the optical properties of the filter are not important as the definition of the lens is not affected. In general, this position is practical only where the light source is small, although filters over the light source have been used in motion picture photography and for infrared photography in total darkness.

2. *In front of the sensitive material.* This involves the use of larger filters than when placed over the lens and requires filters of good quality if the definition of the image is not to be affected. In this position, the plane of sharp focus is shifted forward by a distance equal to the thickness of the filter. This, however, is the most convenient position in tricolor cameras and in repeating backs for three-color photography.

3. *Between the lens combinations.* This position is possible only with the film filters and has the disadvantage that it is inconvenient to change the filter when another is required.

4. *Before the lens.* In general, this is the best position for the filter. It is more accessible and has the further advantage that any imperfections in the filter from an optical standpoint have less effect on the definition of the image than if placed behind the lens.

With all except film filters, there is a displacement of the image when a filter is used. A ray of light entering a glass filter is refracted upon entering and again by an equal amount *but in the opposite direction* upon emerging (Fig. 4.6). Thus, there is a

lateral displacement but not a change in direction. The displacement of the ray of light, however, has the effect of causing the emerging ray to have the effect of originat-

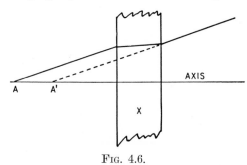

FIG. 4.6.

ing at a point nearer the filter. The distance between A and A' is

$$AA' = t \ (n-1)/n,$$

where A and A' are the real and apparent points of origin, t the thickness of the filter, and n the refractive index of the glass. If we assume the use of glass with a refractive index of 1.5, this means that when the filter is placed in front of the lens the distance of the object will be reduced by an amount equal to $\frac{1}{3}$ the thickness of the filter. This is of no practical significance with distant objects but may require consideration when photographing objects at or near exact size unless the image is focused on the ground glass with the filter in place over the lens.

5. *Behind the lens.* Again assuming the use of glass with a refractive index of 1.5, the effect of placing the filter *behind* the lens is to shift the point of sharp focus back away from the lens by a distance equal to $\frac{1}{3}$ the thickness of the filter. With ordinary glass filters, this shift in the position of the image is too great to be ignored and focusing scales must be corrected accordingly. Of course, if the image is focused on the ground glass with the filter in place, no correction need be made.

Care of Filters. Because gelatin filters are easily marked, they should be handled as little as possible. The best way to use them is, when possible, to place the filter between the combinations of the lens where it will be protected. Film filters may also be used in caps that slip on over the front of the lens, but exposure to moisture will in time cause them to cloud.[10]

Cemented filters should receive the same careful attention as a lens. They should be kept clean by polishing them from time to time with a piece of lens tissue or silk. If necessary, a clean cloth moistened with alcohol may be used to clean the glass surface of a filter. In doing so, care should be taken not to allow the alcohol to reach the edges, as the cement may be softened, allowing air to enter. Cemented filters should be protected from heat because, by its softening the balsam, a strain may be set up which may affect the definition of the lens with which the filter is used.

Most filters are quite stable to light; yet excessive exposure to strong light should be avoided.

Polarizing Screens. While polarizing screens are not color filters and only affect the rendering of color indirectly, there is a similarity in that both are used to control the tone values of a photographic image. The term *polarized,* as applied to light, does not have reference to its color nor its intensity, but to another property which, unlike the other two, is invisible and has to do with the way in which a ray of light vibrates. Ordinarily, the rays of light from the sun, or a source of artificial light, such as a tungsten lamp, vibrate in all directions at right angles to the ray itself. When the ray of light is polarized, however, the vibrations in all but one direction are cut out. A ray of light which is polarized will pass through a polarizing body if

the vibration of the ray is in line with the vibration plane of the body, but is absorbed more and more as the screen is rotated away from this position.[11]

Polarizing materials have been known for years but not until the introduction of *Polaroid* by Land [12] was it possible to obtain such material in a form suitable for photographic use and at a reasonable price. Polaroid combines a polarizing material in the form of minute-rod-like crystals parallel to one another, imbedded in a sheet of plastic. For photographic use, the sheet material is cemented between glass plates. Two types of polarizing screens are now available for photographic purposes; one for general use over the lens, the other for use over the light source.

Light which is polarized in one plane is fairly common; e.g., light from a clear blue sky at a right angle to the sun's rays is strongly polarized, and when this sky light is reflected from water, the reflected light is also polarized. In addition, light specularly reflected from any nonmetallic surface at an angle of approximately 32° to the surface is strongly polarized by the reflection. A lesser amount of polarization is produced at other angles of reflection, and none at zero or at an angle of 90°.

Polarizing screens over the lens alone are useful for:

1. *Controlling the brightness of the sky.* A polarizing screen placed over the lens enables the brightness of a clear blue sky to be darkened as desired simply by rotating the screen until the effect desired is obtained. The use of polarizing screens

---

[10] Some gelatin filters are now lacquered and may be cleaned with soft cloth.

[11] For a detailed explanation of polarization, see any standard text book on light, as, for example, Barton, *A Textbook on Light*, Longmans Green and Co., New York (1939); or Hardy and Perrin, *Principles of Optics*, McGraw-Hill Book Co., New York (1936).

[12] Land, U.S.P. 1,918,848; 1,951,664; 1,956,867; 1,989,371.

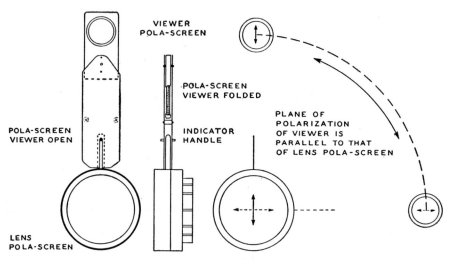

FIG. 4.7.   Pola-screen holder.

for controlling the brightness of the sky has the advantage over filters in that (1) the color rendering of the objects in the foreground is not altered, (2) filters may be used independently to secure the desired effect in the foreground, and (3) the effect produced by the polarizing screen is easily determined from the appearance of the image on the ground glass or in the finder.

Polarizing screens, however, are ineffective when photographing against the sun or directly away from it, or when the sky is overcast. The maximum effect is obtained when the sun is to one side of the camera at a right angle to the optical axis of the lens.

2. *Control of contrast.* The use of polarizing screens makes it possible with certain subjects to control the relative brightnesses of different parts of the image without changing the lighting. Among the subjects offering such possibilities are the walls and roofs of buildings, sunlit water, wet pavements, etc.

3. *Photographing through glass or water and to control reflections.* Reflections from glass, water, linoleum, polished woods, glass tile, painted and lacquered surfaces,

leather, fabric and other nonmetallic reflecting surfaces can be removed to show detail beneath by the use of a polarizing screen over the lens if the camera angle and the illumination are at an angle of approximately 30° to the surface. At other angles, the reflections may be partially but not entirely removed except at an angle of 90° when the polarizing screen is ineffective.

4. *As a neutral density filter.* Two polarizing screens used together in front of the lens form a variable neutral density filter with a density range of from 0.5 to 2.8 (transmission 32% to 0.16%).

On reflex and other cameras in which the image is focused on the ground glass, the effect produced by the polarizing screen may be determined from the appearance of the image on the screen. On twin-lens cameras, the effect may be determined by placing the screen on the viewing lens and then transferring—without change—to the camera lens. On other cameras, a small screen set in a handle rotating with the polarizing screen on the lens (Fig. 4.7) enables the user to determine the effect produced with the screen at different angles.

The use of a polarizing screen over the lens necessitates an increase in exposure of approximately four times with panchromatic and six times with orthochromatic material, but this exposure factor is the same for all positions of the screen.

When the light reaching the subject is polarized by means of polarizing screens placed over the light sources and a second polarizing screen is placed over the lens, the position of the camera and light source is not limited to a single effective angle as is the case when a single polarizing screen is used over the lens. Thus, by using polarizing screens over both the light sources and the lens, the commercial photographer is able to eliminate or at least greatly subdue troublesome reflections when photographing such subjects as oil paintings, carved and polished wood, lacquered surfaces, articles in transparent wrappings, glass, clinical specimens, in copying photographs on rough-luster papers, etc. The exposure is increased considerably, but in most cases this is of no consequence.

McFARLANE AND TUTTLE, "Photographic Possibilities of Polarized Light," *J. Soc. Mot. Pict. Eng.* **25**, 69 (1935).

McFARLANE, "Demonstration of Photography by Polarized Light," *J. Soc. Mot. Pict. Eng.* **26**, 679 (1936).

Chapter 5

PHOTOGRAPHIC SHUTTERS

Types of Shutters. There are two basic types of shutters in use today, the between-the-lens shutter and the curtain or focal-plane shutter. As the name implies, the between-the-lens shutter is located in an air space between the lens elements. The curtain, or focal-plane, shutter is directly in front of the sensitized material. A slit across the curtain admits light as the curtain moves over the film to make the exposure.

Each of these two types has its merits and shortcomings, making each particularly adaptable to specific photographic tasks, to be covered in later discussion.

Blade Movement. In between-the-lens shutters the light is admitted by the opening and closing of blades made of thin

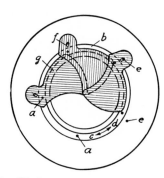

FIG. 5.1. Blade operation in a lens shutter.

material shaped and arranged to open from and close toward the center. For this reason between-the-lens shutters are sometimes called central shutters. Whereas cheap and simple shutters have only one or two blades with holes, which are driven across the lens aperture, better shutters

usually have from three to six blades, hinged about pivots and moved by pins closely adjacent to these pivots. Blade operation is illustrated in Fig. 5.1. Five pivots a are mounted in a blade ring b

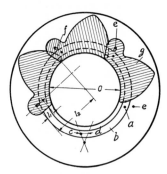

FIG. 5.2. Blades open.

which can be turned freely in both directions c and d. Pins e are mounted in a plate corresponding to the number of blades (in this case five) and slots f are provided in the blades g to control the movement of these blades. In Fig. 5.1 the blades are shown closed. If the blade ring is rotated in direction c, pivots a will force the blades to a rotating movement whereby slots f will slide around pins e until the blades are in the "open" position, admitting light freely through the aperture "O" (Fig. 5.2). Fig. 5.3 shows the blades in half open position whereby a star-shaped, small opening is formed, characteristic of all central shutters with more than two blades. The ratio between the length l_1 and l_2 (Fig. 5.2) explains why a relatively short movement of the blade ring pivot a will cause the relatively long opening movement of the blade within a very short time interval. Movement of the blade ring in one direction *c* will open the shutter, and movement in the opposite direction *d* closes it. Consequently, one full operating cycle of the shutter consists of

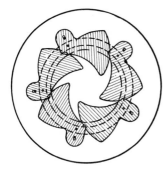

Fɪɢ. 5.3. Blades half closed.

ring and blade movement in one direction, stoppage of that movement, and then reversal. This acceleration, stoppage, and reversal of the masses consumes time and energy, and places limitations on the speed obtainable from this type of shutter. Attempts have been, and are still being, made to overcome these limitations. Shutters with double-ended blades were designed, shaped like two regular blades combined (Fig. 5.4). Arrangement of these double-ended blades is such that one end keeps the shutter closed; but, when actuated, they swing through in one direction, fully open the shutter, and as they continue their swing in the same direction, enter the shut-

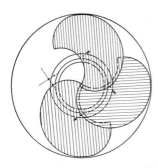

Fɪɢ. 5.4. Shutter with double-ended blades.

ter opening from the other side, thus closing the shutter in an uninterrupted operation. For the next operating cycle the blades must reverse their direction, a condition which requires special mechanical provisions. Obviously, in this manner higher top speeds can be achieved, since no time loss is suffered through stoppage and reversal of blade motion. This design requires larger shutter proportions, since the nearly double-size blades need a larger housing, which is its principal disadvantage.

The Diaphragm. In very simple shutters, the diaphragm consists of a disc, or strip, of metal with two or three holes of different diameter. In most shutters, however, an iris diaphragm is employed. The name "iris" diaphragm is derived from its resemblance to the iris in the human

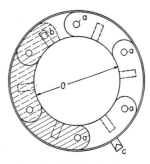

Fɪɢ. 5.5. Detail of iris diaphragm (open).

eye which enlarges and contracts concentrically, with the intensity of the light. The iris diaphragm consists of from 5 to 12 (or more) leaves which can be opened or closed by turning an indicator on the outside of the shutter case. The greater the number of diaphragm leaves, the more nearly will the aperture approach the shape of a perfect circle, although there is no actual need for a perfectly circular opening. The technical elements and their principal arrangement in an iris diaphragm are shown in Fig. 5.5, illustrating a six-leaf diaphragm. These arc-shaped leaves are

fastened to rotate about pins *a* mounted
circularly in the case. Above the leaves
a movable ring may be placed, slotted to
receive pins *b* on the opposite end of the
leaves. By turning this ring, pivots *b*, en-
gaged by the slots, force the leaves to rotate
about pivots *a*, thus increasing or decreasing the size of the diaphragm opening.
Fig. 5.5 shows the diaphragm at full aper-

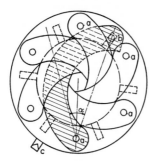

Fig. 5.6.   Detail of iris diaphragm
(partly closed).

ture. By turning the ring clockwise, the
diaphragm opening is reduced and is shown
at minimum aperture in Fig. 5.6. The ring
is usually connected with outside indicator
c which moves over corresponding aperture
"stop-numbers" on the face plate of the
shutter. A large number of leaves requires

greater axial space. High-speed lenses usually allow only a small air space between
front and back elements; hence fewer leaves
are preferred in modern shutters.

**Source of Energy in Between-the-Lens
Shutters.** The blade movement (opening
and closing the shutter) needs a source of
energy, or motor, which in practically all
shutters consists of a spring to be wound
up before every operation. This winding-
up, called "setting" or "cocking" the shutter, is a separate operation in all *pre-set*
shutters. In *automatic* shutters the spring
winding is performed by the same lever
that releases the shutter, thus combining
setting and releasing into one operation.
The release operation of the shutter must
be smooth to avoid jarring the camera.
For this reason the combined set-and-release
operation cannot cope with springs requiring great winding effort. Therefore, automatic shutters do not yield speeds as high
as those of the pre-set shutter which can
be built with stronger springs. A sketch
of a winding mechanism in a pre-set shutter is shown in Fig. 5.7. To hold the
wound-up spring *h* in its set-position a
latch-lever *i* snaps into a latch *p* of set-

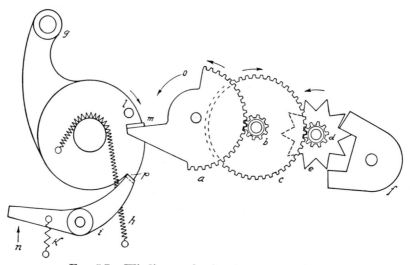

Fig. 5.7.   Winding mechanism in a pre-set shutter.

lever g. When the release-lever or trigger (not shown) actuates latch-lever i in the indicated direction n, the wound-up set-lever g returns (clockwise) to its original position under the driving power of spring h, actuating suitably arranged levers (not shown) which operate the reciprocating movement of the blade ring, thus opening and closing the shutter as previously described.

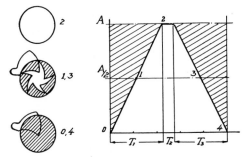

FIG. 5.8. Graphical representation of shutter operation at maximum speed.

Fig. 5.8 represents a graphic interpretation of a complete shutter operating cycle at maximum speed. It is assumed (1) that the opening time is $2\frac{1}{4}$ milliseconds (one millisecond is 1/1000th of a second), (2) that the closing operation requires the same, and (3) the blades stay open for only $\frac{1}{2}$ millisecond. A shutter with double-ended blades, as shown in Fig. 5.9 has no stopping or reversing action, and therefore closes immediately following the open-

ing period, as shown in Fig. 5.8. Obviously, it must be possible to take a picture using a longer exposure time, with full aperture. Hence, the only period in the entire shutter operating cycle to be retarded for longer exposure time is the fully open period (time T_2 in the example of Fig. 5.8, lasting only $\frac{1}{2}$ millisecond).

Retarding Mechanism. To obtain a range of speeds, a retarding mechanism is required. A well-designed retarder must

1. Slow down the shutter mechanism during the wide open period.
2. Be easily adjustable to the speeds required.
3. Provide speed settings which can be uniformly repeated.

During the evolution of the shutter in the past sixty years many different kinds of retarding devices have been used, from simple friction devices to air brakes. Many of these proved unreliable because of changing conditions due to wear, temperature, and climate. Temperature change, for example, influences density of the air and with it the retarding power of the air brake. The wheel retarder, which is not influenced by temperature changes, has superseded all other retarders. Its principle is relatively simple. A rotating movement is transformed into short oscillating movements of an element of relatively heavy weight. The

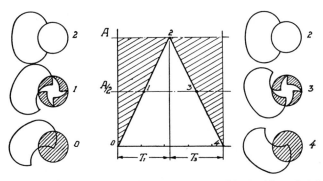

FIG. 5.9. Graphical representation of shutter with double-ended blades.

inertia of this oscillating weight retards the driving movement, similar to the action of an escapement in clocks and watches. The oscillating element is called a "pallet," and its oscillation is the result of its coordinated movement with a star-shaped ratchet wheel; Fig. 5.10 demonstrates the two phases of a pallet functioning as retarder. A star

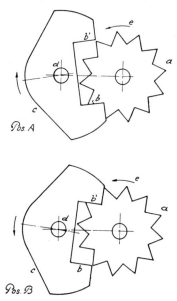

FIG. 5.10. Two phases in the functioning of the retarding mechanism of a lens shutter.

wheel *a* fits into the jaws *b* and *b'* of a pallet *c* in such close coordination that its rotation (indicated in counterclockwise direction by arrow *e*) pushes the pallet out of its way (position *A*). Simultaneously the other jaw *b'* of the pallet is moved into the path of the star wheel (position *B*). The star wheel, always driven in the same direction, now repulses the pallet from its path to the opposite direction, thus causing the oscillating movement of the pallet, in turn retarding the star wheel which might otherwise rotate freely. The retarding power of such a device can be increased by increasing the weight of the pallet, or by increasing its inertia by giving it special

shape, or by imparting greater frequency to the oscillating movement. Of these three factors, faster oscillation exerts the greatest influence on retardation. This is the reason why the star wheel is located at the end of a gear-train in all shutters. Fig. 5.7 shows such a gear-train with star-wheel and pallet. If the first wheel *a* has, for example, 50 teeth, and the pinion on axle *b* has 10 teeth, one rotation of wheel *a* will cause 5 times as many or 5 rotations of axle *b*. On the same axle *b* there is another wheel *c* with 50 teeth driving axle *d* also with a 10-tooth pinion. The same gear ratio will drive axle *d* 5 times as fast as axle *b* and 25 times as fast as axle *a*. Now assume that the star wheel *e* on axle *d* has 10 teeth and rotates 25 times in the same time interval during which gear *a* has turned only once. Since every star-wheel tooth entering the jaws of the pallet *f* causes a single oscillation, the pallet will oscillate 250 times for every one turn of gear *a*, based on the established ratio, thus resulting in considerable retardation. In actual practice, the first wheel usually does not make a complete revolution. The arm *m* of the first gear *a*, hit by pin 1 of spring-driven set lever, or motor member *g* sets the entire gear train in motion. The retarding power of the gear train in motion reacts to motor member *g*, thus slowing its action, that of opening and closing the shutter blades. This motion, completed in a fraction of a second without the retarding mechanism, will now, under the reacting retardation of gear train and pallet, perhaps require about one second.

If by a cam, or other speed-regulating mechanism, arm *m* is moved partly out of the path of pin *l*, as indicated by arrow *o* in Fig. 5.7, it is obvious that only part of the motion will be retarded, thus resulting in a speed of less than 1 second, e.g., ½, ⅕, or ⅒ of a second. Thus the retarding mechanism controls all instantaneous speeds and, although this presentation covers the basic principles, there are many modifications in actual design.

Time and Bulb Exposures. For time exposures the settings B and T are provided on the speed control ring. By turning the speed control ring to B, an interceding lever of suitable shape is shifted into the path of the motor member g stopping its spring driven motion at the very instant when the shutter blades are wide open. This stoppage will last as long as the finger release lever is depressed. On being released the interceding lever is removed and motor member g is set free to continue its closing motion. At setting T another lever is placed across the path of the motor member g by the speed control cam, which again stops the motion of the shutter mechanism at full opening, but needs a second tripping of the trigger to remove it permitting the shutter to close. In certain small shutters used exclusively on hand-held cameras, the T setting is omitted, since the B setting allows for adequate time exposures, thus resulting in a simpler mechanism.

Press-Focus Adjustment. In some shutters an additional lever or push button is found—the so-called "press focus button." It is primarily required by, and was originally designed for, the press photographer. This press focus button facilitates ground-glass focusing by eliminating the need for resetting on T and, after focusing, returning to the desired speed setting. In some shutters the press focus button must be depressed and the trigger actuated simultaneously (Kodak); in others a separate lever opens and closes the shutter blades (Wollensak); and in still others depressing the push button automatically opens the shutter, necessitating only recocking the shutter for the next exposure (Ilex).

Synchronization for Flash Lamps. The principal requirements of a good synchronizer in a shutter are as follows:

(a) The shutter must function properly with all types of flash lamps,

(b) After time delay for a certain type lamp has once been set synchronization must be correctly maintained.

Principle of Built-in Synchronizers. The primary technical principle of all synchro-devices in shutters with built-in synchronization is an electric switch mechanism. First it closes the electric circuit ahead of the shutter opening so that after the required time-delay (5, 20, 23 milliseconds) the full opening of the shutter is simultaneous with the flash peak. Fig. 5.11 is a diagram of the basic design of the Ilex "Acme Snychro" shutter. If synchro-lever 1 has been set by being locked

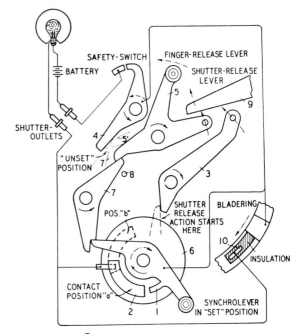

FIG. 5.11. A flash-lamp synchronization mechanism of the Acme Synchro Shutter.

through latch-lever 7, release of trigger 5 will actuate latch-lever 7 and permit synchro-lever 1 with its contact to slide over contact 2, closing the flash bulb circuit. After having traveled for a predetermined time, synchro-lever 1 hits lever 3 starting the shutter release 9. Stop 8 prevents trigger 5 from releasing the shutter if synchronizer is set. The duration of time-delay between closure of the electric circuit and start of the shutter opening can be adjusted by means of control disc 6 which carries contact 2. If adjustable contact 2 is in position *a*, contact will be made shortly after synchro-lever has started its travel; in other words, the longest available time-delay elapses from the time the electric circuit was closed until the time of shutter release. If contact 2 is shifted into the dotted position *b*, contact will be made shortly before shutter opening, the first part of the path being traveled through idly, resulting in shorter time lag. Safety-switch 4 is controlled by the trigger as well as latch-lever 7 in their "unset" positions, as indicated in the diagram by 5' and 7'. This safety-switch keeps the electric circuit automatically interrupted just so long as the synchro-lever is not set for action and the trigger is not operated. This establishes a fully independent synchro-unit which is wound up and brought into coordination with the regular shutter mechanism by setting the synchro-lever.

To secure perfectly synchronized flash with X type High Speed lamps at full shutter opening, the Ilex shutter has a second contact 10. For 0 (zero) or X setting, the control disc 6 is turned clockwise so far that it moves contact 2 entirely out of the reach of synchro-lever 1. Going through the same mechanical operation, synchro-lever 1 will release shutter over lever 3 without closing the electric circuit. The blades, moving into a predetermined position at full shutter opening, now closes

the firing circuit over the second contact 10. The setting of the synchro-lever provides in this case not only mechanical shutter release but permits also the safety-switch 4 to keep the electric circuit uninterrupted and ready for closure through the bladering contact.

The Kodak "Flash Supermatic" shutter with built-in flash synchronization also has a separate setting lever, whereas the Wollensak "Rapax" needs no extra cocking, but requires setting the time-delay indicator back to the "Off" position, in case a flash lamp should be in the battery case and no circuit closure for synchro-flash is desired. The flash contacts in the new Kodak "Synchro Rapid 800" shutter are automatic in operation and, therefore, no special cocking for flash is required.

Shutter Speeds and Exposure Time. The concept of shutter speed is not as simple as it seems and requires exact definition. Consider a complete shutter operation cycle as graphically represented in Fig. 5.12. In this graph the opening of the

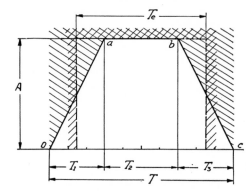

Fig. 5.12. Graph representing the opening of a lens shutter plotted against the time.

shutter is plotted in relation to time. At start of the shutter operation, i.e., at the instant of shutter release (time $t = 0$) the shutter blades begin to open. Time T_1 is required by the shutter to open fully aperture A (point *a*). The shutter blades stay wide open for a time, T_2 (from a to b), after which the shutter begins to close again. After elapse of closing time T_3 the entire cycle is completed, having consumed the "Total Open Time T." Assume that Total Open Time T is 1/100th of a second = 10/1000th of a second, or 10 milliseconds. Obviously, the actual amount of light admitted is not all the light which could pass were aperture A fully open during the entire cycle (Total Open Time), because a considerable part of it has been consumed by the opening and closing period, during which only a part of full aperture A admitted light. As can be seen from Fig. 5.12, the shutter was wide open only during time T_2.

Efficiency of Between-the-Lens Shutters. The actual exposure time, therefore, will be the time which would permit an equivalent amount of light to pass through an ideal shutter, i.e., one in which the full aperture is open during the entire operation cycle. The area within the line o-a-b-c in Fig. 5.12 represents a measure of the actual amount of light admitted during the entire shutter operating cycle. By geometrical relation this trapezoidal area is

$$A. \left(T - \frac{T_1 + T_3}{2} \right), \quad \text{whereby}$$

$$\left(T - \frac{T_1 + T_3}{2} \right) = T_e,$$

the effective exposure time.

The Total Open Time T would be equal to the actual or effective exposure time T_e, if a shutter existed which could open and close so rapidly that the two periods T_1 and T_3 would become infinitely small. Fig. 5.13 is an operating diagram of such an ideal shutter of 100% efficiency, but this, of course, is practically impossible; therefore, the efficiency of a shutter at full aperture is always below 100% and may be expressed mathematically by the ratio of the

effective exposure time T_e to the Total Open Time T

$$\text{Efficiency} \quad E = \frac{T_e}{T} \cdot 100\%$$

$$= \left(\frac{T}{T} - \frac{T_1 + T_3}{2T} \right) \cdot 100\%$$

$$= \left(1 - \frac{T_1 + T_3}{2T} \right) \cdot 100\%.$$

It can be seen from this formula that the Efficiency E would become 100% if the subtracted part, consisting of T_1 and T_3, would become zero, i.e., if opening and

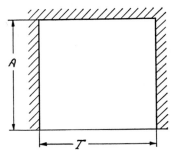

FIG. 5.13. Graph representing the operation cycle of an "ideal" shutter with an efficiency of 100%.

closing time were to disappear. In a correctly designed shutter, the opening and closing times remain constant for any speed, since only time T_2, during which the shutter blades stay wide open, is prolonged for longer exposures. It can further be seen that term $\dfrac{T_1 + T_3}{2T}$ will become smaller, as T, Total Open Time, becomes larger, since T appears in the denominator, while the numerator remains constant. This may be proved graphically in Fig. 5.14, where the opening and closing times already appear to be relatively small as compared with Total Open Time T. In other words, efficiency quickly improves with longer exposure times, and consequently, the effective or actual exposure time will not differ much from the Total Open Time T. An example with actual figures will make this clear. Assume that a shutter has a top speed of 5 milliseconds Total Open Time. The worst possible performance from any shutter of this type is that case wherein Total Open Time consists only of opening time T_1 and closing time T_3, and where no time is left for the wide open period T_2. As a practi-

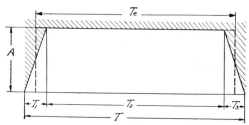

FIG. 5.14. Graph representing the operation cycle of an efficient lens shutter.

cal example, this case could occur with a double-ended blade shutter, where there is no reversal of blade movement; hence no stoppage of blades occurs when wide open. The operating diagram of such a shutter is shown in Fig. 5.15. The shutter opens in

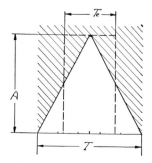

FIG. 5.15. Graph representing the operation cycle of a double-ended blade shutter.

$2\frac{1}{2}$ milliseconds and immediately starts to close, completing its closure in another $2\frac{1}{2}$ milliseconds. The actual exposure time T_e would be

$$T_e = T - \frac{T_1 + T_3}{2} = 5 - \frac{2.5 + 2.5}{2}$$

$$= 2.5 \text{ milliseconds,}$$

2.5 milliseconds corresponds to 1/400 of a second effective exposure time. The efficiency in this case is:

$$E = \left(1 - \frac{T_1 + T_3}{2T} \right) \cdot 100\%$$

$$= \left(1 - \frac{5}{10} \right) \cdot 100\% = 50\%.$$

In other words, the lowest possible efficiency in a between-the lens shutter can be no less than 50%.[1] Now, assume that an exposure time of 1/25th of a second or 40 milliseconds is desired. If the effective exposure time T_e is to be 40 milliseconds, the Total Open Time T must be $42\frac{1}{2}$ milliseconds in a shutter with opening and closing time of $2\frac{1}{2}$ milliseconds each. The efficiency in this case is

$$E = \left(1 - \frac{5}{85} \right) \cdot 100\%$$

$$= (1 - 0.0588) \cdot 100\% = 94.12\%.$$

With an actual exposure time of 1/25th of a second, the Total Open Time T and the effective exposure time T_e are not much different (only 6%), since the efficiency has risen to about 94%. It is to be noted, also, that in the previous example of 5 milliseconds Total Open Time, the actual exposure time was 1/400th of a second, although 5 milliseconds are equivalent to 1/200th of a second. This enormous discrepancy was caused by the 50% efficiency at top speed.

Possible Exposure Errors. The length of exposure time is not the only factor that influences shutter efficiency. Efficiency and effective exposure time also depend considerably on the chosen aperture. If, for example, the diaphragm has been stopped down two stops, which means that the lens aperture has been reduced to one quarter of its full light-admitting area, the effi-

[1] All statements to the effect that shutter efficiency may run lower than 50% are therefore wrong.

-iency of 50% (Fig. 5.15) will be changed decidedly, as shown in Fig. 5.16. Assuming that opening time T_1 and closing time T_3 are reduced to one fourth the original opening and closing times at full aperture

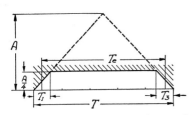

FIG. 5.16. Graph of the operation cycle of a lens shutter showing the effect of the size of the diaphragm on exposure.

and that T_1 and T_3 are equal, which is correct for all practical purposes,

$$T_1 = T_3 = \frac{2.5}{4} = 0.625 \text{ milliseconds.}$$

The actual exposure time will be $T_e = 5 - 0.625 = 4.375$ milliseconds or 1/230th of a second. This considerable difference in effective exposure time reveals a considerable change in efficiency which now is

$$E = \left(1 - \frac{1.25}{10}\right) \cdot 100\% = 87.5\%$$

(compared with only 50% at full aperture). The actual amount of light admitted in this case is

$$\frac{A}{4} \cdot 4.375 = 1.094A.$$

A photographer who expects an exposure time of $\frac{A}{4} \cdot 2.5 = 0.625A$ with the diaphragm stopped down to one quarter of full aperture would, therefore, overexpose 75%, if he were not aware of this efficiency change. Were he aware of the changed efficiency (87.5%) at the smaller opening, he would have figured $5 \cdot 0.875 \cdot \frac{1}{4} A = 1.094 A$ and accordingly would have exposed correctly.

This example was chosen to show that not only speed, but aperture as well, affects the efficiency of a shutter. This explains why an exact definition of speed is not easy, and also why data on shutter efficiency at top speed and at full aperture is of little help to the practical photographer, who certainly cannot be burdened with lengthy calculations or elaborate tables whenever he changes speed or aperture.

Fortunately, the situation is not so critical in practice, because small apertures and top speeds are rarely used in combination, especially with slow color film, the small latitude of which allows for no such error.

With slower speeds, an error resulting from change of aperture is not very great. For example, at a speed of 1/100th of a second (10 milliseconds), the operation diagram of that same shutter would appear like Fig. 5.17. With opening and

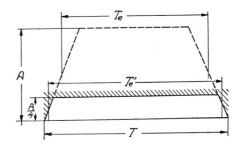

FIG. 5.17. Graph of the operation cycle of a lens shutter at 1/100 second.

closing time T_1 and T_3 remaining constant at all speeds (in the chosen example 2.5 milliseconds each), the effective exposure time at full aperture $T_e = 10$ milliseconds and the efficiency of the shutter is

$$E = \left(1 - \frac{T_1 + T_3}{2T}\right) \cdot 100\%$$

$$= \left(1 - \frac{5}{25}\right) \cdot 100\% = 80\%,$$

and the Total Open Time is 12.5 milliseconds. At an aperture equal to one-quarter of full aperture, the efficiency would then become

$$E = \left(1 - \frac{1.25}{25}\right) \cdot 100\% = 95\%,$$

since all figures remained constant except opening and closing time which were reduced to one-quarter of corresponding periods of full aperture. The effective exposure time would be $T.E. = 11.875$ milliseconds. The actual amount of light admitted, considering the smaller aperture, would be $11.875 \cdot \frac{A}{4} = 2.969\ A$ compared to the (erroneously) expected exposure of $\frac{10}{4} A = 2.5\ A$. In this case the error amounts to only 18% which lies suitably within the latitude of color film.

To minimize exposure errors at top speeds (1/300th or 1/400th of a second and beyond) it has been suggested to determine the efficiency E, not at maximum shutter opening but at half the area of the maximum shutter opening. By comparing the diagram in Fig. 5.18 with that in Fig. 5.15, the difference is readily noted. Efficiency E at half the area is now

$$E = \left(1 - \frac{T_1 + T_3}{2T}\right) \cdot 100\%$$

$$= \left(1 - \frac{2.5}{10}\right) \cdot 100\% = 75\%.$$

If the photographer considers his shutter to be 75% efficient at top speed, he would only make the following errors in changing aperture:

TABLE 5.1

Aperture	Total Open Time	Opening and Closing Time	Efficiency	Actual Amount of Light Admitted	Amount of Light Expected if E is Considered Constant at 50%	Exposure Error in % ($E=50\%$)	Amount of Light Expected if E is Considered Constant at 75%	Exposure Error in % ($E=75\%$)
A	T	$T_1 + T_3$	E	$T_e \cdot A$				
1	5	5	50%	2.5	2.5	0%	3.75	−33%
½	5	2.5	75%	1.88	1.25	+50%	1.88	0%
¼	5	1.25	87.5%	1.06	0.625	+75%	0.94	+10%

These phenomena are the result of geometric conditions and cannot be escaped. The object lesson is that slower speeds are the means to accurate exposure wherever change of aperture is involved.

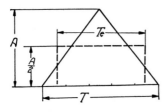

FIG. 5.18. Graph of the operational cycle of a lens shutter showing method of determining efficiency (E) from half the maximum diaphragm opening.

From Table 5.1 it is seen that the maximum error is only 33% if the shutter is considered 75% efficient, as against a maximum error of 75%, if efficiency at maximum aperture is considered as the basis of computation.

Most photographers are not concerned with efficiency, and rightly so; but to those who are, this demonstrates the difficulty of stating definite speeds for a shutter. It is impossible to make positive statements as to shutter speed unless all circumstances and influencing factors are carefully considered. As previously pointed out, the error is considerable only at the highest speed where efficiency might drop almost o 50% (see graph in Fig. 5.19). The graph shows how quickly efficiency increases at small apertures as well as at lower speeds.

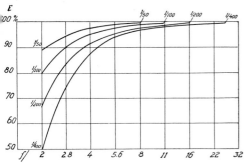

FIG. 5.19. Shutter efficiency in relation to exposure time and f/number.

Exposure to Stop Motion. Stopping motion with high-speed exposure deserves consideration because of popular misconceptions:

(1) An absolute motion-stopping speed is nonexistent; although the outlines in the picture appear to be sharp and clearly defined, blurr resulting from motion is merely not visible to the unaided eye.

(2) With increasing enlargement this blurr becomes increasingly visible; there-fore, the degree of final enlargement governs the amount of permissible blurr.

(3) The angle between the line of motion and the focal plane controls the depicted travel of a moving object and, therefore, determines the maximum shutter speed to be used.

The diagrams in Fig. 5.20 show how direction of motion influences the extent of blurr. When the angle is zero, or the direction of motion is parallel to the film plane, the recorded travel of a moving object may have length a. When the angle (b in Fig. 5.20) lies between 0° and 90°, length b is recorded; whereas with the movement directly toward the camera (90° angle), only a point c is registered, which means that despite the object movement a considerably lower shutter speed is permissible.

Testing of Shutter Speeds. There are basic methods of measuring shutter speed: (1) actual light admitted, (2) "Total Open Time," and (3) methods recording the complete cycle of shutter operation through its three periods.

Complete measurements of shutter speeds must show the three important periods of

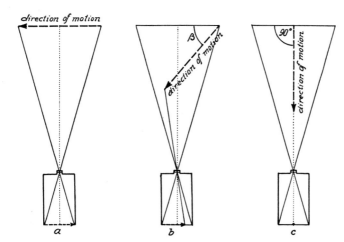

Fig. 5.20. Effect of direction of a moving object on the displacement of the image on the film.

the entire shutter operation cycle, the opening, the wide open, and the closing period.

Because of their very nature, methods measuring actual amount of light admitted are the simplest. Many of them can be performed by any amateur of even little mechanical ability.

Measurement of Actual Exposure Time. A simple, and for all practical purposes sufficiently exact, method is the measurement of actual exposure time by the result as it appears on the exposed film. It is based on the assumption (not absolutely correct scientifically) that, for example, 200 exposures at 1/200th of a second and one single exposure at one second will produce the same negative density. The practical tester will, for example, compare 20 times 1/200th with 10 times 1/100th, or with 5 times 1/50th, or with 1/10th (or 5 times 1/25th with two times 1/10th, or with one 1/5th). If the recorded density on the film is uniform, then speeds may be assumed to be approximately correct.

Other simple methods for testing shutter speeds are based on making a photographic record of a body moving at a known velocity. To mention only a few of these, the full swing of a pendulum with predetermined period of oscillation, or the trace of any object falling freely under the acceleration of gravity. In this latter case the calculation is based on the well-known formula $v = 2gs$ in which g is the acceleration of gravity (980.6 cm. per sec.^{2}) and s is the space through which the body has fallen up to the moment when the recording of its speed begins.

Another means of achieving a predetermined speed is that of using a white mark on the turntable of a phonograph, or a disc driven by a synchronous motor.

In all these methods the moving object will record a trace on the negative, the length of which will permit evaluation of the time the shutter was open. A con-

venient modification of these methods consists in photographing a Neon lamp while moving the camera. In this case the camera need not be moved at any specific speed, since Neon lamps glow alternately with the frequency of AC current. For example, on 60 cycle AC current, the Neon lamp will glow 120 times per second and a series of bright dots similar to beads on a string will be recorded, each dot representing 1/120th of a second. Obviously, this latter method can be used only for testing speeds up to 1/100th of a second, or slower.

It should be remembered that all these methods record actual exposure time, since the opening and closing time of the shutter will be recorded only in part. The records all begin and end in a faded line, becoming brighter and stronger as the opening increases. Since the exact point where the visible trace begins to be recorded on the film cannot be accurately determined, these methods are sufficiently accurate for all practical purposes, but they do not render an exact picture of the entire shutter operation cycle.

Measurement of Total Open Time and Efficiency. Measurement of Total Open Time and Efficiency is only possible with more complicated apparatus. Some of these methods are based on the principle of recording the opening and closing of the shutter on a moving film; others employ electronic methods of time measurement.

Electronic methods are being used to measure the amount of light admitted as well as the Total Open Time. In measuring the amount of light admitted a photoelectric cell charges a condenser as soon as the shutter begins to open, and the charging stops at the instant closure is complete. The greater the amount of light passing through the shutter, the greater will be the electrical charge of the condenser. By discharging the condenser into a ballistic galvanometer the amount of the charge will be indicated. If correctly calibrated, the galvanometer reading will give a measurement of the amount of light actually admitted.

To measure Total Open Time, an electronic circuit is employed which measures the time interval from the very beginning of light admission to its very end, and not, as in the previous case, the actual amount of admitted light. This "Total Open Time" remains the same regardless of diaphragm opening chosen, since the shutter opens from the center and closes toward the center.

A very exact method of recording the entire shutter operating cycle was developed by A. H. Katz, of the Aerial Photographic Laboratory at Wright Field, during the war.

Testing for Synchronization. The problem here is to measure the time-lag between the closing of the electric circuit and the instant the shutter is wide open. Again, testing principles may be classified into (1) those producing a photographic record and (2) those based on electronic devices. Electronic methods are faster and therefore more suitable for testing shutters in large numbers.

The simplest method, which may be applied by any amateur photographer, consists of photographing a flashing bulb. A piece of bromide paper (in place of the film) exposed at the top shutter speed with the synchronizer in action will show, after development, a picture of the flash bulb. If the flash bulb appears absolutely black, the shutter is well synchronized; but, if it is partly shaded or if the fine wires or foil shreds can be seen, synchronization is not accurate. If, with the same synchro-setting, another picture is taken at a slower speed, and a well-exposed picture of the lamp is obtained, it proves that the synchro-delay is too short, and this is now compensated for by the longer exposure. If no picture

is obtained even then, time-lag is too long, i.e., the shutter does not begin its operating cycle until after the flash bulb had already reached its peak.

Various electronic devices have been designed which permit fast and reliable determination of the accuracy of synchronization. One of these methods involves a basic electronic circuit with a thyatron tube, a condenser, and a resistor. A condensor is charged from the instant the electric circuit of the synchronizer closes. At the start of the shutter opening, light passes through the opening blades, activating a photocell which in turn stops charging of the condenser. The amount of charge in the condenser is a measure of the time interval between circuit closing and shutter opening. This condenser charge is applied to a degenerative vacuum tube voltmeter which, calibrated in time units, directly indicates the elapsed time.

Technical Aspects of Higher Shutter Speeds. With the advent of faster emulsions and lenses of larger aperture, a demand for still higher shutter speeds has developed. Although ordinarily it is seldom that the top speed of present-day shutters is required, there does exist for certain purposes a definite need for still higher shutter speeds. Attempts to design between-the-lens shutters with higher speeds are being made constantly, but the problem is extremely difficult and no satisfactory solution is in sight at present. The problems involve mechanical considerations and, to a lesser degree, limitations in size and cost. For example, the parts of a shutter blade, pins, pivots, etc., must be as light as possible but sufficiently strong to withstand the strains set up in the rapid movements in opening, stoppage and closing, which involves a reversal of motion. Since the blades must be close together to be light-tight, friction is inevitable. Stronger springs would provide greater power for higher speeds but would increase strain and result in greater wear and tear of all parts. Heavier parts to withstand the added strain, would require more space and increased driving power of the spring. Jewel bearings would lessen friction but cannot withstand the shocks and rough handling which many shutters receive. Lastly, all of these would require a larger and more costly shutter, and the trend in modern hand cameras is toward greater compactness, thus limiting the over-all size of the shutter.

All this should not be construed to mean that faster shutters cannot or will not be designed. Attempts to design shutters with higher speeds are continually being made. Besides the aforementioned method involving double-ended blades, some inventors have attempted to use two sets of blades timed so that one set is opening while the other is closing. This idea is not new and has been revived time and again. The principal objection to such a mechanism is that in the achievement of higher speeds the blades of the open set will have to start closing even before the closed set has completed its opening. Consequently, they will meet somewhere in a half-open and half-closed position, reducing maximum aperture just when it is most needed.

Focal-Plane Shutters. The focal-plane shutter has provided one answer to the need for extremely high shutter speeds up to 1/1000th of a second and higher.

Focal-plane shutters operate according to an entirely different mechanical principle. Instead of moving blades between the lens elements, a curtain is positioned near the focal-plane. The curtain is opaque and highly flexible and is tensioned between two rollers. A slit in the curtain across the line of movement admits light to the film, and various adjustable spring tensions pull the curtain across the focal-plane at different speeds. Slits of different width in combination with different spring tensions result in a great variety of speeds.

Total Exposure Time vs. Local Exposure Time. Distortion. Fig. 5.21 indicates the outlines of the picture size *a*, the curtain *c* with slit *s*. When curtain *c* moves across frame *a*, slit *s* admits light to the film. Unlike the between-the-lens shutter, such an

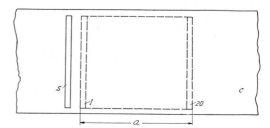

Fig. 5.21   Exposure with the focal plane shutter.

exposure will not be completed at the same instant, but rather strip by strip. Assume that slit *s* equals 1/20 of frame size *a*, then exposure of the entire frame is actually accomplished in consecutive strips of width *s*. The fact that there is no reversal from an opening to a closing movement, as in a between-the-lens shutter, but only one continuous motion also accounts for faster speed. It should be observed that "Total Exposure Time" is the time from exposure of the first strip of the film to the moment when the last strip has been exposed, while "Local Exposure Time" is the period in which each point on the film is actually exposed. If, for example, 1/1000th of a second (one millisecond) exposure time is required, and the curtain has been adjusted so that it moves at such a speed that the width of slit *s* is traversed in that exact time, then the last strip "20" in Fig. 5.21 will be traversed 20/1000 (20 milliseconds) after the first width "1" has been exposed. Obviously, a fast moving object photographed at 1/1000th of a second may well be "stopped" in motion and a satisfactorily sharp picture, strip by strip, may result.

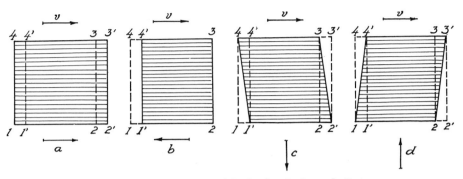

FIG. 5.22. Distortion with the focal plane shutter.

However, after 20 milliseconds, when the last strip is being exposed, the position of the fast moving object might well have changed in the interim, inevitably resulting in a distortion of the pictured object. The extent of this distortion will depend largely on the relationship between the direction of the moving object and the direction of the moving curtain slit. A square-shaped object, moving left to right in the focal plane at a certain speed v in Fig. 5.22, moves from its original position (1, 2, 3, 4) to its new position (1', 2', 3', 4'). If the curtain travels in the same direction a in Fig. 5.22, and requires the same time for the complete cycle of exposure from the very first strip to the last, this last strip of film will be exposed when the image of the square in the film plane has already moved to the new position (1', 2', 3', 4'). Consequently, the image of the square will assume rectangular shape (1, 2', 3', 4) in Fig. 5.22a, i.e., it will appear longer (distorted). Should the slit move in a direction opposite to that of the pictured object motion, as indicated by arrow b, then the image of the square will become rectangular with shortened horizontal sides (1', 2, 3, 4') in Fig. 5.22b. If the curtain moves in the direction of arrow c, then the last strip at the bottom will be exposed when the edges (1, 2) will have moved to a new position (1', 2'), and the resulting image

of the square will be distorted into a parallelogram (1', 2', 3, 4) in Fig. 5.22c. With the curtain moving in direction d, the last strip will image line (3, 4) in the new position (3', 4') to which it has proceeded in the meantime, resulting in a parallelogram (1, 2, 3', 4') as shown in Fig. 5.22d.

In general, these distortions are not objectionable, since in most cases they will be hardly noticeable. In some photographic applications, however, distortion is highly objectionable, e.g., in aerial photography for mapping, precluding the use of the focal-plane shutter.

Factors Affecting Exposure with a Focal-Plane Shutter. In discussing the factors involved in the timing of the focal-plane shutter its position at a distance in front of the focal plane must be considered (see Fig. 5.23). In some cameras this dis-

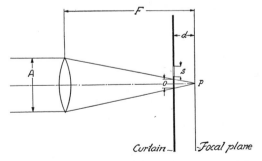

FIG. 5.23. Effect of distance between curtain and focal plane on exposure with a focal-plane shutter.

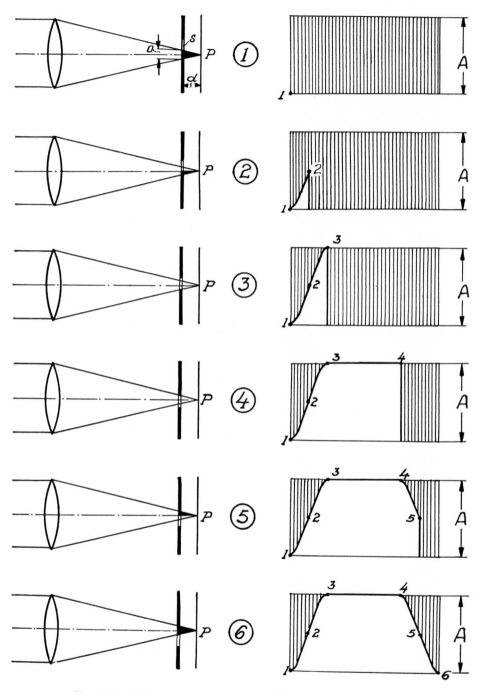

Fɪɢ. 5.24.   The six exposure phases with a focal plane shutter.

tance d is appreciably large. Fig. 5.23 shows how the slit of the curtain with its width s approaches the light cone coming from an infinitely distant point after passing through lens of aperture A, imaging point P in the focal-plane. At distance d, the light cone admitted through slit s has not yet entirely converged to point P and therefore still has a considerable diameter o. The six distinctly different exposure phases of point P are indicated in Fig. 5.24. In phase (1) the light cone is still prevented from reaching the film. The exposure curve in the diagram to the right is about to start at point 1. In phase (2) half the cone o passes through, half of it still being prevented from reaching the film, and the shutter-operation curve has moved to point 2. (3) The slit now fully admits light cone diameter o; the full lens aperture is now utilized and curve has moved to point 3. (4) Slit s has moved further on where its other edge is about to enter into the cone. During this period the full lens aperture is still utilized and the curve continues to point 4. (5) The upper half of the light cone has been cut off by the upper (closing) edge of slit s. Only half of light cone o is admitted. The shutter-operation curve has started its downward trend and moves to point 5. In the last phase (6), cone o has been cut off entirely, all light admission is ended and exposure of the film strip is complete. Curve ends at point 6.

Exposure Curve and Efficiency of a Focal-Plane Shutter. The exposure curve of an individual point P is very similar to that of a between-the-lens shutter. Three major periods may be distinguished:

(1) Phases 1 and 2, in which light admission is steadily increasing, corresponding to opening time T_1 in a between-the-lens shutter.

(2) Phases 3 and 4, where full light admission is manifest, corresponding to wide

open time T_2 in the between-the-lens shutter.

(3) Phases 5 and 6, when light admission steadily decreases, corresponding to closing time T_3 in the between-the-lens shutter.

In an ideal case of a focal-plane shutter, i.e., if it were actually positioned in the focal-plane, Total Operating Time T_{tot}, i.e., the time interval, from the moment the first strip of film of length a is exposed to the instant the last strip of film has been exposed, would be

$$T_{tot} = \frac{a + s}{v},$$

v being the velocity of curtain slit s, and a the length or width of the image frame (depending on whether the curtain travels along or across the film). This exposure time, T_{tot}, governs the extent of distortion, as previously discussed. The "Ideal Actual Open Time," T_a, which name may be given to the time interval during which one individual point on the film is exposed to light through a curtain situated in the focal-plane, would be:

$$T_a = \frac{s}{v}.$$

In all practical cases, however, where the focal-plane shutter is positioned at a certain distance d from the focal-plane, the "Actual Open Time," T, corresponding to the Total Open Time of a between-the-lens shutter, is

$$T = \frac{s + o}{v} \quad \text{(see Fig. 5.23).}$$

The ratio between "Ideal Actual Open Time" T_a and "Actual Open Time" T (of a curtain at distance d) is called Efficiency, E.

$$E = \frac{T_a}{T} = \frac{s}{v} \cdot \frac{v}{s + o} = \frac{s}{s + o}.$$

The undetermined value o, i.e., the diameter of the light cone forming point P on the film, may be replaced by the known values of the focal-length F of the lens and the distance d of the curtain from the focal-plane, by means of the simple geometrical relationship (Fig. 5.23):

$$\frac{A}{F} = \frac{o}{d} \quad \text{or} \quad o = \frac{A \cdot d}{F},$$

$\frac{A}{F}$ is the f/number of the lens; therefore, this equation may be written

$$o = \frac{d}{f}$$

and the Efficiency

$$E = \frac{s}{s + o} = \frac{s}{s + \dfrac{d}{f}}.$$

The Actual Open Time $T = \dfrac{s + o}{v}$ may be written:

$$T = \frac{1}{v} \cdot \left(s + \frac{d}{f} \right) = \frac{s}{v} \cdot \left(1 + \frac{d}{f \cdot s} \right)$$

$$= T_a \cdot \left(1 + \frac{d}{f \cdot s} \right).$$

This last formula indicates that Actual Exposure Time T becomes shorter when curtain speed v is higher, and width of slit s is smaller. It also indicates that the additional term $\dfrac{d}{f \cdot s}$ always prolongs T, and, since it never can vanish completely, Efficiency must always remain smaller than 1 (or 100%). The larger the term $\dfrac{d}{f \cdot s}$, the lower the Efficiency, which becomes increasingly less as distance d increases. If d could be reduced to zero, the additional term would be eliminated, and the "Actual Exposure Time T" would become the "Ideal Actual Exposure Time T_a."

It should be observed that in the additional term $\dfrac{d}{f \cdot s}$, the fraction $\dfrac{d}{f}$ is predetermined by the physical dimensions of cam-

era and lens, and is usually not variable.

Still another matter must be discussed with regard to the action of a focal-plane shutter. In the example shown in Fig. 5.23 slit s was assumed to be wider than cone diameter o. Fig. 5.25 demonstrates the influence of the width of the slit. In Fig. 5.25a slit s is narrower than cone diameter o; in Fig. 5.25b both are of the same exact

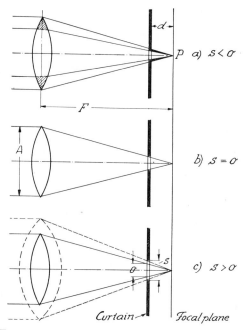

FIG. 5.25.   Effect of width of the slit on exposure with a focal plane shutter.

size, and in Fig. 5.25c slit s is wider than o. As case (a) indicates, a narrower slit would not permit passage of the entire light cone, and, therefore, the result would be equivalent to a smaller lens aperture. In case (b) the full lens aperture may be utilized. If s is wider than o, as in case (C), a still larger lens aperture might be used. As case (a) indicates, the minimum practical slit size s is predetermined by the given lens aperture and the given distance d from the focal-plane. Any slit of size less than the predetermined minimum will result in stopped down lens aperture, offsetting the advantages of a high-speed lens. This minimum slit s may be derived from the previous formula

$$s = o; \quad s = \frac{d}{f}.$$

Since d is constant in a given camera, the smallest usable slit s may quickly be figured for any chosen f-stop. If, for example, $d = \frac{1}{8}''$ with an $f/3.5$ lens, then the smallest permissible slit would be $\frac{.125}{3.5}$ $= .036''$, or somewhat more than $1/16''$. Narrower slits would yield under-exposed pictures.

Testing of Focal-Plane Shutters. Some of the methods used for testing between-the-lens shutters can also be used for focal-plane shutters. Other devices, especially designed for focal-plane shutters, have been developed.

Among the test devices, applicable to both between-the-lens shutters and focal-plane shutters, is one which consists of a transparent drum enclosed in a lighttight housing (Fig. 5.26). A synchronous motor drives the drum at speeds variable from 60 to 4000 r.p.m. A film strip is inserted around the drum's cylindrical circumference by opening the housing at one end. Atop the housing a slit equal to the width

of the drum is provided parallel to the drum axis. The shutter under test is placed over the slit so that the curtain travel is parallel to the drum axis. A light source placed above the shutter at a suitable distance will photographically record a strip as shown in Fig. 5.27. This photo-

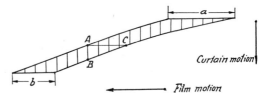

FIG. 5.27. Exposure time record made by shutter speed tested in Fig. 26.

graphic record provides all data necessary to determine the shutter speed. AC is a measure of the effective exposure time at this point in the focal-plane. AB is the chosen width of the curtain slit. The movement of the film is controlled by the chosen speed of the rotating drum V in inches/second; then the effective exposure time is

$$T_a = \frac{AC}{V}.$$

With the f/stop chosen and the distance of the curtain from the focal-plane known, efficiency may be computed as previously explained:

$$E = \frac{s}{s + \dfrac{d}{f}}.$$

Another method makes use of the Strobotac, an electric stroboscope producing from 10 to 240 flashes per second. Directed toward a strip of film which is exposed through a focal-plane shutter, a photographic record of all flashes occurring throughout the entire shutter operating cycle will appear similar to that in Fig. 5.28. The space, traveled from one strip to the next, a, b, will be a measure of the actual curtain speed. If, for example, the

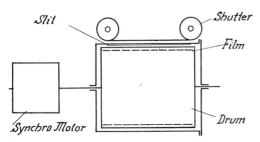

FIG. 5.26. Diagram of a shutter speed tester.

Strobotac were set for 200 flashes, each distance from one strip to the next corresponds to the time interval of 1/200th of a second. The fact that distance *a* is shorter than distance *b* at the end of the total exposure indicates that the curtain speed does not remain constant during the

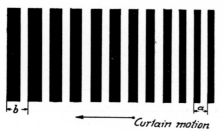

Fig. 5.28.   Exposure time record made by the Strobotac.

entire operating cycle, a condition found in practically every type of focal-plane shutter, which is caused by the greater initial friction of the start of its movement, and because the mechanism needs time for acceleration. This definite disadvantage of the focal-plane shutter may also be observed in Fig. 5.27, where distance *a* is greater than *b*.

Synchronization of Focal-Plane Shutters. Synchronization of the focal-plane shutters involves problems quite different from the between-the-lens shutter because of the difference in the characteristics of the two shutters. A distinction must be made between local exposure time (exposure time of one point of film) and total operation time (time required to expose the entire film), and it must be realized that a shutter with a slit of perhaps 1/8″ and a speed of 1/1000th of a second has to travel 1/8″ in that 1/1000th of a second without considering efficiency. If the film size is 4″ × 5″ and the curtain is to travel across the width of the film, i.e., 4″, there are 32/8″ to be traversed, which will consume 32/1000th of a second until the exposure of the entire film is complete.

Hence, flashbulbs, made especially for use with focal-plane shutters, have a longer peak to allow for this long exposure time.

The difference in the speed of the curtain at the beginning and the end of exposure may also cause different densities in different parts of the negative. In view of the fact that only small strips of film are exposed at a time, not all the light of the flash can be utilized and, consequently, efficiency is lower. Under identical conditions, the low peak of the focal-plane lamp requires larger lens apertures than the high peak lamp used with between-the-lens shutters.

Synchronization of the focal-plane shutter does not present any serious mechanical problems. On almost every focal-plane shutter a part can be found which is accessible from the outside (knob, for example) which moves as the focal-plane shutter operates, and a contact can easily be adjusted to be activated by this part. Some cameras have built-in synchronization with an outlet socket in the back of the camera.

Comparison of Between-the-Lens and Focal-Plane Shutters. In comparing focal-plane and lens shutters it must be realized that one type performs tasks which cannot be fulfilled by the other.

Advantages of the between-the-lens shutter are:

1. Simple handling.
2. Relatively small size, providing convenience in small folding cameras.
3. Freedom from distortion on moving objects because of simultaneous exposure of the entire picture.
4. Even density over the entire negative because of simultaneous exposure.
5. Correct synchronization is more readily achievable with short and high-peak flash lamps.

FIG. 5.29. Synchro shutter of Brownie Reflex. (*Eastman Kodak Co.*)

Advantages of the focal-plane shutters are:

1. Higher speeds to "stop" fast motion.
2. Ready interchangeability of lenses because of separate shutter and lens mount.

The paragraphs which follow describe six representative shutters of American manufacture, namely: (1) the two blade shutter of the Brownie Reflex (Eastman Kodak Company); (2) three precision synchronized, between-the-lens shutters, (a) the Flash Supermatic (Eastman Kodak Company), (b) the Acme Synchro (Illex Optical Company), (c) the Rapax (Wollensak Optical Company) and (3) two focal plane shutters (Graflex and Kodak Ektra).

Some Representative Shutters. Fig. 5.29 illustrates the box camera shutter incorporated in the latest Kodak Brownie Reflex Synchro Model and its principal mechanical elements. If the shutter is set for instantaneous exposures by the time lever (not shown), pressing exposure button 1, partly shown as dashed outline in the direction of the arrow, sets up tension in coil spring 2 and pivots through linkage 3 about point 4 the cover blade 5

and the shutter blade 6 hooked to the former at 7 in clockwise direction. As both blades move as a unit, the opening in the shutter blade remains covered and no light is admitted into the camera. This movement sets spring 8 under tension and, through gear sector 9 on the shutter blade, turns balance wheel 10. During the last part of this movement hook 7 is lifted by stud 11 until disengaged. Accentuated by spring 8 the shutter blade 6 moves counterclockwise. In the sweep its oblong opening briefly (about 1/50 second) uncovers the lens. Again gear sector 9 turns balance wheel 10. This controls the speed of the shutter blade sweep and, consequently, the exposure duration. As the exposure button is released, coil spring 2 returns exposure button 1 and through linkage 3 cover blade 5 to their original positions, where shutter blade hooks on to cover blade at 7.

For photoflash pictures, the electric circuit from a Brownie Flasholder is formed through two prongs on the outside of the camera which extend through the camera body at 13 and 14 and terminate at 15 and 16, respectively. As the exposure button 1 is pressed, contact 16 moves counterclockwise without touching 15. The adjustable screw 17 is moved to the left by link 18. As it approaches the end of the movement, it lifts spring 15 so that the circuit is closed by contact between part 15 and 16 as the opening in the shutter blade 6 commences to uncover the lens. Since the lens remains uncovered for about 1/50 of a second only, "F"-type flashlamps, such as the SM, will flash in synchronism with instantaneous exposures.

If time lever is set at B, its interior extension 12 is turned to the right which pivots cover and shutter blades through about 25°. When going through the pre-

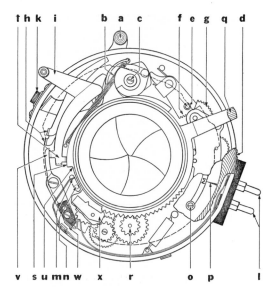

FIG. 5.31. Mechanical elements of the Supermatic Shutter shown in Fig. 30.

at 1/400 seconds an additional spring located under eccentric member *c* is brought into action. Shutter speeds are changed by turning speed-selecting ring *d* which, by means of cams shown as dashed line, actuates controls. The step-shaped cam at *e* controls extent of engagement of gear sector *f* with one member of gear train retard mechanism *g* and a cam, not shown, controls position of an oscillating pallet

FIG. 5.30. Flash Supermatic shutter. (*Eastman Kodak Co.*)

viously described cycle, the returning shutter blade 6 is stopped by lever 12 so that the opening in the blade is in front of the lens keeping it uncovered. Releasing exposure button 1 moves blade 5 to the left, covering the lens. With this setting, and the electric circuit for flashing the bulb being closed as described above, flashlamps of the "M" type, such as Synchro-Press No. 5, can be used to make "bulb" flash pictures.

Fig. 5.30 is the picture of a Kodak Flash Supermatic Shutter, the mechanical elements of which are shown in Fig. 5.31. Setting lever *a* sets up tension in spring *b*;

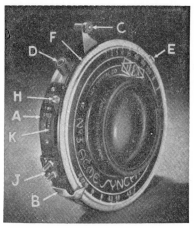

FIG. 5.32. Acme Synchro shutter. (*Ilex Optical Co.*)

FIG. 5.33. Rapax Synchromatic shutter.
(*Wollensak Optical Co.*)

relative to a ratchet (star) wheel. *T* and *B* are determined by positions of levers *h*, also controlled by a cam. The release lever is marked *i* and the socket for the cable release *k*.

Flash discharges with no time lag are synchronized with shutter blade action by an electric circuit formed through prongs *l*, closing it at *m* through post *n* which moves upward when blades open.

Photoflash lamps of 5 milliseconds time lag are synchronized by sliding *F* on the limiting stop *o* opposite index *p*. Clockwise movement of lever *q* sets up spring

FIG. 5.34. Double ended blades of the Kodak Synchro Rapid 800 shutter.

tension through gear train *r* and moves cam *s* upward. Downward pressure on lever *i* now allows its extension *t* to move sideways to cam *u*. Lever *v* follows and opposite end closes contacts *w*. This releases gear train which, through downward movement of step between cams *s* and *u*, actuates lever *t* and releases shutter so blades are fully opened about 5 milliseconds after electric circuit has been closed.

Synchronizing flashlamps of 20 milliseconds time lag is accomplished similarly. Limiting stop *o* at *M* permits movement of lever *q* which, in addition to the action

FIG. 5.35. Driving and control mechanism of the Kodak Synchro Rapid 800 shutter.

described above, engages oscillating pallet *x*. The pallet action slows down counterclockwise travel of "step," and shutter is released so that "fully open" is reached about 20 milliseconds after contacts *w* have closed.

The photograph in Fig. 5.32 shows an Ilex Acme Synchro Shutter, the mechanical principle of which has been diagrammatically explained in Fig. 5.11. In this photograph synchro lever *H* may be seen which, when cocked, sets and connects the otherwise completely disengaged synchro unit. By turning control disc *K* ("6" in

Fig. 5.11) until the colored dot, corresponding to the required time lag, lines up with mark on the indicator plate *A*, the correct time lag for the chosen type flash lamp is set. *J* are two outlets which connect the cord to the battery case. *B* is the diaphragm indicator, *C* the shutter release lever, *D* the socket for the cable release, and *F* the speed control ring. *E* is the press focus button.

Fig. 5.33 is the picture of a Wollensak Rapax Shutter with built-in synchronization. Beneath the two outside electric contact posts *a* is the time-delay indicator *b* for setting time-delay as required for the selected flash lamp. Going clockwise around the shutter case, diaphragm indicator *c*, release lever *d*, cable release socket *e*, and setting-lever *f* are found.

The recently announced Kodak "Synchro Rapid 800" shutter with a top speed of 1/800 second—"the world's fastest shut-

ter of its type"—is shown in Figs. 5.34 and 5.35.

The design of this high speed shutter is based on the principle of the double-ended blades, as described in the previous section of "Blademovement." The double-ended blades (Fig. 5.34) swing through in one direction, opening and closing the shutter in one continuous motion. The shutter mechanism is shown in Fig. 5.35.

Fig. 5.36 shows the shutter curtain *a* with 5 slits, used in the Graflex focal-plane shutter. The top slit is a rectangular opening equal in size to the full picture aperture, and is used if the focal-plane shutter is desired to be completely open, when focusing or using a between-the-lens shutter. The upper shutter roller with its bearing *b* supports the upper curtain end which is not tensioned and rotates freely unless checked by escapement *c*. *d* is a screw and *e* the master gear of top gear roller

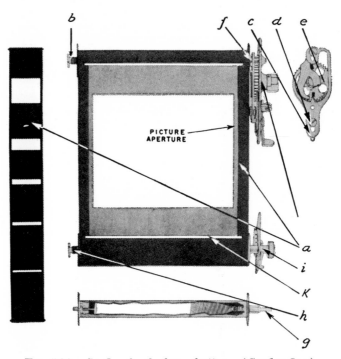

PICTURE APERTURE

FIG. 5.36. Graflex focal plane shutter. (*Graflex Inc.*)

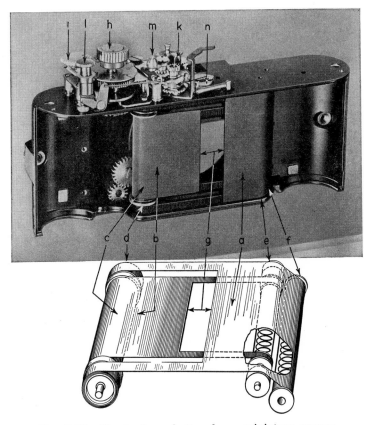

Fig. 5.37. Focal plane shutter for a miniature camera.

assembly f. The bottom tension roller assembly g shows roller with tension spring, carried by curtain roller bearing h and lower plate i; k is the curtain edging slit.

A drawing and photograph of a focal-plane shutter mechanism on a miniature camera are shown in Fig. 5.37. Operating the lever on the back of camera first brings edge of curtain a over edge of curtain b, and then winds them together across film aperture onto rollers c and d, setting up spring tension in rollers e and f. Shutter speeds of 1/50 to 1/1000 second are determined by width of the curtain opening g, regulated by knob h which turns roller c in relation to roller d. Acceleration is compensated for by widening of slit as it travels across film plane due to difference in diameter of rollers c and d. Speeds 1 to 1/25 second are selected with dial i and controlled by an escapement mechanism k which varies the delay of curtain b after curtain a has completed its run. At B setting curtain a moves across when the release button l is pressed down and curtain b follows when button is released. Moving self-timer lever m in clockwise direction winds up a spring-actuated escapement mechanism n which delays automatic tripping of the shutter by 10 to 12 seconds.

NEWMAN, A. S., "Photographic Shutters, Methods and Construction and Measuring Their Speeds," Phot. J. **53**, 220–230 (June 1913).

HAY, ALFRED, Handbuch der wissenschaftlichen und angewandten Photographie, Vol. 2: "Die photographische Kamera und ihr

Zubehör," by Karl Pritschow, Springer, Vienna (1931).

ANDERSON, "A Dictionary of Applied Physics," 1923, Vol. 4, p. 670.

NUTTING, F. G., *Brit. J. Phot.*, p. 349 (1916).

DURHAM, *Brit. J. Phot.*, p. 623 (1934).

YOST, LLOYD, "Testing Focal-plane Shutter," *Amer. Phot.*, p. 808 (December 1936).

CLARK, R. G., "Measuring Shutter Speeds," *Amer. Phot.*, p. 498 (September 1937).

HOLMES, L. S., "On Checking Relative Shutter Speeds," *Amer. Phot.*, p. 626 (September 1937).

WOLCOTT, F. W., "Camera Shutter Speed Experiments," *Camera*, p. 17 (January 1938).

GREENLAW, D. S., "An Accurate Method of Testing Shutter Speeds," *Amer. Phot.*, p. 400 (1938).

WATERS, L. A., "Testing Shutter Speeds," *Camera*, p. 316 (November 1938).

ENGLISH, F. L., "Shutters and Their Testing," *Amer. Phot.*, p. 877 (December 1939), and p. 22 (January 1940).

GRAY, S. MCK., "Performance Characteristics of Camera Shutters," *Photo-Technique*, p. 14 (August 1939).

BARCLAY, C. E., "The Speed Calibration of Photographic Shutters," *Amer. Phot.*, p. 484 (July 1939).

BOND, W. L., "Quick Determination of Shutter Speeds," *Photo-Technique*, p. 54 (January 1940).

TAWNEY, G. L., "Stroboscopic Measurement of Shutter Speeds," *Photo-Technique*, p. 31 (March 1940).

ALMQUIST, E. C., "Measuring Shutter Precision," *Photo-Technique*, p. 53 (1941).

BLADSOE, J. A., "Testing Shutter Speeds and Synchronization," *Amer. Phot.*, p. 36 (January 1942).

HAYES, THOMAS B., "Iris Shutter Analysis," *Amer. Phot.*, p. 34 (November 1942).

BULLOCK, THEODORE H., "Testing Shutters with the Cathode Ray Oscillography," *Amer. Phot.*, p. 24 (September 1944).

DOYLE, IRVING W., AND HAMILTON, JACK, "Aerial Camera Shutters," *Amer. Phot.*, p. 8 (October 1944).

GREENLEAF, ALLEN R., "The Elements of Exposure II," *Amer. Phot.*, p. 8 (January 1945).

BAUDE, JOHN, "Testing a Synchronizer," *Amer. Phot.*, p. 36 (June 1945).

Chapter 6

FUNDAMENTALS OF PHOTOCHEMISTRY

Photochemistry. Photochemistry is the branch of chemistry that is concerned with the chemical changes produced by radiant energy. The reactions may take place between atoms or molecules in either the gaseous, liquid, or solid state, but only the latter is suitable for the photographic process. Photography is concerned with the light sensitive compounds of silver, iron, chromium, and the diazo dyes in the solid state. These are usually suspended in viscous, or jelled, colloidal media, such as gelatin, albumen, glue, casein, agar, cellulose esters, plastics, or glass.

Radiant Energy. Energy due to radiation is emitted, or absorbed, in discrete units called *quanta*. Quanta of light energy are known as *photons*. The energy of the photon varies with the frequency of light in accordance with Planck's law,

$$\epsilon = h\nu,$$

where h has the value 6.62×10^{-27} ergs per second and ν is the frequency of light in reciprocal seconds.

The frequency of light for a particular wave length, λ, is obtained from the expression

$$\nu = \frac{c}{\lambda},$$

in which c is the speed of light, 3×10^{10} centimeters per second and λ is the wave length expressed in centimeters.

It will be noted that quanta of light having short wave lengths will have higher frequencies and, therefore, will be more energetic than those of long wave lengths.

Matter and Energy Levels. The interchange of energy between light and matter takes place in terms of photons, each of which possesses one quantum of energy. Matter may exist in simple forms as atoms and single molecules, or in complex structures as liquids or solids. Atoms and molecules have limited capacities for absorbing energy, due to certain quantum restrictions and, unless the energy of the photon has specific values, it cannot be absorbed. Liquids and solids, on the other hand, are less critical in their requirements; they absorb any energy within specified ranges and have what is known as *continuous energy ranges*. Due to the influence of molecules in liquids and gases upon each other and dissociation of molecules into atoms, continuously varying amounts of kinetic and translational energy are given off.

Matter that contains the least amount of energy is said to be in the normal state, or the lowest *energy level*. When photons are absorbed, the energy content is increased and the matter changes to a higher energy level, called an *excited state*. In this condition matter is unstable, it may lose part or all of its energy reverting toward the normal state, or it can take on additional energy and change to a still higher level.

Band Spectra. It has been shown that a molecule can exist in a number of energy levels and that a change from one state to another results in the absorption, or emission, of energy which results in the production of a line in the spectrum having a definite frequency. In order to account for band spectra, it is necessary to assume that the electronic, vibrational, and rotational energies of molecules are quantized.

The emission of energy, due to the rotation of molecules, gives rise to spectra in the far infrared. Energy emitted, due to the displacement of atoms within the molecule, produces vibration spectra and when these are superimposed on the rotation spectra, bands appear in the near (short) infrared. Electronic spectra are caused by displacement of outer electrons of the atom. These appear as adsorption spectra in the visible and ultraviolet, with the greater energies and larger displacements occurring in the ultraviolet.

Collisions Between Photons and Molecules. Photochemical changes, or reactions, occur as a result of molecules, atoms, or ions, being activated by the absorption of energy due to either collisions or radiation. Molecules activated by light absorb photons, the energy of which varies with the frequency; i.e., *color* of light.

When a photon strikes a molecule, several results are possible: (1) no reaction, the photon does not have the proper energy to be absorbed; (2) *Raman effect:* displacement of atoms in molecules and a photon of different frequency; (3) *Compton effect:* the production of a high speed electron and a photon of lower frequency; (4) the dissociation of the molecule into atoms, one of which becomes excited; the splitting off of an electron with the formation of a positive ion, and the activation, or excitation, of the molecule. Molecules are activated in different ways, depending upon the frequency of the adsorbed radiation.

Energy Requirements for Photochemical Reactions. The energies required for most photochemical reactions range from 20,000 to 100,000 calories per mole. Since visible and ultraviolet light have shorter wave lengths than infrared, hence greater frequency and energy, these are more effective in producing chemical reactions.

The primary result of radiation is the production of molecules or fragments of molecules that have high energy content. According to Einstein's Law, in primary photochemical processes each molecule is activated by the absorption of one photon. The number of molecules activated should be equivalent to the number of quanta absorbed. Since a gram molecule contains 6.02×10^{23} molecules, it should absorb 6.02×10^{23} quanta, a value known as the *einstein*. This concept has been helpful in comparing photo energies with the thermal requirements of chemical reactions.

Calculations for the conversion of photo energy into thermal equivalents make use of the following equations:

The energy of the photon is given by the relation

$$\epsilon = h\nu, \qquad (1)$$

where h is a constant (6.62×10^{-27} erg seconds) and ν is the frequency. Frequency is equal to the speed of light ($3.0 \times$

TABLE 6.1.   EFFECT OF RADIATION ON MOLECULE

Radiation	Wave Length Å	Calories per Molecule	Effect on Molecule
Far Infrared..............	2×10^5–	.... – 1,400	Rotation of molecule
Near Infrared............	8×10^5–4×10^3	1,400– 3,500	Displacement of atoms in molecule
Visible..................	8×10^3–4×10^3	3,500– 71,000	Displacement of electrons in outer orbits of atoms
Ultraviolet..............	4×10^3–2×10^3	71,000–142,000	

TABLE 6.2. ENERGIES FOR TYPICAL RADIATIONS

Wave Length Å	Frequency ν	Region	Energy per Photon, $h\nu$, in Ergs	Energy per Einstein, U, cal. per mol
100,000′	3×10^{13}	infrared	1.99×10^{-13}	2,860
10,000	3×10^{14}	near infrared	1.99×10^{-13}	28,600
7,000	4.29×10^{14}	red	2.84×10^{-12}	40,900
6,000	5.00×10^{14}	yellow	3.31×10^{-12}	47,600
5,000	6.00×10^{14}	blue	3.95×10^{-12}	56,900
4,000	7.5×10^{14}	violet	4.97×10^{-12}	71,500
3,000	1×10^{15}	ultraviolet	$6.62 \times i0^{-12}$	95,300
2,000	1.5×10^{15}	ultraviolet	9.93×10^{-12}	143,000

)¹⁰ cm./sec.) divided by the wave length, in centimeters.

$$\nu = \frac{c}{\lambda}. \qquad (2)$$

n Angstrom unit is 10^{-8} cm. The energy f the einstein will be

$$U = N\epsilon = Nh\nu, \qquad (3)$$

here N is Avogadro's number, 6.02×10^{23}, nd the value of U is expressed in ergs.

Calories per mole are found by convert-ng energy in ergs to joules and dividing y the factor 4.184.

$$k_{\text{cal.}} = \frac{Nh\nu}{4.184 \times 10^7}.$$

'here are 1×10^7 ergs in a joule.

For ultraviolet light with a wave length f 3000 Å., the frequency is

$$\frac{3 \times 10^{10}}{3000 \times 10^{-8}} = 1 \times 10^{15}$$

nd the calories per mole are

$$\frac{6.02 \times 10^{23} \times 6.62 \times 10^{-27} \times 1 \times 10^{15}}{4.184 \times 1 \times 10^7}$$
$$= 95,300.$$

Corresponding energies for other wave engths are given in Table 6.2.

Distribution of Incident Energy. When ubstances are illuminated the energy of he incident light may be dissipated in a number of ways. This may be represented by the general equation

$$E = R + A + T,$$

where E is the incident energy, R is the energy reflected, A is the energy absorbed, and T is the energy transmitted.

In photochemical processes, R may account for the energy lost by reflection from surface of metals, crystals, mediums, or vessels containing the photoactive chemical. Fresnel's law gives the relation between incident and reflected light. It is expressed by the equation

$$\left(\frac{N-1}{N+1}\right)^2 I_0 = R I_0,$$

in which I_0 is the incident light and N is the refraction index of the medium for light of a definite wave length.

Only the energy due to absorbed light can cause photophysical and photochemical changes. Photophysical changes are those in which the physical properties of a substance are altered as: color, crystal shape, solubility, or conductance. Photoconductance is the term applied to the effect where certain crystals that are normally good insulators show conductance when illuminated. Photochemical changes include all changes where a substance undergoes a chemical change due to absorption of light. Typical effects are excitation, ionization, decomposition (photolysis), and photosensitization.

Transmitted energy represents the emission of energy unaltered in manner or form. Processes in which some energy is transmitted include: fluorescence, phosphorescence, the photoelectric effect, and heat. In fluorescence a glow at lower frequency continues only as long as the substance is exposed to the exciting source; while in phosphorescence the glow continues after the exciting source is removed. Quanta of light falling on a metal surface causes the ejection of electrons from the metal, a phenomena known as the photoelectric effect.

Photochemical Laws. In 1818 Grotthus stated the first law of photochemistry; i.e., only radiation which is absorbed can produce a photochemical change. This law was restated by Draper in 1839 and has since become known as the Grotthus-Draper law. Although photochemical reactions are caused by the absorption of radiant energy, it does not follow that all radiation that is absorbed will produce chemical change. Much of the energy is converted into heat, while some may be emitted as light with a different frequency—giving rise to such phenomena as fluorescence and phosphorescence. Ultraviolet and visible radiation are most effective in producing photochemical changes. According to modern theories, the absorption of ultraviolet and visible light produces displacement of outer electrons in molecules, or atoms, causing the molecules to decompose or to react with other molecules. In cases where conditions are not suitable for reaction, the activated molecules emit their energy as radiation of a different wave length, or they may produce violent collisions with other molecules and thus dissipate their energy as heat. Some reactions are sensitive to a wide range of wave lengths, whereas others are affected by monochro-

matic light of definite wave length, or by a narrow band of wave lengths. Einstein's law of photochemical equivalence states that in primary processes the absorption of one quantum is required for each molecule activated. As the energy of the quantum is equal to

$$\epsilon = h\nu$$

and since gram-molecule contains 6.02×10^{23} molecules, a number known as Avogadro's number, N, then to activate the molecular weight of any substance, the number of quanta required will be

$$U = Nh\nu = 6.02 \times 10^{23} \times 6.62 \times 10^{-27}\nu$$

where ν is the frequency, h is Planck's constant. The number of quanta U is called the "einstein."

Quantum Yield. The relation of one quantum absorbed per molecule activated holds for ideal conditions, as rarified gases having reversible monomolecular reactions and a narrow monochromatic absorption band. In most cases the reactions are not simple, but are often followed by a series of secondary or chain reactions. The number of molecules activated by the absorption of a quantum may vary from a fraction to several hundred. The ratio of the number of molecules that have reacted to the number of quanta absorbed is known as quantum yield, ϕ.

$$\phi = \frac{\text{No. of molecules reacted}}{\text{No. of quanta absorbed}}.$$

Primary Photochemical Processes. The Rutherford-Bohr atom furnished the model for quantized adsorption or emission of radiant energy. This and later models for molecules made it possible to visualize the relationship between photochemical processes and spectra. The adsorption of a light quantum by an atom causes the dispacement of an outer electron into a higher quantum orbit or greater energy level.

Similarly, the absorption of light causes molecules or certain atoms in molecules to shift from the normal, nonreactive state into an energized or more active state.

Primary processes which accompany the absorption of light by molecules are:

1. Excitation—raising an electron to a higher level so that molecule retains the additional energy.

2. Ionization—the removal of an electron from a molecule, leaving a positively charged ion.

3. Dissociation—a displacement of an electron which affects vibration of atoms in a molecule sufficient to cause a chemical breakdown.

Secondary Photochemical Processes. The absorption of light quanta is a primary process essential to every photochemical change. This is a physical process and can be represented thus:

$$AB + h\nu \rightarrow AB^*,$$

AB is the normal molecule, $h\nu$ the light quantum having a frequency of ν, and AB^* the activated molecule.

In the complete photochemical reaction, primary processes are followed by secondary processes of either a physical or chemical nature.[1] Typical secondary processes include these effects:

1. Activated molecule returns to normal condition with emission of energy.

$$AB^* \rightarrow AB + h\nu,$$

where $h\nu$ may be heat or fluorescence.

2. Activated molecules may transfer energy to other molecules not affected by the radiation and thus produce photosensitization,

$$AB^* + C \rightarrow AB + C^*.$$

3. Activated molecules may dissipate into radicals, atoms, or ions,

$$AB^* \rightarrow A + B$$
$$AB^* \rightarrow A^* + B^-$$

4. Activated molecules may unite with identical nonactivated molecules and cause polymerization,

$$AB^* + AB \rightarrow AB \cdot AB.$$

5. Activated molecules may undergo intra-molecular rearrangements and form isomers,

$$AB^* \rightarrow BA.$$

6. Activated molecules may react with other molecules producing either direct or indirect chemical reactions,

$$AB^* + C \rightarrow ABC$$

or

$$AB^* + C \rightarrow AC + B.$$

Since secondary processes are sequels to primary processes and can occur either alone or concurrently, they determine the variety of photochemical effects and the quantum yield.

Types of Photochemical Reaction. Photochemical change is not limited to any one type of reaction but includes all types from the simplest molecular changes to the most complex chemical reactions.

Rollifson and Burton, *Photochemistry*, Prentice-Hall, Inc., New York, 1942.

Ellis and Wells, *The Chemical Action of Ultra Violet Rays*, Reinhold Publishing Co., New York, 1941.

Sheppard, *Photography as a Scientific Instrument*, D. Van Nostrand Co., Inc., New York, 1923, 113.

---

[1] Feigl, *J. Chem. Educ.* **21**, 479 (1944).

*Allotropic Change in
   Elements*

$$S\lambda \overset{\text{light}}{\underset{\substack{\text{infra-}\\\text{red}\\h\nu}}{\rightleftarrows}} S\mu$$
(crystalline)   (amorphous)

Synthesis

$$H_2 \quad + \quad Cl_2 \longrightarrow 2HCl$$
hydrogen   chlorine   hydrogen
                                      chloride

*Molecular
Rearrangement
or Isomerization*

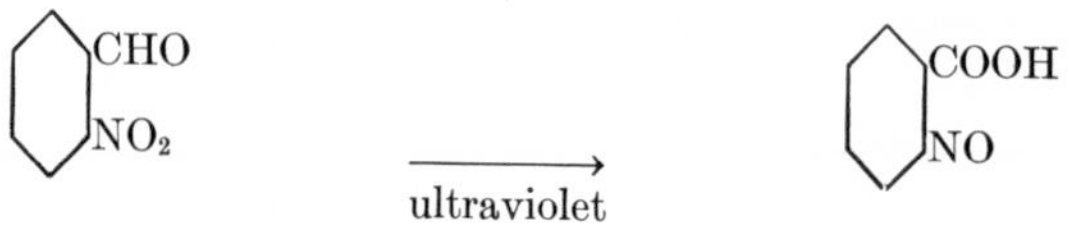

O-nitrobenzaldehyde $\xrightarrow{\text{ultraviolet}}$ O-nitroso-benzoic acid

*Reduction
(Photolysis)*

$$2AgCl \longrightarrow 2Ag \quad + \quad Cl_2$$
silver chloride   silver   chlorine

$$Ag_2C_2O_4 \longrightarrow 2Ag \quad + \quad 2CO_2$$
silver oxalate   silver   carbon
                                  dioxide

$$Fe_2(C_2O_4)_3 \longrightarrow 2FeC_2O_4 \quad + \quad 2CO_2$$
ferric oxalate   ferrous   carbon
                      oxalate   dioxide

Oxidation

$$PbS + 2O_2 \longrightarrow PbSO_4$$
lead   oxygen   lead
sulfide   sulfate

*Polymerization
and Depolymerization*

$$2C_{14}H_{10} \rightleftarrows (C_{14}H_{10})_2$$
anthracene   dianthracene

Autoxidation

$$2FeSO_4 + H_2O + 1/2O_2 \longrightarrow 2Fe(OH)SO_4$$
ferrous sulfate   basic ferric sulfate

$$3Fe(OH)SO_4 \longrightarrow Fe(OH)_3 + Fe_2(SO_4)_3$$
                           ferric   ferric
                           hydroxide   sulfate

Halogenation

Saturation of double bond $C_6H_6 + 3Br_2 \longrightarrow C_6H_6Br_6$
                             benzene   hexabromobenzene

$$C_6H_5CH:CHCOOH \quad Br_2 \longrightarrow C_6H_5C_2H_2Br_2COOH$$
dinnamic acid   dibromocinnamic acid

Decomposition

$$2HI \longrightarrow H_2 + I_2$$
Hydriodic   hydro- iodine
acid   gen

nsitization

$$Hg + h\nu \longrightarrow Hg^*$$
mercury   activated mercury

$$Hg^* + H_2 \longrightarrow Hg + 2H$$
hydrogen   hydrogen
molecule   atoms

ydrolysis

$$(CH_3)_2CO + H_2O \rightleftharpoons CH_3COOH + CH_4$$
acetone   water   acetic   methane
acid

Nature of Photochemical Reactions.

hotochemical reactions differ from ther-
al reactions in that the former take place
the presence of light at normal or low
mperature. In addition to the frequency
f the radiation, other factors such as the
tensity of light and size of vessel affect
e rate of reaction. Photochemical reac-
ions are often accompanied by dark or
ermal reactions in reverse directions, as

$$A \underset{dark}{\overset{light}{\rightleftharpoons}} B.$$

Photochemical reactions may produce
atalysts which in turn cause a thermal
eaction.

$$A \overset{light}{\rightarrow} A^*$$
$$A^* + BC \rightarrow A + B + C.$$

ome reactions have an induction period
uring which enough catalyst is produced
o cause the reaction to proceed with nor-
al speed. Other chemical reactions con-
inue after the illumination is stopped and
xhibit aftereffects of a thermal nature.
While thermal reactions are dependent up-
n the concentration of reacting substances,
hotochemical reactions are often inde-
endent of the concentration. The energy
vailable in photochemical reactions is
reater than that of thermal reactions.
This accounts for the fact that photochemi-
al reactions are often different from
thermal reactions and may be more com-
lex.

Solid and Semisolid Systems.

Most of
the reactions studied in photochemistry
have been in the field of gaseous systems.
Little work has been done with liquid and
solid systems. Of the solids sensitive to
light only a few have been thoroughly investigated. Of these, only the decomposition of silver halides is of interest to
photography.[2]

If certain substances, as gelatin, silver
nitrate, halides of potassium and ammonium, are added to silver halides, the
latter become more light sensitive. Materials of this type act as light catalysts
and are known as "sensitizers." The presence of small quantities of certain sulfur
bodies [3] (as "allyl isothiocyanate") in gelatin greatly increases the sensitivity of
photographic emulsions. It is also known
that the sensitivity of photographic emulsion is dependent on the size range of
silver halide grains. Eggert and Noddack have studied [4] the light absorption
processes of silver halides and found that
they decompose into silver and halogen.
The reaction has a quantum efficiency of
one.[5]

$$AgBr + h\nu = Ag + Br \quad \Phi = 1.$$

Light Sensitive Materials for Photography.

Of the many light sensitive sys-

[2] Franck and Kohn, *Z. Physik* **44**, 607 (1927).

[3] Sheppard and Punnett, U.S.P. 623,499.

[4] Eggert and Noddack, *Z. Physik* **31**, 922 (1925).

[5] Noddack and Weigert, *Sitzber. Preuss. Akad. Wissent.* **38**, 631, 641 (1921).

tems only a few have found commercial applications in photography. Sheppard lists the following: (1) silver halides and salts that produce silver images; (2) iron complexes which produce ferrous salts. The latter are converted into platinum, palladium, or prussian blue images; (3) alkaline dichromates that produce chromium oxides which are capable of tanning gelatin or other colloids; (4) diazo compounds that lose nitrogen and are decomposed into products which may be coupled to form a dye; (5) sensitive dyes that are bleached by light.[6]

Light Sensitiveness of Silver Salts. The relative sensitivity of natural and ammonia fumed silver salts was determined by Turneretscher who measured the intensity of the print-out images.[7]

	Natural Sensitivity	Sensitivity After Ammonia Treatment
Silver Oxalate	2	80
Silver Nitrate	6	8
Silver Tartrate	7	17
Silver Citrate	15	18
Silver Chloride	100	100
Silver Iodide	300	450
Silver Bromide	700	900

Silver halides show the greatest senitivity; however, the order of sensitivity is not the same for all effects. According to the photoelectric effect, electron ejection by light, the sensitivities in decreasing order are AgBr, AgCl, and AgI. The order of darkening in light is AgCl, AgBr, and AgI, although results may differ somewhat according to conditions of preparation. The ease of reduction with developer decreases from AgCl to AgBr to AgI.

Silver Processes. If silver halides, a silver chloride, silver bromide, and silve iodide, or silver salts, as silver nitrate silver citrate, are dispersed in protectiv colloids, as gelatin, agar, albumen, casein collodion, or cellulose esters, suspension formed are known as emulsions which i coated on supports, as glass, film base, o paper, become sensitized goods. Of th silver salts, the silver halides are most im portant.

On exposure to light silver salts exhibi two types of photographic reactions, print ing out—producing visible images—and th formation of latent images which may b developed into visible images. Visible im ages are composed of colloidal silver ad sorbed to or occluded in silver halide. By x-ray studies Koch has shown that th first traces of a visible image are composed of metallic silver.[8] The latent image serves to catalyze the development process causing a reduction of silver halides. There are two basic theories as to the origin of the latent image. Renwick suggests that the colloidal silver acts as a negative sol and is coagulated by the action of light to form a neutral gel which may catalyze the reduction of silver halide. The second theory assumes that on exposure the halogen ion loses an electron which is adsorbed by a silver ion forming a metallic speck.[9]

$$Br^- + h\nu \rightarrow Br + e,$$
$$Ag^+ + e \quad \rightarrow Ag,$$
$$Br \: + Br \rightarrow Br_2.$$

X-ray data show that silver halide crystals have crystal lattices in which the silver and bromine exist as ions.[10] On exposure the ions undergo changes given in the equations above. The silver formed acts as

---

[6] Sheppard, *Ind. Eng. Chem.* **22**, 555 (1930).

[7] *Cassel's Cyclopedia of Photography*, 490 (1911).

FRIEDMAN, "Light Sensitive Systems," *Amer. Phot.* (1940) 294.

[8] Koch and Vogler, *Ann. Physik* **77**, 495 (1925).
[9] Fajans, *Chem. Ztg.* **45**, 666 (1921). Toy and Edgerton, *Phil. Mag.* **48**, 947 (1924). Spencer, *Proc. 7th Int. Cong. Phot.* 358 (1928).
[10] Wilsey, *Phil. Mag.* **42**, 262 (1921).

nucleus, or center, for development of the silver halide grain.

The exposure of photographic emulsions produces latent images that can be developed when the image is treated with a selective reducing, or developing, agent in solution. Latent images are not visible, but when treated with reducing agents the products of the photochemical reaction act as a catalyzer which, in turn, causes reduction of the surrounding silver molecules. The quantum yield for reaction of this type may be as great as 10^9. The exact mechanisms for the processes of latent image formation are still uncertain. A discussion of the various theories will be found in Chapter 10.

Quanta Required for Latent Image Formation. The application of the quantum theory to photographic exposures and latent image formation has been the subject of study for many investigators. Silberstein studied the quantum theory of photographic exposure. James, James and Coleman, and Webb [11] have investigated theoretically the number of quanta required to form the photographic latent image. Silberstein has determined mathematically the number of quanta needed for developability of a silver halide grain.

The question as to the number of quanta utilized in latent image formation is an important problem in photographic theory. One method of approach has been the mathematical analysis of the characteristic H and D curves for an emulsion.[12] A fundamental assumption of the theoretical investigations is that a fixed minimum number of quanta are required to produce a latent image that is just developable.[13]

This minimum number is assumed to be the same for every grain. Analyses of this assumption have led to the conclusion that a small number of quanta, 1 to 4, are involved in latent image formation. Contrary to this Webb has shown that theoretical curves based on a wide variation of sensitivity among grains, 1 to 1000, are also in agreement with experimental H and D curves. Webb and Evans [14] using the method of intermittent exposures found that some grains require more than 64 quanta to become developable. Since 2 or 3 electrons may be placed on a speck without requiring neutralization, the number of quanta required for latent image formation for some grains may be greater than 100. Although a few grains may require 1000 or more quanta, such are scarce. Eggert and Noddack state [15] that the number of quanta falling on a grain may be as high as several hundred.

[11] For a good bibliography of work up to 1939 consult paper by Webb in *J. Opt. Soc. Amer.* **29**, 309 (1939).

[12] Silberstein, *J. Opt. Soc. Amer.* **31**, 343 (1941).

[13] Helnick, ''On the Quantity of Light Required to Make Developable a Grain of Silver Bromide,'' *J. Opt. Soc. Amer.* **5**, 998 (1922); **9**, 521 (1924).

[14] Webb, *J. Opt. Soc. Amer.* **31**, 348 (1941). Webb and Evans, *J. Opt. Soc. Amer.* **41**, 355 (1941).

[15] Eggert and Noddack, *Z. Physik* **20**, 299 (1923).

SHEPPARD, "The Formation of the Photographic Latent Image," *Phot. J.* **68**, 397 (1928).

SHEPPARD AND WIGHTMAN, "Energy Exchanges in the Formation of the Latent Image," *J. Opt. Soc. Amer.* **5**, 913 (1922).

SILBERSTEIN, "Quantum Theory of Photographic Exposure," *Phil. Mag.* **44**, 257 (1922); **44**, 956 (1922); **45**, 1062 (1923); **5**, 464 (1928); *Proc. Int. Math. Congress*, Toronto, p. 127 (1924).

JAMES AND COLEMAN, "Quantum Theory of the Latent Photographic Image," *J. Chem. Phys.* **2**, 483 (1934).

JAMES, *Quantum Theory of Latent Photographic Image* **2**, 134 (1934).

WEBB, "The Number of Quanta Required to Form the Photographic Latent Image as Determined from Mathematical Analysis of

By applying a method of graphic analysis to photographic exposure and assuming that the sensitivity variation among grains of a photographic emulsion depends on the inherent variation in grain sensitivity among grains of the same size class as well as upon size distribution, Webb was able to derive theoretical equations [16] for H and D curves in agreement with experimental data obtained by Wightman, Trivelli and Sheppard [17] for the exposure grain-count of an actual emulsion.

The number of quanta required for latent image formation does not necessarily agree with the number of silver atoms in the latent image. This difference may be due to the fact that the energy of quanta may not be sufficient to cause the formation of silver atoms, silver atoms formed may be oxidized back to ions by loss of electrons or they may be lost by the speck.

According to Mott,[18] quanta adsorbed by a crystal may undergo three fates, the energy may be converted into heat, remitted as fluorescence, or used in the production of photoelectric energy.

Iron Processes. Ferric salts in the presence of organic acids form complexes which on exposure to light are reduced ferrous salts.

$$Fe^{+++} + 3(C_2O_4)^{--} \rightarrow \begin{bmatrix} C_2O_4 & & C_2O_4 \\ & \searrow \; \swarrow & \\ & Fe & \\ & \updownarrow & \\ & C_2O_4 & \end{bmatrix}^{---}$$

$$\begin{bmatrix} C_2O_4 & & C_2O_4 \\ & \searrow \; \swarrow & \\ & Fe & \\ & \updownarrow & \\ & C_2O_4 & \end{bmatrix}^{---} + h\nu \rightarrow C_2O_4^{--} + \begin{bmatrix} & & C_2O_4 \\ & \swarrow & \\ Fe & & \\ & \nwarrow & \\ & & C_2O_4 \end{bmatrix}$$

This reaction forms the basis of the blueprint and platino-type processes.

Bichromate Processes. The second most important photographic process depends upon the action of light on bichromate colloids. The investigations of Eder, Lumiere and Seyewetz, Bowen [19] and others show that a portion of the exposed bichromate is decomposed to Cr_2O_3 which in turn reacts with the acid bichromate ion $(HCr_2O_7)^-$ to form a complex which is responsible for the tanning of the colloid. Colloids hardened in this manner are utilized in various photomechanical processes and in imbibition and pigment printing processes such as carbon, carbo, gum-bichromate, and bromoil.

The Metal Diazonium Process. Hydrophelic supports are coated with a mixture of a light sensitive water soluble diazonium compound, and a mercurous salt. The action of light decomposes the diazonium compound, and the

an o-oxy-aryl   photon   light decom-   nitrogen
diazonium-sul-   position
fonic acid   product

[16] Webb, *J. Opt. Soc. Amer.* **29**, 314 (1939).

[17] Wightman, Trivelli, and Sheppard, *J. Phys. Chem.* **28**, 529 (1924).

[18] Mott, *Proc. Roy. Soc.* **167A**, 384 (1938).

the H and D Curve," *J. Opt. Soc. Amer.* 29, 309 (1939); 31, 348, 559 (1941).

SILBERSTEIN, "On the Number of Quanta Required for Developability of a Silver Halide Grain," *J. Opt. Soc. Amer.* 31, 343 (1941).

SELWYN, "Number of Quanta Required to Form the Photographic Latent Image as Determined from Mathematical Analysis of the H and D Curve," *J. Opt. Soc. Amer.* 29, 518 (1939).

TOY, *Phil. Mag.* 44, 364 (1922).

[19] Bowen and Yarnold, *J. Chem. Soc.* 164 (1929).

ht decomposition product reacts with
rcuric ions which are present in equi-
rium in the solution of mercurous salt;
., mercurous nitrate.

$$Hg_2^{++} \rightleftarrows Hg + Hg^{++}$$
mercurous   metallic   mercuric
ions   mercury   ions

nce the mercuric ions are removed by
mbining with the light decomposition
oduct, only mercury atoms remain. The
rcury atoms form a latent image that
n be developed with a physical developer
ntaining a silver salt and a reducing
ent, forming a silver image.

Quantum efficiencies as high as 0.5 are
aimed. The effective speed, although 5–
× that of other diazo processes is low
ving to high dispersion of the latent im-
e. The emulsion is grainless and the
solution is good due to high opacity of
e image and low scattering of the emul-
on layer. Maximum sensitivity occurs at
00 Å. Resolving power is in excess of
00 lines per millimeter. By varying in-
nsity of printing light, humidity, time of
velopment, and nature of developer,
mmas from 10 to 1.6 are obtained from
given exposure. 80× enlargements are
ossible. The material is of the negative-
ositive type and is suited to document and
icro copying. Although the mercury la-
nt image is rather unstable, the developed
nage is quite stable.

Other Metallic Salt Processes. Various
mpounds of uranium, mercury, thallium,
latinum, cobalt, nickel, cerium, molybde-
um, and tungsten show light sensitive-
ess. Of these the most important for
hotographic use are: uranium, mercury,
hallium, and platinum. At present, no
rinting emulsions employing these salts
re available, commercially.

IPPEL, "The Metal Diazonium Process," *Phot.
J.* **90B**, 34–41 (1950).

RIEDMAN, "Uranium Printing," *Am. Phot.* 33,
846 (1939).

Dye Processes. With the exception of
bleach-out, diazo, and silver-dye bleaching
processes, photography has not made much
use of the light sensitivity of dyes.

Many dyes are sensitive to light, either
changing in color or more frequently bleaching out to colorless or nearly colorless substances. The exposure required for bleaching varies widely with different dyes. The
exposure required for bleaching of some
dyes is greatly reduced, if other substances,
termed sensitizers, are present. Dyes are
usually sensitive to the shorter wave lengths
of light, chiefly to ultraviolet. Dyes sensitive to light are generally bleached by light
of a complementary color. Dye bleaching
may be either a process of oxidation, reduction, decomposition, or internal rearrangement.

a. The Bleach-out Process. This process
often referred to as *dye bleaching* utilizes
dyes that fade rapidly when exposed to
visible or ultraviolet light. Because a dye
transmits its own color and absorbs those
of the remaining spectrum (complementary
color) it can be used as a sensitive material.
The dye in the dye layer absorbs light in
proportion to exposure received and undergoes a photochemical change which bleaches
the dye. By incorporation of three suitable
subtrative color dyes, each in different
gelatin layer, a color material may be
formed which if exposed to a positive color
image yields a positive color picture.

Negative or positive color images may be
formed depending on the choice of dyes.

Dye bleaching as a photographic process
was first recognized by Liesegang in 1889.[20]
The work of Vallot, Neuhaus, Worel, Szcze-
panik, Smith and Limmer was ably summarized by the latter in 1911.[21]

More recently the reactions involved have

[20] Liesegang, *Phot. Arch.* No. 633,328 (1889).
[21] Limmer, *Das Ausbleichverfahren,* Halle
(1911).

been studied by Koenig, Steigman, Mudrovcic,[22] Kogel,[23] Lasreff,[24] and Wendt.[25] While the action of sensitizing agents on dyes of oxazine, thiazine, azine, phthalein, triphenylmethane, and xanthonium classes has been studied, only basic dyes of the xanthene group sensitized with thiourea derivatives, and acid dyes used with activating and sensitizing agents are employed for the production of images. Fixation is accomplished by treating with agents like sulfurous acid which destroy the sensitivity of the dye. Some xanthonium dyes found suitable for dye bleaching are:

Capri Blue GON	Pyronine G
Flavinduline	Rosinduline 2B
Methylene Blue	Rhodamine S

b. The Diazo Process. The bleaching of dyes finds its most important application in photography in the plan copying papers of which Ozalid and Primuline are examples.

In the diazo process, exposure causes diazonium salts, which are dye intermediates, to undergo chemical changes which affect their capacity to form dyes, i.e.:

1. Exposure of the diazonium salt causes the destruction of the diazonium linkage.

(in paper)   (acid)

[22] Mudrovcic, *Phot. 2nd* **27**, 1913 (1929).
[23] Kogel, *Phot. Korr.* **9**, 15 (1926).
[24] Lasreff, *Zeit. Phys. Chem.* **78**, 657 (1912).
[25] U.S.P. 1,850,162; 1,871,830; 1,880,573; 2,049,005.

PLOTNIKOW, *Allgemeine Photo Chemie*, Walter de Gruyter, Leipzig (1936).
Eder's Handbuch IV, 4 (1929).
FRIEDMAN, "Bleach-out Process," *Am. Phot.* 32, 821 (1938).
"Progress in Color," *Brit. J. Phot.* 87, 419 (1940).

The residual diazonium salt, unexposed portion, may couple to form an azo dye.

(azo dye) (acid)

As coupling takes place in an alkaline medium only, it is necessary to nutralize the acid, e.g. with ammonia vapors.

$$HX + NH_3 \rightarrow NH_4X.$$

With this method a dark colored line positive is obtained from a positive original.

2. On exposure to light the diazonimum salt undergoes an internal rearrangement. The compound is chosen so that only one form of the salt will couple. According to the materials used either a positive or negative image may be produced.

The discovery of the diazo reaction was made by Griess in 1858. West, using diazo salicylic acid and its derivatives, made diazo pictures in 1885. The first practical process was introduced by Freer who discovered that diazo-sulfonates after exposure would couple to form dyes. This reaction yielded a negative image. Green, Cross and Bevan, 1890, discovered that diazotized primuline could not couple after exposure. Their method gave a positive image from the copy. In 1923, Kogel discovered the stable class of light sensitive compounds, the diazo-anhydrides, which gave rise to the first dry development papers. It was possible to incorporate these salts in gelatin solutions together with suitable couplers and organic acids and produce, after exposure and fuming with

[26] Spencer, *Proc. 7th Int. Cong.* 358 (1928).

nmonia, coupled images in the unexposed regions.

c. *Silver-Dye Bleach Process.* The Silver-ye Process (Dye Destruction) differs from he bleach-out process in that dyes are leached by chemical means instead of by he action of light. The silver image may et as a catalyst or it may be made the gent for the destruction or protection of yes. The destruction of the dye may take lace either at a point where the silver image is formed or in areas without a silver mage, the effect varying in proportion to he silver density. In either case, the silver mage determines the position of the dye mage remaining after processing. A survey of dye destruction methods was made y Hymer in 1935.[27]

Dye destruction processes are grouped into two methods, depending on whether he silver image promotes or prevents destruction of the associated dyes.

1. Dyes in the presence of the silver image may be destroyed by either oxidation, reduction, catalytic, or bleaching processes.

Dyes in the presence of silver images may e destroyed by oxidizing agents as hydrogen peroxide,[28] ammonium persulfate, potassium bromate, and lead chromate.[29] Reducing agents, like sodium hydrosulfite and odium stannite,[30] destroy dyes while the ilver image is developed. The silver image may also be converted to substances which are capable of destroying the dye either directly or indirectly. Vanadium

ferrocyanide and chromic acid [31] is used in this way. In other cases the silver image may be bleached with an acid solution of thiourea,[32] or dyed with a dye that can be easily reduced to a leuco base.[33] The latter produces a reversed dye image when silver is removed. Two essentials necessary for these processes are the use of a silver halide solvent and an acid reaction.[34]

2. Dyes may be destroyed in areas that do not contain a silver image. In this case, dyes in the presence of silver halides are bleached. Typical bleaching reagents are: calcium hypochlorite and glacial acetic acid,[35] sodium bromate and sulfuric acid,[36] or iodic acid with sulfuric acid.

Dye destruction methods have been employed successfully in Gasparcolor. In this process the developed silver image is bleached with a silver solvent containing ferric salts. The silver salts are then converted to silver, and the dye in the emulsion is bleached by exposure and treatment with hydrosulfite and bromine solutions.

Among the dyes found suitable for such a process are: Diamine Pure Blue FF, Benzopurpurine 10B, and Mordant Yellow G.D.

Quantum Yields for Photographic Reactions. Reaction processes and quantum yields for four photographic systems have been summarized by Eggert.[37]

[27] Hymer, *Sci. Pub. Agfa Central Lab.* **4**, 177 1935).

[28] Schingel, *Brit. J. Phot.* **52**, 608 (1905).

[29] Schweitzer, Fr. P. 496,217 (1915).

[30] Christensen, *Jahrbuch* **29**, 164 (1915); 27,591.

[31] Luther and Holleben, D.R.P. 369,485.

[32] Gaspar, *Zeit. Wiss. Phot.* **34**, 119.

[33] Crabtree, *Abridged Scientific Publications of Kodak Research Laboratories*, **4**, 198 (1919–20).

[34] Luppo-Cramer, *Eder's Handbuch* **2** (1927).

[35] Gaspar, *Brit. J. Phot. Colour Supplement* **27**, 41 (1933).

[36] Schweitzer, B.P. 249,530.

[37] *Phot. J.* **76**, 17 (1936).

SAUNDERS, *The Aromatic Diazo Compounds*, Arnold & Co., London, 1936.

FRIEDMAN, "Gaspar Process," *Am. Phot.* **32**, 130 (1938); **35**, 855 (1941).

Sensitive Substance	Reaction Mechanism	Quantu Yield
Gelatino-silver	$Cl^- + h\nu = Cl + \theta$ $\theta + Ag^+ = Ag$	$\Phi =$
Gelatino-silver bromide	$AgCl + h\nu = Ag + Cl$	
	$Br^- + h\nu = Br + \theta$ $\theta + Ag^+ = Ag$	$\Phi =$
	$AgBr + h\nu = Ag + Br$	
Diazo	$C_6H_5NHC_6H_5N \equiv N + H_2O = h\nu$ $\quad\quad\quad\mid$ $\quad\quad\quad SO_3H$ $= N_2 + C_6H_5NHC_6H_5OH + H_2SO_4$	$\Phi = 0$
Chromate-gelatin	$CrO_4 + 3H$ (from gelatin) $+ h\nu = CrO3OH'$ $CrO + gel \rightarrow$ Adsorption Product	$\Phi = 0$

Dippel[38] has determined the quantum yield for the Metal-Diazonium Process:

Metal-
Diazonium

$$CH_3C_6H_2(OH)(SO_3^-)N^+ \equiv N + h\nu$$
$$CH_3C_5H_3(SO_3^-)COOH + N_2$$
$$Hg_2^{++} \rightleftarrows Hg + Hg^{++}$$ $\Phi = 0$

Energy Requirements for Photographic Silver Image. It is reported that only about 60% of the incident energy is absorbed by the photographic emulsion and that only a small portion of this is absorbed by the silver halide grains; the remainder is lost by scatter, or by absorption, due to gelatin and other materials in the film. Eggert and Noddack, in studies on quantum efficiency of latent image formation, have calculated that only 10% of the incident light is absorbed by the silver halide grain and is useful in latent image formation. Unless the emulsion is sensitized with dyes it is sensitive only to the violet and blue portions of the spectrum. The silver halide crystals in the emulsion are composed of silver and bromide ions, arranged alternately in rows and planes forming a crystal lattice of cubic form in which each silver ion is surrounded by six halide ions, a condition which holds true for all but the ions along the surface and edges.

During exposure, if the light has th proper frequency to be absorbed, the e ergy of the quantum is transferred to th valence electron associated with the bromic ion and raises an electron from the satu rated energy band to a higher level corr sponding to conductance band of the silve halide where the electron is free to mov until it comes in contact with the silver su fide speck, or a particle of free colloid silver, as found in the interior of the crys tal. On contact, the electron loses part o its energy, becomes trapped, and the spec or silver particles, assume a negativ charge.

Since some of the silver ions in the crys tal are not in the proper lattice position the interstitial ions migrate at normal tem peratures until they are attracted to th negatively charged specks where they be come neutralized, forming an atom of fre silver on the speck. This process may b repeated until this speck has a sufficien number of silver atoms to render it develop

^{38} Dippel *Phot. J.* **90B**, 36 (1950).

ble. The number of silver atoms required make the speck developable varies in different emulsions but is generally agreed to ange from one to ten.

The developer provides the energy required to reduce silver ions from the silver alide crystal, the reduction starting at the ilver latent-image speck and continuing as peck grows.

The reduction of silver bromide crystals ollowing exposure is therefore the combined effect of a number of processes:

1. Photoconductivity—results from the bsorption of a quantum of light by the ilver halide lattice and transfer of a hotoelectron to the conductance band where it moves freely due to thermal enrgy until trapped at a sensitivity speck.

2. Ionic Conductivity—the electrostatic otential of the negatively charged speck ttracts the migrating interstitial silver ions, which are neutralized by contact at the speck with electrons, forming free silver atoms. Alternate processes of electron trapping and silver ion neutralization cause the speck to grow until the silver nuclei is developable.

3. Development—reduction starts at the speck and continues to expand until the entire crystal is reduced to metallic silver.

Photography is, therefore, a process in which the light sensitive material absorbs radiation and undergoes certain photochemical changes. Conversion of the latent image to a visible image is brought about by chemical energy supplied by the developer.

Unless the sum of all the energies affecting the silver halide crystal is equal to, or grater than, that corresponding to the heat of formation no reduction will take place.

Chapter 7

THE PHOTOGRAPHIC EMULSION

The photographic emulsion is not, strictly speaking, a true emulsion but a dispersion of crystalline silver halide in a colloid. The term *emulsion* has been in use so long, however, and is so generally understood, that the distinction is largely academic.

The silver halides employed are the chloride, bromide, and iodide. Negative emulsions employ silver bromide and a small quantity of silver iodide; while emulsions for developing papers are composed of silver chloride, silver bromide, or both, the ratio of the two halides depending upon the end in view.

The silver halide, or halides, are produced by adding silver nitrate to a solution of the halide, potassium bromide for example, in a solution of gelatin. In the absence of gelatin, the crystals of silver halide are precipitated and settle to the bottom, but in gelatin they remain uniformly distributed in the solution. The photographic emulsion is thus a *suspension* of crystalline silver halide in gelatin.

The gelatin functions, also, as a protective colloid. Without the protective action of a colloid, such as gelatin, all possibility of developing the image is eliminated as the silver halide, whether exposed or not, is immediately reduced to silver on contact with the developer.

Gelatin. The superiority of gelatin[1] over other colloids is due to its physical properties and to its favorable influence on the sensitivity of the silver halide. Of primary importance is the easy reversibility of the transition from the hydrosol to the hydrogel at convenient temperatures. This property makes it possible to prepare suspension of silver halide crystals which can be spread on paper, film base or glass plates, chilled and dried to form a medium which will hold the photosensitive silver halide uniformly distributed and permanently in position on the base and at the same time is sufficiently permeable to allow the free passage of the solutions used in processing.

Indirectly, gelatin contributes importantly to the light-sensitivity of the silver-halide. The sensitivity of crystals of pure silver halide is comparatively low regardless of the halide or the size of the crystal. The sensitivity of photographic emulsions is due to the formation of sensitivity centers, or nuclei, on the silver halide crystals from the decomposition of substances found in gelatin. Gelatin lacking in these substances (inert gelatin) is in

---

[1] Gelatin has the disadvantage that it is of animal origin and therefore subject to unordered variations. Moreover, it is costly to produce in a highly refined condition and is subject to attack by animal and vegetable organisms, insects, and bacteria. In an attempt to overcome these disadvantages by the substitution of a synthetic material which can be made in the laboratory and standardized, considerable attention has been given in recent years to the use of water-permeable cellulose esters. The problems of emulsification, ripening, washing, sensitizing, however, remain to be solved and it is not possible as yet to prepare emulsions of high speed except with gelatin. See Thorne-Baker, "Plastics in Photography," *Ame Phot.* **43**, 14 (January 1947).

Other colloids which have been used include albumen, agar, and casein, but none of these is as suitable as gelatin.

pable of producing emulsions of high
nsitivity, unless it is converted into active
latin by the addition of a sensitizer. A
rge number of such sensitizers are known
t it appears that the group

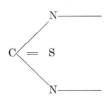

necessary for sensitizing and that in all
ses the final product, i.e., the composition
the sensitivity center, is silver sulfide.

Classification of Emulsions. Photo-
aphic emulsions may be divided as fol-
ws:

1. *Emulsions for Printing-out.* Emul-
ns of this type contain free silver nitrate
d an organic silver salt which functions
a halogen absorbent.

2. *Emulsions for Development.* Emul-
ns for development contain an excess of
lide and, therefore, no free silver nitrate.

(A) Negative emulsions
    (1) Neutral or boiled
    (2) Ammonia
(B) Positive emulsions
    (1) Chloride emulsions
    (2) Bromide emulsions
    (3) Chloro-bromide emulsions
    (4) Brom-chloride emulsions.

This chapter will deal only with negative
d positive emulsions for development.

The Preparation of Emulsions. The
ore important steps in the preparation of
emulsion are as follows:

GUE, *The Chemistry and Technology of Gelatin and Glue*, McGraw-Hill Book Co., New
   York, 1922.

EES, *The Theory of the Photographic Process*,
   The Macmillan Co., New York, 1942.

HORNE-BAKER, *Photographic Emulsion Technique*, American Photographic Publishing
   Co., Boston, 1941.

1. A part of the gelatin required by the
particular formula is soaked in water and
finally dissolved by heat.

2. The soluble bromide and iodide are
added—in solution—with or without the
addition of ammonia.

3. A solution of silver nitrate is added;
the concentration, rate of addition, temperature, and other factors being controlled
to produce a fine and uniform dispersion
of the crystals of silver halide in gelatin
(*emulsification*).

4. The emulsion is then heated to a temperature of from 50° to 80° C. to bring
about a recrystallization of the silver halide
and fix the size-frequency distribution of
the silver halide crystals (*first ripening*).

5. The remainder of the gelatin is added
and the emulsion thoroughly mixed with
the new gelatin, then chilled quickly.

6. When set, the emulsion is placed in
a press and forced through a wire screen
to break it up into small noodles.

7. These noodles are washed in running
water to remove the excess salts. Emulsions
for printing papers are only partially
washed.

8. The emulsion is now heated a second
time to facilitate the formation of the sensitivity centers, or nuclei, on the silver halide
crystals and thus increase the sensitivity
and contrast of the emulsion. This operation either is omitted or is of minor importance in the case of positive emulsions
(*after-ripening or second ripening*).

9. The following may be added at this
stage: (1) color sensitizing dyes, (2) antifoggants or stabilizers, (3) preservatives,
(4) flexibility-promoting substances to facilitate coating and (5) in the case of positive materials, for the control of image
color.

10. The emulsion is then coated on the
final support.

Emulsification. The operation in which the silver halide crystals are formed by precipitation in gelatin is generally termed *emulsification*. Emulsification is the first and one of the most important operations, as the basic characteristics of the emulsion are largely determined by the conditions existing during emulsification. The first requirement is that the crystals of silver halide be sufficiently small to remain uniformly dispersed in the gelatin; i.e., emulsified. Beyond this, it is necessary that the size-frequency distribution of the crystals of silver halide be such as to produce, after ripening, an emulsion suitable for the purpose intended.

The conditions during emulsification that affect the size-frequency distribution are:

1. *The concentration of the gelatin in which the silver halide is precipitated.* Other factors being constant, lower concentrations of gelatin result in a greater proportion of the larger crystals. At the higher concentrations the average crystal size is smaller and more uniform. In paper emulsions most, and sometimes all, of the gelatin is present during emulsification.

Mees states [2] that in negative emulsions precipitation normally takes place in a solution containing from 1 to 5% of gelatin and that this gelatin is of the inactive type —i.e., one free of sensitivity-promoting substances.

2. *The concentration of alkaline halide present during the precipitation of the silver halide.* In emulsions for development, the amount of soluble bromide present during precipitation is invariably greater than is necessary to combine with the silver to form silver halide. Silver bromide is soluble in an alkaline bromide and the increased solubility from the excess halide results in the formation of

larger crystals. Baker states that pa emulsions often contain little excess hal and sometimes may have free acid.

3. *The rate of addition and concentrat of the silver solution.* The solution of sil nitrate is added to the potassium brom gelatin solution at a constant rate and w stirring to prevent any local accumulat of silver nitrate. Other factors being c stant, the rapid addition of the silver trate, or the use of a concentrated soluti leads to small, uniformly sized cryst The slow addition of the silver nitrate lution, or the use of less concentrated sc tions, results in a wider range in the si of the silver halide crystals as those form in the earlier stages increase in size w time.

4. *Temperature.* As would be expec from the general relationship between te perature and solubility, an increase in te perature tends to increase the size-f quency distribution and the average size the silver halide crystals.

5. *The presence of ammonia, or ot solvents of silver halide.* The addition ammonia increases the solubility of silver halide in the solution and favors formation of larger crystals. The a monia may be added before the addition the silver nitrate, with the silver nitrate after emulsification. Ammonia added af emulsification does not change the size-f quency distribution but does facilitate formation of sensitizing nuclei on the sil halide grain.

Ammonia is apparently necessary in preparation of emulsions of the high sensitivity; an excess, however, is state to produce clumping of the silver hal grains resulting in coarser-grained depos of silver in the developed image and low resolving power.

6. *The addition of iodide.* Most negat materials contain silver iodide and it

---

[2] Mees, *The Theory of the Photographic Process*, The Macmillan Co., New York, 1942.

[3] Carrol, *Brit. J. Phot.* **79**, 654 (1932).

pears essential for high-speed negative materials. The amount seldom exceeds 5 mol. per cent.

The iodide is generally added as potassium iodide before precipitation. The evidence available indicates that silver iodide in the amounts used does not form separate crystals of AgI, but forms a solid solution with the bromide and enlarges the lattice without altering its structure. Renwick and Sease [4] found that the amount of silver iodide tends to increase with the size of the crystal.[5]

Ripening. After precipitation of the silver halide, negative emulsions are heated to a temperature which varies between 45° and 50° C., in the case of ammonia emulsions; and 80° to 90° C. with neutral emulsions, for a period which varies apparently from ten minutes to two hours. This operation is known as *ripening* or *digestion*. This treatment results in an increase in the average size of the crystals of silver halide or, in terms of colloid chemistry, a decrease in the dispersity. In the presence of a solvent such as alkaline halide or ammonia, an increase in temperature causes the larger crystals to grow at the expense of the smaller; thus, while the number of crystals present is reduced the average size is increased.

The operations of emulsification and ripening are closely related and together they determine the average size and the size-frequency distribution of the crystals of silver halide in the emulsion.

Little appears in the literature on the ripening of paper emulsions. Since the chief technical requirements of emulsions of this type are low sensitivity, fine grain, and comparatively high contrast, ripening by heat might be expected to employ lower temperatures than are common with negative materials.

Eliminating the Soluble Salts. In the case of negative emulsions only a small quantity of the gelatin required for the finished emulsion has been used up to this point. The remainder is added after ripening and the emulsion chilled quickly. The gelatin added after ripening has a decided effect on the sensitivity of the emulsion and, for high-speed materials, it must be of the active type; i.e., it must contain sensitivity-promoting substances. With the added gelatin, the emulsion sets to a rather stiff jelly. It is then cut up into fine shreds, or "noodles," by placing it in a press and forcing it through a screen of silver wire. The shredded emulsion, which now resembles ordinary spaghetti, is washed in running water for one to ten hours to remove the excess salts.

The water used for washing must be free of organic or metallic substances which cause fog or affect the gelatin. The pH is also important as alkaline water may cause fog, whereas water which is acid lowers the sensitivity. The temperature of the water is kept to about 10° C. to prevent undue swelling of the gelatin and further change in the silver halide crystals.

The keeping properties of an emulsion are improved if the alkaline bromide is not completely washed out. On the other hand, if much is left the emulsion is not suitable for color sensitizing with some dyes.

Paper emulsions receive only a super-

[4] Renwick and Sease, *Phot. J.* **64**, 360 (1924).

[5] Huse and Mulendyke found that the spectral sensitivity of bromoiodide emulsions shifts toward the longer wavelengths with an increase in the percentage of iodide up to about 30%. *Phot. J.* **66**, 306 (1926).

Chibisoff and Makaroff have recorded that the quantity of silver iodide has a marked effect on the resolving power. A series of emulsions of equal speed, in which the iodide was increased from 0 to 5%, increased in resolving power from 30 to 60. *Kino-Phot. Res. Inst. Moscow* **3**, 30 (1935).

ficial washing and, apparently, in some cases none at all.

After Ripening. After washing, negative emulsions are again melted and heated to a temperature which varies, according to the formula, from 50° to 70° C. for a period up to one hour. This operation is known as *after-ripening*. This second heat treatment, unlike the first, has but little effect on the size or the size-frequency distribution of the crystals of silver halide but results in a marked increase in their sensitivity to light. The increase in sensitivity is particularly striking in neutral emulsions and those containing iodide. It has been recorded by Baker[6] that modern high-speed negative materials gain most of their speed during this second ripening.

The increase in sensitivity is the result of the absorption of the sensitizing substances by the silver halide crystals and possibly the formation of small centers of colloid silver. The sensitizing substances are added with the bulk of the gelatin and react with some of the silver halide to form small centers of silver sulfide. The way in which these centers increase the sensitivity of the silver halide will be discussed in Chapter 10.

Carried too far, ripening leads to fog; if not completed, it continues while the emulsion is in storage or after it has been coated. Thus high-speed negative emulsions which have not been fully ripened before coating may continue to increase in speed for three or four months.

Little has been published on the after-ripening of emulsions of silver chloride, or mixtures of silver chloride and bromide, employed for printing papers. There is reason to believe, however, that emulsions of this kind are also ripened by heat but less completely, and in many cases they are allowed to ripen slowly in storage before being coated and dried.

Emulsion Hardeners. An addition of chrome alum, formaldehyde, or acrolein, all in small quantities, for the purpose of hardening the gelatin layer and preventing it from softening and frilling in hot weather, has long been common practice. The use of these in excess, however, causes the emulsion to become brittle. While this may be partially overcome by the addition of glycerol, hardening substances largely free of this drawback have been found in certain aldehydes, diketones, glyoxal and their derivatives.[7]

Emulsion Sensitizers. It has recently been disclosed that the addition of gold salts in the form of aqueous solutions of ammonium or alkali aurous thiocyanates at this stage, or to the melted emulsion before coating, results in an increase in emulsion speed to as much as four times, with practically no affect on graininess. Gold sensitizers have been used since about 1937 for ultra-speed materials and to increase the speed of fine-grain materials.[8]

The addition of silver tungstate, sodium trithionate, potassium acetate, phosphonium and their derivatives, for the purpose of increasing speed, has been the subject of several patents but there is no evidence that these are being used in commercial emulsions.

Antifoggants and Stabilizers. One of the greatest problems of the emulsion maker is to obtain high sensitivity without excessive fog. All methods of increasing speed lead eventually to fog which, if not immediately serious, develops progressively with the passing of time. The addition of small amounts of iodide, or potassium bichromate, to prevent fog was recommended by Eder as early as 1884, but these tend to reduce speed. In recent years a large number of patents have been granted for

---

[6] *Brit. J. Phot.* **72**, 349 (1925).

[7] For patents on such additions, see: *Photographic Abstracts* or *Chemical Abstracts*

[8] Muehler, *P.S.A. Journal* **16B**, 47 (June 1950).

substances described as "fog preventatives" or "stabilizers." Presumably substances of the first class tend to restrain fog in the emulsion during preparation, whereas stabilizers prevent the growth of fog in the material after coating.

Substances patented include:[9] pyrimidine, salicylamide, acetyl and diacetyl aminophenol, phenylmorpholine, pyrimidine, di- and triphenylamine, acetamides, benzamides, carbamides, thiazoles, selenomercapto-hydroxyprimidine.

There is good reason to believe that these substances find an important application in modern emulsion practice.

Additions to Paper Emulsions. Various substances, the nature of which is disclosed only by the patent literature, are added to paper emulsions, these additions being necessitated by the properties of the paper base or to prevent fog and control the color of the image. The latter will be considered here.

The addition of alkaline citrates, phosphates, borates, and chlorides is mentioned by Baker[10] for the purpose of increasing contrast and to restrain development in obtaining warm tones.

The addition of iodide, either as an alkaline iodide or as an organic compound with iodide,[11] produces green-colored images.

A comparatively large number of patents have been granted for substances which combine with free chloride ions in the emulsions to form sparingly soluble halides and thereby serve to prevent fog and, particularly, the yellow fog which appears when development is forced. These additions also assist in obtaining blue-black images.

[9] See *Photographic Abstracts* or *Chemical Abstracts* for patent literature.
[10] Baker, *Photographic Emulsion Technique,* American Photographic Publishing Co., Boston, 1941.
[11] Steigmann, *Phot. Ind.* **34**, 764, 872 (1936). *Brit. J. Phot.* **85**, 167 (1937); B. J. Almanac, p. 229 (1939).

Among the compounds mentioned in the literature are quinine, nitrobenzimidazole, benzatriazol, nitroimdazol, nitrosoquanidine, thiosemicarbazone, thioglycollic acid, 5-amidoquanide, quinone chloride, iodosobenzene, alkyl and aralkyl quinolines, and methylol nitromethane.[12]

Variable Contrast Emulsions. A number of printing papers have been placed on the market in which the exposure scale may be varied to suit the density scale of the negative by changing the color of the exposing light; e.g., *Multigrade, Varigam.* With these papers it is possible to duplicate on one paper by means of filters the range of contrast obtained on several contrast-grades of other papers.

These materials are based on one of two principles: (1) the use of two emulsions, coated separately or mixed, one of which is unsensitized; the other color sensitized and differing in contrast;[13] (2) color sensitizing with a sensitizer in which the gamma varies widely with the wave length.[14]

Experimental Emulsions. Below will be found references to publications containing formulas and directions for the preparation of emulsions. Although these may prove of value for experimental or teaching pur

[12] Schwartz, *Sci. et Ind. Phot.* **7**, 113 (1936). Seyewetz, *Sci. et Ind. Phot.* **6**, 300 (1935). Steigman, *Camera* (Luzern) **13**, 100 (1934).
[13] Renwick, *Phot. J.* **80**, 320 (1940). Renwick and Waller, B.P. 547,883 (1940); B.P. 541, 510–541, 515.
[14] Potter, *Photo-Technique* **2**, 59 (1940). Potter and Hagaman, U.S.P. 2,280,300.

DAVEY, KNOTT, AND EASTMAN KODAK COMPANY, U.S.P. 2,318,597.
POTTER, "Gradation Control in Photographic Emulsions," *J. Phot. Soc. Amer.* **8**, 507 (1942).
MITCHELL AND ILFORD LTD., B.P. 494,088; 547,060; 547,062.
STEVENS, B.P. 580,173 (1943) to Kodak Ltd.
CARROL, U.S.P. 2,384,598 to Eastman Kodak Company.
KODAK LTD., B.P. 552,368 (1941).

poses, it should be borne in mind that emulsion making is a highly skilled and exacting process and one must not expect to succeed at once or to produce emulsions that are of practical value. It is difficult for the amateur emulsion maker to obtain the proper raw materials, particularly a suitable gelatin, and even the resources of the average chemical laboratory are hardly adequate for the precise control necessary at every stage in the preparation of a usable emulsion. Difficulty is experienced also in coating the emulsion on paper, glass or film base—the difficulty increasing in the order named.

CARROL, "A Summary of Emulsion Knowledge," *Brit. J. Phot.* **79**, 627, 1932.

CARROL, "The Preparation of Photographic Emulsions," *J. Chem. Ed.* **8**, 2341, 1931.

EDER, *Handbuch der Photographie*, Vol. III, Part 1, Wilhelm Knapp, Halle a/Salle, 1930.

GREENWOOD, *British Journal Almanac 1941*, 94.

KIESER, "Emulsion Coating Device for the Laboratory," *Phot. Ind.* **30**, 627, 1932.

LEROY, "Preparation of Fine-Grain Plates," *Brit. J. Phot.* **77**, 125, 1930.

MIDDLETON, "Photographic Transfer Papers (Emulsions)," *Brit. J. Phot.* **75**, 512, 1928.

"Preparing Unwashed Silver Chloride Emulsions," *Photo-Technique* **1**, 41, 1939.

STEIGMANN, GREEN, AND BROWN, "Developing Emulsions," *Phot. Ind.* **34**, 764, 1936; G. P. 505,012 silver iodide emulsion for green tones.

STEIGMANN, "Unwashed Silver Chloro Bromide Emulsions for Enlargement," *Brit. J. Phot.* **93**, 140, 1946.

THORNE-BAKER, "A Homemade Chloride Emulsion," *Amer. Phot.* **37**, 12, March, 1943.

THORNE-BAKER, "The Coating and Testing of Laboratory Emulsions," *Amer. Phot.* **34**, 398, 400, 1940.

THORNE-BAKER, *Photographic Emulsion Technique*, American Photographic Publishing Co., Boston, 1941.

THORNE-BAKER, "Making Bromide and Chloride Papers," *Amer. Phot.* **34**, 469, 1940.

WALL, *Photographic Emulsions*, American Photographic Publishing Co., Boston.

Chapter 8

COLOR SENSITIZING OF PHOTOGRAPHIC EMULSIONS

PART I

SENSITIZING DYES FOR PHOTO-GRAPHIC EMULSIONS

Introduction. As ordinarily prepared, photographic emulsions are not sensitive to red or green, their sensitivity being limited to blue and violet and to the invisible ultraviolet regions of the spectrum. In 1873, H. W. Vogel found that the addition of certain dyes to an emulsion made it sensitive approximately to the spectral region absorbed by the dye. Thus, a yellow dye sensitizes to the blue, a red dye to the green, and a blue dye to the red region of the spectrum. The difference in the sensitivity of an emulsion made by the addition of such photographic sensitizing dyes may be illustrated by a series of spectrograms given in Fig. 8.1. Here we see: (a) the sensitivity of the unsensitized emulsion, (b) the sensitivity of an emulsion sensi-

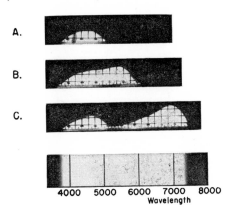

4000 5000 6000 7000 8000
Wavelength

Fig. 8.1. Spectrograms of (a) unsensitized, (b) green, and (c) red sensitized emulsions.

tized by a red dye which imparts additional sensitivity in the green, (c) the extra sensitivity in the red caused by addition of a blue dye.

In the period that followed Vogel's discovery, he and others examined practically all of the then known classes of dyes. Relatively few were found that gave sensitizing action to any great extent. Among these were the triphenyl methane dye Ethyl violet, the pyronine dyes Eosin, Erythrosin and Rose Bengal, the azo dyes Fast Red, Congo Red, Glycine Red, and Benzo Nitrol Brown. Also found to be of value were Acridine Orange, Alizarin Blue, and lastly "Cyanine." This was a dye which had been made by Williams in England in 1856 and found to be too unstable to light to be useful as a fabric dye.

"Cyanine," or Quinoline Blue, was the first representative of what was later proved to be an important class of sensitizing dyes, generically known as the cyanines. The structure and systematic name of "Cyanine" are given below.

$$Am—N \langle \bigcirc \rangle =CH— \langle \bigcirc \rangle N \langle ^I_{Am}$$

1,1'-Di-*n*-amyl-4,4'-cyanine iodide ("Cyanine" or Quinoline Blue)
(1)

The Cyanines. The cyanines may be defined as dyes conforming to the amidinium ion system in which both of the nitrogen atoms are included in heterocyclic ring systems and in which the conjugated chain join-

125

ing these nitrogen atoms passes through a part of each heterocyclic ring. The formula of a typical cyanine dye is shown as follows:

$$\left[\text{—CH=CH—CH=} \right] I^- \leftrightarrow$$

with Et, Et labels

$$\left[\text{=CH—CH=CH—} \right] I^-$$

with Et, Et labels

1,1'-Diethyl-2,2'-carbocyanine iodide (*Pinacyanol*)
(2)

Two extreme resonance structures of the dye are shown between which the actual dye is considered to be a resonance hybrid.[1, 2] The chain stretching between the nitrogen atoms in the formulas consists of an even number of alternating double and single bonds, three double and three single bonds, and this circumstance makes it possible to draw the second structure identical with the first, but with the sequences of linkages in the conjugated chain reversed and the positive charge located on the second nitrogen atom. The formulas show two nitrogen-containing heterocyclic rings, derived from quinoline, linked together through a conjugated trimethine chain. The dye molecule is a positively charged ion, and is satisfied by an acidic radical, in this case iodide, but which may be chloride, bromide, *p*-toluenesulfonate, etc. Ethyl groups are shown attached to the nitrogen atoms but other alkyl or aryl groups may be used.

Cyanine dyes are conveniently classified according to the chain length between the ring systems. The simple cyanines are those in which there is one methine group in the chain between the heterocyclic nu-

[1] Pauling, *Proc. Nat. Acad. Sci.* **25**, 577 (1939).
[2] Brooker, *J. Amer. Chem. Soc.* **62**, 1116 (1940).

clei. An example of this class is Williams' "Cyanine" (Formula 1).

The carbocyanines are those in which there are three methine groups in the conjugated chain, a formula of which has already been shown (Formula 2).

Polycarbocyanines have conjugated chains of more than three methine groups; e.g., dicarbocyanines have five methines, tricarbocyanines have seven, and tetra- and pentacarbocyanines have nine and eleven, respectively. These dyes may be illustrated by the following general formula in which R is alkyl or aryl and n = 1, 2, 3, 4, etc., and x is an anion. If n = 0 the formula represents a monomethine or simple cyanine.

$$\text{=CH(—CH=CH)}_n\text{—}$$

with R, R X labels

(3)

Thus far the dyes shown have been derived from quinoline. Many other heterocyclic nuclei have been employed for making cyanine dyes. Some of the more important are (a) thiazole, (b) thiazoline,

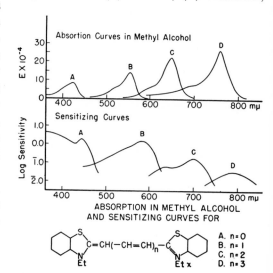

FIG. 8.2. Sensitizing curves for a vinyline homologous series of dyes.

(c) pyridine, (d) benzoxazole, (e) benzothiazole, (f) benzoselenazole, (g) 3,3-dimethylindolenine, (h) naphtho(2,1)-oxazole, (j) naphtho(2,1)thiazole, (k) naptho-(1,2)thiazole.

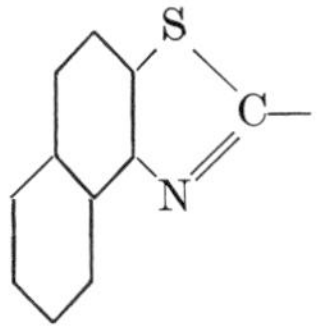

The number of heterocyclic nuclei it is possible to employ is increased many times by the introduction of substituents in the ring; e.g., (1) 4-methylthiazole, and (m) 6-chloroquinoline.

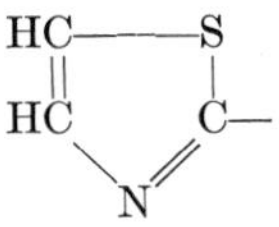

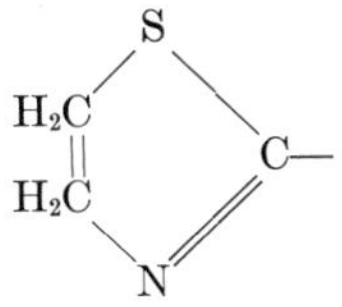

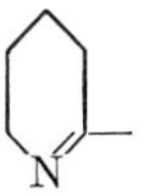

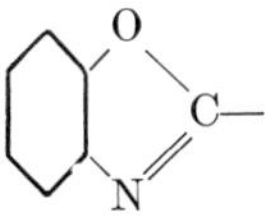

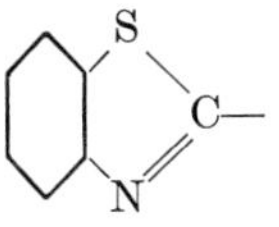

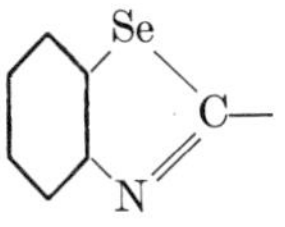

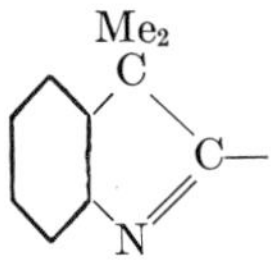

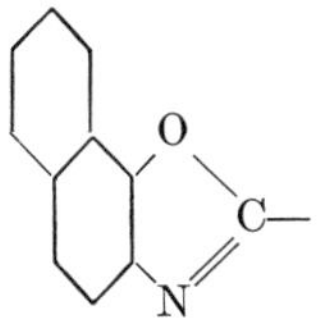

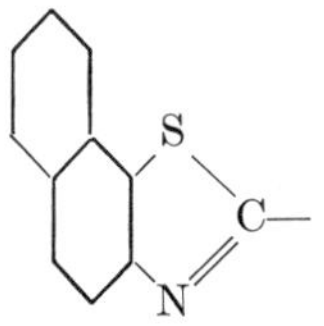

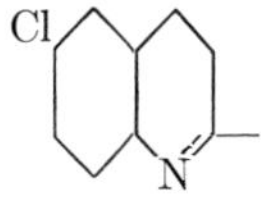

The absorption and sensitizing curves for a vinylene homologous series of dyes from benzothiazole are shown in Fig. 8.2. (The group —CH=CH— by which the chain is lengthened with increase in value of n in Formula 3 is called vinylene.) Nearly the whole range of the visible spectrum is covered by these curves.

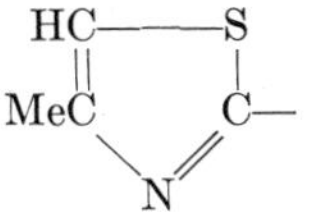

The absorption maximum of the dyes and the sensitizing action in this vinylene homologous series shifts to longer wave length with increasing chain length by an almost constant amount when methyl alcohol is used as solvent. However, the sensitizing maximum for a given dye is seen to lie at somewhat longer wave length than the corresponding absorption maximum determined in methanol. The absorption of the silver halide-dye complex, however, agrees, within the limits of experimental error, with the sensitizing band.

In Fig. 8.3 is given the absorption of a representative group of carbocyanine dyes illustrating the effect on absorption of changing the heterocyclic nucleus. A wide range of the visible spectrum is also covered by these absorption bands and the same may be said of the corresponding sensitizing bands.

Preparation of Cyanine Dyes. According to Brooker[3] the most important intermediates for the preparation of cyanine dyes fall into three main classes:

(A) Quaternary salts of heterocyclic bases which possess reactive hydrogens, usually in the form of methyl groups situated on the α- or γ- positions relative to the nitrogen atoms.

(B) Compounds containing reactive negative atoms or groupings such as halogen, cyano, alkyl- or aryl-mercapto, alkoxy, anilino, or acetanilido.

(C) A condensing agent which may be of either acidic or basic nature depending on the groups being eliminated.

Some of the reactions used in the preparation of the cyanines will now be given.

[3] Brooker, *Mees' Theory of the Photographic Process,* The Macmillan Co., 1942.

A reaction which gives monomethine dyes is the following one:

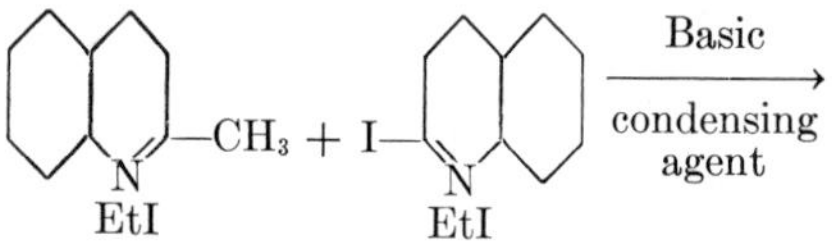

(4)   (5)

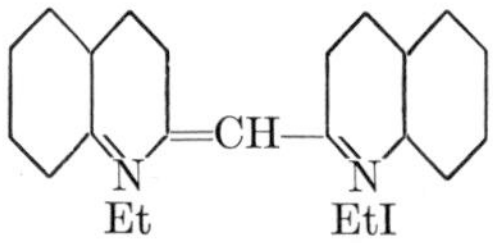

(6)

1,1'-Diethyl-2,2'-cyanine iodide

Quinaldine ethiodide (4), a reactant of type A, is condensed with 2-iodoquinoline ethiodide (5), a reactant of type B, in the presence of a basic condensing agent, a reactant of type C, two moles of hydriodic acid being eliminated during the reaction. Potassium hydroxide was the original condensing agent used in this reaction,[4, 5, 6] but triethylamine was found to be much superior[7] as are also the alkali carbonates.[8] In (6) the nuclei are derived from the same base and the dye is said to be "symmetrical."

2-Methylbenzoxazole ethiodide (type A) and 2-alkyl- or aryl-mercaptobenzothiazole ethiodide (type B) can be condensed together in the presence of a basic condensing agent (type C) to give a cyanine (9) in which the two heterocyclic rings are different. Such a dye is said to be an "unsymmetrical" cyanine. This method appears to be of very general applicability,

being limited only by the availability of the mercapto intermediates.[9, 10, 11]

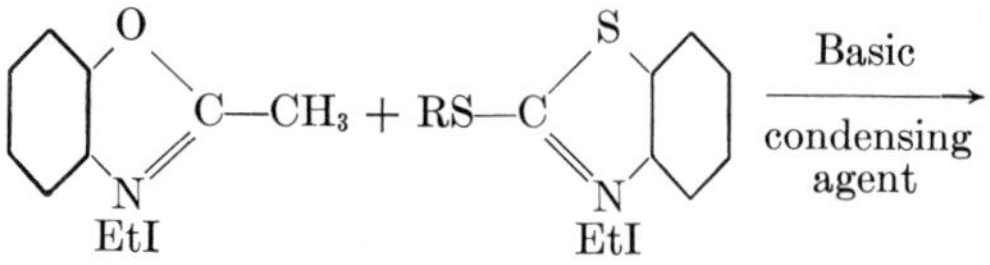

(7)   (8)

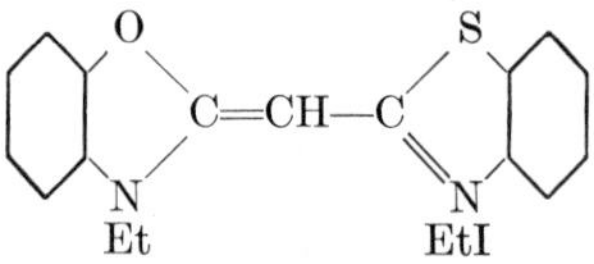

(9)

3,3'-Diethyloxathiacyanine iodide

A third reaction, used to make symmetrical cyanines only, is one in which two proportions of the quaternary salt react with isoamylnitrite in the presence of acetic anhydride. This reaction was used by Fisher and Hamer[12] to prepare the first colorless cyanine (10). Kuhn, Winterstein, and Balser[13] also used this method.

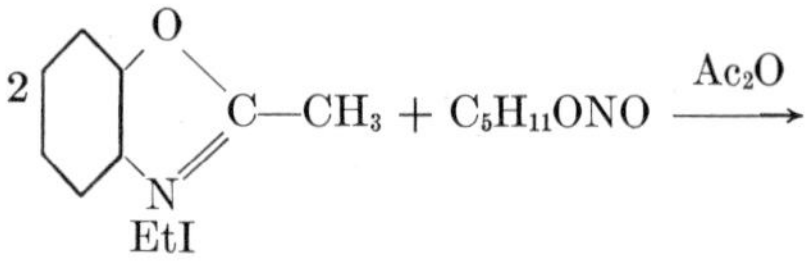

(7)

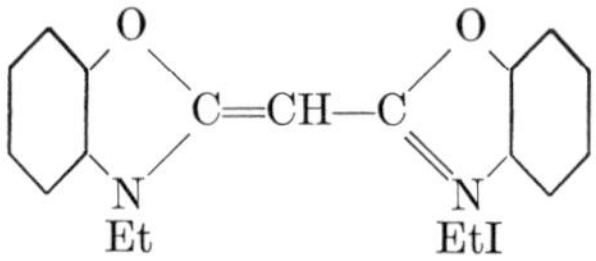

(10)

3,3'-Diethyloxacyanine iodide

A fourth reaction, mainly of historical importance, has been used to make isocyanines. A quaternary salt of type A is condensed with a quinolinium salt in the

[4] Kaufman and Vonderwahl, *Ber.* **45**, 1404 (1922).

[5] Fischer and Scheibe, *J. für Prak. Chim.*, II, **100**, 86 (1920).

[6] Hamer, *J. Chem. Soc.*, 206 (1928).

[7] Brooker and Keyes, *J. Amer. Chem. Soc.* **57**, 2488 (1935).

[8] Beilenson and Kodak Ltd., B.P. 435,542.

[9] I. G. Farbenindustrie A.–G., B.P. 423,792.

[10] Kendall, B.P. 424,559; 425,609; 438,420.

[11] Brooker and Keyes, U.S.P. 2,117,936; 2,202,-827; B.P. 454,687.

[12] Fisher and Hamer, *J. Chem. Soc.*, 926 (1934).

[13] Kuhn, Winterstein, and Balser, *Ber.* **63**, 3176 (1930).

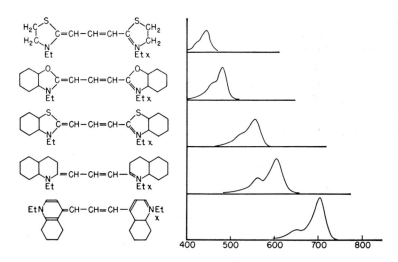

Fig. 8.3. Absorption curves of a set of carbocyanine dyes in methyl alcohol.

presence of alkali as shown by the following illustration:

(4)

(12)

1,1'-Diethyl-2,4'-cyanine iodide

Many of the early known cyanines [14, 15, 16] were made using this method.

Carbocyanines. The first carbocyanine used as a sensitizer was discovered by Homolka in 1905 and named *Pinacyanol.* This dye was made by the condensation of quinoline ethiodide, quinaldine ethiodide (type A) and formaldehyde (type B), in

the presence of alkali (type C). The quinoline salt plays no direct part in the reaction but it acts as a mild oxidizing agent and its use gives rise to increased yields. The structure of the dye was elucidated by Mills and Hamer.[17] The reaction may be sketched as follows:

(4)

(1)

In place of formaldehyde, glyoxylic acid has been used. Later haloforms and chloralhydrate were used.

However, the best general method for preparing carbocyanines is by the use of orthoformic esters. This method was dis-

[14] Williams, *Trans. Roy. Soc. Edinburgh* **21**, 377 (1856).

[15] Hoogewerff and Van Dorp, *Rec. Trav. Chem.* **2**, 317 (1883).

[16] Spalteholz, *Ber.* **16**, 1874 (1883).

[17] Mills and Hamer, *J. Chem. Soc.* **117**, 1550 (1920).

covered by W. König [18] who used acetic anhydride as the condensing medium. Hamer [19] found that increased yields were obtained by using pyridine as the condensing medium. By using orthoacetic esters, Hamer [20] prepared carbocyanines with a substituent on the central carbon atom of the chain. This reaction is sketched as follows:

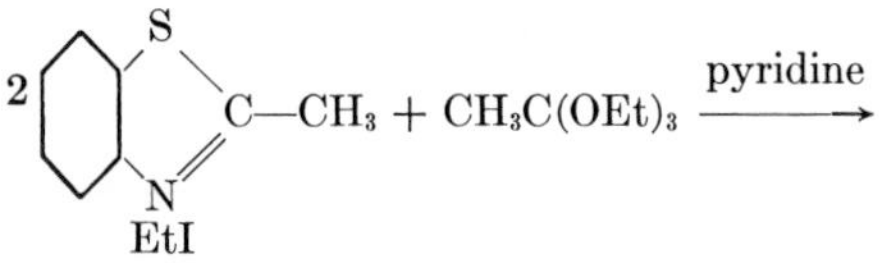

(13)

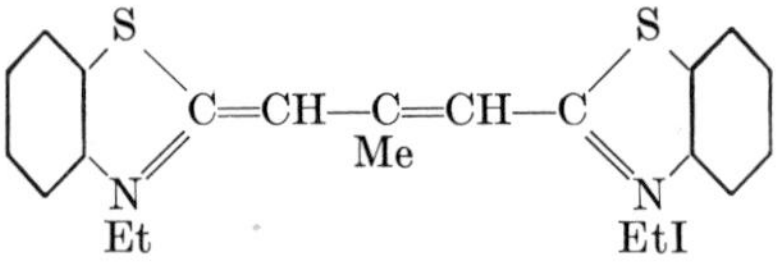

(14)

3,3'-Diethyl-9-methylthiacarbo-
cyanine iodide

A large number of symmetrical carbocyanines of this type but containing groups other than methyl in the central position were described by Brooker and White [21] using ortho esters of acids higher than acetic acid.

Unsymmetrical Carbocyanines. Unsymmetrical carbocyanine dyes, containing two different heterocyclic nuclei, have been prepared by several different methods. Some of the most important are given below. These depend upon first making an intermediate containing one heterocyclic nucleus which is then treated with a quaternary salt containing the second. Piggott and Rodd [22] described intermediates formed by condensing diphenylformamidine with quaternary salts of type A by fusion or in

acetic anhydride which may be illustrated by the following:

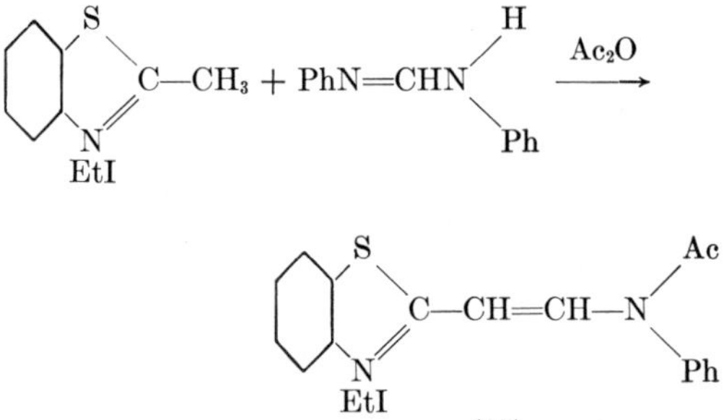

(15)

The use of such intermediates in the preparation of dyes was also patented by Piggott and Rodd [23] and a typical reaction is as follows:

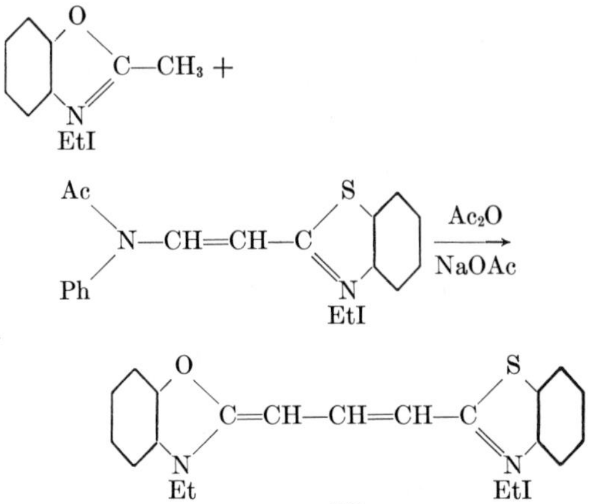

(16)

3,3'-Diethyloxathiacarbo-
cyanine iodide

Acetic anhydride and sodium acetate were used in the above reaction. However, pyridine, quinoline, and alcohol and triethylamine have been used.

Another method is by the use of heterocyclic aldehydes [24, 25] which are formed by the alkaline hydrolysis of the intermediates such as 2-β-acetanilidobenzothiazole ethio-

---

[18] König, *Ber.* **55**, 3293 (1922).

[19] Hamer, *J. Chem. Soc.*, 2796 (1927).

[20] Hamer, *J. Chem. Soc.*, 3160 (1928).

[21] Brooker and White, *J. Amer. Chem. Soc.* **57**, 547, 2480 (1935).

[22] Piggott and Rodd, B.P. 344,409.

[23] Piggott and Rodd, U.S.P. 2,071,898–9; B.P. 354,898.

[24] I. G. Farbenindustrie A.–G., B.P. 438,278.

[25] Brooker, U.S.P. 2,165,218; 2,165,692; B.P. 466,268.

dide (15). Such aldehydes react to give dyes as follows: [26, 27]

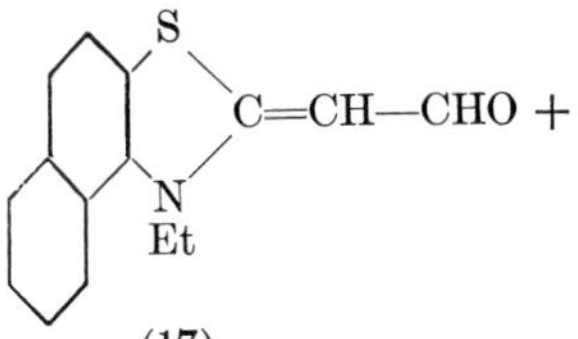

(17)

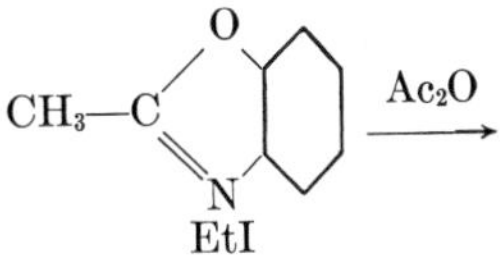

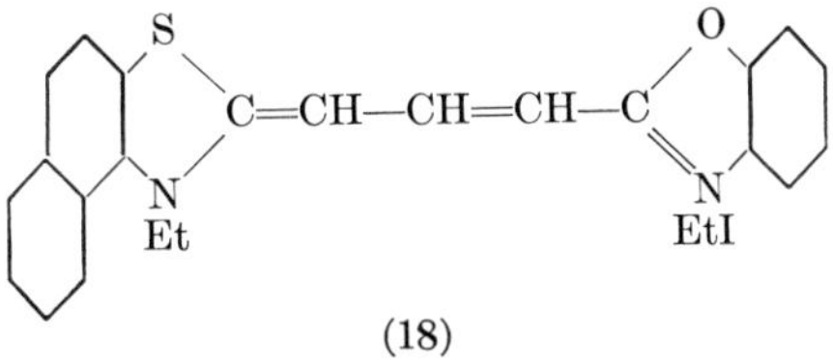

(18)

3,3′-Diethyl-4′,5′-benzo-oxathiacarbocyanine iodide

Reactive pseudo-ketones [28] have been prepared from quaternary salts of type A as illustrated by:

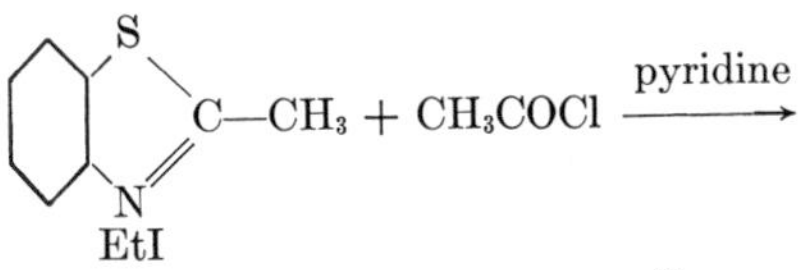

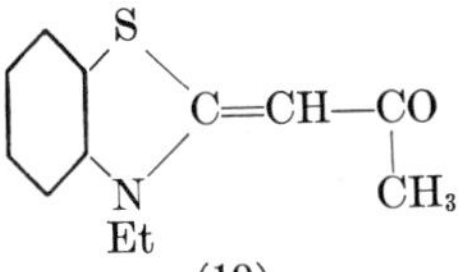

(19)

These pseudo-ketones may be used for the preparation of unsymmetrical chain substitued carbocyanine dyes.[29] In another method [30] the pseudoketones (19) were treated with phosphorous oxychloride to give chlorointermediates which were also capable of reacting to give dyes (22).

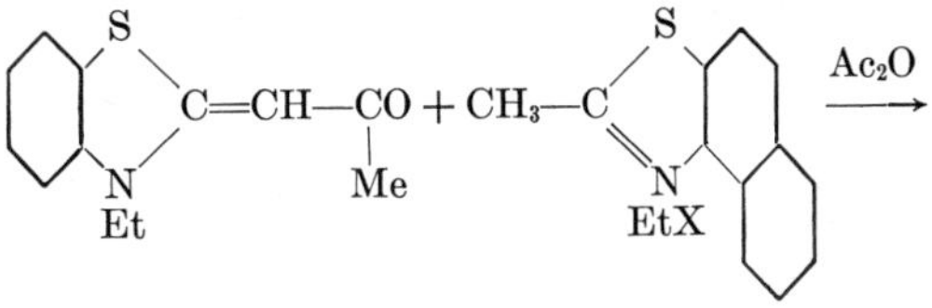

(20)

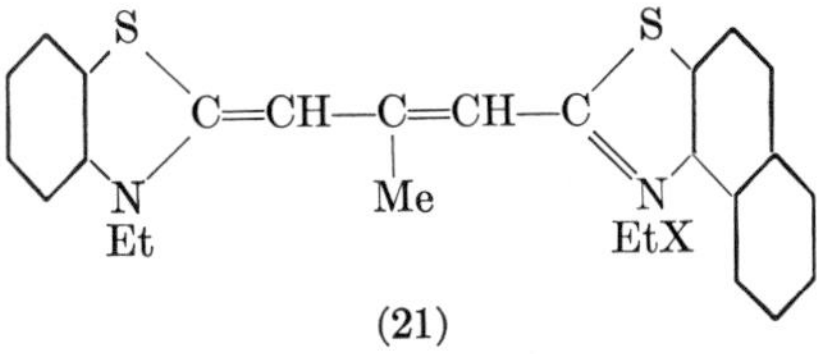

(21)

3,3′-Diethyl-9-methyl-4,5-benzothia-carbocyanine iodide

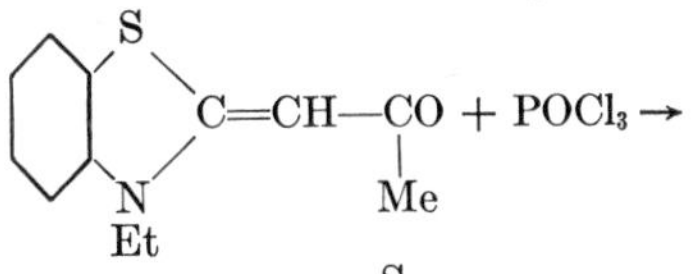

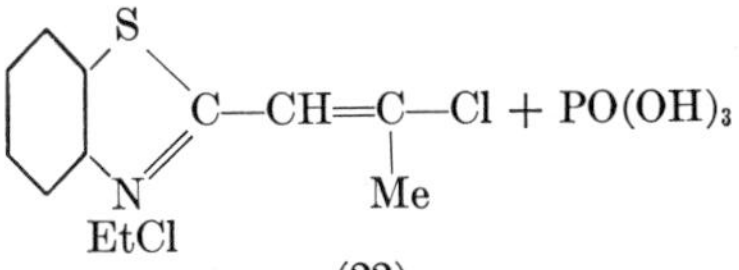

(22)

Still another method consists in using mercapto intermediates. These may be formed by several methods. They may be obtained from thioketones, which in turn may be made by several different methods,[31] one of which is as follows:

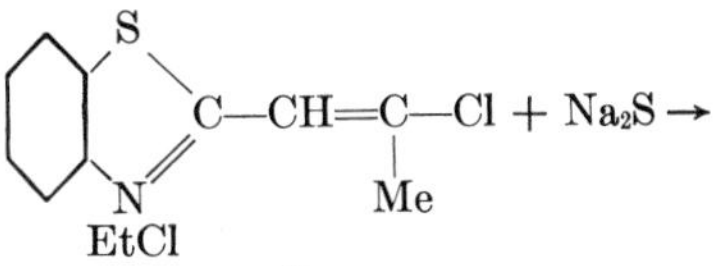

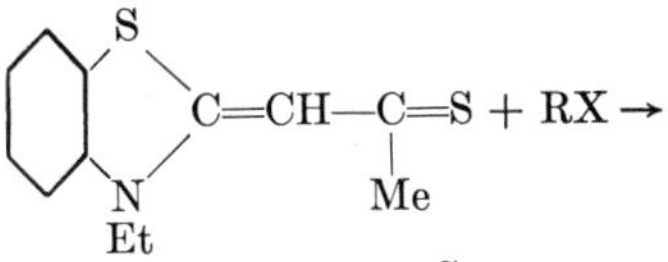

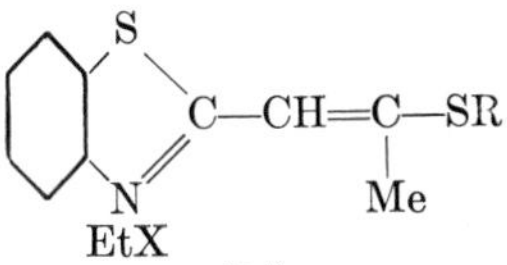

(24)

26 I. G. Farbenindustrie A.-G., B.P. 438,603.

27 Brooker, U.S.P. 2,165,219; B.P. 466,245.

28 Brooker and White, U.S.P. 2,112,139; 2,341,-357; B.P. 466,269.

29 Brooker and White, U.S.P. 2,112,140; B.P. 466,246.

30 Kodak Ltd., B.P. 533,425; U.S.P. 2,231,659.

31 Brooker and Keyes, U.S.P. 2,315,498; 2,369,646; 2,369,647; 2,369,657.

Kendall[32] has prepared intermediates such as (24) using the reactions sketched below:

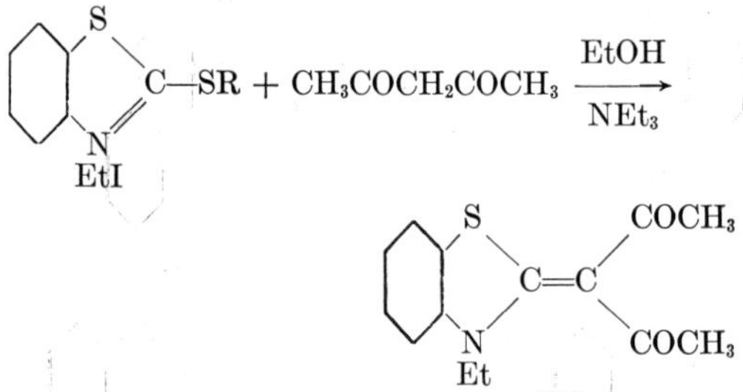

(25)

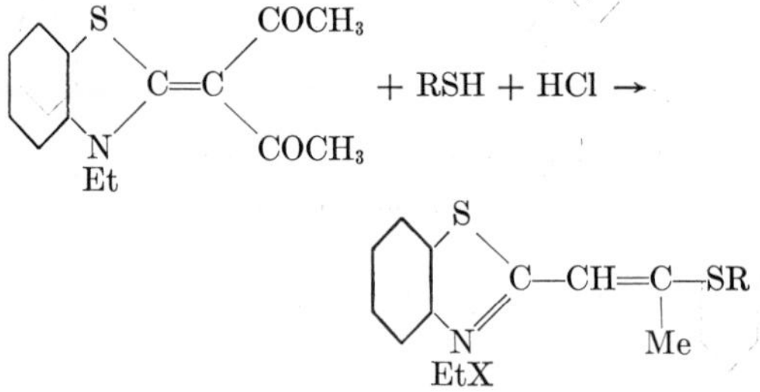

A still further method of preparing chain-substituted unsymmetrical carbocyanines is that of Koslowsky[33] who condensed quaternary salts of type A with compounds such as ethyl isothioacetanilide. The structure of the product is said to be either (26 a or b) according to the conditions of preparation.

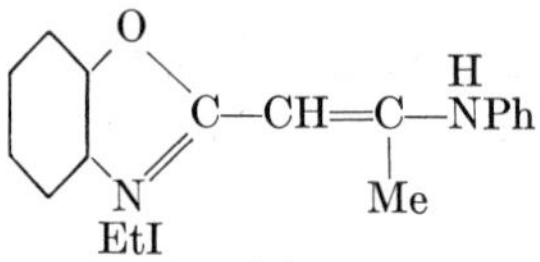

(a)

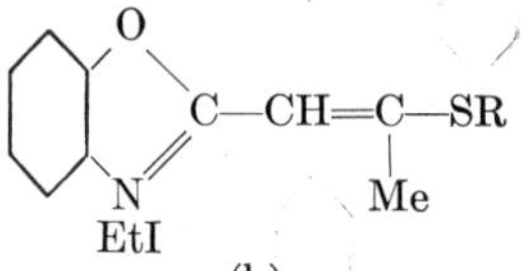

(b)

(26)

Polycarbocyanines. The chief use of this class of dyes is in infrared photography. A brief history of the development of dyes used as infrared sensitizers may be of interest. Among the first dyes used for this

purpose were those of dicyanine type (27) which were marketed by the Hoechst Dye Works. In 1919 Adams and Haller[34] of U. S. Bureau of Chemistry discovered

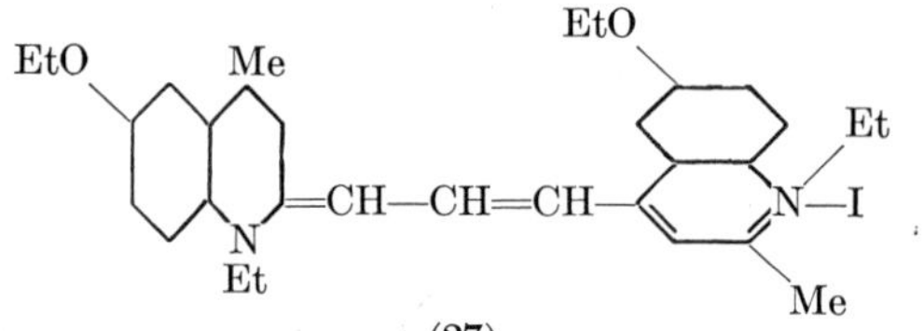

(27)

6,6'-Diethoxy-1,1'-diethyl-2',4-dimethyl-2,4'-carbocyanine iodide
Dicyanine A

Kryptocyanine (28), which is a better sensitizer for the region of the spectrum up to 9000 Å but beyond this point is inferior to Dicyanine A.

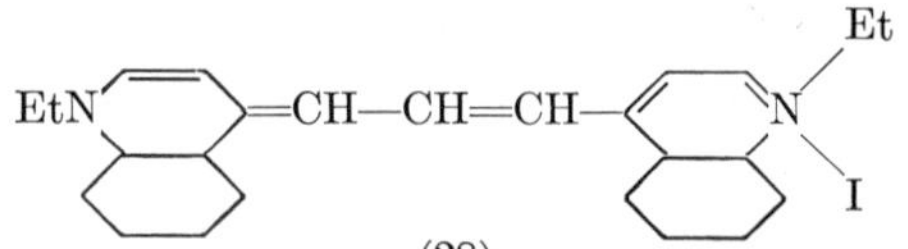

(28)

1,1'-Diethyl-4,4'-carbocyanine iodide
Kryptocyanine

The next advance in this field was made by H. T. Clarke[35] who isolated Neocyanine during the preparation of Kryptocyanine. Up to the end of 1931 Neocyanine was the best known sensitizer for the infrared. The structure of this dye was finally determined by Hamer[36] in 1947.

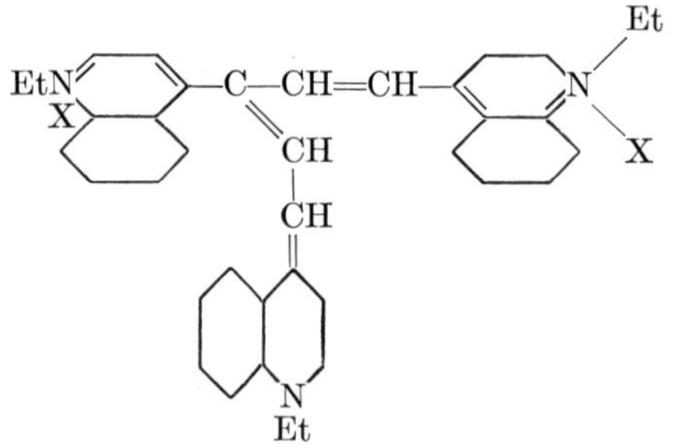

(29)

Neocyanine

[32] Kendall, B.P. 553,264.
[33] Koslowsky, U.S.P. 2,107,379; B.P. 412,309.
[34] Adams and Haller, *J. Amer. Chem. Soc.* **42**, 2661 (1920).
[35] Clarke, U.S.P. 1,804,674.
[36] Hamer, Rathbone, and Winton, *J. Chem. Soc.*, 1434 (1947).

Further improvements came through the use of dicarbocyanines and some dyes of this class are efficient deep red and infrared sensitizers. The first account in detail of the preparation of dicarbocyanines was by Beattie, Heilbron, and Irving [37] who made dyes having substituents on the five carbon chain. They were made from a quaternary salt of type A and substituted β-anilinoacrolein anil according to the following scheme:

$$2 \underset{\underset{\text{EtI}}{\overset{\text{S}}{\big\langle}}}{} C\text{---}CH_3 +$$

$$PhN\text{=}CH\text{---}\underset{\overset{|}{Br}}{C}\text{=}CH\text{---}\underset{\overset{|}{Ph}}{\overset{H}{N}} \cdot HBr \rightarrow$$

$$\underset{Et}{} C\text{=}CH\text{---}CH\text{=}\underset{\overset{|}{Br}}{C}\text{---}CH\text{=}CH\text{---}C \underset{EtI}{}$$

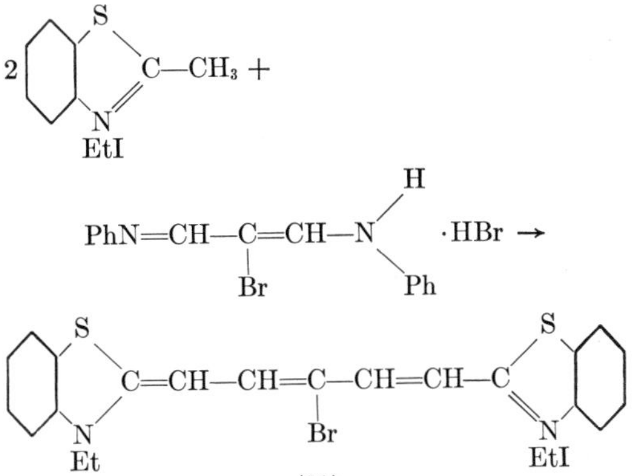

(30)

10-Bromo-3,3'-diethylthiadi-
carbocyanine iodide

Chain unsubstituted dyes of this class were made by Kendall [38] using propargyl aldehyde acetal, a method first suggested by W. König.[39] Hamer and Beilenson [40] reported similar dyes. Unsymmetrical dyes of this class may be made by methods similar to those used for preparing unsymmetrical carbocyanines.[41, 42, 43]

Wahl [44] was the first to report the preparation of tricarbocyanines. He used intermediates which had been reported as early

[37] Beattie, Heilbron, and Irving, *J. Chem. Soc.*, 260 (1932); B.P. 353,889; U.S.P. 2,111,183.

[38] Kendall, B.P. 390,808.

[39] König, U.S.P. 1,524,791; B.P. 232,740.

[40] Hamer and Beilenson, *J. Chem. Soc.*, 1225 (1936).

[41] Piggott and Rodd, B.P. 355,693.

[42] Zeh, U.S.P. 2,131,865; B.P. 434,234; 434,235.

[43] Kendall, B.P. 553,143; 553,144.

[44] Wahl, U.S.P. 1,878,557; G.P. 499,967.

as 1905 by Zincke and Würker.[45] They found that amines cleave dinitrophenyl pyridinium salts to give glutaconic aldehyde derivatives according to the following scheme:

$$2HN\underset{\overset{\diagdown}{Me}}{\overset{\diagup}{Ph}} + \underset{\underset{NO_2}{\overset{|}{\big\langle}}}{\overset{Cl,NO_2}{N}} \rightarrow$$

$$\underset{Me}{\overset{Ph}{N}}\text{=}CH\text{---}CH\text{=}CH\text{---}CH\text{=}CH\text{---}N\underset{Me}{\overset{Ph}{}} \cdot HCl$$

$$+ O_2N\underset{NO_2}{\big\langle}NH_2$$

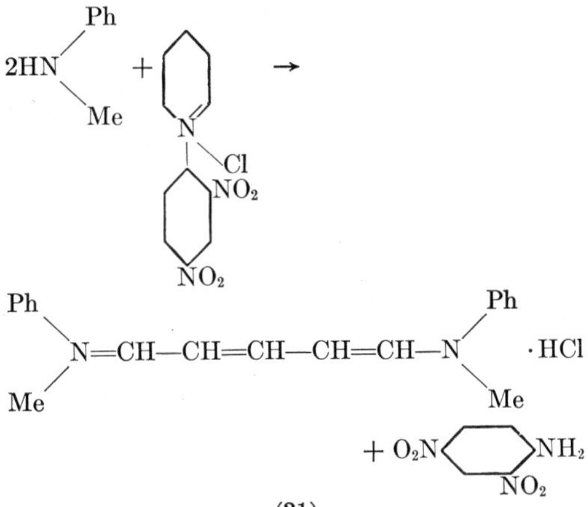

(31)

Wahl condensed intermediates such as (31) with quaternary salts of type A, the reaction being shown below:

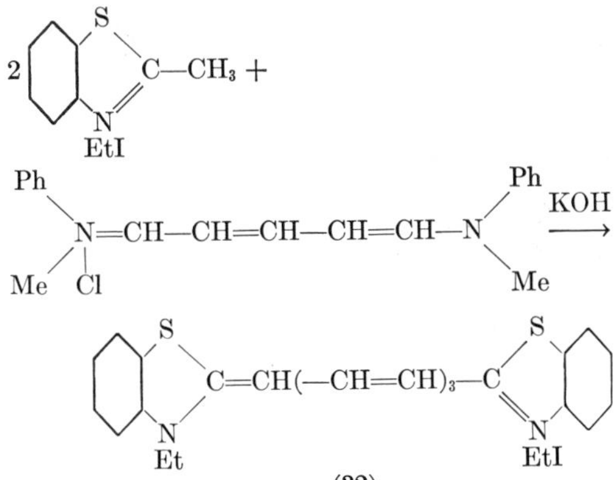

$$2\underset{\underset{\text{EtI}}{}}{\overset{\text{S}}{\big\langle}} C\text{---}CH_3 +$$

$$\underset{Me\ Cl}{\overset{Ph}{N}}\text{=}CH\text{---}CH\text{=}CH\text{---}CH\text{=}CH\text{---}N\underset{Me}{\overset{Ph}{}} \overset{KOH}{\longrightarrow}$$

$$\underset{Et}{}C\text{=}CH(\text{---}CH\text{=}CH)_3\text{---}C\underset{EtI}{}$$

(32)

Many such dyes of this type have been reported by Fisher and Hamer [46] and by Piggott and Rodd. Brooker [47] found that piperidine or triethylamine gave greatly improved yields and by this method was able to prepare the 4,4'-tricarbocyanine called "Xenocyanine" (33), which ex-

[45] Zincke and Würker, *Ann.* **338**, 107 (1905).

[46] Fisher and Hamer, *J. Chem. Soc.*, 189 (1933).

[47] Brooker, U.S.P., 2,161,332; 2,165,337; 2,189,- 599; B.P., 408,571; 436,941; 437,017.

tended sensitivity of the photographic plate beyond 10,830 Å.[48]

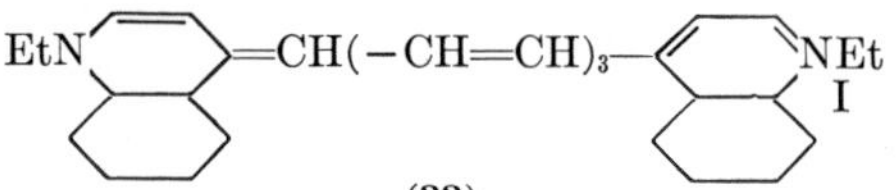

(33)

W. König [49] showed that the ring of furfural could be cleaved by aromatic amines in the presence of acid to give hydroxysubstituted intermediates of the type illustrated below:

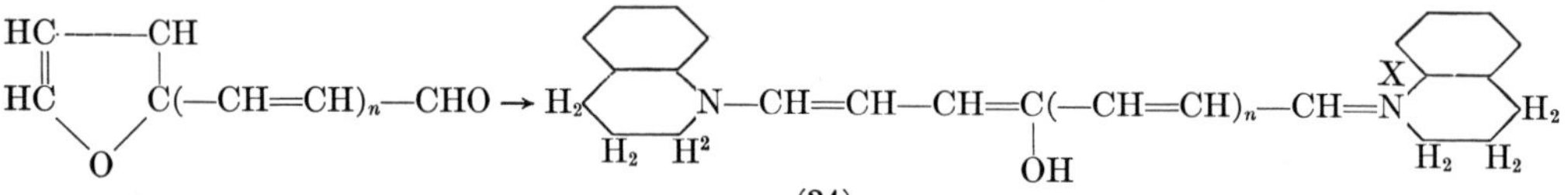

(34)

These intermediates were stabilized by acetylation and by their use tetra- and pentacarbocyanine dyes with acetoxy groups in the chain were made.[50, 51] Such dyes have been found to give sensitivity in the far infrared to beyond 13,000 Å.

Unsubstituted tetra- and penta-carbocyanine dyes were subsequently prepared by Dieterle and Riester,[52] using the following series of steps:

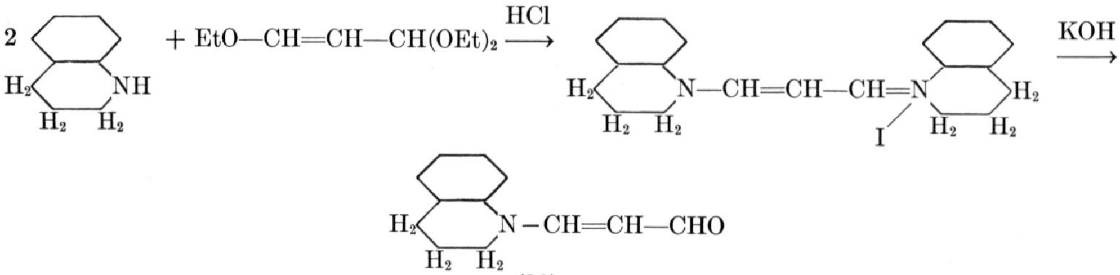

(36)

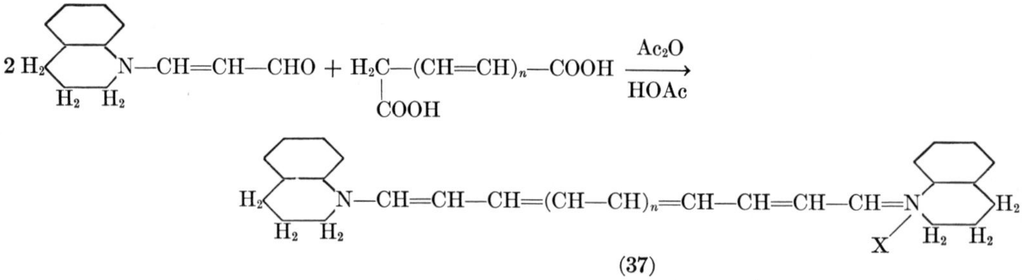

(37)

Such intermediates when condensed with quaternary salts of type A give tetra- and pentacarbocyanine dyes with no substitu-

ent in the chain, the dyes being more powerful infrared sensitizers than the corresponding chain-substituted dyes.

The Merocyanine Dyes. A group of dyes which differ in structure from the cyanines in that they have a conjugated amide system in place of the amidinium ion

[48] Brooker, Hamer, and Mees, *J. Opt. Soc. Amer.* **23**, 216 (1933).

[49] W. König, *J. für Prak. Chim.* II **72**, 555 (1905).

[50] Brooker and Keyes, *J. Franklin Inst.* **219**, 255 (1935).

[51] I. G. Farbenindustrie A.-G., B.P. 441,624.

[52] Dieterle and Riester, *Z. wiss. Phot.* **36**, 68, 141 (1937).

system of the cyanines are known as the *merocyanines*. They were independently discovered by Kendall [53] of the Ilford Laboratories and by Brooker et al.,[54] of the Eastman Research Laboratories.

These dyes may be illustrated by the following typical formula:

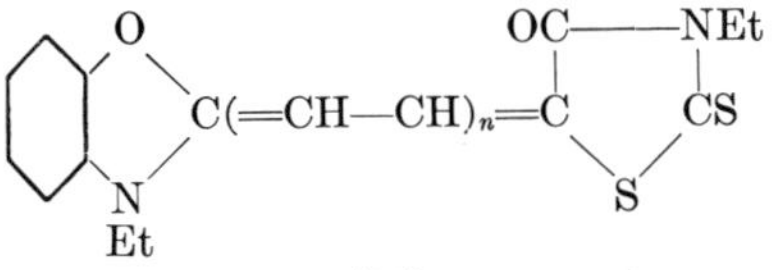

(38)

They are formed by condensing a reactive ketomethylene compound with intermediates of type B (see page 127). A great number of compounds are known which have this reactive ketomethylene group. They may be chain compounds such as acetylacetone, ethyl malonate, ethyl acetoacetate, benzoylacetonitrile, etc., or more frequently cyclic compounds such as: (a) rhodanines, (b) 2-thio-2,4-oxazolidindiones, (c) 2,4-thiazolidindiones, (d) thianaphthenones, (e) indandiones, (f) oxindoles, (g) thiohydantoins, (h) pyrazolones, (j) barbituric acids, (k) isoxazolones, and many others.

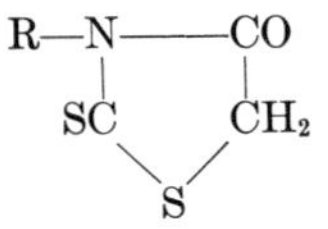

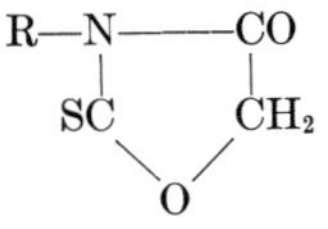

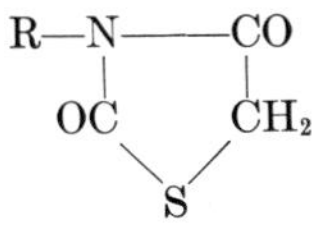

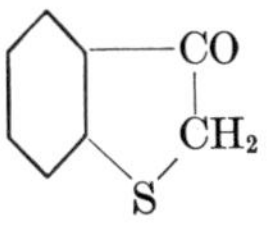

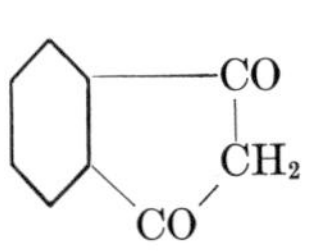

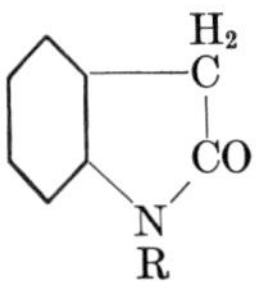

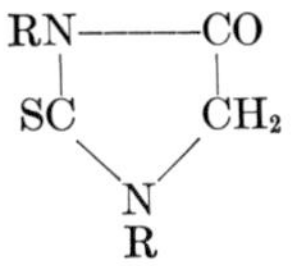

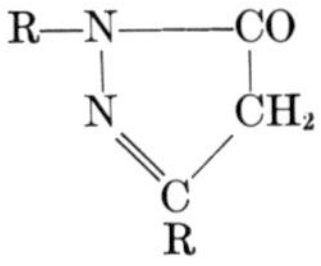

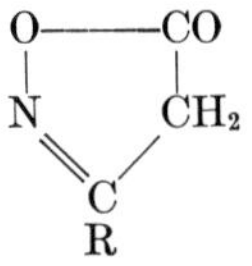

It may be seen from formula (38) that merocyanines may form a vinylene homologous series. The dyes in which n = 0 may [55] be prepared by treating one of the ketomethylene compounds with either an intermediate having reactive halogen, as for example:

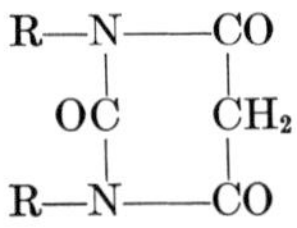

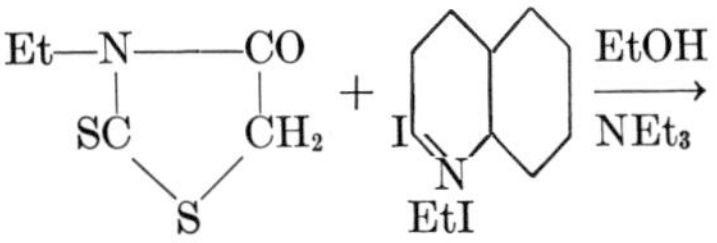

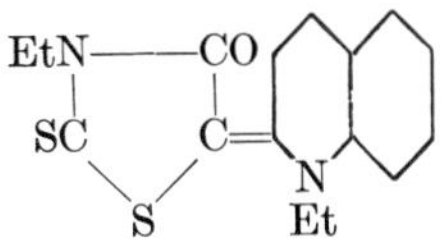

(39)

or with a reactive mercapto intermediate as shown below:

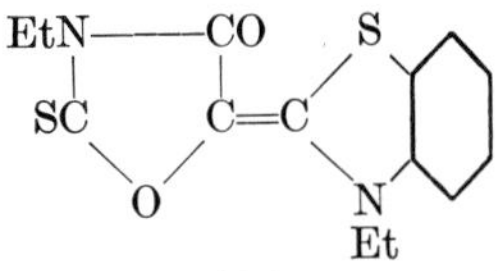

(40)

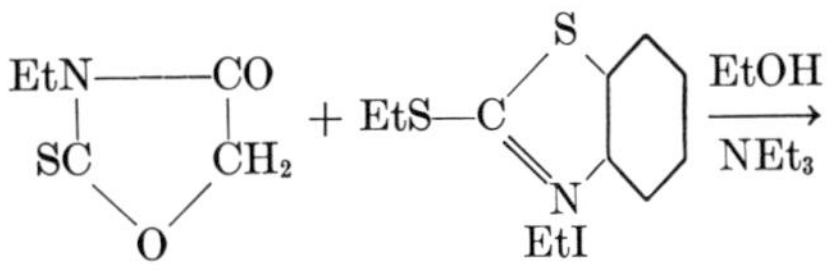

The merocarbocyanines are those in which n = 1 (formula 38). These may be made by a wide variety of methods only a few of which will be given here. One of

[53] Kendall, B.P., 426,718; 428,222; 428,359; 428,360; 432,628.

[54] Brooker et al., U.S.P., 2,078,233; 2,153,169; 2,161,331; 2,165,219; 2,165,338; etc. B.P., 450,-958; 466,097.

[55] Brooker, U.S.P., 2,185,182 (1940).

the earliest was the following:

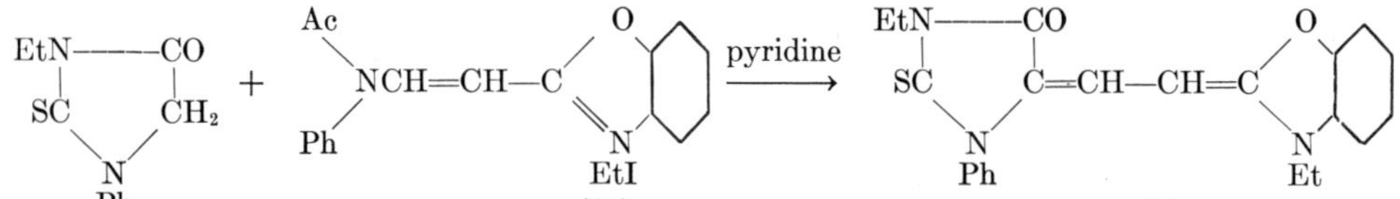

(41)   (42)

Another important method is the use of intermediates originally described by Dains [56] in which the ketomethylene compound is treated with diphenylformamidine as shown in the following:

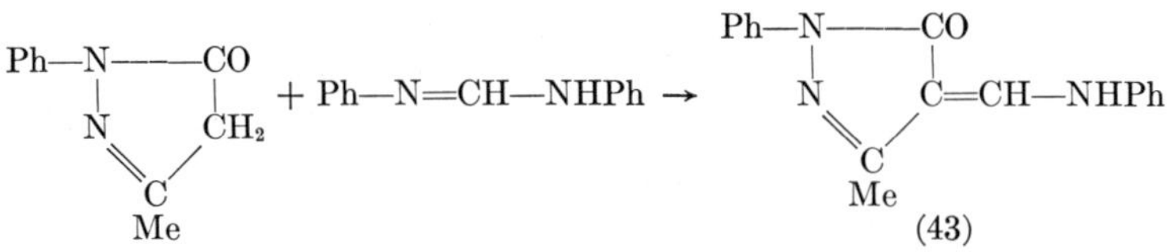

(43)

This type of intermediate is often made more reactive by acetylation and as such is condensed with a quaternary salt of type A usually in pyridine to give dyes as shown below:

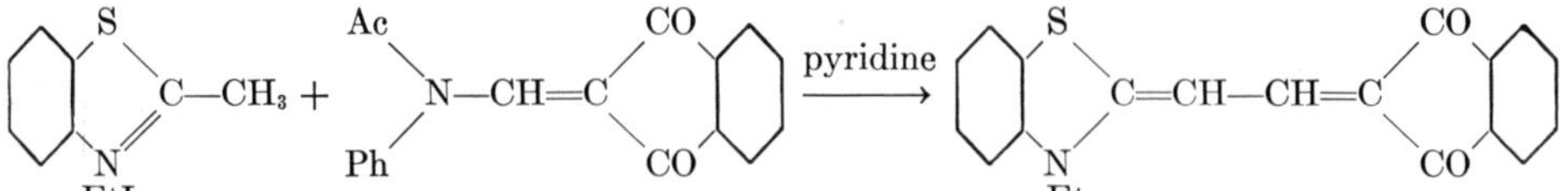

(44)   (45)

Chain-substituted merocarbocyanines have been made by a variety of methods, most of which are similar to the preparation of the chain-substituted carbocyanines (p. 128) using a ketomethylene compound instead of a quaternary salt of type A. The following will serve to illustrate the reaction.

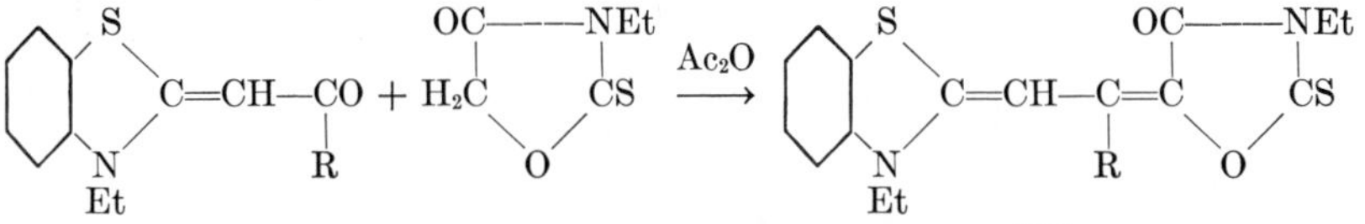

(46)

As in the preparation of the chain-substituted carbocyanines such chloro intermediates as (22) or the intermediates from such thioketones as (23) [57] may be substituted for the ketones.

The following methods have been patented by Kendall, the first of which [58] uses an intermediate which is prepared from the ketomethylene compound and esters of ortho acids. The second method leads to a mixture of dyes, two symmetrical dyes

[56] Dains, *Ber.* **35**, 2496 (1902); *J. Amer. Chem. Soc.* **31**, 1148 (1909); **35**, 959 (1913); **38**, 1510 (1916); **40**, 562 (1918); **44**, 2310 (1922).

[57] Brooker, B.P. 533,425; U.S.P. 2,231,659.
[58] Kendall, U.S.P. 2,319,547; 2,394,068.

and one merocyanine thus: [59]

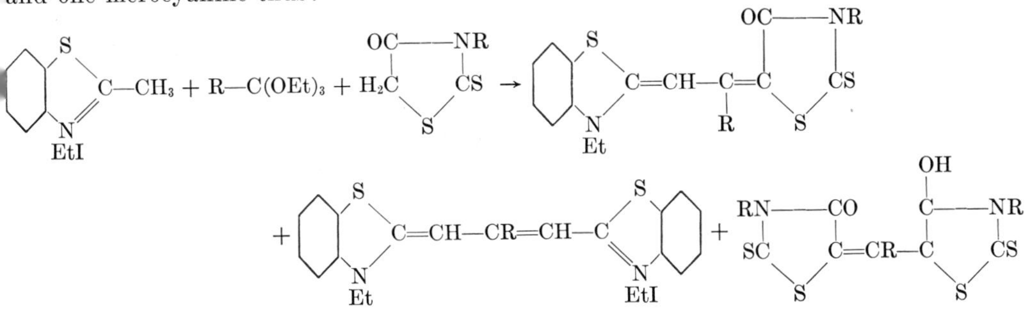

$$\text{C—CH}_3 + \text{R—C(OEt)}_3 + \text{H}_2\text{C} \begin{array}{c}\text{OC}\!-\!\text{NR}\\ \text{CS}\\ \text{S}\end{array} \rightarrow \text{C}=\text{CH—C}=\text{C}\begin{array}{c}\text{OC}\!-\!\text{NR}\\ \text{CS}\\ \text{S}\end{array}$$

$$+ \quad \text{C}=\text{CH—CR}=\text{CH—C} \quad + \quad \begin{array}{cc}\text{RN}\!-\!\text{CO} & \text{C}\!-\!\text{NR}\\ \text{SC}\quad\text{C}=\text{CR—C} & \text{CS}\\ \text{S} & \text{S}\end{array}$$

The preparation of the higher vinylene homologs, called meropolycarbocyanines, is closely similar to the preparation of unsymmetrical polycarbocyanines and intermediates such as the following are used where $n = 1$ or 2:

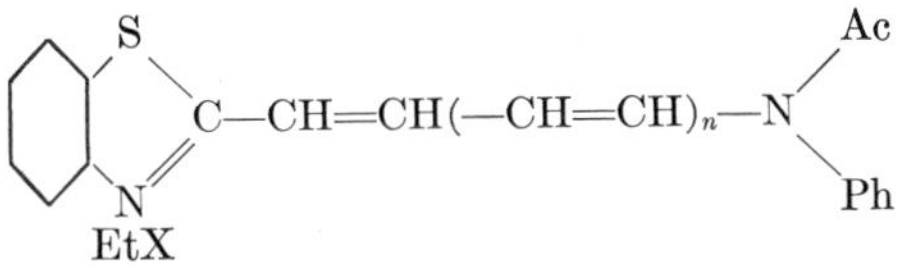

$$\text{C—CH}=\text{CH(—CH}=\text{CH)}_n\text{—N}\begin{array}{c}\text{Ac}\\ \text{Ph}\end{array} \quad \text{or} \quad \begin{array}{c}\text{EtN}\!-\!\text{CO}\\ \text{SC}\quad\text{C}\end{array}=\text{CH(—CH}=\text{CH)}_n\text{—N}\begin{array}{c}\text{Ac}\\ \text{Ph}\end{array}$$

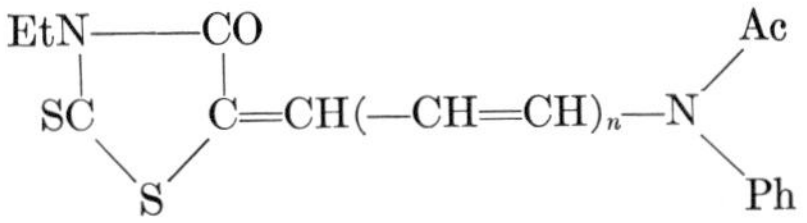

Merocyanines containing the thioamide group —NR—CS— in the ketomethylene part of the dye are capable of adding alkyl salts (such as ethyl iodide or ethyl p-toluenesulfonate) to form reactive intermediates of type B. They may then react further to give more complex dyes thus: [60, 61]

(a)
$$\text{C}=\text{CH—CH}=\text{C}\begin{array}{c}\text{OC}\!-\!\text{NEt}\\ \text{CS}\\ \text{N}\\ \text{Ph}\end{array} + \text{EtI} \rightarrow \text{C}=\text{CH—CH}=\text{C}\begin{array}{c}\text{OC}\!-\!\text{NEt}\\ \text{CSEt}\\ \text{N}\\ \text{Ph}\end{array} +$$

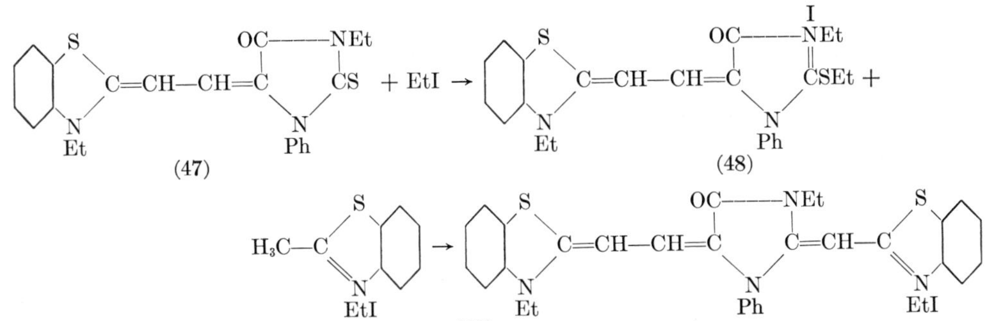

(47)   (48)

$$\text{H}_3\text{C—C} \rightarrow \text{C}=\text{CH—CH}=\text{C}\begin{array}{c}\text{OC}\!-\!\text{NEt}\\ \text{C}=\text{CH—C}\end{array}$$

(49)

(b)
$$\text{C}=\text{CH—CH}=\text{C}\begin{array}{c}\text{OC}\!-\!\text{NEt}\\ \text{CSEt}\\ \text{N}\\ \text{Ph}\end{array} + \text{H}_2\text{C}\begin{array}{c}\text{OC}\!-\!\text{NEt}\\ \text{CS}\\ \text{S}\end{array} \rightarrow$$

$$\text{C}=\text{CH—CH}=\text{C}\begin{array}{cc}\text{OC}\!-\!\text{NEt} & \text{OC}\!-\!\text{NEt}\\ \text{C} = \text{C} & \text{CS}\\ \text{N} & \text{S}\\ \text{Ph}\end{array}$$

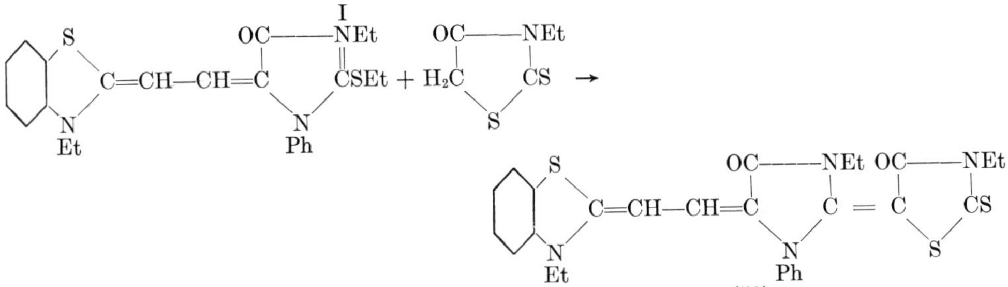

(50)

[59] Kendall, B.P. 519,895; U.S.P. 2,265,908.
[60] Kendall, B.P. 487,051; 489,355; 557,549.
[61] Fry and Kendall, U.S.P., 2,388,036.

The complex dye (50) also contains the thioamide group —NEt—CS— and this may be submitted to further reactions to give rise to still more complex dyes.

The Hemioxonol and Hemicyanine Dyes.

Intermediates such as (44) were found by Keyes [62] to react with secondary amines such as piperidine, morpholine, tetrahydroquinoline, etc., to give dyes which are known as hemioxonols, such as:

$$EtN—CO \qquad CH_2—CH_2$$
$$SC \quad C=CH(—CH=CH)_n—N \qquad CH_2$$
$$S \qquad CH_2—CH_2$$

(51)

Dyes of this type with a number of different chain lengths may be made from a wide variety of ketomethylene compounds.

Hemicyanines are dyes of analogous structure prepared from intermediates such as 2-β-acetanilidovinylbenzothiazole ethiodide (15) and primary and secondary amines. A typical dye of this class is:

$$C—CH=CH—N$$

EtI

(52)

Cyclic amines such as morpholine, piperidine, and tetrahydroquinoline may also be used. These dyes have been independently described by Ogata [63] and by White and Keyes.[64]

PART II

CHARACTERISTICS OF OPTICALLY SENSITIZED EMULSIONS

The increase in sensitivity of an emulsion to light of longer wave lengths than that absorbed by the silver halide itself is called *"optical sensitization."* In contrast to optical sensitization is the increase in sensitivity effected by the ripening process, which, except for minor gains in long-wave

[63] Ogata, *Proc. Imp. Acad. Tokyo* **13**, 325 (1937).

[64] White and Keyes, U.S.P. 2,166,737; B.P. 515,145.

sensitivity, is confined to the spectral region absorbed by the silver halides. For nearly all practical purposes, optical sensitization is achieved by incorporating in the emulsion one or more sensitizing dyes of the types described in the preceding pages.

Formerly, optically sensitized emulsions were prepared by bathing the emulsion-coated plate for a few minutes in a dilute solution of the dye, but in modern practice the dye is added in solution, usually in an organic solvent, to the ripened emulsion just before application to the support. The best solvent, concentration and temperature must be determined by trial for each dye.

Sensitometric Characteristics of Optically Sensitized Emulsions. The user of an optically sensitized emulsion normally is mainly interested in the extension of its sensitivity beyond the wave-length range of the unsensitized emulsion, but it is also important to remember that the other characteristics may change as a result of the presence of the dye. The behavior of the sensitized emulsion toward blue light, to which the sensitizing dye may be inert, usually is different from that of the same emulsion without dye; and, in the sensitized emulsion, the characteristics may differ in the optically sensitized region of the spectrum from those in the region of the halide absorption band.

[62] Keyes, U.S.P. 2,216,441; 2,186,608.

A. *Spectral Sensitivity.* By a suitable choice of dyes, emulsions can be rendered sensitive to all wave lengths from the absorption band of silver halide throughout the visible spectrum into the infrared region as far as about 13,000 Å. The general spectral distribution of sensitivity in photographic emulsions can be conveniently shown in "wedge spectrograms," examples of which are shown in Figs. 8.4 and 8.5. The manner in which these spectrograms are obtained is described elsewhere, and it need only be mentioned here that the distance of the envelope of the curve from the base at any wave length is, with certain important qualifications (*loc. cit.*), a meas-

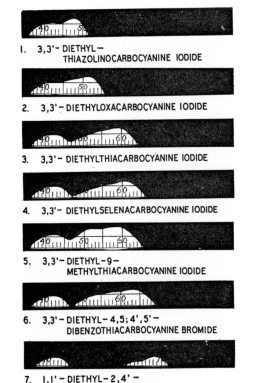

Fig. 8.4. Wedge spectrograms of a chlorobromide emulsion sensitized with carbocyanine dyes. (From Mees, *The Theory of the Photographic Process,* The Macmillan Co, New York, 1942.)

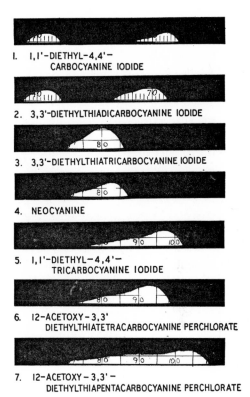

Fig. 8.5. Wedge spectrograms of a chlorobromide emulsion sensitized with infrared sensitizers. (Mees, *The Theory of the Photographic Process,* The Macmillan Co., New York, 1942.)

ure of the sensitivity, on a logarithmic scale, of the emulsion at that wave length.

Sensitization over a wide spectral region is usually accomplished by adding mixtures of dyes, each sensitizing strongly at different wave lengths. It is occasionally convenient to use emulsions in which high sensitivity is restricted to a fairly narrow spectral region; e.g., emulsions with high sensitivity only in the region of the red line of the hydrogen spectrum have been useful in astronomy.

B. *Effect of Optical Sensitization on Speed.* In spite of the greater spectral range to which an optically sensitized emulsion may respond, the increase in speed to white light as compared to the speed of the same emulsion without dye is often disappointingly small. The sensitivity of a dyed emulsion to violet light is often lower than that of the corresponding undyed emulsion, and decreases to 50% of the sensitivity of the undyed emulsion at 400 mμ are not uncommon. Since the effect is noticed with dyes which have no measurable absorption in the violet, it is unconnected with any loss of light by absorption by the dye, and it appears that a true desensitizing action of optical sensitizers exists. This phenomenon has been studied carefully recently by Spence and Carroll,[65] whose results will be discussed later.

The desensitization appears to be quite independent of the sensitizing properties of the dye, no clear relation between the two phenomena having been observed. Although conclusive proof is difficult to obtain, it seems probable that the degree of desensitization produced by sensitizing dyes is independent of wave length; hence, the sensitized speed is probably also lower than it would otherwise be, and it will therefore be obvious that a dye showing too pronounced desensitization cannot be a good practical sensitizer.

C. *Contrast of Optically Sensitized Emulsions.* The contrast of the sensitized emulsion, as measured by gamma (Chapter 17), may differ for exposure to light in the sensitized spectral region from that for light absorbed directly by the silver halides, but no invariable rule can be given for the change of contrast with wave length. Usually, the gamma is higher in the sensitized spectral region than in the absorption band of the silver halide. An explanation often advanced for this increase in gamma is that, since the smaller grains in the emulsion have the greatest ratio of surface to volume, these grains will adsorb relatively more of the dye than the larger— i.e., the smaller grains will be preferentially sensitized. These are the grains which contribute a large portion of the density in the developed image at the higher exposures. For the same grain-size distribution, a relatively greater density is therefore obtained at the higher exposures in the sensitized spectral region than in the absorption band of the silver salt, i.e., the gamma increases.

D. *Reciprocity-Law Failure in Optically Sensitized Emulsions.* As is well known, the density of the developed image produced by the incidence of a given amount, It, of monochromatic light-energy on the plate is not constant, but depends on the intensity, I, and the time, t, of the exposure. This lack of reciprocity between intensity and time of exposure is called the *Failure of the Reciprocity Law* (Chapters 11, 32), and is signaled by the fact that the plot of the exposure, It, required to produce a specified density as a function of the exposure time, t, is not a straight line parallel to the t-axis. Several studies have been made of the manner in which the failure of reciprocity varies with wave length, with results which are conveniently summarized in an article by Biltz and Webb.[66] The essential result is that, so long as comparisons at different wave lengths are made at the same density, the curves showing the variation of the exposure, It, required to produce this density, with the exposure time, t, are nearly parallel to each other for different wave lengths; i.e., in this sense, reciprocity failure is nearly independent of wave length. This holds for the absorption bands both of the silver halide and the dye. At first sight, it may seem difficult to reconcile this result with the increase in contrast often observed in the sensitized spectral region, but Biltz and Webb show how this difficulty is resolved by the limit-

[65] Spence and Carroll, *J. Phys. and Coll. Chem.* **52**, 1090 (1948).

[66] Biltz and Webb, *J. Opt. Soc. Amer.* **38**, 561 (1948).

ation of the law to a fixed density, as stated above.

Hypersensitization of Opically Sensitized Emulsions. The sensitivity of dyed emulsions in the optically sensitized region can often be considerably increased by bathing the plates in a solution of ammonia, a process known as *"hypersensitization."* One minute's bathing in a solution made by diluting 4 cc. of concentrated ammonia (28%) to 100 cc. with distilled water at a temperature not exceeding 55° F. is a convenient procedure. The plate should be dried as quickly as possible in a stream of dust-free air and used immediately. Acceleration of the drying process by rinsing in alcohol after bathing is advantageous. Hypersensitized plates tend to produce fog if kept, although they can be kept for some weeks in a refrigerator.

The response to ammonia treatment depends on both the dye and the emulsion, and the greatest increases in sensitivity tend to be realized in slower emulsions. It is frequently useful in practice with plates sensitized to infrared radiation.

Carroll and Hubbard,[67] in studying hypersensitization, found that increased speed in the optically sensitized spectral region could often be realized by bathing in distilled water and drying. This is often nearly as efficient as the ammonia process. Only for infrared emulsions did the ammonia treatment yield much more sensitivity than water-bathing.

The effect depends on an increase in the concentration of silver ion at the grain surface—the ammonia dissolves some of the silver bromide as the complex cation $Ag(NH_3)^+_2$, which, on drying, decomposes to Ag^+, the equilibrium condition at the boundary between the emulsion and bathing solution being such that after drying there is an excess of silver ion over bromide

ion in the emulsion. In the case of water-bathing, the effect is presumably due to an increased silver-ion concentration following removal of bromide ion.

Factors Influencing Optical Sensitization. As shown earlier in this chapter, silver bromide does not absorb the longer wave lengths to any appreciable degree. On exposure of the undyed emulsion to long-wave radiation, no energy is absorbed, and no change can be induced in the silver halide. The function of the sensitizer is to absorb these longer wave lengths, and, by some interaction of the adsorbed dye with the silver halide not completely understood, to transfer, in effect, this absorbed energy to the grain, bringing about the same process as occurs in the silver halide by direct absorption of light.

The behavior of the dye as a sensitizer can therefore be analyzed in terms of the adsorption of the dye to the grain, the absorption of light by the adsorbed dye, and the efficiency of transfer of the absorbed energy to the halide, each of which merits some discussion.

Adsorption of Sensitizing Dyes to Silver Halides. The transfer process from dye to silver salt requires intimate molecular contact between the sensitizing molecule and the grain. Not only have dye molecules the requisite high intensity of light absorption, but their chemical nature is such that relatively large attractive forces between dye and silver halide exist. The long conjugated chains in the organic nuclei and in the chromophoric bridge of dye molecules bring large van der Waals forces into play, and these may be supplemented by electrostatic forces between dye ions, such as the cyanines, and the surface ions of the silver halide lattice, or between neutral dye molecules of a dipolar nature, as the merocyanines, and the lattice ions. Only intensely colored molecules held by such forces to the silver bromide surface

[67] Carroll and Hubbard, *Bur. Stand. J. Res.* **10**, 211 (1933).

can sensitize; dye merely dissolved in the gelatin of the emulsion is ineffective.

When a quantity of dye is added to an uncoated photographic emulsion, there is, at a given temperature, a definite distribution of the dye between the halide grains and the suspension medium. A little dye added is usually taken up practically completely by the grains; as more dye is added, more is adsorbed to the grains, but also more remains free in the liquid. Fig. 8.6, from a study by E. P. Davey,[68] shows typical "adsorption isotherms" for sensitizing dyes in emulsion, i.e., the relation, at a given temperature, between the amount of dye taken up by the grains and that left unadsorbed in the gelatin solution. Many isotherms end in a plateau parallel to the axis of concentration of unadsorbed dye—i.e., the surface of the solid has taken up as much as it can at the temperature in question, and any additional dye is simply left unadsorbed in the solution.

Several of the curves, too, suggest adsorption in more than one stage. Sheppard, Lambert, and Walker [69] obtained similar isotherms for dyes adsorbed to colloidal silver bromide in water and in gelatin emulsions and, interpreting the saturation plateau as indicating complete coverage of the silver-bromide surface by a layer of dye a single molecule thick, arrived at certain conclusions with respect to the orientation of the dye molecules on the surface. The area of a single dye molecule in contact with silver bromide can be estimated for various orientations from known bond-length and bond-angle data and from the distances of closest approach of the atoms as estimated from crystal-structure studies and in other ways; the total area of the halide surface can be estimated from photomicrographic determinations of the size-frequency distribution of the grains, and the total number of molecules of dye

[68] Davey, *Trans. Farad. Soc.*, **36**, 323 (1940).

[69] Sheppard, Lambert, and Walker, *J. Chem. Phys.* **7**, 265 (1939).

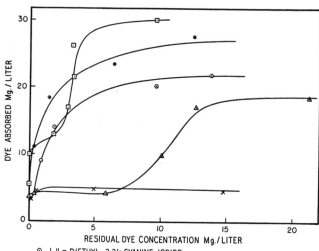

○   1,1′ – DIETHYL-2,2′-CYANINE IODIDE.
×   SAME DYE PARTIALLY DISPLACED BY COMPETING ADSORBATE.
▫   3,3′- DIMETHYL-9-ETHYLTHIACARBOCYANINE BROMIDE.
●   3,3′- DIETHYL-9-METHYLTHIACARBOCYANINE BROMIDE.
△   3,3′,9-TRIETHYL-6,6′-DICHLOROTHIACARBOCYANINE IODIDE.

FIG. 8.6. Adsorption isotherms of sensitizing dyes. (Davey, *Trans. Farad. Soc.* **36**, 323 (1940).)

adsorbed at complete coverage is known from the isotherm. One can therefore calculate the area of surface claimed by each dye molecule and compare this value with the molecular area for various orientations. In this way, Sheppard, Lambert, and Walker concluded that the saturated monolayer of cyanine dyes contained close-packed assemblages of dye molecules held "edge-on" to the surface, i.e., with the plane of the organic nuclei perpendicular to the surface, and with the internuclear bridge parallel to the surface. The first stage of adsorption in some of the curves of Fig. 8.6 may correspond to adsorption of molecules at random over the surface, possibly lying flat, which, at a critical concentration, assume the "edge-on" orientation characteristic of the second stage.[67] It is found also that the absorption spectra of the adsorbed dye are different at concentrations corresponding to the two branches of these isotherms,[67] strong evidence that the state of the adsorbed molecules is different in the two stages.

Effect of Concentration of Sensitizing Dye on Sensitization. As the concentration of sensitizing dye added to the emulsion increases, the photographic effect increases, at first nearly proportionally to the concentration, then more slowly, and finally often reaches a maximum beyond which further increase in concentration causes a decrease in photographic sensitivity. Fig. 8.7 from a paper by Spence and Carroll [64] illustrates the phenomenon for two thiocarbocyanine dyes. In this figure, the ordinates, $1/E$, are measures of the optical sensitization. The concentration of dye at which the sensitivity is a maximum is called the photographic optimum; this quantity depends on the dye, the type of emulsion and other factors. Direct comparison of the optimum with the saturation limit of the adsorption isotherm shows that, for a number of dyes, the optimum occurs

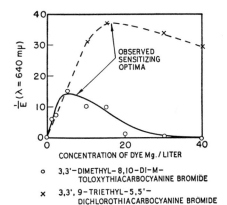

FIG. 8.7. Plots of observed Optical Sensitization against Concentration. (Spence and Carroll, *J. Phys. and Colloid Chem.* **52,** 1090 (1948).)

at concentrations considerably below that corresponding to complete coverage by a monolayer of dye molecules.[67, 68]

This is also clearly indicated by data of Spence and Carroll, showing that the absorption of light by the adsorbed dye continues to increase at concentrations above the photographic optimum. Moreover, beyond the optimum, the decrease in the sensitivity conferred by the dye is accompanied by a parallel decrease in the sensitivity of the dyed emulsion to blue light, and a decrease in the sensitivity of a dyed emulsion to blue light compared with that of the same emulsion without dye sets in even below the optical sensitization optimum. Since this effect toward blue light is obtained by dyes with practically no absorption in this region, there must be a true desensitizing action of the sensitizing dye. The desensitization increases regularly with concentration, while the rate of increase of absorption and hence of sensitization levels off with increasing concentration as the absorption approaches completeness. At sufficiently high concentration, therefore, the increase in desensitization more than offsets the increased sensitization, with the result that an optimum concentration for sensitization occurs.

This desensitizing action of dyes is an important factor in determining the usable concentration in sensitized emulsions. The effect varies greatly among dyes, and no clear relation has been found between their sensitizing and desensitizing properties.

Absorption Spectra of Sensitizing Dyes. Since, according to the general laws of photochemistry, the spectral region for which a dye sensitizes is determined by its absorption spectrum as it exists in the adsorbed state on the silver halide, the analysis of the behavior of a sensitizing dye in terms of the factors which determine the sensitization requires a knowledge of this property. A general account of the absorption spectra of dyes is given on page 127, where it is pointed out that the spectral distribution of sensitivity of a sensitized emulsion runs parallel with the spectral distribution of light absorption by the adsorbed dye. (Fig. 8.2.) Another important observation made by Leermakers, Carroll, and Staud [70] was that some dyes in emulsions possessed more than one sensitization and absorption spectrum: a relatively broad band of sensitization and absorption at low concentrations of the sensitizer, and a band, often remarkably sharp, displaced to longer wave lengths, at higher concentrations. They concluded that these different spectra belonged to absorbed dye molecules in different conditions—the high concentration associated with the appearance of the sharp type of band suggesting some kind of "aggregated state" consisting of units of greater complexity than those causing the broad band, which might be individual molecules. The occurrence of more than one type of sensi-

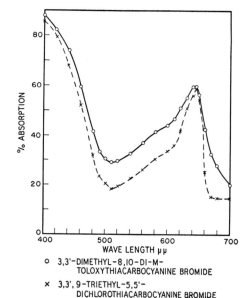

FIG. 8.8. Absorption spectra of two sensitizing dyes in emulsion. Silver halide extends to 510 mμ. (Spence and Carroll, *J. Phys. and Colloid Chem.* **52**, 1090 (1948).)

tization spectrum from a given dye was also observed by Schwarz.[71]

Illustrations of sharp absorption bands are to be found in Fig. 8.8 of this chapter, and the effect of dye concentration on spectral sensitizing of silver bromide in Fig 8.7. It is also interesting that the transition from the first to the second stage of adsorption indicated in some of the isotherms of Fig. 8.3 is accompanied, at least for some dyes, by a well-marked change in the absorption and sensitization spectra— broad bands in the part of the isotherm being associated with low concentration and sharper bands displaced to longer wave lengths in the second stage.[67]

It is not surprising that the sensitization spectrum of a dye differs from its absorption spectrum in an organic solvent, since a molecule in the adsorbed state normally absorbs light of different wave length, usually 20 or 30 mμ longer, than

[70] Leermakers, Carroll, and Staud, *J. Chem. Phys.* **5**, 878 (1937).

[71] Schwarz, *Sci. et Ind. Phot.* **10** (2), 233 (1939).

he free molecule in solution. As is suggested, however, by the behavior of sensitizers just mentioned, the changes occurring in the absorption spectrum of the dye adsorbed to the silver halide are more complicated than is to be expected from a mere adsorption effect on the spectrum of the dye as shown in alcoholic solution. From studies by various investigators it appears that dye molecules, because of the large van der Waals forces emanating from the conjugated chains in the rings and in the internuclear bridge, exhibit, under suitable conditions, a great tendency to associate with each other, forming dimers and polymers or "aggregates" of greater or less complexity. These dimers and more complex aggregates have characteristic spectra which may be displaced to shorter, or to longer, wave lengths from the spectral maximum of the simple molecule. The relatively high solute-solvent forces in alcoholic solution and in other organic solvents nearly always prevent association of the dye molecules at an attainable concentration in these solvents; but the organophobic nature of water, along with its high dielectric constant, which diminishes the repulsive electrostatic forces between similarly charged dye ions, facilitates this association, as does also the presence of dissolved inorganic salts and polar surfaces such as the surface of a silver halide crystal. The units in the aggregated systems of dye molecules are held together by van der Waals forces, which, although strong for this type of force, are still weak compared with valence forces, with the result that the aggregates are easily broken down on dilution or on moderate increase of temperature—the association is reversible.

Aggregation is common on the halide grains, and pronounced maxima of absorption and sensitization may occur, with intensities depending upon the concentration

of the dye added to the emulsion, at wave lengths longer or shorter than the absorption maximum in alcoholic solution.

Of particular interest are the very sharp bands displaced to long wave lengths from the monomeric band already alluded to as associated with an "aggregated state." Such bands were first reported in aqueous solutions of 1,1'-diethyl-2,2'-cyanine chloride by E. E. Jelley [72] and independently, somewhat later, by G. Scheibe,[73] and observed in sensitization by Leermakers, Carroll, Staud, Scheibe, Schwarz, and others. As shown in Fig. 8.8, the intensity of these bands may be very high, and some important practical sensitizers owe their importance to this fact.

Efficiency of Energy Transfer. Having absorbed energy from the light, the adsorbed dye molecule, if it is to act as a sensitizer, must, in effect, transfer the absorbed energy to the silver halide. Other processes may compete with the transfer, such as fluorescence, transfer to foreign molecules or degradation of the absorbed energy as heat, so that the transfer process is not necessarily completely efficient. A quantum efficiency of transfer might be defined, stating the probability that a quantum of light-energy absorbed by the dye is photographically effectively transferred to the grain. An absolute measure of this quantity is difficult, but a value of the efficiency of transfer from the dye relative to the quantum efficiency of direct utilization of absorbed energy by the silver salt can be determined readily by comparing the number of quanta of absorbed light required to produce a specified photographic density in the optically sensitized spectral region with the number absorbed directly by the halide required to produce the same density. Such data have been

[72] Jelley, *Nature* **138**, 1009 (1936).

[73] Scheibe, *Zeit. f. angew. Chem.* **50**, 212 (1937).

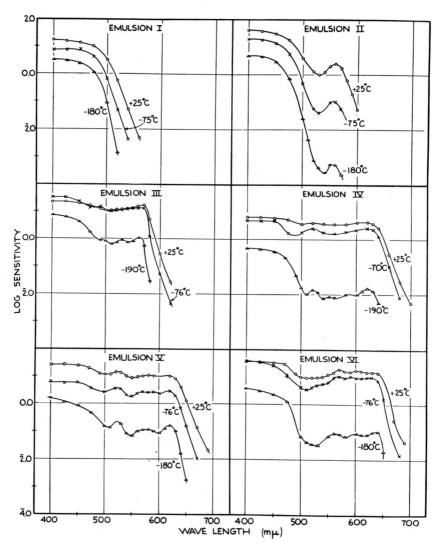

Fig. 8.9.   Effect of temperature on sensitivity of optically sensitized emulsions.
(Evans, *J. Opt. Soc. Amer.* **12**, 214 (1942).)

reported by Leermakers[74] and by Spence and Carroll,[75] showing large variations in the relative efficiency of transfer. The relative efficiency of transfer of some sensitizers approaches unity—a light-quantum absorbed by the dye is nearly as effective

[74] J. A. Leermakers, *J. Chem. Phys.* **5**, 889 (1937).

[75] Spence and Carroll, *J. Phys. and Coll. Chem.* **52**, 1090 (1948).

photographically as one absorbed by the silver salt. These authors also show that some dyes show a high transfer-efficiency although they also desensitize markedly. From these dyes absorbed energy is transferred efficiently enough to the silver halide, but subsequent effects of the dye independent of its sensitizing action interfere with the utilization of the transferred energy in building up latent image.

Mixture of Dyes—Supersensitization.

The sensitization of a mixture of dyes is rarely made up of strictly additive contributions of the separate dyes; a mutual "interference" resulting in a greater or smaller loss of sensitivity is the most common occurrence. Sometimes, however, the presence of one dye, which may itself be an indifferent sensitizer, greatly increases the sensitization of another. For example, auramine, a dye absorbing blue light and with little sensitizing effect, when added to an emulsion containing certain carbocyanines, greatly augments the sensitization of the latter.[76] Other combinations of dyes with a similar effect were discovered by Mees, who termed the phenomenon "*supersensitization.*"[77] The origin of this effect is complex; sometimes the light-absorption of the sensitizer is increased in the presence of the supersensitizer, but increases in sensitivity may also occur without any corresponding increase in absorption, and a true increase in the efficiency of transfer of energy from the sensitizer to the silver salt takes place.[77a]

Effect of Temperature on Optical Sensitization.

As a general rule, the sensitivity of commercial emulsions decreases at low temperatures, and the question arises as to the effect of temperature on optical sensitization as compared with the natural sensitivity of the halide. Fig. 8.9 from a paper by Evans [78] summarizes the result

TABLE 8.1. RATIO OF EFFICIENCY OF SENSITIZER AT TEMPERATURE, T, TO ITS EFFICIENCY AT ROOM TEMPERATURE

Emulsion	Wave Length in Sensitized Region (mμ)	$T(°$ C.)	Ratio	$T(°$ C.)	Ratio
II	560	−76	1/10	−190	1/550
III	560	−76	1	−190	1/5
IV	620	−70	1	−190	1/20
V	620	−76	1	−180	1/4
VI	630	−76	1/2	−180	1/15
VII	600	−75	1/10	−191	1/60

* An exception may occur at very low intensities requiring very long exposures, when diminished reciprocity failure at low temperatures may cause an effective increase in sensitivity.

Emulsion II	Orthochromatic	Coarse grain	Medium speed
Emulsion III	Orthochromatic	Coarse grain	Very high speed
Emulsion IV	Panchromatic	Fine grain	Medium speed
Emulsion V	Panchromatic	Coarse grain	High speed
Emulsion VI	Panchromatic	Coarse grain	Very high speed
Emulsion VII	Panchromatic	Medium grain	Medium speed

of a study of this question. It is seen that, in general, the loss in sensitivity at low temperatures is greater in the optically sensitized spectral region than in the blue, although for some dyes the difference in sensitivity at 25° C. and − 75° C. is small. In Table 8.1 are listed the ratios of the loss in sensitivity at 400 mμ to that in the optically sensitized region for the emulsions represented in Fig. 8.9, these ratios being measures of the decrease in efficiency of optical sensitization compared with the natural sensitivity of the halide at the lower temperatures.

Great variations in the effect of temperature on different emulsions are shown by the data in Table 8.1. The subject is far from thoroughly investigated, but there seems no doubt about its fundamental importance in the theory of sensitization.

---

76 Bloch and Renwick, *Phot. J.* **60**, 195 (1920).

77 Mees, U. S. P. 2,075,046–8 (1937).

77a Carrol and West, in *Fundamental Mechanisms of Photographic Sensitivity*, p. 162, edited by J. W. Mitchell, Butterworth, London 1951: West and Carrol, *J. Chem. Phys.* **19**, 417 (1951).

78 Evans, *J. Opt. Soc. Amer.* **32**, 214 (1942).

Chapter 9

THE MANUFACTURE AND PHYSICAL PROPERTIES OF NEGATIVE MATERIALS

Proper use of negative materials requires some knowledge of the support on which the sensitive emulsion is coated, namely, film base, glass plates or paper. These will be discussed in the present chapter from the point of view of requirements, preparation, treatment, and properties.

Film Base—Requirements. The requirements of a satisfactory film base are rather exacting as indicated by the following:

(1) *Optical Requirements*
   (a) Transparent and optically homogenous.
   (b) Free from haze and visible imperfections.
   (c) Colorless (except where antihalation coatings are applied).

(2) *Chemical Requirements*
   (a) Chemically stable.
   (b) Inert to highly sensitive emulsions.
   (c) Good adherence to the emulsion layer.
   (d) Unaffected by photographic chemicals.
   (e) Moisture resistant.

(3) *Physical Requirements*
   (a) Strong, tough, and hard but not brittle.
   (b) Stiff but also flexible.
   (c) Suitable elastic and plastic properties.
   (d) Tear resistant.
   (e) Free from curl, buckle, etc.
   (f) Dimensionally stable.

(4) *Thermal Requirements*
   (a) High softening temperature.
   (b) Slow burning.

In addition to the general requirement mentioned above, there are certain special requirements for film base which depend on the particular type of photography for which it is intended. For amateur roll film the base must be thin enough to permit winding on a small diameter spool and enable the spool to carry the desired length of film. Film used in film packs must have even greater flexibility because of the sharp radius it must follow when the tab is pulled. Motion picture film requires a stronger tougher base with better wearing qualities because it has to be transported repeatedly at appreciable speeds by mechanical teeth which engage in perforations in the film. It must also have good dimensional stability or the film perforations will not mesh properly with the sprocket teeth.

Sheet film for portrait or commercial use should be flat under all atmospheric conditions so that it will remain in the focal plane. For this reason the base for sheet film is generally made thicker than for other types of film. Film used for three or four color separation work must have especially good dimensional stability to insure proper register.

Some of these requirements are mutually contradictory and many compromises must be made in selecting the best material. It is because the requirements are so rigid that relatively few materials have proved

:actical for film base. So far these in-ude only cellulose nitrate, celluose acetate, ad other organic acid cellulose esters. ellulose nitrate has been the most satis-ctory film base for a great many years t it suffers from inferior chemical stabili-y and great fire hazard. For these rea-ns it is gradually being replaced by the -called "safety base" made from slow-irning cellulose organic acid esters.

Cellulose. When cellulose in the form cotton linters or wood pulp is treated ith nitric acid or acetic anhydride in the ·esence of suitable catalysts, or dehydrat-g agents, cellulose nitrate or cellulose ·etate is formed.

The purer forms of cellulose have an npirical composition which corresponds to $C_6H_{10}O_5)_x$. Chemists have shown by com-ned acetylation and hydrolysis that cot-n forms the octacetate of cellobiose, a ssacharide composed of two glucose units. he cellulose molecule consists of a long ain of glucose units which are linked gether by 1–4-glycosidic oxygen bonds. ccording to Haworth,[1] the formula for llulose is:

162, the molecular weight for cotton cellu-lose is in the order of 120,000. Polymeriza-tion values for other celluloses reported by various investigators range from 10 to 3000, indicating particle weights of 1600 to 450,000.

It should be noted that the cellulose mole-cule is made up of glucose units and that each unit contains three OH, hydroxyl groups, which may become involved in esterification.

Cellulose Nitrate. If cellulose is treated with nitric acid, cellulose nitrate and water are formed. Since the presence of water causes the reaction to be reversible it is necessary to introduce a strong dehydrating agent, as sulfuric acid.

$$(C_6H_7O_2(OH)_3)_x + 3xHNO_3 \rightleftarrows$$
Glucose Unit
$$(C_6H_7O_2(NO_3)_3)_x + 3xH_2O$$

Based on the percentage of nitrogen per glucose unit, cellulose nitrates may be con-sidered to be mono-, di-, or trinitrates if they contain 6.77, 11.13, or 14.16% nitro-gen, respectively. Commercial cellulose nitrate, however, is not any single one of

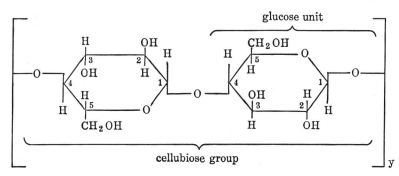

taudinger[2] found that the degree of poly-erization of cotton, as glucose units, is pproximately 750 and, since each glucose nit has a combined equivalent weight of

[1] Haworth, *J. Soc. Dyers and Colorists* **50**, bilee issue.

[2] Staudinger and Jurish, Kunstseide (1) **21**, 6– (1939).

SUTERMEISTER, *The Chemistry of Pulp and Pa-per Making,* pp. 11–19, John Wiley & Sons (1941).

GILMAN, *Organic Chemistry—An Advanced Treatise,* Vol. II, pp. 1535–1583, John Wiley & Sons (1938).

OTT, *High Polymers,* Vol. V, Cellulose and Cel-lulose Derivatives, pp. 29–100, Interscience Publishers (1943).

these three compounds. Different glucose units in any sample, or even in any cellulose molecule, may contain either none, one, two, or three nitrate groups so that the average nitrogen content of a given cellulose nitrate sample may have any intermediate value.

Properties of cellulose nitrate vary with the cellulose used and with conditions of nitration. Chain lengths for cellulose nitrate range from 200 to 3000 glucose units. The solubility depends on the degree of nitration and the viscosity which is a measure of the chain length. Viscosity of nitrate solutions varies with both the source of cellulose and the conditions of nitration.

Cellulose containing two and a fraction nitrate groups per glucose unit, 11 to 12.4% nitrogen, is known as pyroxylin and, because of its solubility, flow, adhesion, and compatibility with suitable solvents, is used for manufacture of film base, as well as plastics and lacquers.

Amor [3] gives as a typical nitrating mixture:

> 60% sulfuric acid
> 20% nitric acid
> 20% water.

The cotton linters are nitrated at 40° C. for 20 minutes under conditions of constant

[3] Amor, *Phot. J.* **78**, 459 (1938).

agitation. The resulting product is washed, neutralized, and bleached.

Cellulose Acetate. As organic acids do not react satisfactorily with cellulose, organic esters of cellulose are prepared commercially by treating the cellulose with a mixture of an acid anhydride, as esterifying agent; an organic acid, as diluent; and an inorganic acid, as catalyst. Cellulose acetate is produced by treating cotton linters with a mixture of acetic anhydride, glacial acetic acid and a catalyst, as sulfuric acid.

$$(C_6H_7O_2(OH)_3)_x + 3_x(CH_3CO)_2O \rightleftarrows \\ (C_6H_7O_2(OCOCH_3)_3)_x + 3_xCH_3COOH$$

By partially hydrolyzing the triacetate first formed, with acetic acid and water, a product is obtained which contains 35 to 40% acetyl, or two and a fraction acetyl groups per glucose unit. This product was found by Miles to dissolve in acetone and form stable films on evaporation.

Cellulose acetate containing 38 to 40% acetyl is slow burning and is used in the manufacture of some safety films. However, it suffers from two major disadvantages: (1) it is less resistant to moisture than cellulose nitrate which means that films made from it are less dimensionally stable, and (2) it is inferior in certain physical properties such as tensile strength and flexibility.

Mixed Organic Acid Cellulose Esters Organic acid cellulose esters other than cellulose acetate have become increasingly important since 1937 in the manufacture of safety film base. Cellulose propionate and cellulose butyrate are more difficult to manufacture than cellulose acetate and

SCHLOTTER, "The Chemistry, Manufacture and Uses of Nitrocellulose," *Chem. Met. Eng.* **25**, 281 (1921).

SHEPPARD AND NEWSOME, "Film Formation with Cellulose Derivatives," *J. Soc. Chem. Ind.* **56**, 1 (1937).

SHEPPARD, "The Removal of Free Acid from Nitrocellulose," *J. Ind. & Eng. Chem.* **13**, 1017 (1921).

WORDEN, *Technology of Cellulose Esters*, Vol. 1, Part 3, Nitrocellulose Theory and Practice, D. Van Nostrand Co., Inc., 1921.

OTT, *High Polymers,* Vol. V, Cellulose and Cellulose Derivatives, pp. 622–663, Interscience Publishers (1943).

WORDEN, *Technology of Cellulose Esters,* Vol. VIII, pp. 2553–2567, D. Van Nostrand Co., Inc., 1921.

OTT, *High Polymers,* Vol. V, Cellulose and Cellulose Derivatives, pp. 671–68, Interscience Publishers, 1943.

suffer from the disadvantages of softness and low strength. However, the mixed esters, *cellulose acetate propionate* and *cellulose acetate butyrate*, give products with improved physical properties compared with regular cellulose acetate and are easier to manufacture than cellulose propionate or cellulose butyrate.[4]

The properties of these mixed cellulose esters depend on (1) the particular acyl groups present, (2) the ratio of acetyl to propionyl or butyryl, (3) the degree of esterification (or conversely, the degree of hydrolysis), and (4) the length of cellulose chain.[5] So far only those esters represented by the small shaded area in Fig. 9.1,

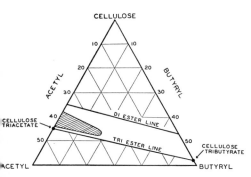

FIG. 9.1. Composition diagram for cellulose mixed esters of acetic and butyric acids illustrating those useful in film base.

have been important in the photographic industry. The major advantage of the mixed cellulose esters in film base compared with regular cellulose acetate is better flexibility and greater moisture resistance, which means better dimensional stability.

Cellulose Triacetate. Fully esterfied cellulose acetate containing three acetyl groups per glucose unit (44.8% acetyl) is

called cellulose triacetate. It is much superior to regular cellulose acetate in moisture resistance and in some physical properties. However, methylene chloride is about the only practical solvent, but until fairly recently this material has not been available in commercial quantities or at an acceptable price. This difficulty has retarded the commercial use of cellulose triacetate for film base for a number of years, although progress was being made in this direction in Europe prior to World War II. More recently cellulose acetate containing 43 to 44% acetyl, slightly less than a theoretical triacetate, has come into use for safety film base in the United States.[6]

Casting Film Base. Photographic film base is made by combining the cellulose ester with suitable solvents, a plasticizer, and sometimes stabilizers. The function of the solvents is to dissolve the ester and permit a thin layer to form and dry. The addition of the plasticizer improves the flexibility and in certain cases reduces the burning rate.

Films are formed from the cellulose ester solutions or "dope": (1) by allowing the solvent to evaporate, or (2) by coagulation with a nonsolvent that is miscible with the solvents used. Solutions used for coating are concentrated and very viscous, having a consistency about that of thick honey.

Nitrate dope is made by dissolving the nitrated cotton containing 11 to 12.4% nitrogen in a mixture of solvents, generally consisting of acetone with methyl or ethyl alcohol and sometimes butyl alcohol. A plasticizer like camphor, dibutyl phthalate, or triphenyl phosphate is added. The amount of plasticizer used varies, but for camphor it is usually 5 to 15% of the weight of cellulose nitrate. The exact formulas for the composition of film base vary somewhat among the different manu-

[4] U. S. P. 2,038,685 (1946).

[5] Malm, Fordyce, and Tanner, *J. Ind. & Eng. Chem.* **34**, 430 (1942).

OTT, *High Polymers*, Vol. V, Cellulose and Cellulose Derivatives, pp. 667–708, Interscience Publishers, 1943.

[6] Fordyce, *J. Soc. Mot. Pict. Eng.* **51**, 331 (1948).

facturers. After filtering, the dope is ready for coating.

An ordinary acetate dope may be made by dissolving cellulose acetate containing 38 to 40% acetyl in acetone with or without the addition of a small amount of alcohol. Cellulose acetate propionate and cellulose acetate butyrate are usually dissolved in a mixture of chlorinated hydrocarbons (such as ethylene or propylene dichloride) together with methyl or ethyl alcohol. High acetyl cellulose acetate may be dissolved in a mixture of methylene chloride and alcohol. Triphenyl phosphate is the most common plasticizer for all types of safety film base because it has good retention and is an effective flame retardant. It is used in amounts varying from 5 to 25% of the cellulose ester.

The base is usually cast by spreading the dope in a uniform layer on a large heated chromium-faced drum which rotates slowly, allowing the solvent to evaporate and the base becomes firm enough so that it can be stripped off in a continuous sheet before the drum has made a complete revolution. The base is then passed through a series of heated chambers to remove the remaining solvent. In this "curing" operation the tension on the sheet must be carefully controlled because stretching the base tends to orient the cellulose ester molecules in the direction of stretch. This in turn affects the mechanical and dimensional properties of the film.[7] The base is then wound into rolls up to 60 inches wide and 2000 feet long. The solvents are recovered from the air and used over again. The approximate thicknesses of film base are:

	Inches	*Millimeters*
Roll Film	0.0033	0.085
Motion Picture Film	0.0053	0.135
Sheet Film	0.0082	0.210

Dimensionally Stable Film Base. In some types of photographic work it is very important that the film used have a high degree of dimensional stability, e.g., in various color processes where accuracy of registration is critical, and in aerial photography where accurate maps are to be made from the film negative. The dimensions of the film should not change with age or when subjected to changes in temperature and humidity. In aerial photography it is particularly important that the film be uniaxial.

Charriou and Vallette[8] claim to have produced "nondeforming" films in the laboratory with a base of cellulose triacetate containing 61.5% combined acetic acid (44.1% acetyl) with 25% triphenyl phosphate dissolved in methylene chloride and ethyl alcohol. They state that the change in the linear dimensions of a gelatin-coated support, after soaking for some days in water and redrying at the initial relative humidity, did not exceed 0.015%. The film, of course, does swell during the water treatment and contracts again during drying. This low shrinkage triacetate film has not been commercialized in France.

Intense study in the United States on the methods and control in manufacture has made possible the production of safety film base from cellulose acetate propionate and cellulose acetate butyrate which, on the basis of shrinkage and distortion, is as satisfactory as nitrate. The susceptibility of these types of safety aerial film for water is no greater than that of nitrate aerial film, and they show the same degree of uniaxialism.[9, 10] In spite of the improved dimensional stability of these safety films

[7] Calhoun, *J. Soc. Mot. Pict. Eng.* **43**, 227 (1944).

[8] Charriou and Vallette, *Publications Scientifiques Et Techniques Du Ministere De L'Air*, No. 116, Paris (1937).

[9] Carver, *Photogram. Eng.* **4**, 223 (1938).

[10] Calhoun, *Photogram. Eng.* **13**, 163 (1947).

TABLE 9.1

Type of Base*	Nitrate	Regular Acetate	Acetate Propionate	Acetate Butyrate	High Acetyl Acetate
Composition of Cellulose Ester Used					
Nitrogen, %	11.95	—	—	—	—
Acetyl, %	—	40.4	30.0	29.5	43.3
Propionyl, %	—	—	13.8	—	—
Butyryl, %	—	—	—	17.5	—
Specific Gravity	1.525	1.300	1.275	1.240	1.290
Refractive Index, N_d	1.506	1.492	1.481	1.475	1.482
Chemical Stability	Low	High	High	High	High
Burning Rate	Extremely high	Very low	Very low	Very low	Very low
Moisture Content (70° F.–90% R.H.), %	2.2	5.5	4.5	2.4	3.5
Linear Swell in Water (from oven-dry), %	0.70	1.75	1.05	0.55	0.90
Tensile Strength (Schopper), psi	15,300	11,000	11,200	11,300	14,400
Ultimate Elongation, %	30	40	45	40	35
Modulus of Elasticity, 10^5 psi	6.4	4.5	4.2	4.6	5.5
Folding Endurance (Schopper), No.	19	7	15	17	14
Tearing Resistance (Elmendorf), gm	67	52	62	52	51

* Tests made at 70° F.—50% R.H. except where stated otherwise.

there are certain special applications where glass plates are still preferred.

Substratum Coating. Since emulsions do not adhere to film base, subcoating is necessary to prevent frilling of the gelatin layer when wet, or stripping when dry. Gelatin is insoluble in organic solvents and the base is insoluble in water, but it is possible to prepare solutions consisting of gelatin and cellulose nitrate, or acetate, dissolved in a mixture of one of the organic solvents and water , The film base is coated with a thin layer of this and then dried. During drying, the organic solvents and water evaporate, depositing on the film base a surface layer of gelatin and cellulose nitrate or acetate. The cellulose nitrate deposited results in good adhesion of the substratum coating to the film base, whereas the gelatin present insures good adhesion of the emulsion.

Physical Properties of Film Base. Some of the more important physical properties of several types of film base in 0.0053 inch thickness are given in Table 9.1.

These film supports were each made from a particular cellulose ester composition, the characteristics of which can be varied over a considerable range. Furthermore, the properties of the base can be varied still more by changing the kind and concentration of plasticizer added and by control in the casting operation. Therefore, the values given in this table should be considered as illustrative rather than exact when considering any one particular type of film base.

FUCHS, "Preliminary Preparation of Photographic Layers," *Phot. Ind.* **34**, 552, 554 (1936).

CHARRIOU AND VALETTE, "Adhesions of Photographic Emulsion to Cellulose Acetate Supports," *Sci. et Ind. Phot.* (2) **8**, 99 (1937).

KOZLOFF, "Mechanism of Adhesion of the Emulsion to the Support," *Proc. International Congress of Photography* (1935).

The high moisture absorption of regular acetate compared with nitrate base means that the former will undergo a greater degree of swell when immersed in processing solutions. This behavior is undesirable in many types of professional photographic work. The high moisture absorption of regular acetate adversely affects many other physical properties as well. The acetate propionate and acetate butyrate film supports on the other hand have much greater moisture resistance and better flexibility but are about the same in strength as the regular acetate. The high acetyl acetate base is much closer to the nitrate in strength and stiffness but it does not have quite as good moisture resistance as the acetate butyrate. The permanent shrinkage of all of these types of film base may be either low or high depending on how well they are cured—that is, on the residual solvent content.

Film Emulsion Coating. Film base is coated with emulsion in rolls 36 inches or more in width and often 1000 to 2000 feet in length. The most common coating method in use involves passage of the film base beneath a roller which is immersed in a long shallow trough containing the liquid emulsion to be coated (Fig. 9.2). Suitable means of accurately controlling the temperature of the emulsion in the trough are available.

It is important that the uniformity and thickness of the applied coating be held to very rigid specifications, because emulsion thickness is very important in controlling the photographic properties of the film. Not only is it essential that the coating be of the proper thickness, but it must be uniform over both the width and the length of the roll and from one roll of base to another. Thickness is controlled by emulsion concentration, emulsion viscosity, and speed of coating.

Immediately after coating, the film is

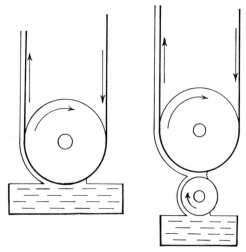

FIG. 9.2. Diagram illustrating principle of trough and roller coating machines. (Baines, *British Journal of Photography*.)

chilled either by passage through a "chill box" containing refrigerated air or by contact with chilled drums. The emulsion which is normally fluid at temperatures above 90° F. sets rapidly to a gel at temperatures of 50° F. and below. Its temperature can subsequently be raised without "remelting" so that it can be dried at temperatures approximating those of normal room air.

The sheet of chilled, coated film is then conducted by automatic machinery to the drying room where it is either looped and dried in the form of festoons or carried over an arrangement of rollers continuously through the drier. The emulsion is dried by clean air of the proper temperature and relative humidity. Drying is a very important operation as lack of uniformity in drying results in a variation in sensitivity, while improper drying conditions may seriously affect the quality of the product in other ways.

Special Coatings. Film base, which has a high degree of flexibility, curls badly as the emulsion dries because of the contraction of the gelatin. This curling is counteracted by treating the opposite side of the base so as to cause it to contract equally, but in the opposite direction. In roll film and sheet film, this so-called *noncurl coating* usually consists of gelatin while in motion picture film a certain degree of control is obtained by treating the back with solvents or solutions of certain cellulose esters which have a similar effect, and, in some cases, also tend to reduce the liability of static electrical discharges upon the unwinding of the roll.

On sheet and roll film, dyes which absorb light, but are decolorized by the processing solutions, may be added to the gelatin coating applied to the rear of the film base to produce a *nonhalation backing*. In motion picture film, where a gelatin backing would be objectionable, nonhalation properties are obtained either by a dye backing or by the addition of suitable light-absorbing material to the film base itself, producing what is termed *gray base* film.

Dyes for nonhalation backings must meet the following requirements:

1. High light absorption particularly in region of maximum emulsion sensitivity.

2. No effect on emulsion or film base under ordinary conditions of storage.

3. No effect on the process of development.

4. Completely bleached or removed either in the developer or the fixing bath, preferably the former. Some films, however, have a permanent low-density, antihalation dye backing.

5. No undesirable residual products left after ordinary fixing, washing, or drying.

Triphenyl methane dyes such as acid fuchsin, and malachite green, have been used most frequently. Colloidal manganese dioxide has been used on unsensitized emulsions. The patent literature[11] mentions bleachable dyes from several other classes such as indophenols and styryls.

Nigrosine has been used for permanent backings.

If a sensitized surface, whether film, paper, or glass plate, is subjected to surface friction, or abrasion, the portions affected by the stress are made developable, or in some cases partially desensitized. This is a surface effect which can be prevented in a considerable degree by applying a thin layer of gelatin over the emulsion, the protective or *super-coating* forming what is sometimes called a *nonabrasion layer* or coating.[12]

Cutting and Packing. The large rolls of film are slit into strips and cut to the desired size.[13] Elaborate testing and inspection of film is carried out at this point by methods which are complicated because film cannot be examined with ordinary illumination. The film is then packed for shipment. The moisture content of the film at the time of packaging must be carefully controlled to insure proper keeping and only specially purified packaging materials can be used because of the danger of contamination. Protection of film against moisture vapor transfer either inward or outward during storage is virtually a necessity, and greatly improved packaging materials and methods have been developed in recent years for this purpose.

---

[11] For the patent literature in this field consult *Chemical Abstracts* (American Chemical Society) or *Photographic Abstracts* (Royal Photographic Society).

[12] The use of shellac, colophony, carnauba, nontan, or cantol wax and various natural and synthetic resins have been patented as emulsion protective layers. For example: Shellac Colophony, B.P. 450,220 (1936), I. G. Farbenindustrie. Carnauba and other waxes, B.P. 468,678 and B.P. 468,780 (1937), Kodak Ltd. Polyvinyl acetal resin, U.S.P. 2,245,218, Murray and Kenyon, Eastman Kodak Company.

[13] The cutting and perforating dimensions for most sizes of film have been standardized by the American Standards Association, 70 East 45th Street, New York City, N. Y., from whom copies of such standards may be obtained.

Physical Properties of the Finished Film. The physical properties of the emulsion coated film differ in several respects from those of the film base itself, notably in moisture absorption, flexibility, curl, and dimensional stability. This is because of the chemical and physical differences between the emulsion and base. The emulsion is much more susceptible to moisture than the base and expands and contracts to a larger extent with changing humidities. It is also softer and sometimes tacky when moist and more brittle than the base when very dry. Each of these factors affects the over-all properties of the film.

Moisture Relationships. Some knowledge of the various moisture relationships of photographic film is fundamental to any understanding of its physical properties. Fig. 9.3 shows how the equilibrium moisture content of different photographic materials varies with the relative humidity of the surrounding air. (It should be emphasized that it is the *relative*, not the *absolute* humidity which determines the moisture content of these and similar materials.)

Different types of film may have a gel-to-base thickness ratio as high as 1:2 or as low as 1:15 when the gelatin backing and emulsion are included together. Typical moisture equilibrium curves for several kinds of film involving different types of base and emulsion are shown in Fig. 9.4. The steep slope of these moisture equilibrium curves above 60% R.H. is noteworthy

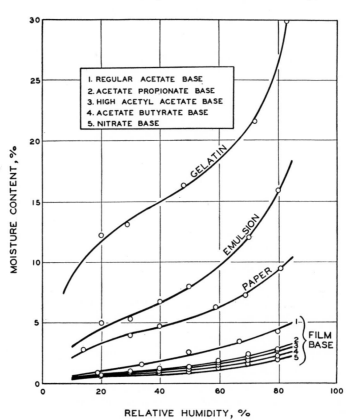

FIG. 9.3.   The equilibrium moisture content of several photographic materials
at various relative humidities at 70° F.

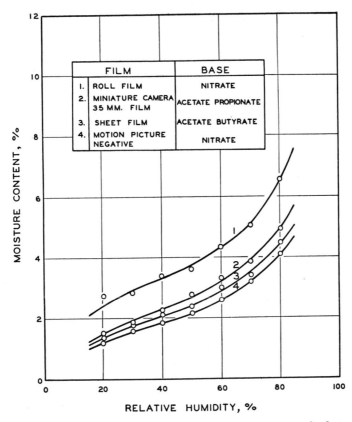

	FILM	BASE
1.	ROLL FILM	NITRATE
2.	MINIATURE CAMERA 35 MM. FILM	ACETATE PROPIONATE
3.	SHEET FILM	ACETATE BUTYRATE
4.	MOTION PICTURE NEGATIVE	NITRATE

FIG. 9.4. The equilibrium moisture content of several types of photographic film at 70° F.

because it is the clue to the many adverse effects of high relative humidities on film. To eliminate the difficulties which sometimes occur in photographic work under adverse humidity conditions, many professional photographic laboratories are now using automatically controlled air-conditioning equipment.

The physical effects on the emulsion of excessive moisture include the tendency for glaze marks to appear, tackiness which may cause sticking to paper or to metal parts, the transfer of backing dyes by contact with the emulsion surface, etc. Damage from mold as well as photographic defects such as mottle, decreased sensitivity and increased fog also occur at high relative humidities. Serious damage to unprotected sensitized materials may be expected in short periods of time at relative humidities of 80% or above and in longer times at relative humidities down to 65%. It is therefore recommended that relative humidities over 60% be avoided in using or storing photographic films.

Mechanical Properties. The physical properties of film such as strength, flexibility, curl, etc., vary with the day-to-day changes in atmospheric conditions. Strength and stiffness decrease with increase in both temperature and relative humidity. Fig. 9.5 illustrates the effect of relative humidity on the brittleness of photographic film determined by placing

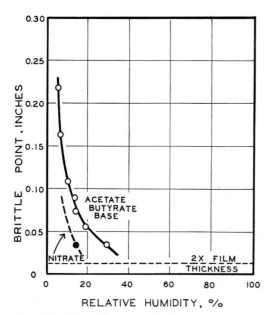

FIG. 9.5. The effect of relative humidity on the vise brittleness of nitrate and acetate butyrate safety base aerial film at 70° F.

a small loop of film emulsion side out between the jaws of a vise which is closed at a uniform speed until the sample breaks.

Above 30% R.H. film is not normally brittle, but below 20% R.H. brittleness increases rapidly. Film on safety base is generally a little more brittle than film on nitrate base but modern mixed cellulose ester and high acetyl acetate safety films are much superior in flexibility to safety films made on regular acetate base. The effect of temperature on the brittleness of film is shown in Fig. 9.6, a marked increase occurring at subzero temperatures, although even under these conditions moisture improves the flexibility as indicated in the diagram.

Deformation. The effort made in manufacture to prevent the curl of photographic film by the use of gelatin backings has already been mentioned. In the case of 35-mm. miniature camera and certain other types of film for which gelatin backings are

undesirable, the curl of the film increases as the moisture content decreases. This is because emulsion contracts about 7 or 8 times as much as the base for a given change in relative humidity and thus pulls the base into a curved position. Even if an anti-curl treatment is incorporated in the base, low relative humidities should be avoided with this type of film to minimize curl.

Film is subject to other types of deformation in addition to curl, e.g., *buckle* and *flute*.[14] Buckle occurs when the edges of a roll or the edges of a stack of film sheets become shorter than the interior as a result of differential shrinkage or differential loss of moisture. Flute is the opposite of buckle and occurs when the edges become longer than the center as a result of differential swelling or stretching.

Dimensional Stability. The various types of dimensional change which photographic films undergo deserves some com-

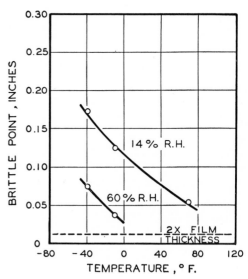

FIG. 9.6. The effect of temperature on the vise brittleness of acetate butyrate safety base aerial film.

---

[14] Carver, Talbot, and Loomis, *J. Soc. Mot. Pict. Eng.* **41**, 88–93 (1943).

ment even though shrinkage is seldom important to the amateur photographer. In some professional fields, on the other hand, the dimensional stability of the film is almost always important and often critical.

The dimensional changes which occur in any photographic film with changes in humidity, temperature, age, and handling are extremely complex and are the result of a number of different effects. The most important of these may be classified as follows:

A. Temporary or reversible dimensional changes.
  1. Humidity expansion and contraction.
  2. Thermal expansion and contraction.
B. Permanent or irreversible dimensional changes.
  1. Loss of residual solvent or volatile material other than moisture.
  2. Plastic flow.
  3. Release of mechanical strain.

The expansion and contraction of film with humidity are generally much more important in practice than thermal expansion, not only because the coefficients are larger but because the range of relative humidity normally encountered indoors is much greater than the range in temperature. The magnitude of the humidity coefficients is directly related to the moisture resistance of the base and the thickness of the emulsion.

The largest portion of permanent shrinkage is caused by the loss of residual solvent from the base. Shrinkage is increased by increase in either storage temperature or relative humidity and is decreased by the use of closed containers which prevent free circulation of air.

The approximate shrinkage characteristics of several types of photographic film are given in Table 9.2. Some variation may be found between individual films or between films manufactured at different times or by different manufacturers. The

TABLE 9.2.   APPROXIMATE SHRINKAGE PROPERTIES OF VARIOUS TYPES OF PHOTOGRAPHIC FILM

	Roll Film Film Pack	Motion Picture 35-mm. Neg. Film	Reversal 16-mm. Film	Miniature Camera 35-mm. Film	Topographic Aerial Film	Sheet Film
Base Type	Nitrate	Nitrate	Regular acetate	Acetate propionate	Acetate butyrate	Acetate butyrate
Base Thickness, Inches	0.0033	0.0053	0.0053	0.0053	0.0053	0.0082
Gel Backing	Yes	No	No	No	No	Yes
Gel-to-Base Thickness Ratio	1:2.5	1:6	1:8	1:6	1:7	1:5
Moisture Content at 70° F.—50% R.H.,	4.1	2:3	3.8	2.8	2.4	2.8
Humidity Coefficient of Linear Expansion per 1° F.$\times 10^5$	11	6.0	11	9.5	8.2	8.0
Thermal Coefficient of Linear Expansion per 1° F.$\times 10^5$	—	3.0	4.7	4.1	4.3	4.0
Processing Shrinkage, %	0.20	0.12	0.20	0.10	0.04	0.10
Aging Shrinkage,* % (Open to the Air)						
1 year at 70° F.—50% R.H.	0.40	0.50	—	0.40	0.09	0.15
1 year at 90° F.—90% R.H.	1.2	0.75	—	0.75	0.05	0.75

* Includes processing shrinkage.

Note. Where precise engineering data are required on current film products, the manufacturer should be consulted.

shrinkage characteristics of films for professional use are controlled more closely than those for amateur use. However, there has been a marked trend in recent years toward lower shrink films of all types and the shinkage of even most amateur films is considerably less than it was ten years ago. This has improved the resistance of films to buckle as well as increased their dimensional stability.

Glass Plates. Glass for photographic purposes must be clear, free from color, bubbles, striae and other imperfections, and reasonably flat.

An emulsion coated directly on glass has a tendency to frill when wet or to strip off when dry. The surface of the glass, therefore, must first be treated to obtain good adhesion of the emulsion layer. The glass substratum ordinarily consists of a thin coating of gelatin strongly hardened by chrome alum, or chemical etching may be employed.

Glass plates are coated with emulsion by a machine (Fig. 9.7) which spreads a thin and uniform layer of emulsion over the glass plates as they are conducted past the coating apparatus on a moving belt. Several coating devices have been described in the literature. In one of the earliest machines the emulsion simply flows over the lips of a long, narrow trough onto the glass plate. The emulsion must, of course, be kept at a suitable temperature in order

that it may flow readily. In another machine described by Cadett, the arrangement is very similar except that directly behind the trough from which the emulsion issues is a light-weight roller which acts as a spreader and smooths out the layer of emulsion on the plates. In still another machine, described by B. J. Edwards, the emulsion was contained in a long trough the width of the glass to be coated. In this trough a glass cylinder is revolved. A scraper, or squeegee, on one side of the cylinder removes the emulsion carried around the cylinder and allows it to drain down onto the glass plate.[15]

After being coated with the emulsion, the plates are carried on a movable belt through a cold chamber or compartment in which the emulsion is chilled and set to a gel. Upon reaching the end of the conveyor system, the plates are removed and dried under controlled conditions.

Paper Base. Paper is used as an emulsion support chiefly for positive rather than negative materials. As far as the latter are concerned, the use of paper as a support is confined to:

1. Photocopying papers for the reproduction of documents (a) with special copying cameras such as the *Photostat* and *Recti-*

---

[15] Smith, *Eder's Jahrbuch*, 1892, p. 385; Cadett, B.P. 9,886 of 1886, and 13,725 of 1887; Edwards, *Phot. News* (1884), p. 541; Wenzel, *Die Chemi-Photographische Industrie.*

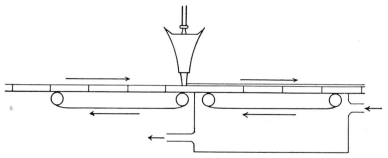

FIG. 9.7. Diagram of plate coating machine. (From Baines, *British Journal of Photography.*)

graph and (b) by the reflex copying process.

2. Direct positive papers in which the negative image is reversed to a positive.

3. As a base for emulsions which are subsequently transferred to othe supports. Stripping materials of this type may be divided into two classes: (a) those in which the emulsion after exposure and processing is stripped from the paper and transferred to glass (lithography and other photomechanical process materials), and (b) those in which the emulsion is affixed to metal, or other suitable support, and the paper backing stripped off *before* exposure. Dry stripping materials of this type [16] are employed chiefly in the sensitizing of large sheets of metal for the preparation of photographic templates.[17]

The paper base employed for such purposes is invariably made especially for photographic purposes. Among the major requirements are a high degree of freedom from all foreign substances which would affect the emulsion and physical strength to withstand the various processing baths. Some of these are acid, some alkaline, and

the paper stock must have the physical strength to withstand these changes as well as the temperature changes, prolonged washing, and handling which photographic papers ordinarily receive in practice.

The paper is usually coated or "sized" before the emulsion is applied. This coating may consist of hardened gelatin or barytabarium sulfate in gelatin. The purpose of such coating is:

1. To form an insulating layer between the paper base and the emulsion preventing (a) too great an absorption of the emulsion by the paper base, and (b) separating the emulsion from metallic or other impurities which may be present accidentally in the paper base to prevent desensitizing or fogged spots.

2. To obtain satisfactory adhesion and facilitate uniform coating of the emulsion on the paper base.

3. To control the surface. For a gloss surface two or more coatings may be applied after which the paper is passed between highly polished, heated rollers under high pressure. Special surfaces are obtained in the same way except that embossed rollers are used.

4. To control, through the addition of dyes or other materials, the color of the surface.

[16] For information on stripping layers see: Lane, U.S.P. 2,391,171; Stand, U.S.P. 2,398,056; Hart, B.P. 577,230; Nadeau and Starck, B.P. 553,383; Batley, Branch, and Soper, B.P. 554,292, 554,300, 568,652.

[17] Nelson, *Airplane Lofting Methods*, McGraw-Hill Book Co., New York.

WENTZEL, "Photographic Raw Paper," *Phot. Rund.* **62**, 56 (1925); **64**, 217 (1927).

Chapter 10

THE SILVER HALIDE GRAIN, THE MECHANISM OF EXPOSURE, AND THE LATENT IMAGE

The usefulness of present-day photographic materials is a result of the behavior of the tiny individual particles of silver halide which are contained in photographic emulsions. In many cases these particles are extremely sensitive to light and store up the effect of an exceedingly small amount of light. This effect can, in turn, be multiplied manyfold by the action of a developer. This stored-up effect of light is known as the latent image. It is so small that it cannot be detected by any means other than by development itself. Consequently, the nature of the latent image and the nature of the development process are closely related. Studies of the behavior of the latent image under different conditions of development and exposure and its reactions with certain other chemicals have led to a fairly clear conception of its nature and the mechanism of its formation. An understanding of these processes requires a knowledge of the structure of the silver halide grains themselves.

THE STRUCTURE OF THE SILVER HALIDE GRAINS

The methods of making photographic emulsions and the silver halide grains that they contain have been discussed in an earlier chapter. These grains are minute crystals of silver halide completely insulated from each other by gelatin. All emulsions contain a range of grain sizes, but the average within a given emulsion ranges from exceedingly small—less than 0.1 micron in diameter—in slow emulsions to several microns in fast negative-type emulsions. A photomicrograph of the grains of

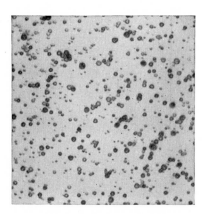

Fig. 10.1. Photomicrograph of the silver halide crystals of a positive emulsion, × 2500.

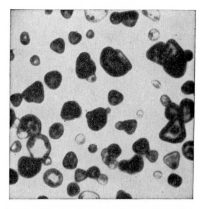

Fig. 10.2. Photomicrograph of the silver halide crystals of a negative emulsion, × 2500.

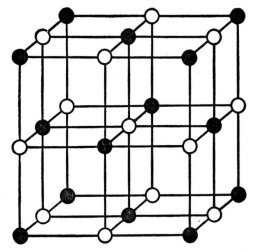

FIG. 10.3. Diagram of the cubic lattice of silver chloride and silver bromide.

a slow positive emulsion is shown in Fig. 10.1; one for a fast negative emulsion, in Fig. 10.2. From the latter it can be seen that the grains are thin platelets with triangular, hexagonal, and a variety of other shapes. These shapes result from the fact that the silver halide crystal has a cubic lattice structure. This structure is shown diagrammatically in Fig. 10.3. Each ion of silver is surrounded by six ions of halide, and vice versa.

One face of this structure can be shown in a plane, as in Fig. 10.4. This represents the face of a crystal. In an actual emulsion the surfaces of the grains are not formed in this manner but have an octahedral surface in which all of one kind of ions or the other are on the surface. This makes it possible for two types of crystals to exist—those which have all silver ions on the surface and those which have all bromide ions on the surface. Such a condition can be visualized by passing a plane through Fig. 10.3 at such an angle that it touches either all of one kind of ions or all of the other. These types of crystals are shown in Fig. 10.5. An additional condition is also indicated in this figure.

The silver surface grain has adsorbed to it an excess of bromide ions with their associated potassium ions. The potassium ions are free to wander away or be replaced by other ions, but the bromide ions are firmly attached so that the crystal has a negative charge in relation to the rest of the solution. This condition arises when the grain is formed in an excess of halide ions and is one of the requirements for the formation of a developable latent image. In the case shown in Fig. 10.5b where the grains have silver adsorbed, they were made in the presence of excess silver. Such grains are immediately reduced by the action of a normal developer even without exposure.

In addition to the adsorbed bromide ions, the grains in an emulsion have gelatin adsorbed to their surfaces as well as sensitizer dyes and a variety of other materials.

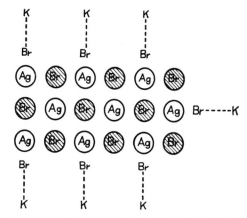

FIG. 10.4. Diagram of the silver bromide lattice showing potassium bromide adsorbed to cubic faces.

Most high-speed emulsions contain a small percentage of iodide. In such cases the iodide ions of the crystal lattice are haphazardly spaced, replacing some of the bromide without any essential change in the type of crystal lattice. Silver iodide itself has a different lattice structure but does not affect the silver bromide struc-

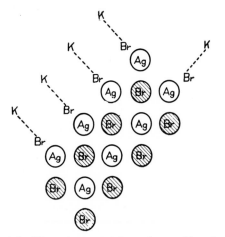

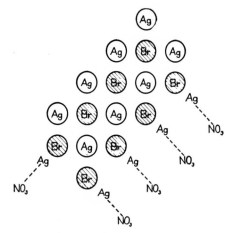

(a) Silver ion crystal surface with adsorbed bromide ion.

(b) Bromide ion crystal surface with adsorbed silver ion.

FIG. 10.5. Diagram of decahedral faces of silver bromide.

ture. If 32% or more of iodide is present when the grains are formed, two types of grains are formed—those composed of the bromide-type lattice structure and some grains of pure silver iodide. No commercial emulsions contain this amount of iodide. Chlorobromide emulsions crystallize with a cubic structure with the chloride and bromide haphazardly distributed.

In addition to their normal crystal structure, the grains contain certain specks of foreign material called sensitivity specks. These specks are extremely important and will be taken up more completely later.

Quantum-Mechanical Description of Crystal Sructure. Recent applications of quantum mechanics to the study of crystals have given considerable information concerning the behavior of crystals of silver halide. This method describing crystals specifies the energy content of electrons in the crystal and also the possible energy levels which electrons might have. For example, in a metal there is a certain energy-level band which is broad enough and continuous enough so that electrons can move around freely. Furthermore, there are electrons in this energy level under

normal circumstances. These electrons are perfectly free to move and, when a potential is applied, the electrons do move and thus a current flows. For this reason, metals are conductors. The situation in nonconductors such as crystals of silver halide is quite different. A graphical representation of this condition is shown in Fig. 10.6. The crosshatched band la-

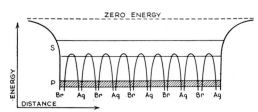

FIG. 10.6. Quantum-mechanical description of the energy levels occurring in a crystal of silver bromide.

beled p represents the energy level of the electrons related to the ions of bromide. This level is filled with electrons and they are firmly bound so that they cannot move around from one position to another. The higher level marked s is associated with the valence electron level of silver and here electrons could move around freely.

However, there are no electrons in this band in a normal crystal of silver bromide. If an electron were put in this energy band by some outside means or by the addition of a certain amount of energy to one of the electrons in the p band it could move around freely through the crystal. The usefulness of this concept in explaining some of the characteristics of silver halide and the latent image will be taken up later.

REACTIONS OF THE SILVER HALIDES WITH LIGHT

As was explained earlier, light is a form of electromagnetic wave energy which occurs in small units called quanta. When a quantum of light strikes an object, any one of three things may happen. It may be reflected, it may be transmitted, or it may be absorbed. When the light is absorbed it is converted to some other type of energy; it is changed into heat or may cause some reaction to take place. In such photo reactions it is only the light that is absorbed which is effective, and not that which is transmitted or reflected.

A number of the reactions that can be caused by the absorption of light have been explained in an earlier chapter. Those which silver halide undergoes are of interest in the study of the latent image.

Photoelectric Effect. When light of the proper wave length and energy content is absorbed by certain crystals, electrons are ejected from the surface of the crystal. This is the principle on which ordinary photoelectric tubes operate. If the material is in a vacuum, the emitted electrons can be collected by means of an applied voltage. A measure of the current obtained is a measure of the photoelectric effect; or, after this has been established, is a measure of the amount of light which has been absorbed.

Silver bromide exhibits the photoelectric effect to a certain extent. In the early days of photographic science it was thought that this might be the mechansim of latent-image formation. However, an accurate measurement of the wave length of the light which will cause the ejection of electrons from silver chloride, silver bromide, and silver iodide [1,2] has shown that the effect is not caused by visible light at all, but only by much higher energy ultraviolet radiation. This can be taken as evidence that latent-image formation, which can be caused by visible light, is not related to the photoelectric effect.

Photolysis. Photolysis of silver halide is the decomposition of silver halide by light. The reaction which takes place can be written as follows:

$$2\, AgBr + light = 2\, Ag + Br_2.$$

The reaction is much more efficient if it takes place in surroundings that will remove the halogen which is formed, for otherwise the reaction tends to proceed in the opposite direction to use up some of the silver which is formed. The reaction in the presence of water, which acts as a halogen acceptor, can be written as follows:

$$2\, AgBr + H_2O + light$$
$$= 2\, Ag + Br^- + OBr^- + 2\, H^+.$$

Mutter [3] studied photolysis under a variety of conditions and found that in the presence of nitrite, an excellent halogen acceptor, the reaction may proceed with a quantum efficiency of one. This means that for every quantum of light *absorbed*, one atom of silver is formed.

This type of reaction is made use of in ordinary print-out proof papers. The

[1] Fleischmann, *Ann. d. Phys.* **5**, 73 (1930).

[2] Toy, Edgerton, and Vick, *Phil. Mag.* **43**, 482 (1927).

[3] Mutter, *Z. wiss. Phot.* **26**, 193 (1939).

silver image is produced directly by light so that fairly long exposures are required. The process is made as efficient as possible by having an excess of silver on the grains which acts as a halide acceptor. Even so, free chlorine is formed and can be detected by its odor if a print-out paper is exposed to a very intense light.

The relative efficiency of different wave lengths of light in producing the print-out effect is, in general, the same as the spectral sensitivity distribution for latent-image foramtion. This is evidence that the mechanisms of the two are related.

Internal Photoelectric Effect—Photovoltaic Effect—Photoconductance. When two similar silver-silver bromide electrodes are electrolytically connected and one of the electrodes is exposed to light, a potential is developed.[4] This is called the photovoltaic effect. The exposed electrode becomes negative in relation to the dark electrode, indicating that the electrons within the silver bromide which are released by the exposure to light migrate into the adjacent silver. The investigations of this phenomenon were made with light of such a wave length that no electrons could be ejected from the halide by the normal external photoelectric effect, indicating that the electrons were released within the halide.

Another phenomenon which results from the internal release of electrons in silver halide crystals is known as photoconductance. When silver bromide crystals, which are normally extremely weak conductors, are exposed to light, an electric current will pass through the crystal if the proper voltage is applied. Toy[5] investigated the effects of various wave lengths of light in producing the photoconductance

effect and found that it closely paralleled the spectral sensitivity for latent-image formation.

THE NATURE OF THE LATENT IMAGE AND ITS FORMATION

Since the beginning of photography, workers in the field have speculated as to the nature of the photographic latent image and its formation. A large amount of experimental work has been done in the study of this phenomenon so that at present a fairly clear picture of its nature has been established. This differs quite considerably from some of the earlier theories.

Carey Lea[6] suggested that the exposure to light formed a subhalide of silver such as Ag_mCl_n in which m is larger than n. It was assumed that this subhalide was more easily affected by a developer than ordinary silver chloride. This theory was quite widely accepted before 1900, and a good deal of work was done in an attempt to prove the existence of such a subhalide, but without success.

Bredig[7] suggested that a grain was disintegrated to a number of much smaller grains whose solution pressure would cause development. Bose[8] suggested a vibratory strain which raised the grains to a higher energy and made them developable. Hurter and Driffield,[9] Chapman Jones,[10] and Namias[11] suggested a change of state of the silver halide as a result of exposure, such as a polymerization, depolymerization, or conversion to a metastable state.

[4] Vanselow and Sheppard, Pt. I, *J. Phys. Chem.* **33**, 331 (1929). Sheppard, Vanselow, and Hall, Pt. II, *ibid.* **33**, 1403.

[5] Toy, *Nature* **120**, 441 (1927).

[6] Lea, *Am. J. Sci.* **37**, 476 (1889) (3). Lea, *ibid.* **33**, 349 (1887) (3).

[7] Bredig, *Eder's Jahrbuch.* **13**, 357 (1899).

[8] Bose, *Phot. J.* **42**, 146 (1902).

[9] Hurter and Driffield, *Phot. J.* **22**, 145 (1898).

[10] Jones, Chapman, *Science and Practice of Photography*, 4th Edition, p. 383, Iliffe and Sons Ltd., London (1904).

[11] Namias, *Phot. Korr.* **42**, 155 (1905).

As recently as 1930 Weigert [12] suggested a micelle theory of the latent image as a result of his experiments on induced optical anisotropy. According to his theory the latent image is formed from physically changed micelles, dense yet amorphous aggregates of molecules of all constituents of the emulsion, the original silver, dye, silver sulfide, and the silver halide itself. The change upon exposure to light, which represents a spatial orientation of the micelle elements, corresponds simultaneously to an increased catalytic activity toward the developer.

Schwarz [13] advanced the surface discharge theory. According to his views the exposure to light was supposed to shift electrons from the surface of the grains into their interior so that the negative charge on the surface was decreased, making the grain more easily attacked by the developer. Hanson and Evans [14] believed that a slight modification of this theory was adequate to explain a number of the characteristics of the latent image. It is well known that halide grains prepared in the excess of halide rather than silver ions are essential for the formation of the latent image, but the work of James [15] has shown that the direct influence of the surface charge on developability is of secondary importance.

More recently Huggins [16] has suggested that the effect of light is to convert a grain or a portion of a grain of silver bromide from the cubic lattice structure to the B3, or cubic zinc sulfide, structure. This structure is stabilized by the presence of excess electrons, a higher energy state, and would presumably be developable. This theory has never received a great deal of attention.

All these theories, which have been presented in a chronological order, have one thing in common: they all assume that the substance of the latent image is something other than metallic silver. In many instances they have resulted from experimental data which could not be as easily explained at the time by other mechanisms. In some cases they have been advanced with the aim of encouraging further experimentation. The fact that present knowledge leads overwhelmingly to the conclusion that the latent image is metallic silver and that most of the workers in the field accept this hypothesis does not detract from the value of these theories in their contributions to the present knowledge of the photographic latent image and its formation.

Silver Speck Theory. Since the first discovery that the action of light on the silver halides was to form metallic silver it was logical to assume that the substance of the latent image was metallic silver itself. Such a theory has been held, of course, for a long time. The major work which has been done in relation to this theory is that involved in determining the mechanism of the formation of the silver, its distribution on or in the grains, and the nature of the development process whereby the presence of a bit of silver makes a grain developable.

The behavior of the latent image, when treated with certain chemicals, leads to some knowledge as to its nature. It can be destroyed by the action of oxidizing agents which should have sufficient oxidation potential to oxidize metallic silver.

Physical development of an exposed emulsion leads to further information. A physical developer is a solution composed of a weak reducing agent and a soluble

[12] Weigert, *Z. wiss. Phot.* **29**, 191 (1930); Pt. II, *ibid.* **30**, 217 (1931).

[13] Schwarz, *Phot. Korr.* **69**, 27 (1933), Beilage 5.

[14] Evans and Hanson, *Phot. J.* **77**, 497 (1937).

[15] James, *J. Phys. Chem.* **43**, 701 (1939).

[16] Huggins, *J. Chem. Phys.* **11**, 412 (1943).

salt of silver. The weak reducing agent is not powerful enough to reduce the grains of an emulsion but can slowly reduce a silver salt in solution. Metallic silver speeds up the reduction of the silver salt. An exposed emulsion can easily be developed in such a developer. This is evidence that the exposure has produced silver. In fact, such development can be carried out after the emulsion is fixed. Bullock [17] has investigated the amount of exposure that is required for both pre- and post-fixation physical development. It was found that a greater exposure was required than for a normal type of development. This might be taken as evidence that the image for physical and that for chemical developers is not exactly identical, so it does not prove beyond a shadow of a doubt that the latent image for normal development is metallic silver.

Koch and Volger [18] studied the crystal structure of exposed silver bromide by the x-ray diffraction method and found evidence of the metallic silver crystal lattice in addition to the silver bromide lattice. After fixing, only the silver lattice structure remained.

Development Centers. In 1917, Hodgson [19] studied the process of development by stopping the development before a visible image had formed and examining the grains under the microscope. A number of specks were visible on the grains, indicating that the development had started at discrete points. It was observed that on continued development a grain which contained these specks developed to completion and that the development continued by the growth in size of these specks, not by the continued formation of new specks all over the grains. This observation originated the idea of development centers.

It was later shown by the use of the electron microscope, with which magnifications up to 50,000 times were obtained, that exposure of silver bromide forms discrete specks of silver. However, the exposure level which formed detectable silver specks was much greater than is required for latent-image formation.

The presence of these development centers leads to several possibilities as to the formation of the latent image: the light may be absorbed in specks, the effect of over-all absorption is concentrated into specks, or simply the development must start somewhere. In any case it leads to the conclusion that the specks are already present on the grains of an emulsion.

Sensitivity Specks. The presence of "sensitivity specks" of silver sulfide on the silver halide grains of an emulsion was discovered by Sheppard.[20]

Clark [21] assumed that sensitivity specks are silver sulfide; then oxidizing agents which would attack metallic silver but not silver sulfide, could be used to destroy the latent image without much effect on sensitivity. Treatment in such oxidizing agents had a much larger effect on sensitivity than was predicted, and he concluded that the sensitivity specks must contain some metallic silver as well as silver sulfide. However, some doubt was thrown on this conclusion by Sheppard,[22] who showed that the size of the particles of silver sulfide would have a great influence on the attack of oxidizing agents—the smaller the speck, the more easily it was attacked.

The work just discussed has not only

[17] Bullock, E. R., *Chemical Reactions of the Photographic Latent Image*, Eastman Kodak Co., Rochester, N. Y., 1927.
[18] Koch and Volger, *Ann. Physik* **77**, 495 (1925).
[19] Hodgson, *J. Franklin Inst.* **184**, 705 (1917).

[20] Sheppard, *Phot. J.* **65**, 380 (1925). Sheppard and Hudson, *Ind. Eng. Chem.*, Anal. Ed. **2**, 73 (1930).
[21] Clark, *Brit. J. Phot.* **74**, 227, 243 (1927).
[22] Sheppard, S. E., *Brit. J. Phot.* **75**, 207 (1928). (A letter to the editor.)

stablished that the grains in an emulsion ontain definite "sensitivity specks" and hat the development begins at discrete pecks, but has established fairly well the ature of these specks. It has not, however, iven any information as to the manner in which the specks enhance sensitivity and oncentrate the latent image. That their ffect is not a result of the absorption of ight by the specks themselves can be estab-ished quite easily by a study of the spectral ensitivity distribution of a variety of emulion types. The spectral sensitivity disribution of emulsions of silver chloride, ilver bromide, or of bromo-iodide is closely elated to the spectral absorption distribuion of the particular crystals. This is rue even after the grains have been treated with an oxidizing agent which destroys the pecks and decreases the total sensitivity y a large factor. According to the laws of photochemical reactions, a reaction can e caused only by light which is absorbed. Since it is very unlikely that the spectral bsorption characteristics of the sensitivity pecks for the different types of emulsions would be similar to the absorption of the rystals themselves, we may conclude it is bsorption of light by the crystals themevles, not the sensitivity specks, which orms the latent image.

This leaves open the question as to the mechanism whereby the specks increase speed and concentrate the effects of the exposure to light. Toy[23] concluded that "the function of the traces of foreign matter at the centers is to facilitate, catalytically, the decomposition by light." However, since the presence of the specks does not change the spectral sensitivity distribution and since the quantum equivalence law of photochemical reactions,[24] as propounded by Einstein[25] had been shown to hold for the photolysis of silver halide, Sheppard, Trivelli, and Loveland[26] state that (1) the relative spectral sensitivity, (2) the number of quanta absorbed, and (3) the number of silver atoms formed per quantum of light absorbed were not affected by the presence of the sensitivity specks. From these ideas they developed the concentration speck theory of the latent image which assumed that the function of the sensitivity centers is to "concentrate the silver atoms reduced by the light absorbed by the silver bromide." Although the specific mechanism by which the specks concentrated the silver was not established, it was assumed that the silver atoms which were formed by light would collide with the specks and remain there so that the specks would grow in size during exposure and would reach a critical size which would make a grain developable. This fitted in completely with the sensitizing action of the specks.

Later data, which will be discussed in a following section, have given evidence that the formation of the latent image is a two-stage process in which the light energy absorbed is transferred to an electron and later results in the formation of metallic silver. If the energy is lost by the electron before metallic silver is formed, the actual amount of silver formed by the absorption of a given amount of light could be a function of other circumstances such as the presence of a speck, without the Einstein quantum-equivalence law's being disobeyed. These later data have resulted in a modification of the concentration speck theory, but this theory was a great contribution to the advancement of the knowledge of la-

[23] Toy, *Trans. Farad. Soc.* **19**, 290 (1923).

[24] This law applies to the primary product of photo-reactions. Secondary products may be formed in greater or smaller amounts.

[25] Einstein, *Ann. d. Phys.* **37**, 832, IV (1912). Einstein, *ibid.* **38**, 881.

[26] Sheppard, Trivelli, and Loveland, *J. Franklin Inst.* **200**, 51 (1925).

tent-image formation and in its general form has stood up until the present time.

Size of the Latent Image. The size of the sensitivity specks and the additional size required to make a grain developable has been the subject of a number of experiments. The amount of silver which is formed by exposure is so small that no direct measurement has been possible. Reinders and Hamburger [27] attempted to determine the number of atoms of silver which were required in a speck to initiate physical development by depositing silver on a glass plate in a vacuum by distillation. Their results indicated that three or more silver atoms were required. However, their results are based on certain assumptions as to the sizes of the specks formed on the plate in relation to their statistical analysis and cannot be accepted without some doubt.

A number of attempts have been made by mathematicians to develop equations for

the H and D curve of an emulsion with th aim of getting some clue as to the size o the latent image. These equations, whic need not be included here, take the forr of various types of probability functions an most of them contain a factor which migh be considered as related to the minimur number of absorbed quanta or silver atom required to make a grain developable. series of H and D curves derived from on of these equations with the assumption fo a number of values of this factor, r, i shown in Fig. 10.7. It can be seen tha for all but small values of the factor, r the curves are very steep, not at all lik actual H and D curves obtained in practice This indicates that a small number, les than ten, of atoms of silver are required t make a grain developable. A recent wor of Webb [28] has shown that other assump tions can be made such that the shapes o practical H and D curves can be calculated with large values of r so that the mathe

---

[27] Reinders and Hamburger, *Z. wiss. Phot.* **31**, 32 (1932); *ibid.* **31**, 265 (1933).

[28] Webb, J. H., private communication.

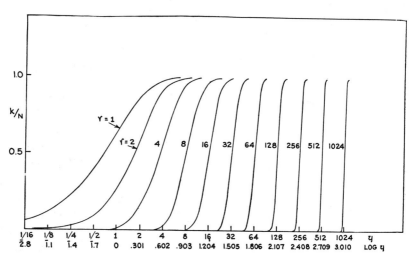

FIG. 10.7. Curves corresponding to different values of — in the probability equation

$$\frac{K}{n} = \sum_{n=r}^{n=\infty} \frac{e^{-y}y^n}{n!}$$

in which K/n is the fraction of grains rendered developable and — is the minimum number of quanta required to make a grain developable.

natical analyses cannot be considered as strong evidence that such a small number of atoms are required. However, it is generally accepted that silver specks containing a small number of atoms, probably less than ten, are responsible for the latent image.

Gurney-Mott Theory of Latent-Image Formation. Recent advances in quantum mechanics and the application of these principles to the structure and behavior of crystals have contributed a great deal of knowledge to the problems of latent-image formation. Webb [29] first applied the principles of quantum mechanics to an explanation of the formation of the latent image. Following the work of Gurney,[30] which explained the coloration of crystals of the alkali halides, and the quantum-mechanical explanation of the photoconductance effect in silver bromide, Webb described the latent image as a concentration of electrons at a speck, or trap. The electrons were supposed to be transferred to a higher energy level by the absorption of light and in this energy level they could wander through the crystal at will as in the photoconductance effect. The sensitivity specks were supposed to contain energy levels slightly lower than this conductance level, so that when an electron traveled to such a speck it gave up a bit of energy in going to this new level and was trapped. This gave an excellent explanation of the speck concentration of the effect of absorbed light but was at variance with the formation of metallic silver as latent-image substance.

Gurney and Mott [31] presented a theory for the photolytic formation of silver from silver halide as follows: the energy structure of a crystal of silver halide can be described as in Fig. 10.6. The silver and

bromide represent the silver and bromide ions which are present alternately in a crystal. The crosshatched area labeled p represents the energy level of the electrons connected with the bromide ions. This energy band is filled and electrons cannot move around in it. The clear energy band labeled s represents the energy level corresponding to the conductance level in metallic silver. In a crystal of silver halide all the valence electrons are associated with the bromide ions and none with the silver, so that this band is empty. Electrons cannot have energy represented by the areas not included by these two bands. The photoconductance phenomenon can be explained by this diagram. When light is absorbed, its energy is transferred to one of the electrons in the p band and the electron is lifted up to the s band where it is free to wander around just as the conductance electrons flow around in metallic silver. If a voltage is applied to a crystal while it is illuminated, the electrons which are lifted into the s band by light will flow to the positive pole, causing conductance. Studies of photoconductance have shown that the current increases with increasing voltage, even at constant illumination, until a certain value is reached beyond which the current is unaffected by voltage, only by the intensity of light. This has been taken to indicate that some of the electrons in the s band get caught by some means before they reach the electrode. This can be explained by the energy-level structure of metallic silver itself. This is shown in Fig. 10.8. If the lowest energy level in the

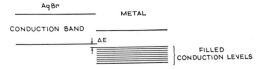

FIG. 10.8. Relation between energy level in the silver bromide conduction band and in metallic silver.

[29] Webb, *J. Opt. Soc. Amer.* **26**, 367 (1936).

[30] Gurney, *Proc. Royal Society* **A141**, 209 (1933).

[31] Gurney and Mott, *Proc. Royal Society* **164A**, 151 (1938).

conduction level of the silver bromide is higher than the lowest filled level in the conduction band of metallic silver, an electron passing from silver bromide to a speck of silver would give up a small amount of energy and be trapped. Thus, atoms or specks of metallic silver might be the traps which prevent the electrons from reaching the positive pole when too low a voltage is applied.

Another concept which was applied to the theory of photolysis by Gurney and Mott was the presence of interstitial ions in a crystal lattice. A perfect crystal would contain a uniform spacing of ions as shown on page 163. However, it has been found that in many cases crystal contains some ions which are not in their proper place, but in the interstitial positions. Presumably these are caused by thermal motion of the ions in the crystals. This condition is shown in Fig. 10.9. These ions and their movement through the crystal, either by going from one interstitial position to another or by moving to one of the holes

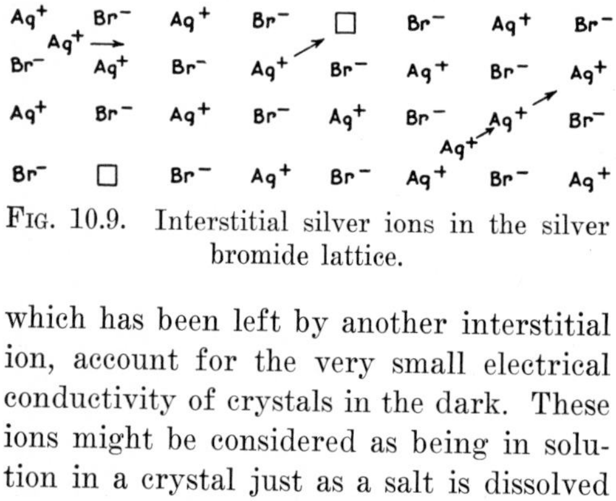

FIG. 10.9.   Interstitial silver ions in the silver bromide lattice.

which has been left by another interstitial ion, account for the very small electrical conductivity of crystals in the dark. These ions might be considered as being in solution in a crystal just as a salt is dissolved in water. The conductivity of such crystals follows the same laws as the conductivity of ionized salt solutions. This conductivity decreases with decreasing temperature.

Gurney and Mott also assumed that silver bromide contains particles of colloidal silver.

These concepts and assumptions were combined to give the following hypothesis: when such crystals are exposed to light some electrons are elevated to the higher conductance band and on wandering around come in contact with a speck of silver and are trapped. This charges the speck negatively, and this negative charge attracts some of the interstitial ions of silver which migrate to the specks and are neutralized by the electron to form an atom of silver which is attached to the speck already present. This mechanism affords a complete explanation of how the effect of light which is absorbed all over the crystal can be concentrated at discrete specks.

In order to apply this theory to the formation of a latent image as well as to the photolytic formation of metallic silver, it is necessary to postulate that the sensitivity specks, silver sulfide, or whatever their complete composition might be, can serve the same function as the colloidal silver specks; i.e., they can act as traps for electrons in the conductance level of the crystal.

Experimental Support for the Gurney-Mott Theory. Such a clearly defined mechanism for latent-image formation suggests the possibility of a number of experiments which could support or disprove the theory. A number of experiments aimed at separating the primary (electron trapping) and secondary (wandering of silver ions to make metallic silver) process have been performed by Berg and Mendelssohn [32] and by Webb and Evans [33] who investigated the effect of exposures at low temperature. The H and D curves of a normal emulsion exposed at room temperature and at temperatures of liquid

[32] Berg and Mendelssohn, *Proc. Royal Society* **168A**, 168 (1938).

[33] Webb and Evans, *J. Opt. Soc. Amer.* **28**, 249 (1938).

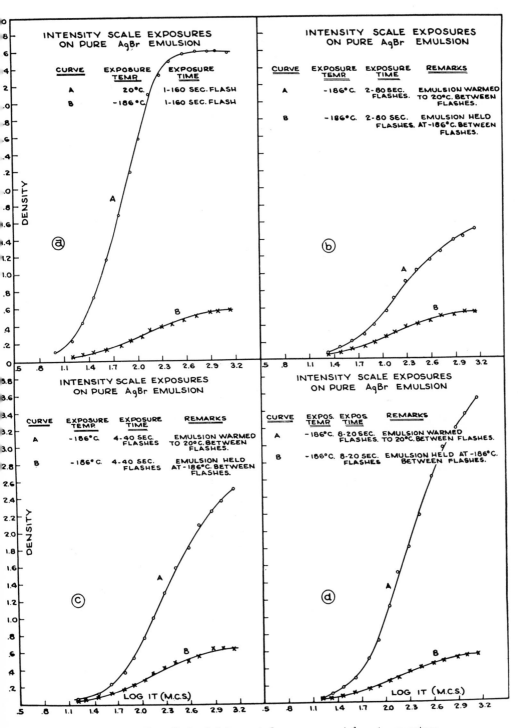

FIG. 10.10.   The effect of interrupted exposures at low temperature.

air are shown in Fig. 10.10a. The low-temperature exposure gives very little density. However, if the film is given only half the exposure at the low temperature, then warmed up, then cooled again and given the other half of the exposure, much more density is obtained as shown in Fig. 10.10b. Increasing numbers of interruptions to the exposure with a warm-up in between each interruption lead to increasing density as shown by Fig. 10.10c and d. Webb and Evans concluded that if the exposure were interrupted a sufficient number of times with a warm-up in between each interruption, the effect of the exposure at low temperature would be identical with that given at room temperature. This effect is explained as follows: during the exposure at low temperature the electrons are lifted to the conductivity band where they can wander around and some of them are trapped at the centers. However, at the low temperature the interstitial silver ions cannot wander to and neutralize this charged speck. The charged speck repels other electrons so that they cannot accumulate at the specks and are finally trapped in the interior of the grains or give up their energy by emitting light (fluorescence) and dropping back into the lower energy level. In fact, when silver bromide is exposed at low temperatures it does fluoresce with a green glow. When the emulsion is warmed up, the silver ions can wander through the crystal and neutralize the few electrons which have been trapped at the specks, and a small amount of metallic silver is formed. When the exposure is interrupted and the film is warmed up, some atoms of silver are formed. The specks are no longer charged and, upon subsequent cooling and exposure, a few more electrons can be trapped before the charge becomes sufficient to repel further electrons. These data fit in perfectly with the Gurney-Mott theory and demon-

strate that the primary process, the release and trapping of electrons, occurs at low temperatures and can be separated from the secondary process, the wandering of the silver ions to neutralize the trapped electrons, which cannot occur at low temperatures.

Distribution of the Latent Image. The distribution of the latent image on the surface and in the interior of the grain was first investigated by Kogelmann in 1894. He dissolved away the surface of the grains in order to lay bare to the developer the latent image in the interior of the grains. A number of other investigators have studied this problem during the years. Lainer noticed that a small amount of iodide in a developer caused an increase of density, or effective latent image, and it was later assumed by Lüppo-Cramer that this was due to the cracking of the grains by the iodide entering the crystal lattice to replace bromide. A number of the unusual photographic effects, such as reciprocity

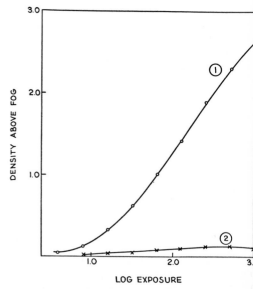

FIG. 10.11. *H* and *D* curves of the developed surface latent image after treatment with an oxidizing bleaching solution: (1) dilute bleach, (2) concentrated bleach.

failure, the Clayden effect, and others, have been explained by the assumption of the formation of a greater or lesser amount of internal latent image. However, it was not until 1941 that an adequate technique for investigating the internal latent image was established. Berg, Marriage, and Stevens [34] used a "surface" developer containing glycine in the absence of sodium sulfite or any other silver halide solvent, and were able to obtain good separation of the surface and internal latent image. In order to investigate the internal latent image it was necessary to destroy the surface latent image. This was accomplished by a dilute solution of the oxidizing agent potassium dichromate in the presence of sulfuric acid. It was necessary to establish the concentration of these ingredients and the time of

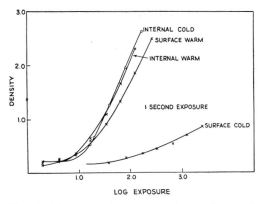

Fig. 10.13. *H* and *D* curves for surface and internal latent images exposed at high and low temperature.

treatment for each emulsion investigated in order not to destroy some of the internal latent image. As a developer for the internal latent image after the surface image had been destroyed they used a developer containing hypo to act as a solvent for the silver bromide. This solvent action made the internal latent image available for development. Figs. 10.11 and 10.12 show the H and D curves of the surface and internal latent images. This procedure was used in investigating the formation of latent images at low temperatures. The results obtained are shown in Fig. 10.13. As can be seen from the figure, the surface latent image resulting from the low-temperature exposure is quite low, in agreement with the work of Webb. However, the internal latent image resulting from the low-temperature exposure is very similar in amount to the internal latent image resulting from exposure at room temperature. This result indicates that the released electrons are trapped at internal specks.

Kornfeld [35] also presented a satisfactory method for separating the surface and internal latent image.

The development of the Gurney-Mott theory of latent-image formation and the

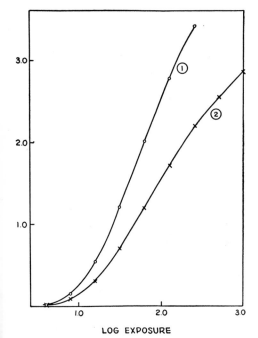

Fig. 10.12. *H* and *D* curves of the developed internal latent image after treatment with a bleaching solution: (1) dilute bleach, (2) concentrated bleach.

[34] Berg, Marriage, and Stevens, *J. Opt. Soc. Amer.* **31**, 385 (1941).

[35] Kornfeld, *J. Opt. Soc. Amer.* **31**, 598 (1941).

means of separating the surface from the internal latent image are powerful tools in the hands of workers in the field of photographic theory. They give such a clear explanation of a number of the latent-image phenomena which had not been thoroughly understood before that it can be expected that work along these lines in the future will lead to a still clearer picture of the process which takes place in the photographic emulsion.

Optical Sensitizing and Latent-Image Formation

The present knowledge of the manner in which these dyes function as sensitizers is still far from complete.

One of the basic laws of photochemical reactions states that only light which is absorbed by a material can have any effect in causing a reaction to take place. It is, therefore, obvious that the spectral sensitivity which is conferred upon an emulsion when it is sensitized must be closely related to the color of the sensitizing dye. For many years this exact relation was not clearly understood. It was not until 1937 that Leermakers, Carroll, and Staud,[36] using the spectrophotometer developed by A. C. Hardy, measured the amount of light which was reflected from and transmitted by a sensitized emulsion, and by subtracting the sum of these from the total incident light determined the light which was absorbed. The spectral absorption and the relative spectral sensitivity of the emulsion are both shown in Fig. 10.14. The two are practically identical in distribution.

This same figure also demonstrates another very important point. It can be seen that the sensitivity in the sensitized region has the same relation to the absorp-

[36] Leermakers, Carroll, and Staud, *J. Chem. Phys.* **5**, 878 (1937).

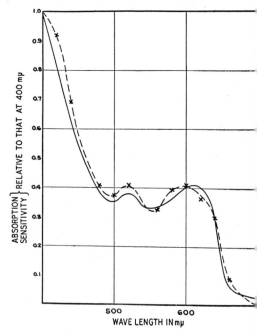

Fig. 10.14. The relation between light absorption and sensitivity in a sensitized emulsion: *solid line*, relative absorption; *broken line*, relative sensitivity.

tion in this region that the sensitivity in the blue region (the region of absorption of the silver bromide itself) has to the absorption in this region. This correspondence of absorption and sensitivity throughout the spectrum means that in forming a latent image the emulsion makes just as efficient use of the light which is absorbed by the sensitizer as it does of the light absorbed by the silver bromide itself. A number of other experiments have shown that not all sensitizers are so efficient, but it is of a great deal of interest that some sensitizers are 100% efficient.

Nature of the Latent Image Formed in Sensitized Emulsions. The data on the efficiency of certain sensitizers may be taken as evidence that the latent image formed from light absorbed by a sensitizer is similar to that formed when the silver bromide absorbs the light.

Berg, Marriage, and Stevens [37] investi-
ated the depth distribution of the latent
mage obtained by exposure in the sensi-
zed region by using the surface and
epth developer technique described earlier.
heir results are shown in Fig. 10.15. The
elation between the yellow and blue ex-
osure is identical for the internal latent
mage and the external latent image. This
esult is further evidence that the nature
f the latent image in the two cases is the
ame.

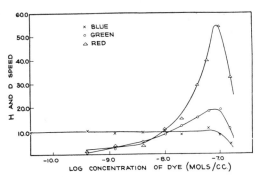

FIG. 10.16. Influence of sensitizer dye concentration on sensitivity.

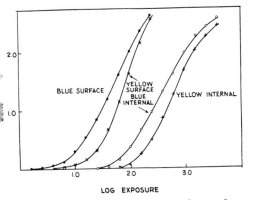

FIG. 10.15. *H* and *D* curves for the surface
and internal latent images exposed to blue and
to yellow light.

Sensitizer Adsorption. Since the energy
bsorbed by the sensitizer is so readily
ransferred to the silver halide it is logical
o assume that there must be some chemi-
al or close physical connection between
he sensitizer and the silver halide. In the
early days of the use of sensitizers it was
found that they were adsorbed strongly to
the silver halide grains and that dyes which
were not adsorbed would not act as sensitizers. However, it was not until 1928 that
any very thorough study of the adsorption
was made. Sheppard and Crouch [38] measured the amount of dye removed from a
solution by a given amount of silver halide.

At intermediate concentrations the grains
were covered by a monomolecular layer of
the dye. At much higher concentrations
of the dye, increased adsorption took place.

The relation between the state of adsorption of sensitizer dye and the sensitivity
which was conferred was studied by Leermakers, Carroll, and Staud.[39] Their results are shown in Fig. 10.16. As the
amount of dye was increased the sensitivity
to red and green increased, and the sensitivity to blue, the inherent sensitivity of
the emulsion, stayed constant. At a certain
critical concentration the sensitivities to
red, green, and blue dropped sharply. At
the same time the contrast to all three ex-

FIG. 10.17. Effect of dye concentration on
spectral sensitivity produced by a thiacarbo-
cyanine; *upper figure,* 5 mg. dye per 100 cc.
emulsion; *lower figure,* 0.02 mg. dye per 100 cc.
emulsion.

37 Berg, Marriage, and Stevens, *op. cit.*

38 Sheppard and Crouch, *J. Phys. Chem.* **32,**
751 (1928).

39 Leermakers, Carroll, and Staud, *J. Chem.
Phys.* **5,** 893 (1937).

posures dropped sharply. Eggert and Biltz[40] showed that the condition of optimum sensitizing corresponds fairly closely with the adsorption of a monomolecular layer of the dye.

Leermakers, Carroll, and Staud[41] also showed that the sensitizing resulting from a given dye may take on more than one distribution. Fig. 10.17 shows spectrograms of an emulsion containing two different concentrations of the same dye. These two sensitivity distributions correspond with the absorption characteristics of the dye adsorbed in the molecular and the aggregated state, the higher concentration giving the aggregated state. Schwarz[42] studied the same phenomenon and published an extensive paper on the different types of sensitization obtained from a single dye.

A number of investigators have studied the orientation of the dye molecules on the surface of the silver halide grain. The dye orientation is of importance because there is some evidence that the exact orientation of the dye molecules on the surface of the silver halide grains has some influence on its ability to transfer the energy obtained by absorbing light to the silver halide grain with consequent latent-image formation. Brooker and Keyes[43] found that isomers of certain sensitizing dyes did not act as sensitizers. Leermakers, Carroll, and Staud observed that these same dyes were adsorbed to the grains and other investigators found that the equilibrium adsorption of these dyes agrees well with that calculated from the size of the dye molecules.

Mechanism of the Transfer of Energy From the Sensitizer to Silver Bromide. It has been shown that the first step in the transfer of the energy absorbed by the sensitizer to the silver bromide grain is the adsorption of the dye to the grain, this adsorption being in a certain specific orientation. The series of events which might occur when the sensitizer transfers its light absorbed energy to the grain may be numerous—the dye may be destroyed by giving up an electron and the formation of metallic silver; the energy may be transferred with the release of metallic silver and bromine; the bromine released may destroy the dye; or some reducing agent present in the environment may regenerate the dye after it is destroyed. A number of experiments have been carried out which throw some light on these possibilities. Leszynski,[44] Tollert,[45] and Bokinik and Iljina[46] investigated the number of atoms of silver that were formed per molecule of adsorbed dye when silver bromide particles in different types of media were exposed to light absorbed by the sensitizer. The results vary from four to sixty molecules of silver per molecule of adsorbed dye, indicating that the dye is not destroyed but merely transfers its energy to the silver bromide. This experiment does not rule out the possibility that the dye is regenerated.

Sheppard, Lambert, and Walker[47] investigated the action of light on dyes adsorbed to silver bromide. The dye was destroyed progressively by exposure to blue light absorbed only by the silver bromide, indicating that the dye was being destroyed by the bromine which was released. In the presence of a halogen acceptor the dye was not destroyed. Addition of a solution of

[40] Eggert and Biltz, *Trans. Faraday Soc.* **34**, 892 (1938).

[41] Leermakers, Carroll, and Staud, *op. cit.*

[42] Schwarz, *Sci. et Ind. Phot.* **10**, 233 (1939).

[43] Brooker and Keyes, *J. Amer. Chem. Soc.* **58**, 659 (1936).

[44] Leszynski, *Z. wiss. Phot.* **24**, 275 (1926).

[45] Tollert, *Z phys. Chem.* **140**, 355 (1929).

[46] Bokinik and Iljina, *Acta Physicochimica,* U. S. S. R. **3**, 383 (1935).

[47] Sheppard, Lambert, and Walker, *J. Chem. Phys.* **7**, 426 (1939).

bromine to a solution of dye in the presence of a halogen acceptor decolorized some of the dye, but when the adding of bromine was ceased the dye was regenerated. These experiments indicate that the dye can be destroyed by bromine and that it can be regenerated by halogen acceptor, but they do not rule out the possibility of the direct transfer of the energy from the dye to the silver halide grain.

That the presence of the halide ion is necessary for the formation of metallic silver from the light absorbed by at least some sensitizers was shown by Sheppard, Walker, and Lambert. Silver erythrosinate has the same spectral absorption distribution as silver bromide dyed with erythrosin, but it does not show the same photolytic effect. An exposure which liberated considerable silver from the sensitized grains of silver halide gave no appreciable silver from the silver salt of the dye.

Thus, the information which is available to date does not definitely establish the exact mechanism of the energy transfer. The energy may be transferred directly or the dye may give up an electron to the silver halide and later regain an electron. The quantum-mechanical principles as applied to the formation of the latent image by Gurney and Mott can also be used for expressing the energy-level requirements of the electrons in the dye and their relation to the energy level of the electrons in the silver bromide. However, this treatment does not shed any further light as to the exact mechanism of the energy transfer.

Chapter 11

PHOTOGRAPHIC EXPOSURE EFFECTS

Sources of Developability Other than Exposure to Radiant Energy. A latent image, i.e., the condition of developability, may be produced in a number of ways other than by exposure to light or other forms of radiant energy. Toward the end of the last century, W. J. Russell[1] found that many substances, including freshly scratched metals, many fats and volatile oils and numerous organic bodies, such as wood, straw, and resin, would produce developability in a photographic emulsion without exposure to light. The activity of all of these materials was traced to the formation of hydrogen peroxide as a result of the oxidation of the substances in moist air. Hydrogen peroxide itself exhibits the phenomenon in a much more marked degree.[2] Since Russell's first experiments, it has been found that many mild reducing agents, such as sodium arsenite,[3] very dilute ferrous oxalate, sodium hypophosphite, stannous chloride, some dilute acids, certain neutral salt solutions and some dyes, confer developability. The materials which have been investigated most thoroughly are sodium arsenite and hydrogen peroxide. Their action on the photographic emulsion shows an extraordinary parallelism with the action of light and other forms of radiant energy. The action of hydrogen peroxide and sodium arsenite, for example, increases with time, or with concentration, giving rise on development to a characteristic curve similar to that produced on exposure to light. In both cases, there is a well-defined reversal portion and the sensitivity to hydrogen peroxide and sodium arsenite in general, parallels that to light. The distribution of the latent image produced by bathing in solutions of sodium arsenite has been studied by Svedberg[4] and by Toy and has been found to be distributed among the grains of silver halide in accordance with the same laws that govern the formation of latent images by light.

Photographic Reversal Effects. *Reversal from Overexposure (Solarization)*

The term solarization was applied originally to the bronze appearance of shadows produced on printing-out papers by great overexposure. The term is more generally employed today to describe a condition, resulting from extreme overexposure of negative materials, which tends to destroy the developability of the latent image and causes the image to develop as a positive rather than as a negative. Reversal by overexposure varies with different emulsions; a few commercial emulsions show partial reversal at exposures which are of practical significance but in general the exposures required are so much greater than those required in practice that reversal from this source is comparatively rare. Emulsions with a high percentage of iodide tend to show reversal effects at lower exposures than those of silver bromide.

The presence of halogen acceptors, as for

---

[1] Russell, *Brit. J. Phot.* **44**, 437, 490 (1897).

[2] Sheppard and Wightman, Hydrogen Peroxide, *J. Franklin Inst.* **195**, 337 (1923).

[3] Clark, Sodium Arsenite, *Phot. J.* **63**, 237 (1923); **64**, 91 (1924).

[4] Svedberg, *Phot. J.* **62**, 186 (1922).

[5] Toy, *Phil. Mag.* **44**, 352 (1922).

xample hydrazine, prevents or reduces the ossibility of reversal [6] as does a silver alide solvent in the developer. Most ordiary developers with sodium sulfite do not ow reversal effects from overexposure if evelopment is prolonged, although it may e in evidence in the earlier stages. The ndency to reverse disappears at low temeratures.

Herschel Effect. In 1839, F. W. Herhel [7] observed that an image on a silver hloride printing-out paper is destroyed bleached out) upon exposure to red light. his is now known as the *visual* Herschel ffect. The destruction of a latent image y subsequent exposure to diffused white or ed light, or infrared radiation, is known s the *latent* Herschel effect. The latent Ierschel effect is produced by the action of ght, or radiation of longer wave length han the dominant wave length of the initial xposure. Hardly any single photographic xposure phenomenen has been investigated

as thoroughly as the Herschel effect, more particularly for its bearing on the formation of the latent image.[8]

Sabattier Effect. This effect is a reversal phenomenon observed with photographic materials under certain conditions as when the developed image is exposed to diffused light and redeveloped. Reversal of the image under these conditions is usually due to the first negative image acting as a stencil during the second exposure, the positive image being formed by the exposure of the undeveloped silver halide.

Reversal of the image, however, may also be produced by the substitution of certain chemicals, such as sodium arsenite, for exposure to diffused light. Exposure to x-ray under these conditions does not result in reversal. It is now generally agreed that the Sabattier effect in this case is a different phenomenon connected apparently with the development of the image.

Albert Effect. A reaction of light sensitive photographic materials discovered by E. Albert in 1899. Albert found that if a wet collodion plate is considerably overexposed and the latent image destroyed with nitric acid, a positive image is produced upon exposure to white light and subsequent development. Albert's observations with wet collodion have been shown to hold also for gelatin emulsion by Luppo-Cramer, J. Precht, and others. The effect is produced by chromic acid, ammonium persulfate, and other substances that destroy the latent image as well as by nitric acid.

Clayden Effect. A photographic effect discovered by A. W. Clayden (1900). A photographic material which is first given

---

[6] Crowther patented the addition of paraphenylnedimine to emulsions for the purpose of preventg reversal. B.P. 29,919 (1912). Caldwell atented the addition of hydrazine to the emulsion or the purpose of preventing reversal. Plates repared in accordance with this patent were laced on the market by the Paget Prize Plate Co., f Great Britain, under the trade name of Hydra." *Brit. J. Phot.* **59**, 367 (1912).

[7] Herschel, *Phil. Trans.* **131**, 1 (1840).

ODSEY, "Simple Experiments in Solarization," *Pop. Phot.* **21**, 56, 164 (October 1947).

IARCELIUS, "Solarize for Striking Effects," *Pop. Phot.* **14**, 26 (April 1940).

WAHN, "Solarized Negatives," *Amer. Phot.* **40**, 18 (December 1946).

ARD, "Solarization," *Pop. Phot.* **19**, 34 (October 1945).

OVING, "Solarized Negatives," *Amer. Phot.* **37**, 16 (April 1943).

"Pseudo-Solarization as a Practical Process," *Brit. J. Phot.* **83**, 510 (1936).

AGE, "Some Thoughts on Solarization," *Brit. J. Phot.* **95**, 542 (1948).

EHR, "What is Solarization?", *Pop. Phot.* **23**, 68 (October 1949).

[8] Mees, *The Theory of the Photographic Process,* The Macmillan Co., New York. Clark, *Photography in Infrared,* John Wiley & Sons, Inc., New York. Blair, *Practical and Theoretical Photography,* Pitman Publishing Corp., New York. Mack and Martin, *The Photographic Process,* McGraw-Hill Book Co., Inc., New York.

a partial exposure to diffuse light produces a reversed image if exposed a second time to a brilliant source of light. The effect is observed frequently in photographing lightening. If the lens is left open to await a flash in the proper position, other flashes occurring in the meantime (street lights, etc.) produce a general exposure. Then when a brilliant flash occurs the shutter is closed and the image developed. The image of the flash may develop as a positive, or as a negative, depending upon the relation of the two exposures.

Villard Effect. This is a special phase of the Clayden effect and was discovered by Villard in 1900, who found that a latent image on a photographic plate, or film, which had been produced by x-rays, is partially destroyed upon exposure to diffused white light.[9]

The Reciprocity Law and Its Failure. In 1876, Bunsen and Roscoe, as a result of their investigations on the darkening of silver chloride papers, established what is called the Reciprocity Law according to which the photochemical reaction (or blackening) is dependent simply on the total energy incident on the sensitive material; i.e., the product of time and intensity, and is independent of the actual values of either of these two factors. Scheiner, and later Abney, found that the latent image does not obey the Reciprocity Law, and the density obtained upon development depends upon the actual values of intensity and time and not simply on their product.

The amount of departure from the reciprocity law is apparently a characteristic of the emulsion but does not correlate very well with other emulsion characteristics. Reciprocity failure varies with the wave length of the source of radiation by which the exposure is made, but the relationship

is a comparatively simple one: the relative exposure required to produce a given density for two different wave lengths remain constant as the time of exposure is varied. In other words, the spectral sensitivity of an emulsion is independent of exposure time in the sense that the relative *amount* of exposure required to produce the same density at two wave lengths remain constant for any *time* of exposure provided that the exposure times for the two wave lengths are the same.[10]

The reciprocity failure varies also with the temperature of the material at the time of exposure, disappearing in many cases at very low temperatures, i.e., $-185°$ C.

Closely connected with the failure of the reciprocity law is the "intermittency effect" discovered by Abney who found that the photographic effect of an intermittent exposure is not equal to a continuous exposure for the same time but differs by an amount which depends upon the degree of intermittency and the speed of the sensitive material. Later studies have shown that the intermittency effect depends on the rate of intermittency and the intensity level of exposure. The photographic effect of an intermittent exposure lies between the effects produced by a continuous exposure with an intensity equal to that of the light used in the intermittent exposure and a continuous exposure of intensity equal to the average intensity over both the light and dark periods. An intermittent exposure and a continuous exposure of the same average intensity produce an equal photographic result if the degree of intermittency is above a certain critical level which varies with the intensity.

In practice the failure of the reciprocity law concerns the photographer most frequently: (1) in exposing with electronic flash lamps, (2) in exposing multi-layer

[9] For a discussion of these, and other exposure effects, see Mees, *The Theory of the Photographic Process,* The Macmillan Co., New York.

[10] Mees, *The Theory of the Photographic Process,* p. 249.

olor materials at low intensity levels and 3) in projection printing, if exposures are ong.

It is necessary with most materials to develop exposures made with electronic flash amps from 50–100% longer than for comarable subjects exposed to sunlight or ungsten light in order to obtain adequate ontrast and density in the negative. The elative speed of a material when exposed y electronic flash, as compared to exposures by sunlight or tungsten illumination, aries with different materials. Cases are ot unknown where the slower of two films o sunlight and tungsten light is the more apid when exposed by electronic flash.

Reciprocity failure with multi-layer color aterials is complicated by the fact that, n general, the three emulsions do not behave alike and the variations in contrast and ensity make it impossible to obtain the roper color balance. In general, the deiciencies in color reproduction, arising rom the failure of the reciprocity law, annot be corrected by the use of filters.

Positive emulsions, as a rule, are particlarly subject to reciprocity law failure, ut it is seldom of concern in ordinary ractice. With long exposures it may be ound difficult to obtain good contrast and one values.

Hypersensitizing and Latensification. Iethods of increasing the speed of an emulion before exposure are termed hypersenitizing, whereas methods of increasing the atent image, or its developability, after xposure but before development are ermed latensification.[11]

---

[11] This terminology was suggested by Sheppard, anselow, and Quirk, *J. Franklin Inst.* **240**, 439 1945).

'or a summary of the work on reciprocity failure to 1945, see Mees, *The Theory of the Photographic Process,* Chap. 6.

ILKINGTON, "Further Notes on Reciprocity Law," *Photography* (London) **5**, 22 (1950).

Methods of hypersensitizing include:

1. *Uniform exposure of the sensitive material to light before exposure in the camera.* (Pre-exposure.) The amount of exposure must be less than that producing appreciable fog. The effectiveness of this method varies greatly with the sensitive material and the conditions of exposure, and the results are often complicated by fog. The increase in speed is largely confined to the lowest exposures; i.e., the extreme toe portion of the D log E curve.

2. *Bathing in solutions of (1) ammonia, (2) ammonia and a silver salt, (3) hydrogen peroxide before exposure.*[12] These methods are generally effective only with panchromatic materials, and little or no increase in speed is obtained with blue-sensitive or orthochromatic materials. With panchromatic materials, the increase in speed is chiefly for the longer wave-length region and becomes less and less as the initial sensitivity of the emulsion in the long-wave region increases. All of these methods have the disadvantage of increasing fog which becomes so great within a few days that the emulsion is no longer usable. Hydrogen peroxide is of theoretical interest only as it is too unreliable for practical use.

3. *Exposure to mercury.*[13] Exposing either the unexposed or *exposed* emulsion to

---

[12] Ammonia, Schumann, *Phot.-Woche.* **2**, 394 (1885). Ammonia, Burka, *Brit. J. Phot.* **67**, 479, 496, 504 (1920). Ammonia, Wightman and Quirk, *J. Franklin Inst.* **203**, 279 (1927). Ammonia and silver salts, Jacobsohn, *Amer. Phot.* **20** (1929); *Brit. J. Phot.* **76**, 315 (1929). Ammonia, Mecke and Zobel, *Brit. J. Phot.* **84**, 304 (1937). Hydrogen peroxide, Luppo-Cramer, *Phot. Korr.* **52**, 135 (1915). Sheppard, Wightman, and Trivelli, *J. Franklin Inst.* **200**, 335 (1925); **203**, 261 (1927). Hydrogen peroxide and silver salts, Schmieschek, *Brit. J. Phot.* **77**, 276 (1930).

[13] Dersch and Duerr, *J. Soc. Mot. Pict. Eng.* **28**, 178 (1937). Smethurst, *Brit. J. Phot.* **84**, 337 (1937). English, *Amer. Phot.* **90** (1939). Emmerman, *British Journal Almanac,* 1938, p. 198.

mercury in a sealed glass, bakelite, or hard rubber container for 36 to 72 hours at room temperature increases the effective emulsion speed of some materials as much as 100%. The increased speed is obtained chiefly in the toe portion of the D log E curve, the gamma, for the same time of development, being less than for untreated material. The color sensitivity of the emulsion is not altered nor is fog increased appreciably, except with high speed materials where the increased fog may offset the gain in effective speed. The process is most effective when applied to medium-speed panchromatic materials and varies greatly with the relative humidity during the exposure; 50 to 60° R.H. is recommended. The increased speed following treatment with mercury recedes after two or three weeks, but there is no increase in fog so that mercury hypersensitized emulsions do not need to be used at once.

Methods of latensification include:

1. *Uniform exposure to light (post-exposure)*. Historically, this method dates back to the early days of wet collodion.[14] On some low- and medium-speed panchromatic materials, the effective emulsion speed is increased from 2–4 times by uniform exposure for 30–60 minutes to light sufficient to produce a fog density of approximately 0.2.[15] The increased speed is not obtained with shorter times of exposure at higher intensity levels and is small with high-speed emulsions. The color of the exposing light is not important nor is the color sensitivity of the emulsion affected. Con-

trast is reduced, however, necessitating increased development.

2. *Treatment with hydrogen peroxide, ammonia, and certain amines.*[16] These substances used after exposure increase the effective emulsion speed and the mechanism of the reaction is presumably the same as when the emulsion is treated before exposure. From a practical standpoint, these substances are less interesting than those below.

3. *Treatment with mercury.* The increase in speed from exposure to mercury after exposure in the camera is as great and in some cases greater,[17] than if used prior to exposure.

4. *Treatment with organic acids.*[18] High speed panchromatic emulsions are increased in speed if exposed before development to acetic, formic, proponic, oxalic, or sulfurous acid. The material may (1) be placed in a closed container with a tuft of cotton wet with a few drops of acid and left for one or two hours, or (2) immersed in an acid solution prepared by dissolving a 50/50 solution of acetic and formic acids in benzene, or alcohol, for about 15 minutes, rinsing and developing in the usual way. The maximum speed increase is obtained in metol-hydroquinone-borax type developers. The effect is largely within the toe portion of the D log E curve and, like most other methods, this is more effective with high than low-speed emulsions. Fog is increased appreciably only on old emulsions.

Hopkinson, *Brit. J. Phot.* **85**, 183 (1938). Sheppard, Vanselow, and Quirk, *J. Franklin Inst.* **240**, 439 (1945). Schmieschek, *Photo-Technique* (October 1941), 52.

[14] Eder, *Handbuch*, Band I, Teil 3, p. 316.

[15] Moore, *Phot. J.* **81**, 27 (1941). Berg, B.P. 572,633 (Kodak Ltd.) 1941; *Brit. J. Phot.* **93**, 107 (1946).

[16] Hydrogen peroxide, Luppo-Cramer, *Phot. Korr.* **52**, 135 (1915). Wightman, Trivelli, and Quirk, *J. Franklin Inst.* **200**, 335 (1925). Ammonia, Wightman and Quirk, *J. Franklin Inst.* **203**, 279 (1927). Morens, U.S.P. 2,201,591. I. G. Farbenindustrie, B.P. 431,916. Trivelli and Sheppard, *Silver Bromide Grain of Photographic Emulsions*, D. Van Nostrand Co., Inc., New York, 192.

[17] Roudier and Vassy, *Sci. et Ind. Phot.* **1**, 253 (1943).

[18] Muehler and Bates, *J. Phot. Soc. Amer.* **10**, 586 (1944).

5. *Treatment with sulfur dioxide.*[19] Exposure of the latent image to sulfur dioxide has been found to increase the effective speed from two to four times. The results are similar to those obtained with acetic and other organic acids but in general show less fog.

Desensitizing. The sensitivity of the silver halide to light can be reduced without affecting the developability of the latent image by the application after exposure and before development of a number of substances which are known as *desensitizers.* The use of a desensitizer, either as a preliminary bath or as an addition to the developer, makes it possible to develop even high-speed panchromatic emulsions in a fairly bright light without danger of fog.

The first practical desensitizer (phenosafranine) was discovered by Luppo-Cramer in 1920. Since then many more have been found chiefly among quinoid dyestuffs and particularly among the azines, cyanines, triphenylmethanes, and oxyazines.[20] There is, apparently, a close connection between sensitizers and desensitizers, as both are found in closely related dyes, and Mills and Smith found that the replacement of the CH linkage of the quinolin rings in the iso- and pseudo-iso cyanines by N converted sensitizers into desensitizers. No adequate theory of desensitizing, or the chemical constitution of desensitizers, has yet been evolved. Certain facts, however, are well established: (1) the effect on sensitivity varies with the wave length; (2) the reduction in sensitivity generally increases with average grain size of the emulsion, but varies with different desensitizers; (3) many active desensitizers are not practical because of their fogging action; (4) in many cases, the latent image is destroyed by desensitizing if not developed within a few hours; (5) the latent image is reduced or destroyed if exposed to yellow or orange light before development.

The most effective desensitizers up to now are three closely related dyes discovered by Schuloff and introduced by Agfa as pinakryptol, pinakryptol green, and pinakryptol yellow,[21] the latter having the formula

EtO — CH=CH — NO2 — N — MeCl

Pinakryptol green may be used either as a preliminary bath or as an addition to the developer, but pinakryptol yellow, which is a more efficient desensitizer, must not be added to the developer as it is destroyed by sulfite. A 1:2000 solution should be used as a preliminary bath for 3–5 minutes before development.

Effect of Time on the Latent Image. The latent image is remarkably permanent. Many records of the successful development of the latent image 15 to 20 years after exposure may be found in the literature and the exposed film of the ill-fated Andre polar expeditions were developed with usable results 38 years later. Such changes as occur with time are due more to the growth of fog than to any change of the latent image itself.[22]

---

[22] Cannon, *Phot. J.* **57**, 72 (1917).

[21] Schuloff, *Eder's Handbuch* **III** (3), 149 (1932).

---

[19] Simons (Eastman Kodak Co.), U.S.P. 2,368,-267. Muehler and Bates, *J. Phot. Soc. Amer.* **10**, 586 (1944). Sheppard, Vanselow, and Quirk, *J. Phot. Soc. Amer.* **12**, 301 (1946).

[20] Mercuric cyanide 1:3000 is a desensitizer when added to certain developers. B.P. 280,525 (1926); *Brit. J. Phot.* **75**, 233,692 (1928).

HAMER, A Chemical Study of Desensitizers. (1) *Proc. VII International Cong. of Phot.*, London, 1928, 92, (2) *Phot. J.* **70**, 232 (1930).

See also: Mees, *The Theory of the Photographic Process*, Chap. XXIV, The Macmillan Co., New York.

With high-speed negative materials, the latent image grows for a period of several months, then remains very nearly constant for a much longer period before fading begins.[23] The increase in speed in the months following an exposure is most in evidence with panchromatic materials where it may amount to as much as 200% within a year; is much less in blue sensitive materials, and is not found at all on low-speed materials such as positive motion picture film. The growth in the latent image

during this period appears to be confined to the lower densities; in the higher densities the increase is either proportionally less or there may be a loss in density. As a result, the shape of the D log E curve is changed, the period of decreasing gradient beginning at a lower density and comprising a larger part of the curve. With multilayer films for color photography, these changes are sufficient to upset the balance of the different emulsions resulting in false colors. Such materials must be developed as soon after exposure as possible. See Chapter 32.

The graininess of the image appears to increase with the time elapsing between exposure and development and is independent of the growth, or fading, of the latent image.

[23] Mees, *Photography and Focus* **39**, 338 (1915); Jausseran, *Revue d'Optique* **8**, 119 (1929); Heisenberg, *Die Veranderung des latenten Bildes in Halogensilbergelatineschichten bei der Lagerung; Veroff des wiss. Zentral-Lab. Agfa*, Leipzig, 1933, p. 47; Famulener and Loessel, *J. Soc. Mot. Pict. Eng.* **36**, 374 (1941); Famulener and Judkins, *J. Phot. Soc. Amer.* **8**, 517 (1942).

Chapter 12

THE THEORY OF DEVELOPMENT

The development of the photographic latent image is, of course, tied up very closely with the nature of the latent image itself. The process is essentially the reduction of grains of exposed silver halide to metallic silver according to the equation:

$$Ag^+ + electron = Ag \text{ (metal)}.$$

During normal development only exposed grains containing a latent image are reduced. The question is often asked, "Why does a developer not develop the unexposed as well as the exposed grains?" Actually, if development is extended over a long enough period of time, all grains are developed. Thus, the development of the latent image is a rate phenomenon, the development of the exposed grains taking place at a greater rate than the development of the unexposed grains.

In order for a reducing agent to be a developer it must fall within the proper range of reducing power. If it is too weak a reducing agent it cannot reduce silver halide at all, and if it is too powerful it will immediately reduce the unexposed grains as well as the exposed grains. Certain organic reducing agents such as p-methyl-aminophenol, hydroquinone, catechol, para-phenylene-diamine, and inorganic reducing agents such as ferrous oxalate fall within the proper range and are developers. The strong reducing agents such as sodium stannite and hydrosulfite are too potent and completely reduce or fog all the grains in the emulsion.

Although there are many types of developers there are only two basic types of development. These are known as chemical development and physical development. In a physical developer the silver which is reduced is supplied by silver ions in the solution itself. In chemical development the grains of the emulsion are themselves reduced. Most normal chemical developers contain some silver halide solvent so that some of the grains can be dissolved and be reduced from solution by physical development, but in most cases this is a minor effect and does not basically change the nature of the chemical development process.

In the early days of photography when collodion emulsions were in use, physical development was the only type used, but now it is only used in rare instances, mainly for experimental purposes in the investigation of the development process and the nature of the latent image. Since silver ions in solution are more easily reduced than silver halide grains, physical developers must be weaker reducing agents than chemical developers. Chemical development is usually carried out in alkaline solutions where the reducing agents are more powerful. The power of ferrous oxalate is not a function of acidity or alkalinity so it can be used in a wide range of conditions; it is quite useful in theoretical studies but is seldom, if ever, used in practice.

Physical Development. A physical developer contains a reducing agent, such as elon, an acid, and a source of silver ions, frequently silver nitrate. It is fairly unstable and in time will deposit metallic silver all over the container and throughout the solution. However, this deposition of silver is greatly speeded up by the presence of specks of silver. As mentioned in the previous section, Reinders and Hamburger and Reinders and DeVries determined the size of the silver specks which were required to initiate the deposition of silver from a physical developer and concluded that four atoms were sufficient. Arens and Eggert [1] studied the amount of silver deposited in the presence of a silver sol and found that the amount was a function of the number of specks of silver rather than their size. The same relation was observed for gold sols.

Bullock [2] investigated the amount of exposure which an ordinary photographic plate required to be developed by physical development and found that it was approximately five times that required for ordinary chemical development. He used a slow type of emulsion. There is evidence that a greater differential is required for faster emulsions. Thus, the fact that an exposed emulsion can be developed in a physical developer cannot be taken as evidence that the latent image for chemical development is composed of metallic silver.

That the latent image for physical development is metallic silver can hardly be questioned. Further evidence is derived from the fact that even after it is fixed an exposed emulsion can be developed in a physical developer. This is known as post-fixation physical development as opposed to the normal or pre-fixation physical development. In fixing the film for post-fixation physical development, great care must be taken to avoid dissolving away some of the fine particles of the latent-image silver. In this dispersed

condition the silver is quite easily oxidized and the fixing agents which complex the silver ion aid the oxidation. Owing to the partial loss of silver during fixing, the conclusions drawn from a good deal of the experimental work done with post-fixation physical development are subject to question.

The nature of the mechanism of physical development has been the subject of a good deal of speculation. One of the first theories, generally held for a good many years, was the supersaturation theory proposed by Ostwald.[3] It was supposed that the developer reduced some of the silver ions to metallic silver which remained in solution in the supersaturated state. This supersaturation prevented the further reduction of silver ions. In the presence of metallic silver specks the supersaturated solution of silver deposited metallic silver, which relieved the supersaturation and allowed more silver to be reduced, etc. The second important theory was based on the catalytic action of the silver speck in increasing the rate of reduction of silver ion rather than the deposition of silver. This catalytic action was explained in a different manner by different investigators, but for the most part it was assumed that the developer was adsorbed by the silver and the resulting increase in concentration of the developer caused the increased rate of reduction.

Recent work by James [4] has shed a good deal of light on the mechanism of physical development. He investigated the rate of formation of silver from silver ion in solution by a number of developing agents. It was found that in the presence of silver specks the rate was a linear function of the concentration of certain developing agents,

[1] Arens and Eggert, *Z. Elektrochem.* **35**, 728 (1929)

[2] Bullock, E. R., ''Chemical Reactions of the Photographic Latent Image,'' *Monograph No. 6 on the Theory of Photography*, Eastman Kodak Co., Rochester, N. Y. (1927).

[3] Ostwald, W., *Lehrbuch der allgemeinen Chemie*, 2nd Edition, Engelmann, Leipzig, 1893, *Band II*, Teil 1: 1078.

[4] James, *J. Amer. Chem. Soc.* **61**, 648 (1939). James, *ibid.*, 2379 (1939).

the normal characteristic of a homogeneous reaction. However, the rate was a fractional power of the silver ion concentration. This is characteristic of heterogeneous reactions in which adsorption occurs and can be taken as very strong evidence that adsorption of silver ions to the specks plays the major role in physical development. This result is in agreement with the catalytic theory mentioned earlier and is in opposition to the supersaturation theory.

Chemical Development. Chemical development, or the reduction of the exposed silver halide grains in an emulsion, is quite different in nature from physical development. There have been a number of theories formulated to explain its mechanism. These have varied according to the theory of the nature of the latent image held by the various investigators and according to the variety of facts observed about the characteristics of development under a variety of conditions. The kinetics of development are influenced by a large number of variables—total salt content of the developer solution, pH, the developing agent itself, certain dyes, oxidation products of the developer, bromide, antifoggants, silver halide solvents, and a number of others. Interpretation of the results of many experiments has frequently been confused by some of these factors that were unknown at the time. It is only in recent years that a number of these variables have been correlated to form a fairly clear picture of the development process.

The theory of the mechanism of chemical development which was most generally held in the early days was the supersaturation theory mentioned earlier in relation to physical development. There is now a good deal of evidence against this theory, the most conclusive of which is that obtained by means of the electron microscope. Until fairly recently the appearance of the individual grains of a developed emulsion was

described as being coke-like, a solid chunk. However, with the higher magnification which is possible with the electron microscope, it has been found that the developed grain is composed of a large number of tiny filaments so that it looks like a mass of seaweed, as shown in Fig. 12.1. Filamentary

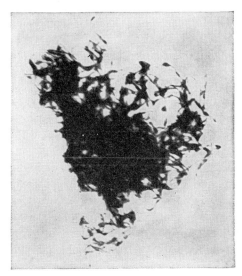

FIG. 12.1. The filamentary structure of the silver formed by the development of a silver halide grain with amidol. × 40,000.

silver is not formed by physical development, a very distinct difference between the two types of development. This evidence in itself does not refute the Ostwald supersaturation theory for *physical* development, but it is very difficult to see how that theory would account for the formation of the filamentary silver by chemical development.

Bancroft [5] suggested the adsorption theory of development. If the exposed grains adsorb developer more strongly than the unexposed, then they will be developed more rapidly. This theory has been modified in a good many ways by various investigators, including the restriction of the adsorption of the developer to the silver

[5] Bancroft, *Trans. Farad. Soc.* **19**, 243 (1923).

halide, to the silver specks of the latent image, or to the interface between the two.

Studies of the induction period, the time between the immersion of film in a developer and the appearance of the image have been the subject of many experiments. Lainer [6] found that small amounts of iodide in a developer caused a significant decrease in the induction period with a hydroquinone developer. Lüppo-Cramer [7] explained this on the basis of the fact that iodide, which forms a silver salt less soluble than silver bromide, tended to crack the grains and lay bare some of the latent-image specks. Others explained it by the assumption of increased developer adsorption by the iodide; many dyes are more strongly adsorbed by silver iodide than by silver bromide. It was also observed that certain basic dyes had the same effect. It was found that neither dyes nor iodide gave the accelerating effect with a metol developer, but both did with para-aminophenylglycine. The dye effect has been explained by the assumption of the formation of a complex between the dye and the developer which was more strongly adsorbed than the developer itself. Recent clarifications of these effects will be discussed later.

Sheppard and Meyer [8] proposed the theory that the developing agent forms a complex with the silver halide at the surface of the grains. At the interface of the silver speck of the latent image this complex breaks down to form metallic silver and oxidized developer. The importance of the speck of latent-image silver is twofold. It provides the necessary ionic deformation to initiate the decomposition of the complex and also gives a break in the adsorbed barrier layer which acts as a starting point for the formation of the complex.

Wulff and Seidl [9] attempted to investigate the direct influence of the adsorption of the developer by the grains. Since the adsorption could not be separated from the development process, a compound similar to a developing agent but which was not itself a developer, resorcinol, was added to the developer, and it was found that development was greatly decreased. This was presumed to be caused by the competing adsorption of the resorcinol. However, these investigators did not control the pH of their developer and their interpretation of the results is doubtful. Furthermore, it has been found recently that resorcinol influences the effects of the developer oxidation product on the course of development, and so might have a specific effect on development not connected with its adsorption characteristics.

As mentioned earlier, the effect of dyes on development has been investigated. As little as 0.008 gram per liter of oxidized amidol decreases the induction period of a hydroquinone developer. The absence of sulfite causes a decrease in the induction period and, in the absence of sulfite, the absence of air causes a great increase in the induction period. Bromide added to the developer causes a much greater increase in the induction period in the absence of air than in its presence. In fact, Frötschner [10] reached the conclusion that it was likely that no development could take place in the complete absence of air and the oxidation products of developer. Oxidation products, when used as a prebath, also decreased the induction period, which led to the conclusion that the oxidation products were adsorbed to the silver halide

[6] Lainer, *Phot. Korr.* **28**, 12 (1891).

[7] Lüppo-Cramer, *Phot. Korr.* **49**, 118 and 501 (1912); *ibid.* **50**, 61 (1913).

[8] Sheppard and Meyer, *J. Amer. Chem. Soc.* **42**, 689 (1920).

[9] Wulff and Seidl, *Z. wiss. Phot.* **28**, 239 (1930).

[10] Frötschner, *Phot. Ind.* **35**, 801 (1937).

grains or to the latent image. Staude[11] found that the oxidation products of the developer had no effect on the amount of fog developed. He concluded that the latent image was a concentration of electrons at a speck and that these attracted the oxidized developer. Thus only reducing agents which form a complex with their oxidized form could act as developers. This theory could not account for the developing properties of ferrous oxalate.

Schwarz and Urbach,[12] in relation to their surface discharge theory of latent image, approached the problem of development from the point of view, "Why do the unexposed grains not develop?" This inactivity was explained by the presence of a barrier layer of adsorbed gelatin and bromide ion which gave the grain a negative charge. The negatively charged developer could not approach the grain unless the charge of the surface of the grain had been decreased by the migration of some of the electrons on the surface to the interior of the grains. Hanson and Evans[13] accepted and extended this theory in the explanation of a number of the known characteristics of the latent image and development. However, recent work by James[14] has shown that, although the negative charge on the surface of the grains is quite important in preventing unexposed grains from being developed and does influence the rate of development with certain types of developers, it is of no direct primary importance in the development process.

Rabinowitsch[15] assumed that the latent image was metallic silver and that the developing agent was adsorbed to this silver and not to the silver halide grain. His experimental work demonstrating this adsorption to metallic silver could not be substantiated by Perry, Ballard, and Sheppard.[16] Recently James has found no evidence for adsorption of several developing agents to silver specks in physical development, although there was evidence indicating that paraphenylene-diamine and hydroxyl amine are adsorbed.

The quantum-mechanical principles recently applied to the explanation for the photographic latent image have also been applied to the development process. Gurney and Mott[17] proposed a so-called "electrode" theory. The silver speck of the latent image was supposed to act as an electrode and receive electrons from the developing agent. The speck now charged negatively attracts some of the interstitial silver ions which migrate to it and form metallic silver. When the interstitial silver ions are all used up, more are formed and the process continues until the grain is completely developed. The theory does not explain how the bromide ions get out of the crystals. Furthermore, the rates of development of silver chloride, silver bromide, and silver iodide are not at all in relation to the mobility of the interstitial silver ions in the different types of crystals.

Webb has extended this theory into fairly complete form, and Berg[18] has also extended it to eliminate some of the objections mentioned. He assumed that the mechanism of development proposed held

[11] Staude, *Z. wiss. Phot.* **38**, 65 (1939). Staude, *Gebrauchsfot. Atelier Fot.* **46**, 84 and 108 (1939). Staude, *Z. wiss. Phot.* **37**, 3 (1938).

[12] Schwarz, *Phot. Korr.* **69**, 27 (1933—Beilage 5). Schwarz and Urbach, *Z. wiss. Phot.* **31**, 77 (1932).

[13] Evans and Hanson, *Phot. J.* **77**, 497 (1937).

[14] James, *J. Phys. Chem.* **43**, 701 (1939).

[15] Rabinowitsch, Peissachowitsch, and Minaev, *Ber. VIII*, Internat. Kongr. Phot., Dresden, 1931, 186. Rabinowitsch, *Z. wiss. Phot.* **33** (1934).

[16] Perry, Ballard, and Sheppard, *J. Amer. Chem. Soc.* **63**, 2357 (1941).

[17] Gurney and Mott, *Proc. Royal Society* **164A**, 151 (1938).

[18] Berg, *Trans. Farad. Soc.* **39**, 126 (1943).

only during the induction period. After
the interstitial silver ions are all used up
and the speck of silver has become large
enough, the charged speck will actually pull
some of the adjacent silver ions from the
crystal lattice itself. These are replaced
by some farther away, etc. However, this
theory does not explain how the induction
period varies with the charge on the developing ion.

The recent work of James has thrown
so much light on the nature of the development process and has eliminated so much
of the confusion resulting from the variety
of results obtained on the effects of dyes,
oxidation products, and the like, that it will
be treated in its entirety as a separate unit.

James[19] first studies the rate of formation of silver from silver ions in solution
by a variety of developing agents in the
presence of specks of metallic silver. This
parallels physical development. Reduction
with hydroquinone and catechol is directly
proportional to the concentration of the
developing agent but is proportional to a
fractional power of the silver ion concentration, indicating that the developer is not
adsorbed to the silver specks but that the
silver ions are adsorbed.

The role of adsorption in increasing the
rate of chemical reactions can be clarified
by quantum-mechanical principles.[20] Fig.
12.2 indicates the energy relations which
might exist in a given reaction. For the
reactants, silver ion and developer, to react
in homogeneous solution they must go over
a certain potential barrier as shown by the
solid line. This requires a certain energy
of activation, E_{hom}. The number of atoms
which react will be a statistical function,
depending upon the number which obtain
this amount of energy from thermal agitation. However, when one or more of the

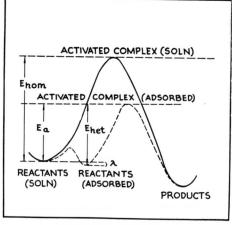

Fig. 12.2. Quantum-mechanical description of
energies involved in a homogeneous reaction
(E_{hom}) and in a similar reaction with absorption on a catalysis ($_{het}$).

reactants are adsorbed onto some active surface, the energy required for the reaction
is decreased, as shown by the dotted line,
so that much less energy is required for the
reactants to get over the hump, or react.
Under this condition the reaction will proceed at an increased rate.

In the case of development with paraphenylenediamine, the ratio is a fractional
power of developer concentration and linear with silver ion concentration, indicating
that the reaction proceeds by the adsorption
of this developer.[21]

Development of ordinary emulsions in a
variety of developers at different values of
pH shows that the active ingredient of the
developer is the ionized form of the developing agent. Ionization increases with
pH; hence, development is more rapid at
higher pH. For hydroquinone, the doubly
ionized state

[19] James, *J. Amer. Chem. Soc.* **61**, 648 (1939).
James, *ibid.* **61**, 2379 (1939).
[20] James, *J. Chem. Ed.* **23**, 595 (1946).
[21] James, *J. Franklin Inst.* **240**, 15 (1945).

is the active agent; for elon and catechol, the singly ionized state; for hydroquinone monosulfonate, the triply ionized state; and for the derivatives of paraphenylenediamine, the neutral or un-ionized state. This variation in ionic character leads to the possibility of the classification of the developing agents into groups depending on their ionic charge. A study of the induction period of a number of developers shows that their behavior falls into a very neat pattern depending on the ionic charge,[22] as shown in Fig. 12.3. The curves, appropriately marked, show the course of the growth of density with the developers with 0, 1, 2, and 3 negative charges. The scale of the time of development has been adjusted for each developer so that the straight portions of all the curves have the same slope. For the strong developers the total time represented by the diagram is fairly short and for the weak developers it is fairly long, but with this adjustment all of the developers fall into this pattern. This change in induction period with ionic charge can be interpreted as indicating that the induction period is connected with the negatively charged barrier layer which

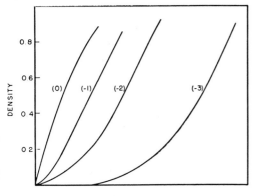

TIME OF DEVELOPMENT

FIG. 12.3. Dependence of shape of time-density curve upon ionic charge of the developing agent.

[22] James, *J. Franklin Inst.* **240**, 83 (1945).

surrounds the grains. The greater the charge on the developer the longer it takes to penetrate this layer.

The nature of the barrier layer has been demonstrated by a number of experiments. The presence of certain salts in a developer frequently has a large effect on the rate of development, caused by the effect of the salt on the charge layer contributed by gelatin. Gelatin, being amphoteric, has a negative charge in solutions with pH higher than its isoelectric point and a positive charge at pH values lower than its isoelectric point. At values of pH greater than 4.8, the isoelectric point of gelatin, development with ferrous oxalate is slowed down by the negatively charged gelatin barrier layer. Addition of potassium nitrate causes a large increase in the rate of development. At values of pH lower than 4.8, the positively charged gelatin layer increases the rate of development with ferrous oxalate. The addition of potassium nitrate to the developer with a pH lower than 4.8 gives a large decrease in the rate of development. At a pH of 4.8, the addition of salt has no effect. The different effects of the salt additions at different values of pH indicate that the neutral salt tends to decrease the barrier layer contributed by gelatin. The salt effect does not occur in developers containing a zero charge action ingredient, such as the paraphenylenediamine derivatives. In fact, James[23] states that this technique can be used as a method for determining the isoelectric point of gelatin in an emulsion. This effect of neutral salt on development parallels the effect on certain dyes which will not penetrate gelatin except in the presence of neutral salt.

The effect of certain dyes and developer oxidation products on the charge barrier layer is due to their effect on the bromide

[23] James, *J. Chem. Phys.* **12**, 453 (1944).

ion barrier layer. Phenosafranin, when added in very small quantities to certain developers, enormously decreases the induction period.[24] This is true in a ferrous oxalate developer at pH values both above and below the isoelectric point of gelatin. The effect is greatly reduced by the addition of bromide to the developer which builds up the bromide barrier layer. The accelerating effect of phenosafranin does not occur in developers with a zero or minus one charge. A number of basic sensitizer dyes have the same accelerating effect when added in small quantities to a developer. It is likely that the sensitizers present in a normal panchromatic emulsion may have the same effect.

The presence of the oxidation product of hydroquinone has an effect on the bromide ion barrier layer. This effect leads to abnormal behavior in certain developers [25] as shown in Fig. 12.4. The developer was a hydroquinone caustic developer, with

[24] James, *J. Franklin Inst.* **240**, 229 (1945).
[25] James, *J. Franklin Inst.* **240**, 229 (1945).

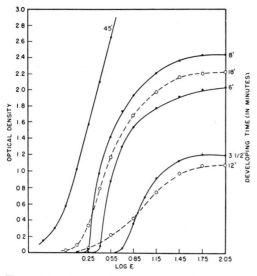

FIG. 12.4. *H* and *D* curves for development in caustic hydroquinone solution: *solid lines,* no sulfite; *broken line,* 5 grams Na_2SO_3 per liter.

bromide but no sulfite. The exceedingly high contrast and short toe of the solid lines is a result of the effect of the oxidation product of hydroquinone. It can be explained as follows: development of a given exposure step starts with the release of the oxidation product. This catalyzes the development of other exposed grains in that exposure step which immediately develops, giving a high density. As soon as development of a lower exposed step begins the previous step has already attained a very high density leading to the very short toe. At longer times of development where all of the steps have had time to develop, the curve is perfectly normal. In the presence of a small amount of sulfite, which reacts with and removes the oxidation product, the curves are perfectly normal as shown by the dotted lines. It is concluded that the abnormal result under these particular conditions is due to the influence of the oxidation product on the bromide barrier layer because the effect does not occur in a developer containing no bromide. Furthermore, the effect only decreases the induction period of the exposed grains with no change of fog density. The oxidation products of a number of developers have no influence on the course of development.

Sulfite, in addition to its effect caused by the removal of oxidized developer, changes the behavior of bromide barrier layer. It gives a significant increase in emulsion speed, at low development gamma, when added to developers with a double or triple negative charge but has very little effect on the singly or uncharged developers.[26]

This work clarifies to a large extent the effect of a number of additions to developers. Those materials which influence the barrier layer charge have an effect proportional to the charge on the developer. Thus hydroquinone, para-aminophenylgly-

[26] James, *J. Franklin Inst.* **240**, 327 (1945).

TABLE 12.1. COMPARISON OF DEVELOPING AGENTS AT MAXIMUM DEVELOPMENT

Agent	Relative Speed	Agent	Relative Speed
Hydroquinone (carbonate)	100.0	p-Amino-o-cresol	100.0
Catechol	97.8	D-19	93.3
Ferro-oxalate	95.5	Hydroquinone (caustic)	89.9
Elon	100.0	p-Aminophenylglycine	72.5
Elon monosulfonate	95.5	Hydroxylamine	72.5
Diaminodurene	95.5	p-Hydroxyphenylglycine	69.3
E–H	95.5	Ascorbic Acid	64.6

cine, and ferrous oxalate show a number of effects which do not occur with elon or the derivatives of paraphenylenediamine.

James [27] has also found that the maximum emulsion speed which can be obtained with a given emulsion and optimum development is practically the same for many developers. The formula which he chose was a caustic solution of the developer in the absence of air and sulfite, thus eliminating all but the essential ingredients. The caustic was chosen as the alkali because it gives complete ionization of all of the developers. Complete development was defined as that stage of development where the growth of density of fog was about equal to the growth of the image. The fog density involved was between 0.7 and 1.1, much more than occurs in practical cases. The time of development was different for the different developers. The emulsion speed for the various developers is shown in Table 12.1. Two standard developers, D19, and another elon hydroquinone developer, were included as a point of reference. Except for the last four in the table, all of which are fairly unusual developers, the speeds are not significantly different. It can be concluded that the basic mechanism of development is the same for all of these developers and that probably the size of the latent-image speck which is required to make a grain developable is about the

same for all. This result must not be confused with normal practice where development is stopped far short of completion and a number of factors influence the rate of the development to that stage.

The practical advantage of a complex developer such as elon hydroquinone mixtures used in practice, according to James,[28] derives from the use of a developer with a single charge (elon) with a more powerful developer which has a double charge (hydroquinone). The one with the shorter induction period starts the grains developing and the more powerful one continues the development. On this principle he predicted that mixtures of hydroxylamine (one charge) and hydroquinone monosulfonate (three charges) would give greater densities than the sum of the two acting separately. His experiments upheld this. This result may be taken to indicate that the earlier held theory that elon and hydroquinone form a complex which is more active than either developer is not necessary to explain the behavior of the mixture.

The work of James does not make it possible to choose definitely between the two general types of theories of the mechanism of development which are held today. These are the "electrode" type which are based on the silver speck of the latent image accepting the electron from the developer and in turn passing it on to a silver ion of

27 James, *J. Franklin Inst.* **239**, 41 (1945).

28 James, T. H., Reference 26.

the crystal to produce a silver atom, and the catalytic theory whereby the latent image, be it silver or otherwise, is presumed to catalyze the reduction of silver ions in the crystal itself, particularly at the interface between the latent image and the remainder of the crystal. However, James [29] has found that in certain pH regions development with hydroquinone is a function of a fractional power of the concentration of the hydroquinone (different from physical development) and, since he has found no evidence for the adsorption of hydroquinone to metallic silver, he concludes that the hydroquinone must be adsorbed to other portions of the grain, either the silver halide itself or at the interface between the silver halide and the latent image. This being the case, it would not give up its

electron to the silver speck. He concludes that development takes place at the interface of the grain and the latent image, with the latent image acting as a catalyst following the description given earlier with relation to physical development. This conclusion is in line with the earlier theory of Sheppard and Meyer.

The formation of the filamentary silver as shown by the electron microscope is explained by the wandering of individual silver atoms, after they are formed by reduction, to spots on the silver already present which are most free to add a silver atom to form a crystal. Jelley [30] has observed that the appearance of the filaments often suggests that the filament structure is a crystallization phenomenon.

[29] James, *J. Phys. Chem.* **44**, 42 (1940).

[30] Jelley, *J. Phot. Soc. Amer.* **8**, 283 (1942).

Chapter 13

PHOTOGRAPHIC DEVELOPERS.
I. SILVER IMAGES

Photographic development is a process of chemical reduction, and developing agents are a class of reducing substances which, under certain conditions, are capable of reducing crystals of silver halide that have been exposed to light without attacking the unexposed grains within a similar or somewhat longer period of time. In addition to the ability to differentiate between exposed and unexposed silver halide, a development agent to be practical must (1) have sufficient energy to develop the latent image adequately; (2) free from tendency to fog; (3) must be reasonably stable in solution; (4) must be soluble in water or in the presence of sulfite or an alkali; (5) must not soften or disrupt the gelatin layer; (6) its developing properties must not vary too greatly with changes in temperature, dilution, or composition of the solution, and (7) it is desirable, but not necessary, that it be nontoxic.

Inorganic Developing Agents. Practically all developing agents in general use are para or ortho diphenols, diamines or aminophenols. There are, however, a number of inorganic developing agents, although none remain in common use and some are only of theoretical interest. Hydroxylamine [1] (NH_2OH) and hydrazine [2]

(NH_2NH_2), for example, develop slowly in an alkaline solution but bubbles of nitrogen and nitrous oxide are formed which tend to disrupt the gelatin. Ferrous fluoride (FeF_2) develops in an acid solution but is impractical because of the formation of hydrofluoric acid. Hydrogen peroxide [3] (H_2O_2) develops in a strongly alkaline solution but fogs badly and decomposes too rapidly to make its use practical. Some of the compounds of copper, chromium, tungsten, [4] vanadium, [5] and molybdenum develop under certain conditions but are only of theoretical interest. Sodium hydrosulfite [6] ($Na_2S_2O_4$) is a better developer than any of the above but tends to fog, oxidizes rapidly, and is unstable in solution decomposing according to the reaction:

$$3Na_2S_2O_4 \rightarrow 2Na_2S_2O_3 + Na_2S_2O_6.$$

The only inorganic developing agent of practical utility is ferrous oxalate, [7] which is made by adding ferrous sulfate to an excess of potassium oxalate, the whole being acid. This forms the double salt $K_2Fe(C_2O_4)_2$ which disassociates into FeC_2O_4 and $K_2C_2O_4$, the actual developing

[1] Egli and Spiller, *Phot. News* **28**, 613 (1884). Sheppard and Mees, *Investigations on the Theory of the Photographic Process*, Longmans Green and Co., London, 1907. Nichols, *J. Amer. C. S.* **56**, 841 (1934). James, *J. Amer. C. S.* **61**, 2379 (1939).

[2] Andresen, *Phot. Mitt.* **28**, 286, 296 (1892).

[3] Andresen, *Phot. Korr.* **36**, 260 (1899).

[4] Liesegang, *Phot. Arch.* 1895, 282.

[5] Lumiere and Seyewetz, *Bull Soc. franç.* (2) **10**, 108 (1894).

[6] Eder, *Handbuch* (1890), Band III, 124. Steigman, *Phot. Ind.* **19**, 379 (1921). Luppo-Cramer, *Phot. Korr.* **45**, 405 (1908). Brooks and Blair, *Photo-Technique*, May, 1941, 41. Durham, *Brit. J. Phot.* **87**, 169 (1940).

[7] Carey Lea, *Brit. J. Phot.* **27**, 292 (1880).

ion being $Fe(C_2O_4)_2$. The reaction taking place in development may be

$$Ag^+ + Fe(C_2O_4)_2^{--} \rightleftarrows$$
$$Ag(metal) + Fe(C_2O_4)_2^{-}.$$

As a developer, ferrous oxalate is notable for its fog-free, pure black silver deposit. It requires more exposure, however, than the more energetic organic developers and is no longer in general use.

Ferrous citrate, tartrate, lactate, and formate develop but are less effective than the oxalate.

Organic Developers. Below are shown the structural formulas of a number of well known organic developing agents.

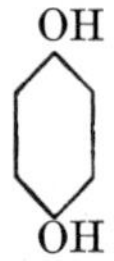

OH

Paradihydroxybenzene (hydroquinone)

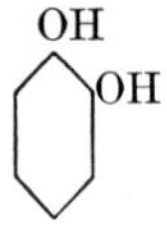

OH

OH

OH

Orthodihydroxybenzene (catechol)

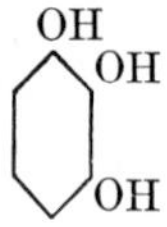

OH

OH

OH

Trihydroxybenzene (pyrogallol)

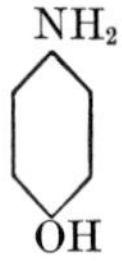

OH

NH_2

Paraminophenol

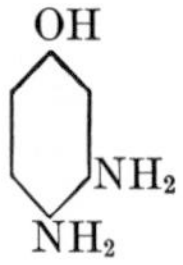

OH

OH

NH_2

Diaminophenol

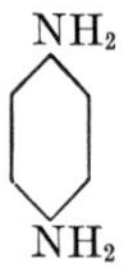

NH_2

NH_2

NH_2

Paraphenylenediamine

NH_2

OH

Cl

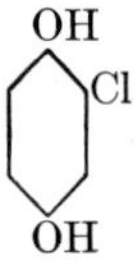

Chlorohydroquinone (Adurol)

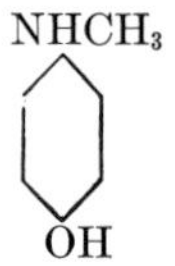

OH

$NHCH_3$

Monomethyl paraminophenol (Metol, Elonj etc.)

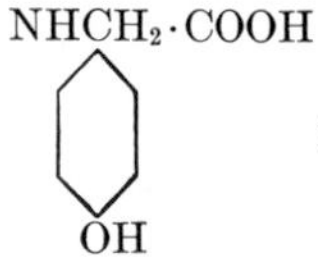

OH

$NHCH_2 \cdot COOH$

(Glycin)

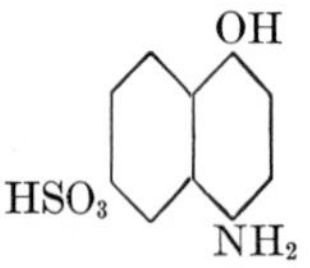

OH

OH

(Eikonigen)

HSO_3

NH_2

It will be noted (1) that all of these contain at least two hydroxyl (OH), two amino (NH_2) or one hydroxyl and one amino group and (2) these are either in the ortho or para position in the benzine ring. There are a few developing agents that contain only one of these groups, but all known organic developers contain at least one. These two groups appear, therefore, to be the active groups in all organic developers. The hydrogens in an amino group may be replaced with an $—NHCH_3$ as in monomethyl paraminophenol, with an $—N(CH_3)_2$ group as in dimethyl paraphenylenediamine and —Cl, —Br, —I, and $—CH_3$ may be substituted at other points in the ring as in chlorohydroquinone and toluhydroquinone. The substitution of a carboxyl group (—COOH), as in glycin or a sulfonic acid group ($—HSO_3$), as in eikonigen, results in low energy but useful developers. The addition of a nitro group (NO_2), however, destroys the developing properties completely.[8]

Early in the present century Andresen in Germany and, independently, Lumiere in France, attempted to discover the connection between chemical structure and de-

---

[8] A useful list of substances which have been described or patented as developers will be found in the *Handbook of Photography* by Henney and Dudley, McGraw-Hill Book Co., Inc., New York.

veloping properties from a study of the similarities in the chemical structure of the known developing agents and their characteristics as developers.[9]

As a result of these studies it was concluded that:

1. Aromatic compounds to be capable of development must contain two hydroxy, two amino or one hydroxy and one amino group.

2. In benzine derivatives, the hydroxy and amino groups must be in the ortho or para position to each other.

3. Compounds containing groups in the para position are more energetic developers than those with the groups in the ortho position.

4. If hydrogens of the amino group are replaced with alkyl groups the new compound is a more energetic developer.

5. The substitution of bromine or chlorine for hydrogen in the benzene nucleus increases the developing power.

6. Replacement of hydrogen in the benzene nucleus with acid groups such as COOH, HSO_3 lowers the activity of the substance as a developer.

7. Compounds containing two hydroxyl groups require an alkali for development. Developing agents containing one hydroxy and one amino group will develop without an alkali but not with sufficient rapidity for general use.

8. Compounds containing three active groups, not in a symmetrical arrangement, are more energetic than those containing two.

9. Increasing the number of amino groups increases the developing power.

10. The energy of a benzene derivative which is already a developer is increased if a methyl (CH_3) group is added.

---

[9] Andresen, *Phot. Mitt.* **28**, 286 (1892). *Eder's Jahrbuch* **7**, 486 (1903). Lumiere, *Bull. Soc. franç. photo.* (2) **7**, 310 (1891); **13**, 415 (1897).

Kendall,[10] much later, suggested that any compound having the grouping

$$-\underset{\underset{X}{|}}{C}-(CH-CH)_n=\underset{\underset{Y}{|}}{C}-.$$

Where n may be zero, 1,2, etc., X and Y are either O H or N R' R'', where R' and R'' are hydrogen or alkyl groups, can act as a developer. There are, however, a number of exceptions particularly among substances forming a dye image simultaneously with the silver image, as, for example, thioindoxyl.[11]

Characteristics of the Principal Developers

ADUROL (chloro-hydroquinone, chloroquinol, CHQ, Quinitol, chloronol) chloro or bromo-1.4-dihydroxybenzene, C_6H_4-$(OH)_2 \cdot Cl$.

As developers, these compounds are similar to hydroquinone but have a higher reduction potential and are less affected by temperature, and there is less tendency to fog and less stain than with hydroquinone. Despite these advantages, the combination of hydroquinone and metol is more popular and the chloride substituted products are used chiefly to obtain warm-tones on chloride and chlorobromide developing papers.

---

[10] Kendall, *Proc. IX Cong. International Phot.,* Paris, 1935, 227.

[11] Homolka, *Phot. Korr.* **44**, 115 (1907). *Eder's Jahrbuch* **28**, 22 (1914).

SEYEWETZ, "The State of Our Knowledge of Organic Developing Agents," *Brit. J. Phot.* **66**, 186 (1920).

Preparation of Developing Substances

Adurol: BRAMER AND ZABRISKIE, U.S.P. 1,912,-774 and Beilensen and Kodak Ltd., British Patent 563,541 (1943).

Developing Agents in General: STARNES, *Manufacturing Chemist* **8**, 396 (1937); **9**, 47 (1938); GROGGINS, Unit Processes in Organic Syntheses, 2nd Edition, 1938, McGraw-Hill Book Co., Inc., New York.

THORPE, *Dictionary of Applied Chemistry*, Vol. 4, 182 (1913).

AMIDOL (Acrol, Dianol) 2.4-diaminophenol hydrochloride, $C_6H_3(OH)(NH_2).2HCl.$

Diaminophenol is an energetic developer with sodium sulfite alone. It develops, but more slowly, in an acid solution. The white or gray-white, needle-like crystals are readily soluble in water but oxidize rapidly without appreciable discoloration and solutions are no longer useful as developers within a few hours.[12]

Diaminophenol is now used principally for the development of chloride and bromchloride papers producing rich, cold-black tones. It is nearly always used alone, although diaminophenol-pyro has been recommended as a negative developer, the pyro functioning as a developer without an alkali in the presence of diaminophenol.

CATECHOL (Pyrocatechin, Kachin, Catechin. 1–2-dihydroxybenzene, $C_6H_4(OH)_2$.

Catechol is similar chemically to hydroquinone which is the corresponding para derivative. The oxidation products of catechol, like those of pyrogallol, tan the image:[13] this property has been utilized to produce gelatin relief images for three-color printing.

Catechol differs from other organic developers in functioning almost normally in

the presence of hypo which makes it especially suitable for combined fixing and developing.

A combination of catechol and paraphenylenediamine has been introduced by Johnson and Sons Ltd. for fine grain development under the trade name of *Meritol*.

GLYCIN (Athenon, Kodurol, Monazol). N-(1.4-hydroxyphenyl) glycin. $HOC_6H_4 \cdot NHCH_2CO_2H$.

As a developer, glycin is slow but powerful. It is especially notable for the fine grain of the reduced silver and freedom from fog. Unlike other organic developers, glycin is not directly oxidized by air and it does not produce a stain image. It keeps well in solution and is well suited to continuous use in tanks. Today it is used chiefly in combination with paraphenylene diamine or metol for fine grain negative development and with hydroquinone for warm tones on chlorobromide and chloride papers.

HYDROQUINONE (Hydrochinon, Hydrokinone, Quinol). 1.4-dihydroxybenzene, $C_6H_4(OH)_2$.

Hydroquinone is a slow but powerful developer. The induction period is comparatively long, but the addition of density proceeds quite rapidly after the image has appeared, with the result that the arithmetical coefficient (Watkins factor) is low. In this respect, hydroquinone is almost the exact opposite of metol, diaminophenol, paraminophenol, etc.

Hydroquinone is used alone chiefly for work in which extreme contrast and density are required (process work). It may be used with the alkaline carbonates or the caustic alkalies, the latter producing greater density and contrast, or with paraformaldehyde. The activity of hydroquinone developers is greatly retarded by low temperature, becoming practically inert below

---

[12] Developing substances containing an amino, or a substituted amino group such as diaminophenol, paraminophenol, methyl paraminophenol (metol), oxidize readily and are commonly supplied in the form of a hydrochloride, sulfate or oxalate. For a discussion of the influence of the acid radical in developers, see Southworth, *Brit. J. Phot.* **84**, 711 (1937).

[13] Warnerke, B.P. 1436 (1881). Sanger Shepherd and Bartlett, B.P. 24,234 (1902). Koppmann, D.R.P. 309,193 (1913). Troland, B.P. 392,785 (1932). Starnes, B.P. 466,625 (1937).

Monomethyl paraminophenol: DICKINS, U.S.P. 1,884,844; WHITTAKER, U.S.P. 1,993,253 and BEAN, U.S.P. 2,315,932.

Paraminophenol: MCDANIEL, SCHNEIDER AND BALLER, *Trans. Elect. Chem. Soc.* 39, 441 (1921).

55° F. At temperatures above 70° F. excessive fog and staining may be encountered.

Other than for process work, hydroquinone is usually used with metol (monomethyl paraminophenol). The two supplement one another admirably to form a developer which for general purposes is greatly superior to either alone and which because of its adaptability is by far the most widely used developer at the present time.

METOL (Elon, Enol, Genol, Monol, Monotol, Photol, Pictol, Rhodol, Veritol). 1.4-methyl paraminophenol sulfate HOC_6H_4-$(NHCH_3)$.$\frac{1}{2}H_2SO_4$.

Metol is an energetic developer. The induction period is short and the arithmetical coefficient high; in other words, the image appears quickly but density and contrast increase more slowly.

The addition of hydroquinone produces a developer with the energy and detail-producing characteristics of metol and the density and contrast-producing properties of hydroquinone. The properties of a metol-hydroquinone developer, however, are not simply the sum of the properties of the two agents. The speed of development, as measured by either the growth of density or contrast, is greater for the two agents when used together than the sum of the two used separately. It has been suggested that the increased activity of the metol-hydroquinone in combination is due to the formation of complexes similar to the combination introduced by A. and L. Lumiere as meto-quinone. It now appears, however, that the effect of adding metol to a hydroquinone developer is to reduce the induction period carrying development forward to the point at which the hydroquinone becomes an active developer.[14] The hydroquinone in this way makes its influence felt earlier than would otherwise be the case. The maximum effect is produced within a pH range of 9.0–10.5; as the pH decreases the part played by the hydroquinone becomes less and less.

Ordinarily the alkaline carbonates, or borates, are used, but metol alone will develop without an alkali and metol-sulfite formulas have been recommended (1) as compensating developers—for the development of subjects of extreme contrast, and (2) as fine-grain developers.[15]

PARAMINOPHENOL (K o d e l o n, Rodinal, Azol). 1.4-aminophenol $C_6H_4(OH)$-(NH_2) base $C_6H_4(OH)(NH_2)$·HCl hydrochloride.

When used with the alkaline carbonates, paraminophenol forms a rapid, soft working developer which is notably free from any tendency to produce development fog even at temperatures considerably above normal. It is, therefore, especially suitable for high-temperature development. In practice, however, paraminophenol is less popular than metol because it is more rapidly exhausted.

Highly concentrated developers of exceptional keeping properties may be prepared by adding paraminophenol to a solution of potassium metabisulfite and then adding sufficient sodium hydroxide to dissolve the precipitated free base. A developer of this type was patented and introduced commercially by Agfa as "Rodinal."[16] Numerous others have been introduced since.

---

[14] James, *J. Phot. Soc. Amer.* **9**, 62 (1943).

[15] Veldman, *Atelier* **35**, 30 (1928). Von Ehrhardt, *Amer. Phot.* **28**, 466 (1934). Wiegleb, *Schweiz. Phot.-Ztg.* **37**, 93 (1935). Henn and Crabtree, *J. Phot. Soc. Amer.* **10**, 727 (1944).

[16] On the preparation of "Rodinal type" developers see: Ermen, *Brit. J. Phot.* **67**, 611 (1920). Gray, *Brit. J. Phot.* **80**, 175 (1933). Willcock, *Brit. J. Phot.* **83**, 256 (1936).

PARAPHENYLENEDIAMINE (Diamine, Diamine P, Dianol, Diamine H (hydrochloride) P.D.H. 1,4-diaminobenzene C_6H_4-$(NH_2)_2$ base $C_6H_4(NH_2)_2 \cdot 2HCl$ hydrochloride.

Para and possibly ortho-phenylenediamine are the only developers in which the graininess of the image is definitely lower than other developing agents. The fine grain is due to its solvent action on silver halide and its low reduction potential. These two factors prevent full development of the latent image, thus necessitating an increase in exposure as compared with more energetic developers and it is possible that development is largely of the character associated with physical development in which silver is deposited on the latent image from a silver-bearing solution.

The silver deposit is dichroic, i.e., black by transmitted light and cream-colored by reflected light. The printing density is greater than the visual density so that negatives which appear to be lacking in density and contrast may be of good printing quality.

Para-phenylenediamine is frequently combined with glycin, metol, or similar developers.[17]

Both the free base and the hydrochloride are strongly toxic and contact with the solutions should be avoided. The use of waterproof gloves is advised.

PYRO (Pyrogallol, Pyrol, Pyrox). 1.2.3-hydroxybenzene $(OH)_3C_6H_3$.

Pyro in recent years has been almost completely superseded by other developers and particularly by metol-hydroquinone. The behavior of pyro as a developer depends in a large measure on the dilution.

Thus in a concentrated solution the induction period is relatively long but the image develops rapidly; in diluted solutions, on the other hand, the time of appearance is relatively short but density and contrast are added slowly.

Pyro oxidizes rapidly in solution, and while stock solutions with good keeping properties may be prepared with the addition of a relatively large quantity of an acid sulfite, pyro developers, as generally employed, have a useful life of only a few hours.

The developed image varies in color from a warm black to a yellowish black, depending upon the amount of sulfite or other preservative.

The photographic density and gamma of the pyro-developed image are higher than the visual density and contrast, the difference between the two, or the *color index*, depending primarily on the amount of preservative used.[18]

Development in pyro, particularly with small amounts of preservative, results in the tanning of the gelatin surrounding the silver of the image. This property has led to its use in the development of gelatin reliefs for three-color printing.

Pyro is used alone, in combination with metol to obtain a more energetic developer with a lower threshold value, and less frequently with other developing agents, such as glycin, diaminophenol, or paraphenylene. Used in combination with diaminophenol it develops without an alkali.[19, 20]

The Selectivity of Developing Agents. The relation between the development of

---

[17] Sease, *Camera* (Phila.) **47**, 1 (1933). Lowe, *Camera-Craft* **43**, 558 (1936).

Gallafent and E. I. Dupont patented (B.P. 580,237 of 1944) the combination of orthophenylene and aminophenols and polyhydroxybenzenes to form compounds useful as fine grain developers.

[18] Wilsey, *Brit. J. Phot.* **66**, 721 (1919).

[19] *Bunel Bull. Belge*, **44**, 151 (1922). Hall, *Amer. Phot.* **16**, 326 (1922).

[20] A number of methylated, ethylated or other substituted pyrogallols have been patented: Bayer, B.P. 10,721; Agfa, D.R.P. 155,568; Schultes, U.S.P. 2,017,295 and 2,057,451; Stockelbach, U.S.P. 2,037,742. See also: Emmerman, *Phot. Ind.* **36**, 1085 (1938); **34**, 896 (1936).

he image and the development of fog, as measured by the relationship of the respective densities, is termed the *selectivity* of he developing agent. This characteristic, ike all others, depends considerably upon the conditions under which the developer is used, the formula, and the degree of development. Nietz found no relationship between the fog density and the reduction potential of the developing agent when development is carried to completion.[21] Shiberstoff and Bukin,[22] on the other hand, found that developing agents may be divided into two classes: a low-fog group which includes paraphenylenediamine, glycin, paraminophenol, and catechol; and a high-fog group which, in increasing order, includes bromhydroquinone, chloroquinol, metol, pyro, hydroquinone and metoquinone. Using a developing solution of uniform composition, except for the developing agent, Shiberstoff placed developing agents in the following order of increasing selectivity; hydroquinone, chloroquinol, pyro, metoquinone, metol, glycin, catechol and paraminophenol. He also found that selectivity decreases with increased temperature.

The Developing Agent and Effective Emulsion Speed. Nietz found an 18-fold variation in emulsion speed between different developing agents and concluded that on the whole emulsion speed increased with the reduction potential of the developing agent but probably less than his data indicated.[23] Shiberstoff and Bukin[24] found only insignificant differences. James[25] also found no differences of importance among

eleven developing agents, except in the early stages of development, but his results were obtained with a developer without sulfite and with development to completion, or to a fog density of 0.3, and thus do not duplicate the conditions under which the same developers are used in practice.

Undoubtedly, the capacity of a developing agent to develop the latent image fully depends upon the conditions under which it is used and is not a property of the developing agent alone. The sodium sulfite is a solvent of silver halide and, used in large quantities, most certainly affects the final result. Potassium bromide also lowers the effective emulsion speed early in development, but has been shown to result in higher speeds on prolonged development due to the reduction of fog. The pH of the solution may well be an important factor also.

Reduction Potential of Developing Agents. The relative reducing energy of a developing agent is known as its *reduction potential*. The reduction potential of a developing agent may be determined in one of three ways:

1. *The amount by which density is depressed with a given quantity of a restrainer such as potassium bromide.* For a given concentration of potassium bromide, under fixed conditions of development, the amount by which the density is reduced depends upon the ability of the developer to overcome the resistance of the soluble bromide. Hence, the concentration of bromide will be in direct proportion to the energy, or reduction potential, of the developing agent.[26]

2. *The amount of silver bromide reduced to silver by a given quantity of the developing agent.* By this method a given quantity of the developer is added to silver

21 Nietz, *Theory of Development*, D. Van Nostrand Co., Inc., New York.
22 Shiberstoff and Bukin, *Kino-Phot. Ind.* 1932, p. 101.
23 Nietz, *Theory of Development*, D. Van Nostrand Co., Inc., New York.
24 Shiberstoff and Bukin, *Kino-Phot. Ind.* 1932, p. 101.
25 James, *J. Franklin Inst.* **240**, 41, (1945).

26 Sheppard, *J. Chem. Soc.* (London) **39**, 530 (1906).

bromide, formed by precipitation in water, and the reduced silver is collected and measured. The reduction potential of the developing agent is then expressed in terms of the quantity of metallic silver produced from the reduction of the silver bromide.[27]

3. *Electrometric methods.* Electrometric methods have been utilized by Bredig, Matthews and Barmeier, Frary and Nietz, and more recently by Evans and Hanson.[28] The results obtained by the latter are quite different from earlier measurements made by the density depression method as will be evident from the following table in which the values from the density depression method, used by Nietz, are compared with those obtained by the electrometric method; the potentials given being measured against the standard saturated calomel reference cell.

| | Reduction Potential | |
| | Density Depression Method | Electro-metric Method |
Developing Agent		
Diaminophenol	30	−0.434
Bromhydroquinone	21	−0.327
Monomethylparamino-phenol sulfate	20	−0.308
Pyrogallol	16	−0.388
Dimethylparamino-phenol sulfate	10	−0.293
Chlorhydroquinone	7.0	−0.335
Paraminophenol (HCl)	6.0	−0.291
Toluhydroquinone	2.2	−0.390
Hydroquinone	1.0 (standard)	−0.357
Paraphenylene diamine	0.3	—

The outstanding difference in the values obtained by the two methods is the much higher potential of hydroquinone with the electrometric method than with the older density depression method. It will be observed that the potential of hydroquinone, as measured by the electrometric method,

is higher than that of monomethyl-paraminophenol (metol), while the difference in potential is greater, and in the opposite direction, when measured by the depression of density. The potentials, as measured electrometrically, do not correspond very well with the observed differences in the rate of development, or velocity constant but are in fair agreement with the maximum densities obtainable with the various developing agents.

Differences in Developing Agents With Respect to Rate of Exhaustion. With all developers, there is a loss in activity with use. This loss in activity affects development in two ways: (1) longer development is required to reach a given degree of contrast or gamma, and (2) the lower densities are less fully developed tending to produce the effect of underexposure.

The effect of repeated use on density with different developing agents using a standard formula was investigated by Strauss who found that metol has the longest useful life, followed in order by paraminophenol edinol, ortol, chloro-hydroquinone, glycin pyrocatechin and, much worse than the others, pyro.

Ermen investigated the exhaustion of developers using the time of appearance on developing papers.[29] His results placed the different developing agents in the following order: metol (best), dimethylaminophenol, paraminophenol, metol-chlorohydroquinone, chloro-hydroquinone, and lastly hydroquinone.

Identification of the Principal Developing Agents. Methods of identifying the various organic developing agents have been described by Andresen,[30] Clarke,[31] Er-

27 Andresen, *Phot. Korr.* **35**, 447 (1898). Valenta, *Photographische Chemie und Chemikalien-Kunde*, II, 506, Wm. Knapp, Halle a/S.

28 Evans and Hanson, *J. Phys. Chem.* **41**, 509 (1937).

29 *Brit. J. Phot.* **68**, 64 (1921).

30 Andresen, Valenta, *Photographische Chemie und Chemikalienkunde*, Knapp, Halle a/S.

31 Clarke, *J. Ind. and Eng. Chem.*, November 1918; *Brit. J. Phot.* **65**, 499 (1918).

ien,[32] Lehrman and Tausch,[33] Plauman,[34] nd Huse and Atkinson.[35] Table 13.1 is rom the last mentioned paper.

Dermatitis and Developers. Contact vith solutions of paraphenylenediamine lmost invariably affects the skin, causing t first a redness, then some swelling accompanied, or followed shortly, by an itching and burning sensation and finally, in nany cases, painful blisters. The number vho are affected by metol (monomethylaraminophenol) is comparatively large, ut fortunately sensitivities are much less requent to paraminophenol and diaminohenol which, with hydroquinone, pyro, lycin, and most other developers, are in ommon use. In the case of metol, the presnce of dimethylparaphenylenediamine as n impurity is the most frequent source of he well-known metol poisoning, although netol itself is toxic and can affect those llergic (i.e., hypersensitive) to it. Methods f preparing metol so as to remove all races of paraphenylenediamine have been)atented,[36] and several commercial brands ire now claimed to be free of any poisonous mpurity.

If irritation occurs as a result of the use f a particular developer, either its use hould be discontinued immediately, or the iands protected from contact with the solution when in use.

[32] Ermen, *Brit. J. Phot.* **64**, 390 (1917).

[33] Lehrman and Tausch, *Phot. Korr.* **71**, 17, 35 1935).

[34] Plauman, *Phot. Ind.* **29**, 341 (1931).

[35] Huse and Atkinson, *The Chemical Analysis of lotion Picture Developers and Fixing Baths*, Mo- ion Picture Film Division, Eastman Kodak Co., Iollywood, Calif.

[36] U.S.P. 2,163,166 (1939), Ermen, *Brit. J. Phot. llmanac*, 1924, p. 298.

REES AND ANDERSON, "Simultaneous Deter- mination of Elon and Hydroquinone in Photographic Developers," *J. Soc. Mot. Pict. Eng.* **53**, 268 (1949).

SHANER AND SPARKS, *J. Soc. Mot. Pict. Eng.* **45**, 20 (1945).

Ointments containing lanolin, boric acid, zinc oxide, or ichthymol may be helpful in allaying the pain and irritation, but in an advanced stage, when blisters have appeared, the use of a lotion or ointment is inadvisable. A wet dressing of several layers of surgical gauze saturated with a mild antiseptic and astringent, such as boric acid, potassium permanganate, aluminum acetate or Burrows solution (obtainable as Domeboro Tabs), is preferable. A zinc, or other mildly antiseptic ointment, may be used after new skin is formed.

Developing Solutions. The typical developing solution contains:

1. A solvent; water.

2. A developing agent or agents, such as metol-hydroquinone, pyro, etc.

3. A preservative, or antioxidant, such as sodium sulfite, or an acid sulfite, e.g., sodium bisulfite.

4. An alkali, such as a carbonate, borate, or hydroxide.

5. A restrainer, or antifogging agent, such as potassium bromide.

Some developing agents do not require an alkali, and the restrainer is often omitted from negative developers although frequently it is added in the form of used developer to "condition" the solution.

The Preservative. All organic developing agents have a strong affinity for oxygen.

BOURNE, "Photographic Dermatitis," *Brit. J. Phot. Almanac*, 1945, p. 82.

CRABTREE AND MATHEWS, *Photographic Chemicals and Solutions*, American Photographic Publishing Co., Boston.

SOUTHWORTH, "Developer Constitution and Toxicity," *Brit. J. Phot.* **85**, 390 (1938).

GREENWOOD, "Dermatitis and Toxicity," *Brit. J. Phot.* **92**, 235 (1945).

BLUMANN, "Metol Poisoning," *Brit. J. Phot.* **80**, 72 (1933).

MALLINCKRODT, Chemistry of Photography, Mallinckrodt Chemical Co., St. Louis, 1940.

"Metol Poisoning," *American Encyclopedia of Photography*, Vol. 9, p. 3237.

TABLE 13.1.   IDENTIFYING REACTIONS OF DEVELOPING AGENTS

Agent	Ferric Chloride (in Acid Solution)	Benzaldehyde (in Alkaline Solution)	Sodium Nitrite (in Acid Solution)
Elon (Melting Point Elon base, 85° C.)	Purple color develops slowly in cold	No precipitate if pure	Colorless, needles slightly soluble in water, Melting Point 136° C.
Glycin (Melting Point 200° C.)	Darkens slowly in cold	No precipitate	No precipitate
Amidol (Melting Point base, 79° C.)	Bright red color immediately	Dirty yellow precipitate, Melting Point indeterminate	Dark brown precipitate
P-amino phenol (Melting Point base, 184° C.)	Purple color develops slowly in cold	Yellow precipitate Melting Point 183° C.	Red color with R-acid
P-phenylene diamine (Melting Point base, 140° C.)	Green-blue, changing immediately in brown	Yellow precipitate Melting Point 138° C.	Red color with R-acid

It is necessary, therefore, to add an antioxilizing agent, or preservative, which is usually sodium sulfite, $NaSO_3$ (desiccated), or $Na_2SO_3 . 7H_2O$ (crystal). Sodium sulfite is occasionally replaced wholly, or in part, by sodium bisulfite, $NaHSO_3$, which in an alkaline solution is converted into sodium sulfite and sodium bicarbonate.

The addition of sulfite (1) protects organic developing agents against aerial oxidation; (2) tends to prevent the formation of staining developer products; (3) acts as a silver halide solvent by the formation of complexes, and (4) is a weak alkali and under certain conditions increases the rate of development and the maximum density obtainable.

The reactions involved are not precisely known and may not be the same with all developing agents.[37] With hydroquinone, which has been studied more extensively than other developing agents, in the absence of sulfite, the quinone which is formed as one of the by-products of development, or as a result of the oxidation of the hydroquinone when exposed to oxygen of the air, is immediately converted by the alkali, or by by-products of the first reaction, to an unstable oxyquinone which decomposes to form the compounds which color the solution and stain the gelatin. The addition of sulfite prevents the formation of the oxyquinone by combining with the quinone to form sodium hydroquinone monosulfonate which is colorless and produces no stain. In other words, the sulfite prevents the formation of staining by-products through combination with the developer to form compounds which are colorless. Further-

more, the presence of quinone accelerates the oxidation of hydroquinone; hence sulfite, by removing the quinone from the solution, tends to preserve the solution by lowering the rate of oxidation.

As a solvent of silver halide, sodium sulfite is used in a relatively high concentration in so-called "fine-grain" developers. The solvent action, which is at its greatest with silver chloride and relatively insignificant with silver iodide, acting upon the surface of the grains of silver halide prevents them from attaining their full size in development and reduces the tendency of the grains in close proximity to one another from merging to form larger aggregates of silver.

The addition of sulfite to an alkaline solution of certain developing agents, particularly hydroquinone, paraminophenol, and metol, affects the rate of development and particularly the maximum density. Evans and Hanson have shown that this may be explained as being due to the increased potential of the solution, an increase in the potential of the solution resulting in an increase in the maximum developable density.

The quantity of sulfite employed varies greatly; among the factors determining the amount required are:

1. *The susceptibility of the developing agent, or agents, to oxidation.* The more readily the developing agent accepts oxygen from the air, the greater the amount of preservative required for satisfactory keeping properties in solution.

2. *The concentration of the developer.* The amount of preservative required for a dilute developer is greater than for a more concentrated solution because the proportion of the developing agent to the available oxygen is less.

3. *The temperature at which the developer is kept.* The rate of oxidation in-

37 Andresen, *Eder's Jahrbuch* (1930), Vol. 3. Pinnow, *Z. Electrochem.* **21**, 380 (1915). Rzymkowski, *Phot. Ind.*, 627 (1928). Seyewetz and Szymson, *Bull. Soc. franç. Phot.* **21**, 71, 236 (1934). Lehrman and Tausch, *Phot. Korr.* **71**, 17, 35 (1935). Evans and Hanson, *J. Phys. Chem.* **41**, 509 (1937).

creases with the temperature; consequently, a developer used at a temperature above normal requires a larger amount of preservative.

4. *The keeping properties required and the way in which the solution is used.* Developers which are used once in a tray and then discarded naturally do not need to keep so well as those designed for use in tanks over a long period of time. On the other hand, the conditions under which the developer is used may favor rapid oxidation of the solution. The amount of oxidation, for example, is relatively greater in tray development than in a tank because a larger proportion of the solution is exposed to air.

5. *The alkalinity of the solution.* The more strongly alkaline the developer, the more rapid the rate of oxidation; for satisfactory keeping properties it is necessary, therefore, to use an increased amount of preservative.

Insufficient amounts of the preservative result in rapid oxidation of the developer causing: (1) a loss in developing power, (2) the formation of colored oxidation products which stain the gelatin, and (3) oxidation fog.

Large amounts of the preservative improve the keeping properties of the developer but increase the time of development and reduce the effective emulsion speed through the solvent action on silver bromide.

The Alkali. With but few exceptions, diaminophenol being the most important, all organic developers require an alkali. The function of the alkali is to increase the ionization of the developing agent and to absorb the bromine liberated in development. The alkalies in general use include the alkaline carbonates, the caustic alkalies, borates, and metaborates. Other substances used less frequently include acetone, for-

maldehyde, paraformaldehyde, ammonia alkaloyd amines, trisodium phosphate mono-, di-, and triethanolamine, sodium metasilicate, and sodium aluminate.

Potassium carbonate is more suitable for concentrated developers because of its greater solubility, but is not widely used in the United States because of its higher price. The caustic alkalies are used chiefly in developers for process materials with developing agents of low energy such as hydroquinone. In general, developing solutions containing caustic alkalies are exhausted more rapidly with use than those with the alkaline carbonates.

Borax is used chiefly with metol and hydroquinone in fine-grain developers. It acts as a restrainer with developers of the ortho dihydroxy type, such as pyro and catechol.[38]

Sodium metaborate, unlike sodium carbonate, in the presence of an acid does not evolve a gas, so that there is less danger of blistering in warm weather when the swollen emulsion is transferred from the developer to an acid fixing bath.[39]

Acetone, formaldehyde and trihydroxymethylene disassociate in solution and combine with the sodium sulfite to form an alkali. For example with acetone

$$2CH_3.CO.CH_3 + 2Na_2SO_3 + C_6H_4.OH.OH$$
$$\rightarrow 2CH_3.CO.CH_3NaHSO_3 + C_6H_4.ONa$$

with formaldehyde

$$HCHO + Na_2SO_3 + H_2O \rightarrow$$
$$HCHO—NaHSO_3 + NaOH$$

Trihydroxymethylene reacts with sodium sulfite to form sodium bisulfite and sodium hydroxide.[40]

Sodium metasilicate has been recommended particularly for high temperature

[38] Reinders and Beukers, *Ber. 8th Int. Cong Phot.*, Dresden, 1931, 171.

[39] Russell, U.S.P. 1,976,299 (1934); 1,990,806 (1935).

[40] Bostrom, Nordisk, *Tidskr. Fot.* **26**, 110 (1942).

se as it hardens gelatin but has not come
nto general use.

The use of sodium aluminate prepared
rom the addition of potassium aluminum
ulfate $(KAL(SO_4)_2)$ to sodium hydroxide
NaOH) was patented by Alburger.[41]
This is claimed to produce a solution with
long active life and hardens the gelatin,
ut apparently has attracted little atten-
ion.

For any particular developing agent, the
ate of development is very largely a func-
ion of the pH of the solution. The particu-
ar alkali appears immaterial as long as the
quantity used results in a solution of the
ame pH value. The pH required for de-
elopment varies with the developing agent.
Metol, for example, requires a pH of from
5–7, whereas hydroquinone is inactive at
a pH of less than 9.0. Hydroquinone, how-
ver, is much more sensitive to a change in
pH, and at a pH of 10.5 hydroquinone and
metol develop at approximately the same
rate.[42]

pH of Alkalies

	Molar Conc.	pH
Borax	0.1	9.2
Sodium sulfite	1.0	9.7
Sodium carbonate	1.0	11.6
Ammonium hydroxide	0.1	11.7
Sodium hydroxide	0.1	13.1
Trisodium phosphate	1.0	13.8
Sodium hydroxide	1.0	13.9

pH of Standard Developers. (As determined in the laboratories of the Department of Photographic Technology, Rochester Institute of Technology.)

Kodak	D–1	1:7	9.9
	D–8		11.45
	D–9		12.08
	Dk 15		9.58
	D–16		9.0
	D–19		10.15
	Dk–20		8.28
	D–23		7.80
	D–25		7.00
	Dk–50		9.33
	D–52		9.87
	—	1:1	9.8
	Dk60a		9.65
	D 61a		9.25
	D 72		10.20
	D 76		8.70
	D 76 d		8.4
	D 82		10.3
Ansco	17 M		8.85
	48 M		9.25
	113 (Stock)		7.03
	115 (Stock)		9.72
	130 (Stock)		9.7
	120 (Stock)		9.6
Dupont-Defender	9 D		10.00
	54 D		9.85
	55 D		9.95
	57 D		9.99
	60 D		9.85
Edwal	12		7.5
	102		10.7
	F–R X–33		7.8
	D 76		8.6
	D 76		8.3
Odell Physical			9.3
Rodinal			12.3

Private communication from Professor S. M.
Thronson.

The Restrainer. The presence of an
alkaline bromide, such as potassium bromide, lowers the degree of ionization of the
silver bromide and, by reducing the concentration of silver cations, restrains development.[43] The addition of potassium

---

[41] Alburger, U.S.P. 2,321,345. *J. Soc. Mot.
Pict. Eng.* **33**, 296 (1939).

[42] Reinders and Beukers, *Phot. J.* **74**, 78
(1934).

ELVEGÄRD, "The Course of Development at Different pH's," *Zeit. wiss. Phot.* **41**, 81
(1942).

---

[43] Citrates, tartrates and boro-tartrates behave
similarly. Lobel, *Bull. Soc. franç. Phot.*, 1928,
p. 167.

It has been suggested that the restraining
effect of potassium bromide may be due at least
in part to its effect on the surface absorption
equilibrium at the surface of the grain of silver
halide. Mees, *Theory of the Photographic Process*, The Macmillan Co., New York, 1942.

bromide, however, is ordinarily for the purpose of preventing fog because the restraining effect is greater on fog than on the latent image. Where maximum contrast is required, a relatively high concentration of bromide is usually necessary to prevent fog. In some cases, the restrainer is not included in the formula but is added through a "conditioning" process which consists in (1) developing waste film in the solution before use or (2) in the addition of a small quantity of used developer. It is claimed that developing solutions thus treated produce less fog than those to which potassium is added.

The effect of adding a restrainer varies with the developing agent and is greatest with those of low potential. The depression in density from the addition of potassium bromide is equivalent practically to a loss in effective emulsion speed; this is considerable in the early stages of development and becomes less and less as the degree of development increases.

In recent years, a number of substances have been found which are more effective than potassium bromide in preventing fog.[44] The best known are 6-nitrobenzimidazole and benzotriazole. These may be used to reduce fog on negative materials particularly when developing under conditions likely to give rise to fog, or with silver chloride papers to obtain a cold, blue-black image.

Additions to Developing Solutions.
Calcium Precipitants. The precipitation

of calcium salts in developers before use may be prevented by using distilled water rain water, or chemically softened water for preparing solutions, but this will not prevent sludging as the developer is exhausted This may be prevented by the addition of sodium metaphosphate or sodium tetraphosphate; the latter being the more effective.[45] The amount required varies from 0.5 gram per liter for developers of low alkalinity such as Dk–20 and D–76 to 2.0 grams per liter for carbonate developers, such as D–11, D–19, D–52, D–72. The addition of either the meta- or tetraphosphate to developers containing a caustic alkali is not recommended because of the rapid hydrolysis of the phosphate.

Silver Halide Solvents. The usual purpose of adding a solvent of silver halide to the developer is for the purpose of securing a fine-grain image. The silver halide solvents used include (1) sodium sulfite, (2) thiocyanate, (3) ammonium chloride, (4) and hypo. Metol-hydroquinone-borax formulas for fine grain employ a high concentration of sodium sulfite which with a low pH results in considerable improvement in graininess. The solvent action of the thiocyanates is greater and developers including a thiocyanate produce finer grain but at the expense of emulsion speed. Ammonium chloride has been recommended but has not proved as satisfactory.[46] The addition of hypo has the effect of improving graininess, but at a higher speed loss than the other solvents of silver halide and with a greater tendency toward dichroic fog.

Hydrazine. The addition of hydrazine was found by Stauffer, Smith, and Trivelli [47] to increase the inertia speed and the gamma as compared with normal development. The effect increases with increasing

[44] Trivelli and Jensen, *J. Franklin Inst.* **210**, 287 (1930). Wulff, U.S.P. 1,696,830. Sheppard and Hudson, *Phot. J.* **67**, 359 (1927). Seyewetz, *Bull. Soc. franc. Phot.* (3) **30**, 47 (1933); *Brit. J. Phot.* **80**, 17 (1933). I. G. Farbenindustrie, B.P 280,525. Gossler, B.P. 403,789. Trivelli and Jensen, *J. Franklin Inst.* **211**, 155 (1931). Weissberger and Eastman Kodak Co., U.S.P. 2,324,123 (1943). Falleson and Eastman Kodak Co., U.S.P. 2,384,613 (1944). Dersch and Heimbach, (Ansco), U.S.P. 2,298,093; 2,384,897 (1942).

[45] Crabtree and Henn, *J. Soc. Mot. Pict. Eng.* **43**, 426 (1944).

[46] Kendall, *Amer. Phot.* **41**, 15 (April 1947).

[47] *J. Franklin Inst.* **239**, 291 (1944).

pH but decreases as the sulfite concentration increases. The action of hydrazine is apparently to induce the development of weakly exposed or unexposed grains in the vicinity of grains which are developing normally.

Urea. Urea has a softening action on gelatin which may be used (1) to increase the speed of development, (2) to revive partially exhausted developers, and (3) to facilitate development a low temperature.[48]

The addition of fairly substantial amounts of urea enables development to be carried on at temperatures as low as 40° F. without greatly increasing the time of development and with only a slight loss in emulsion speed. At 40° F. from 300–400 grams of urea per liter are required and the time of development is from 2–4 times greater than at 68° F.

Wetting Agents. The addition of wetting substances to developing solutions for the purpose of facilitating the absorption of the developing solution by the sensitive material and preventing pinholes and other irregularities in development has become quite common in recent years. The substances used for this purpose include *Aerosol*, ethyl alcohol, butyl alcohol, alkanol B (sodium salt of alkyl), naphthlene sulfonic acid, ethylene dichloride, triethanolamine, and hexyl alcohol.

Effect of Dilution on Development.

Slight dilution of the developer affects principally the time of development. The variation in time of development with dilution is more marked with those developers which oxidize readily, such as pyro, than with those which oxidize slowly. With very dilute developers, the action is confined chiefly to the upper layers of the emulsion and, generally speaking, it is not possible to obtain the same density and contrast as with a concentrated developer. Fog tends to increase with dilution, due probably to increased oxidation.[49]

Effect of Use on Developing Solutions. With use, a developing solution becomes slower in action as a result of (1) depletion of the developing agent, or agents, and (2) the restraining effect of by-products of the process of development in the form of sodium bromide, sodium iodide, and developer oxidation products. The decrease in both sulfite and alkali is insignificant.

The by-products of development which accumulate in a used developing solution retard development and, if present in quantity, development is so greatly restrained that there is a loss in effective emulsion speed.

Replenishment of Developing Solutions. The loss in density and contrast due to partial exhaustion of the developing solution may be overcome to a certain extent by the addition of a replenishing solution, which may be either a solution of the same composition as the original formula, but without bromide, or a more concentrated solution containing a larger proportion of the developing agents, and alkali. It is not possible, regardless of the composition of the replenishing solution, to bring a partially exhausted developing solution back to its original condition. However, with suitable replenishment the period over which a developing solution may be used without involving an *excessive* loss in the density and contrast of the image may be greatly extended.

By adding sufficient replenishing solution to maintain the level of the developing solution in the tank, the replenishing solu-

[48] Dersch, *J. Phot. Soc. Amer.* **11**, 467 (1945).

CRABTREE AND HENN, "Wetting Agents," *The Complete Photographer No. 54.*

GREENWOOD, "Wetting in Photographic Processes," *Brit. J. Phot.* **90**, 438 (1943).

[49] Nietz and Whitaker, *J. Franklin Inst.* **203**, 507 (1927). Chibisoff, *Kinotechnik* **11**, 373 (1929).

tion added is equal in volume to that of the developer which has been removed from the tank on the sensitive material. This in turn is directly proportional to the amount of material processed; hence, the amount of replenishing solution added is directly proportional to the amount of sensitive material which has been developed.

The only satisfactory method of determining the best formula and the amount of replenishing solution required is by actual photographic tests made by developing sensitive material under known conditions.

Testing Developing Solutions. Tests of developing solutions may be of value for:

1. Maintaining uniformity of processing through the use of standardized solutions.
2. Ascertaining properties of solutions before use.
3. Determining source of unusual behavior, i.e., fog, etc.
4. Methods leading to the more efficient use of solutions; i.e., eliminating unnecessary waste by replenishment.

For most purposes, comparative photographic tests are adequate. These are best made by sensitometric methods; but, lacking sensitometric equipment, comparative tests can be made by developing test strip exposed to a step wedge. A step wedge much better for this purpose than a camer exposure as comparisons are more easil and accurately made. A large step wedg from which a number of strips may be cu is a decided advantage in the absence of a exposing box of some kind to ensure accu rate and reproducible exposures on the te strips. The test strips should be on a singl emulsion and the conditions of developmen (temperature, time, agitation, volume o solution, etc.) must be the same for all test If the purpose is to study the result on particular emulsion, then that emulsio must be used; but, if the object is simpl to compare developers or to standardiz solutions, any convenient emulsion may b used.

In most cases, comparisons will be mad visually of:

1. Fog, extent of veiling of unexpose portions of the test strip.
2. Threshold value, the first exposur producing a visible density.
3. Density scale, difference in the maxi mum and minimum densities, i.e., tota density range.
4. Differences in density progression, i.e the rate of increase in density from step t step if any significant difference is recog nizable to the unaided eye.
5. Color of the image, if visually notice able.

Properly made, such comparisons, al though qualitative, may be exceedingly use ful in studying different solutions, formu las, the effect of temperature, dilution time, agitation, degree of exhaustion, spee loss, and the effect of replenishment.

ALBURGER, "Mathematical Expression of Developer Behavior," *J. Soc. Mot. Pict. Eng.* **35**, 282 (1940).

BAUMBACH, "Chemical Analysis of Hydroquinone, Metol and Bromide in a Developer," *J. Soc. Mot. Pict. Eng.* **33**, 517 (1939).

BLANEY, "Method of Removal of Excess Halides from Photographic Developing Baths," U.S.P. 2,073,621 of June 10, 1933.

EVANS, "Maintenance of a Developer by Continuous Replenishment," *J. Soc. Mot. Pict. Eng.* **31**, 273 (1938).

HARVEY, WOOSLEY AND BAINES, "Exhaustion and Regeneration of Developers," *Proc. 9th Int. Cong. of Phot.*, Paris, 1935. *Sci. et Ind. Phot.* (II) **6**, 300 (1935).

WEISBERG (Greenwald), "Regeneration of Photographic Developer Solutions," U.S.P. 2,073,664 of September 9, 1933.

ERMEN, "Qualitative Tests for the Commone Developers," *Brit. J. Phot.* **64**, 390 (1917)

EVANS AND HANSON, "Chemical Analysis of a M-Q Developer," *J. Soc. Mot. Pict. Eng* **32** (1939).

Developer Fog. Fog may be produced
y the developer if:

1. The solution is improperly com-
ounded, i.e., contains an excess of alkali,
sufficient restrainer, or is used without
lution.

2. The temperature of the solution is
xcessive.

3. Development is forced; i.e., prolonged
beyond safe limits.

4. The solution is contaminated with
etallic salts of tin, copper, or zinc.

5. The solution contains sodium sulfide
t a result of the reduction of the sulfite to
ulfide by bacterial or fungous growths.
his occurs ordinarily only in developers
deep tanks which are used continually.
he formation of sulfide may be prevented
y sterilizing the tanks, racks and all de-
eloping equipment periodically with a
lution of sodium hypochlorite or a 5%
lution of trisodium phosphate and hot
ater.

USE AND ATKINSON, *Chemistry Analysis of
    Photographic Developers and Fixing
    Baths,* Eastman Kodak Co., Hollywood,
    1939.
VANS, HANSON AND GLASOE. "Iodide Analy-
    sis in an M-Q Developer," *J. Soc. Mot.
    Pict. Eng.* 38, 180 (1942); *Ind. Eng. Chem.*
    (Analyt. Ed.) 14, 314 (1942).
TOTT, "The Application of Potentiometric
    Methods to Developer Analysis," *J. Soc.
    Mot. Pict. Eng.* 39, 37 (1942).
AUMBACH, "An Improved Method for the De-
    termination of Hydroquinone and Metol in
    Photographic Developers," *J. Soc. Mot.
    Pict. Eng.* 47, 403 (1946).
HANER AND SPARKS, "Application of Methyl
    and Ethyl Ketone to the Analysis of De-
    velopers of Elon and Hydroquinone," *J.
    Soc. Mot. Pict. Eng.* 47, 409 (1946).
EVENSON, "Determination of Elon and Hydro-
    quinone in Developers," *Phot. J.* 87B, 18
    (1947).
ENN AND HERTZBERGER, "Equations for Cal-
    culating the Condition of Photographic
    Solutions in Continuous Systems," *P.S.A.
    Journal* 13, 494 (1947).

6. Exposure of the material to air during development (oxidation fog). Under
ordinary conditions oxidation, or aerial fog,
occurs only with developers containing hydroquinone but may be produced with other
agents if the solution contains tin, copper,
or other metallic compounds. The addition of a small quantity (10–15%) of used
developer, or a desensitizer such as Pinakryptol, is usually effective in preventing
aerial fog.

7. An excess of sodium sulfite. The fog
produced by an excess of sodium sulfite is
due to the reduction, by the developer, of
silver halide which is rendered soluble by
the excess of sulfite. Sulfite fog is much
less common than the other sources and
ordinarily may be prevented either by the
addition of potassium bromide, an antifogging agent, or a small quantity of used
developer.

Stain with Developers. Stain with developers may arise from (1) the colored
oxidation products of the developer, and
(2) from the formation of silver in a finely
divided state.

Stains due to excessive oxidation of the
developing solution may be due to:

1. A solution lacking sufficient preservative to prevent oxidation.

2. Developing at a high temperature
with increased oxidation of the solution.

3. Excessive exposure of the sensitive
material, or the solution, to air during development.

4. The use of old, oxidized developer.

Stains arising from the formation of silver are usually dichroic (i.e., two-colored)
with a metallic appearance by reflected
light and a reddish or purplish color by

CRABTREE, "Chemical Fog," *Am. Ann. of Phot.*,
    1920, p. 20.
CRABTREE AND MATHEWS, *Photographic Chemi-
    cals and Solutions,* American Photographic
    Publishing Co., Boston.

transmitted light. Silver stain, frequently termed dichroic fog, is produced by solvents of silver halide, such as hypo, ammonia, an excess of sodium sulfite, by sodium sulfide, or by thiocyanates in fine-grain developers. Silver stains appear most frequently on fine-grain negative and positive materials and when the developing solution is partially exhausted or used at a high temperature.

In most cases, silver and silver sulfide stains may be removed by prolonged immersion in an acid ammonium thiosulfate fixing bath to which has been added 1 grams of citric acid per liter (½ oz. to 3 oz.). This should be used in a well-ventilated room because of the sulfur dioxide fumes which are formed. After reduction of the stain, wash negatives thoroughly.

HENN AND CRABTREE, "Sulfide Stain," *P.S.A. Journal* **13**, 752 (1947).

HOTOGRAPHIC DEVELOPERS.
I. SILVER-DYE IMAGES

COLOR DEVELOPMENT

A number of developing agents used for *eveloping* a photographic latent image *n*, under certain conditions, deposit a *lored* image in addition to the silver *nage*. Such color images become much *ore* apparent when the silver image is re*oved* by some agent such as Farmer's Re*icer*. The well-known developer, pyro*allol*, when used without sulfite, gives a *ery* strong brown "stain" image. This *as* first described by Liesegang[1] in 1895. *ydroquinone*, catechol, amidol, and a *umber* of other well-known developers *lso* give stain or dye images. *o*-Amino*henol*, 4-methoxynaphthol, hydrocoerulig*one*, indoxyl, and thioindoxyl are other *gents* which produce a dye image. The *vo* latter agents were investigated by *[omolka][2]* in 1907.

The exact structure of the "stain" or *ye* images produced by the normal de*elopers* such as pyrogallol and hydroqui*one* is not known, but it is composed of *olymerization* products of the oxidized *evelopers* and is closely related to the type *f* compounds known as humic acids.[3]

The reaction involved when indoxyl is *sed* as a developer is perfectly straight*orward*. This substance is an intermediate *f* the dye *indigo*. During the development of a latent image indoxyl is oxidized to form the insoluble dye which is deposited simultaneously with the silver image according to the reaction

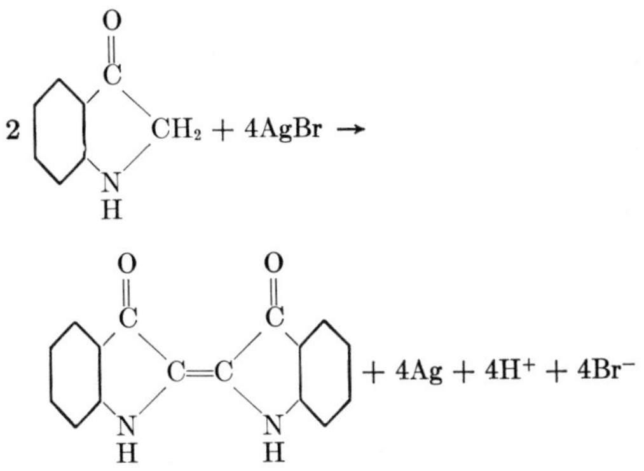

In a similar manner a number of other dye intermediates and leuco cases can be used as developers and form dye images.

The developer, *o*-aminophenol, is not a leuco base but is called a "self-coupling" developer. It forms the dye

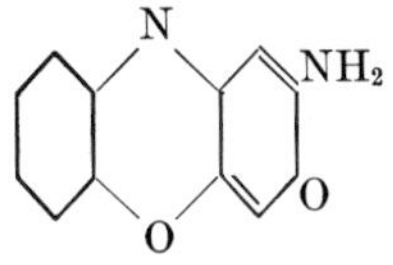

as follows[4]

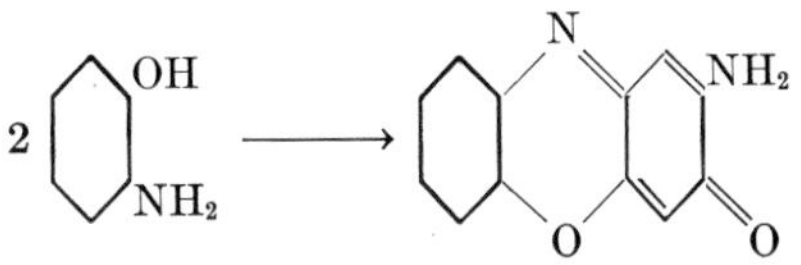

Dye-image formation by development with leuco bases or self-coupling developers has never become of any practical import-

---

[1] Liesegang, *Phot. Arch.* **36**, 115 (1895).

[2] Homolka, *Phot. Korr.* **44**, 55, 115 (1907); **51**, *56*, 471 (1914), *Brit. J. Phot.* **54**, 136, 196, 216 *1907*). Ermen, *Brit. J. Phot.* **70**, 47, 299 (1923).

[3] Tausch, *Thesis*, Dresden (1934).

[4] Von Auwers, Borsche, and Weller, *Ber.* **54**, 1291 (1921).

ance because of the poor color and instability of the images which can be formed or because of the poor latent-image developing properties of the compounds.

In 1912 Fischer [5] found that certain agents, when added to p-phenylenediamine or p-aminophenol developer solutions, would cause the formation of a dye image accompanying the silver image. This was found to be due to the "coupling" of this added material to the oxidized developer and the material was called a "coupler." This nomenclature is still in use. Fischer realized that this principle had many practical applications and he patented [6] the use of such processes for the production of prints in color and for color photography. His patents included images consisting of dyes belonging to five different classes— namely, indophenols, indoanilines, indamines, indothiophenols, and azomethines. The type of coupling development found by Fischer did eventually have practical application in the Kodachrome, Kodacolor, Agfacolor, and Ansco Color processes of the present day.

Types of Dyes Formed by Coupling Development. There are two types of developers which can be used as coupling developers, derivatives of p-phenylenediamine

$$\begin{array}{c}NH_2\\ \bigodot\\ NH_2\end{array},$$ and derivatives of p-aminophenol

$$\begin{array}{c}NH_2\\ \bigodot\\ OH\end{array}.$$ Both couple at the amino group

$$\begin{array}{c}N\\ \|\\ \bigodot\end{array}$$ so that the amino group in the p-amino-

phenol developers and one of the amino groups in the p-phenylenediamine developers must be unsubstituted. There are also two general types of couplers, phenols (or

napthols) $$\begin{array}{c}OH\\ \bigodot\end{array},$$ and materials containing

an active methylene group, $=C—\overset{H_2}{C}—C=$ a CH_2 group connected directly to two unsaturated carbon atoms. A p-phenylenediamine derivative couples with a phenol to form an indoaniline dye. A p-aminophenol derivative couples with a phenol to form an indophenol dye. The dyes formed when either p-phenylenediamine or p-aminophenol couples with an active methylene group are called azomethine dyes.

Couplers. The various elements and groupings that are combined in a compound which behaves as a coupler can be divided into two parts. The first of these is the color-forming part, which determines to a great extent (when used with a given developer) the color of the dye which is formed or the general region of the spectrum in which the dye will absorb light. The other parts of the material influence the stability of the dye formed, the solubility of the dye formed, as well as the solubility of the coupler itself in a developer solution, the diffusibility of the coupler

TABLE 14.1. EFFECT OF ADDED GROUPS ON THE COLOR FORMED FROM PHENOL AND NAPHTHOL COUPLERS (DEVELOPER DIETHYL-p-PHENYLENEDIAMINE)

Coupler	Group Added	Color
Phenol..............		Greenish blue
o-Cresol..............	CH_3	Blue
1,3,6-Xylenol..........	Two CH_3	Deeper blue
α-Naphthol..........		Blue
Dichloro-α-naphthol.....	Two Cl	Cyan
Trichloro-α-naphthol....	Three Cl	Green cyan
Pentachloro-α-naphthol..	Five Cl	Green

---

[5] Fischer, *Brit. J. Phot.* **60**, 595, 712 (1913); **61**, 329 (1914).

[6] U.S.P. 1,055,155; 1,079,756; 1,102,028. D.R.P. 253,335.

through an emulsion layer, and other physical characteristics. These functions will be discussed further in a later section.

All the phenol or naphthol couplers form dyes which absorb light in the red end of the spectrum, thus giving cyan or blue dyes. A few of the well-known couplers and the colors which they form with diethyl-*p*-phenylenediamine are shown in Table 14.1.

Couplers which are pyrazolones, cyanoacetyl compounds, and derivatives of *p*-nitrobenzylcyanide, $O_2N\langle\quad\rangle CH_2CN$, when coupled with diethyl-*p*-phenylenediamine, give dyes with the major absorption in the green region of the spectrum, thus leading to magenta or orange dyes. A few of the better known couplers of this type are shown in Table 14.2.

TABLE 14.2. COUPLERS WHICH GIVE A MAGENTA DYE WITH DIETHYL-*p*-PHENYLENEDIAMINE

1-*p*-Nitrophenyl-3-methyl-5-pyrazolone
1-Phenyl-3-methyl-5-pyrazolone
p-Nitrobenzylcyanide
Benzoylacetonitrile
Naphthoylacetonitrile

Couplers with the active methylene group

$$O$$
$$\|$$

between two —C— groups give dyes which have their major absorption in the blue region of the spectrum and are thus yellow or orange. A few of them are shown in Table 14.3.

TABLE 14.3. COUPLERS WHICH GIVE A YELLOW DYE WITH DIETHYL-*p*-PHENYLENEDIAMINE

Ethyl acetoacetate
Ethyl benzoylacetate
Acetoacetanilide
β-Naphthoylacetone
Diethyl malonate

Thus, the cyan and blue dyes obtained by coupling development are indoaniline or indophenol dyes, and the yellow, orange, and magenta dyes are azomethine.

Coupling Developers.

The most important developers used for coupling to make a dye image are the substituted *p*-phenylenediamines. These may have one or two of the hydrogen atoms on one of the nitrogens substituted by methyl, ethyl, or other groups, and may have similar groups substituted in the benzene ring. However, one of the amino groups must remain unsubstituted in order for the developer to couple.

The exact structure of the developer influences the solubility of the dyes formed, the stability of the dyes, and the exact color which is obtained from a given coupler. Table 14.4 indicates the colors which

TABLE 14.4. EFFECT OF DEVELOPING AGENT ON COLOR OBTAINED WITH DICHLORO-α-NAPHTHOL

Developing Agent	Group Added	Color
p-Phenylenediamine..... *p*-Toluylenediamine.....	CH₃ on ring	Pink or purple Blue
Dimethyl-*p*-phenylene- diamine.............	Two CH₃ groups on N	Cyan Blue
Diethyl-*p*-phenylene- diamine.............	Two C₂H₅ groups on N	Cyan

are obtained when a few different developers are used with a given coupler.

One of the chief disadvantages of the normal *p*-phenylenediamine developers is their strong tendency to cause a severe rash on human skin. In using such developers, extreme care must be exercised to avoid contact with the developer solution. Skin irritations have occurred after repeated use of such developers even when great care has been taken to avoid contact. On continued exposure to *p*-phenylenediamine a person does not develop an immunity to it but actually develops increased sensitivity.

In recent years a number of patents have been granted describing new developers which are stated to be an improvement over the well-known dimethyl-*p*-phenylenediamine and diethyl-*p*-phenylenediamine. U.S.P. 2,210,843 describes a compound $N(C_2H_4 \cdot OH)_2$

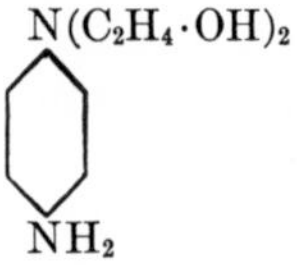

which has OH groups substituted in the two ethyl groups of diethyl-*p*-phenylenediamine. This compound is much more soluble in a developer solution than diethyl-*p*-phenylenediamine. U.S.P. 2,163,166 describes the compounds HNR_1—Y

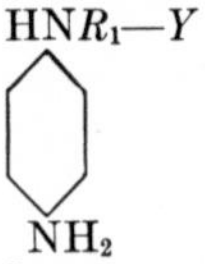

, where R_1 is an alkylene or arylene group and Y is COOH or SO_3H, and the compounds

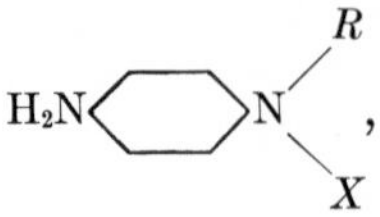

, where R represents H, alkyl, aryl, or hydroxy alkyl and X represents —$(CH_2CH_2O)_n$—CH_2-CH_2OH. These compounds are stated to be more soluble than the usual color developers and to have greatly decreased toxic action on human skin. U.S.P. 2,193,015 describes the developer compounds

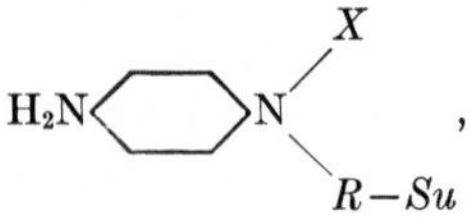

, where X represents hydrogen or alkyl, R represents alkylene, Su represents —SO_2NH_2, —SO_2NHR', or —$NHSO_2R'$, where R' is hydrogen or alkyl. These compounds are also stated to be more soluble than normal color developers and much less toxic.

p-Aminophenol and substituted *p*-aminophenol can also be used as color developers. However, the solubility and the instability of the dyes formed from these developers make them unsatisfactory, and they have not been used in practice.

Developer Solution Ingredients. The constituents of coupling developer solutions

are the coupler, the developer, an alkali which is usually required to dissolve the coupler and to make the developer sufficiently active, a buffer to preserve the alkalinity, a small amount of sulfite to act as preservative (the large amount of sulfite used in normal black-and-white developers usually interferes with the coupling reaction), bromide, and frequently an additional organic antifoggant. In some cases an organic solvent such as alcohol is used instead of an alkali for dissolving the coupler. Formulas for color-developer solutions which give cyan, magenta, and yellow dye images suitable for three-color work, as well as a variety of colors suitable for monochrome, have been published by Colton.[7]

Chemistry of the Coupling Development Reaction. During development or other methods of developer oxidation, the coupler reacts with the oxidized developer as follows:

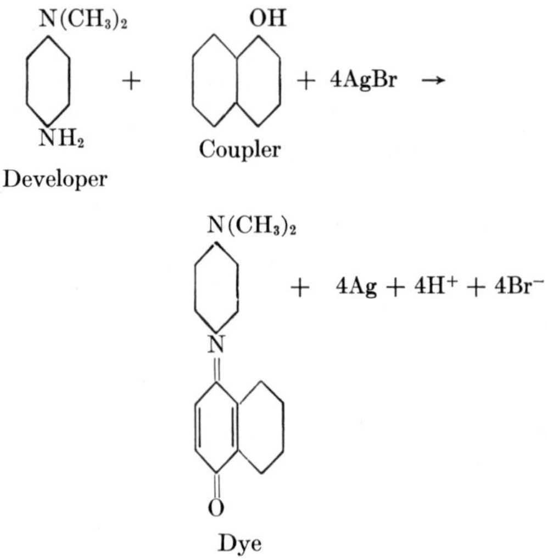

Four molecules of silver bromide are reduced and four molecules of hydrobromic acid are formed. The reaction of a coupler

[7] Colton, *Photo-Technique* **1** (September 1939), 16.

with an active methylene group can be shown by a similar equation:

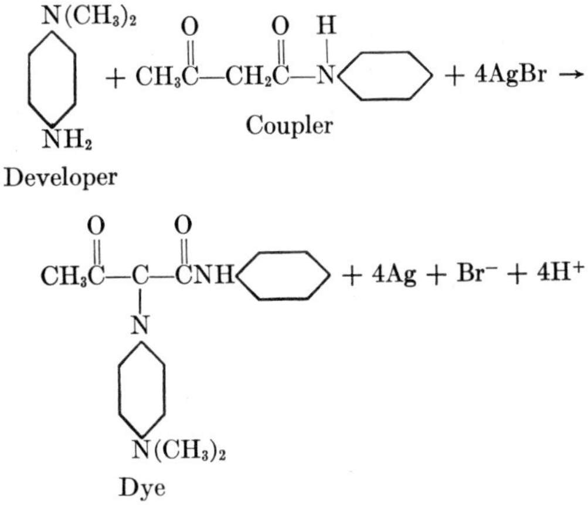

Developer · Coupler + 4AgBr →

Dye

Certain phenol couplers have the coupling position occupied by a chlorine atom rather than the hydrogen. In this case the chlorine is split off during the coupling reaction and the same dye is formed as if the chlorine had not been present. For example,

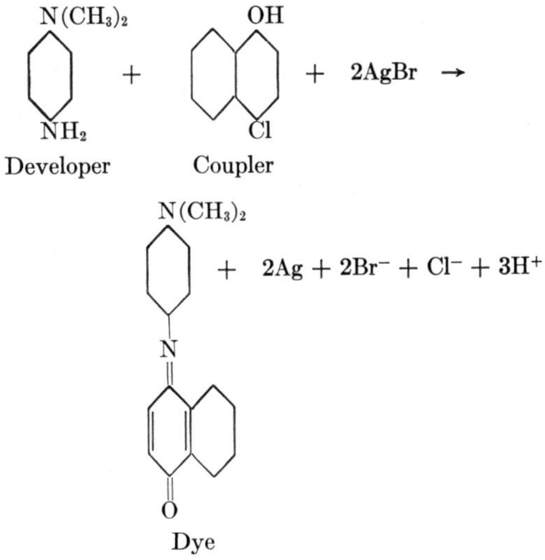

Developer · Coupler + 2AgBr →

Dye

Only two molecules of silver bromide are reduced, and two molecules of hydrobromic and one molecule of hydrochloric acid are released.

In practice, during the simultaneous development of a silver and dye image, re-

actions similar to those shown above take place but, in addition, some of the oxidized developer reacts with sulfite, which is normally included in all developer solutions. The reaction is

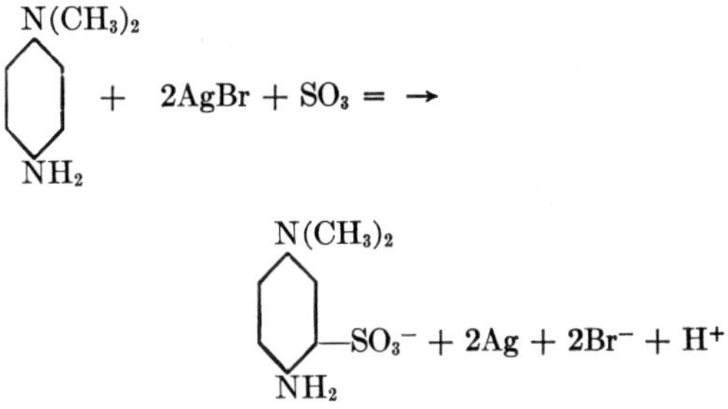

$+ 2AgBr + SO_3 = →$

$-SO_3^- + 2Ag + 2Br^- + H^+$

In addition, some developer is oxidized by the oxygen of the air, thus forming dye without the formation of silver, so that it is quite difficult to demonstrate experimentally the four-to-one ratio of the amount of silver and dye formed (or two-to-one in the case of chloro-substituted couplers) as indicated by the above equations.

The coupling reaction has been investigated by Flannery and Collins.[8] They used developers containing no sulfite but did not mention any specific steps taken to eliminate oxygen. For the cyan coupler, 2,4-dichloro-α-naphthol, they found 1.83 molecules of silver for every molecule of dye formed during the development reaction. This is in fair agreement with the value 2, which would be predicted from the equation for a chloro-substituted coupler. For the magenta coupler, 1-*p*-nitrophenyl-3-methyl-5-pyrazolone, 3.64 molecules of silver per molecule of dye were formed; and for the yellow coupler, furoyl-2-acet-2',4'-xylidide, 3.4 molecules of silver per molecule of dye. These results are in fair agreement with the theoretical value of 4. The deviation of these results from the theoretical values must be attributed to experimental error rather than to any error in the

[8] Flannery and Collins, *Phot. J.* **86B**, 86 (1946).

equations themselves, because the structure of the dyes formed by a number of couplers has been determined and is in agreement with the structure given by the equations.

Practical Use of Coupling Development. In order for coupling development to be used in practice, a number of requirements must be fulfilled. For a dye *image* to be formed, the dye which is formed during development must be insoluble and not be washed out of the film. Resorcinal

OH
⬡
⬡OH

is an excellent coupler, but with the normal coupling developers it forms a dye which is soluble in the developer solution. The dye must also have the proper color, particularly for three-color photography, and must also have adequate stability against fading.

For use in the Kodachrome process [9,10] of the Eastman Kodak Company, the couplers must be adequately soluble in the developer solution and must diffuse freely through the gelatin so that the dye images may be formed in the proper layers. The particular couplers which most adequately fulfill the coupler and dye requirements have required extended technological investigation, but couplers such as 2,4-dichloro-1-naphthol, 1-phenyl-3-methyl-5-pyrazolone and acetoacet-2,5-dichloroanilide are of the types that could be used.

The coupler requirements for a process such as Agfacolor, Ansco Color, or Kodacolor are quite different. In these films the couplers are included in the emulsions themselves and must be of such a nature that they do not wander from one layer to the next. This is accomplished by the attachment of large organic groups to the coupler molecules, the nature of these groups being such that they immobilize the

coupler and yet do not interfere with the coupling reaction, or change, to any large extent, the color of the dye formed. Couplers of the type used in Agfacolor and Ansco Color are described in a number of patents.[11] For example, the compound 1-Stearoylamino-4-(1'-hydroxy-2'-naphthoylamino)-benzene-3-sulfonic acid

$$\text{OH} \quad \underset{\text{SO}_3\text{H}}{\overset{\text{O H}}{\underset{\|}{\text{C}}-\overset{\text{H}}{\underset{}{\text{N}}}}-\underset{}{\bigcirc}-\overset{\text{H O}}{\underset{}{\text{N}-\underset{\|}{\text{C}}}}-\text{C}_{17}\text{H}_{35}$$

is described as a cyan coupler. The group

OH
⬡
⬡

is the coupling or dye-forming part; the group $-\text{C}_{17}\text{H}_{35}$ is the part of the molecule which prevents wandering from one layer to another; and the group $-\text{SO}_3\text{H}$ introduces enough solubility so that the coupler may be properly dispersed in the emulsion. These latter groups do not have any significant effect on the color of the dye formed. The experimental work which led to the development of the nonwandering couplers for use in Agfacolor film has been summarized by Schneider, Fröhlich, and Schultze.[12]

The Kodacolor process of the Eastman Kodak Company, first described by Dr. C. E. K. Mees,[13] makes use of a different method of dispersing the couplers in the emulsions and immobilizing them against wandering from one layer to another. The couplers in their emulsion layers are not dissolved in the gelatin itself but are carried in very small particles of oily organic materials which protect them from the gelatin and, at the same time, protect the silver bromide from any interaction with

---

9 Mees, *J. Franklin Inst.* **233**, 41 (1942).

10 Davies, *Phot. J.* **76**, 248 (1936).

11 U.S.P. 2,186,732; 2,186,849; 2,186,851; 2,179-239; 2,186,719.

12 Schneider, Fröhlich, and Schultze, *Die Chemie* **57**, 113 (1944).

13 Mees, *J. Franklin Inst.* **233**, 41 (1942).

the couplers. When development takes place, the oxidation product of the developing agent dissolves in the organic material and there reacts with the coupler so that the dyes are formed in the small particles dispersed in the layers. A number of liquids which might be used as the solvent for the coupler and a number of compounds which might be used as the couplers themselves have been described in patents.[14]

Several other methods of immobilizing couplers have been described in recent patents. U.S.P. 2,296,306 describes coupler compounds which have attached to them a molecular group which forms an insoluble salt with silver ions. The silver salt of this compound can be put in an emulsion and forms a dye on subsequent color development. A number of patents[15] describe couplers which are prepared by attaching a coupler molecule to certain types of colloidal materials. This material is then used as a carrier for the grains in the emulsion, rather than gelatin which is normally used. Thus, the coupler itself becomes a part of the carrier in which the emulsion is formed.

Colored Couplers. The dyes obtained from coupling development are now in wide use in three-color photography. However, these dyes have certain characteristics which cause a significant loss in quality when a color print is made from a color transparency or when a color transparency is duplicated. In the ideal case, the cyan dye used in a color photograph should have density in the red region of the spectrum, but no density in the green and blue regions. In practice, cyan dyes do have density in the blue and green regions of the spectrum. Magenta dyes which should have density only in the green region of the spectrum also have some density in the blue region. These densities

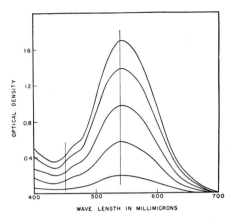

Fig. 14.1. Spectrophotometric curves of a series of concentrations of a typical magenta dye.

of the dyes in the improper region of the spectrum contribute a good deal of darkening and desaturation when a color transparency is duplicated. By the use of colored couplers, as described by P. W. Vittum and W. T. Hanson, Jr.,[16] these imperfections can be canceled. This is accomplished by introducing into the coupler itself a color which contributes density in a given region of the spectrum which is just equal to the undesired density of the dye that is formed from that coupler. Let us take a magenta dye for an example. Fig. 14.1 shows the spectrophotometric curves of a series of concentrations of a typical magenta dye. Here the density is the ordinate and the wavelength is the abscissa. This dye has high density in the green region of the spectrum but also has some density in the blue region. The density in the blue region is the objectional feature of this dye for use in color photography. Now, suppose that the coupler from which this dye was formed is colored yellow and has a spectrophotometric curve in a given concentration, as shown in Fig. 14.2. As magenta dye is formed from this coupler, the color of the coupler itself is

14 U.S.P. 2,322,027; 2,304,940.

15 U.S.P. 2,397,864; 2,397,867; 2,415,381; 2,415,-382; 2,422,680.

16 Vittum and Hanson, Jr., *P. S. A. Journal* **13**, 2 (1947).

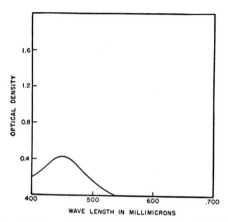

Fig. 14.2. Yellow colored coupler for correcting blue absorption of magenta dye.

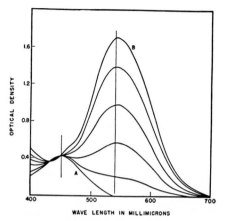

Fig. 14.3. Spectrophotometric curves of a series of concentrations of a magenta dye obtained from a typical yellow-colored coupler.

destroyed. The result is shown in Fig. 14.3. The curve representing the color of the coupler itself is reproduced from Fig. 14.2 and is labeled "A." The maximum concentration of magenta dye which is formed when all of the coupler is used up corresponds to the top curve in Fig. 14.1, and this is labeled "B" At intermediate conditions where some of the coupler has reacted and some magenta dye has been formed, the spectrophotometric curve of the resulting mixture will be the sum of that for the coupler that remains and that for the magenta dye which is formed. A number of these intermediate conditions are shown in Fig. 14.3. It can be seen that the curves representing all of the concentrations of dye pass through the same point in the blue region of the spectrum. This density in the blue region of the spectrum is a constant independent of the amount of magenta dye that is formed, so

that the resultant image behaves effectively as if the magenta dye had no blue absorption.

In a similar manner, an orange-colored coupler with the proper amount of density in the blue and green regions of the spectrum could exactly cancel the blue and green densities of the cyan dye formed from that coupler.

Couplers which will form a dye having the characteristics shown in Fig. 14.3 may be made by attaching a colored component to the active position of that coupler so that when the coupler reacts with oxidized developer to form a dye the colored component of the coupler itself is expelled and destroyed and the normal dye is formed. The type of reaction which occurs is illustrated by the following typical dye-forming reactions, A, with a normal uncolored coupler, and B, with a colored coupler:

A. CH_3—C——CH_2
      ‖   C=O + H_2N⟨ ⟩$N(CH_3)_2$ + AgBr → CH_3—C——C=N—⟨ ⟩—$N(CH_3)_2$
      N   N

Developer   C=O
          N

Coupler

Magenta Dye

B. 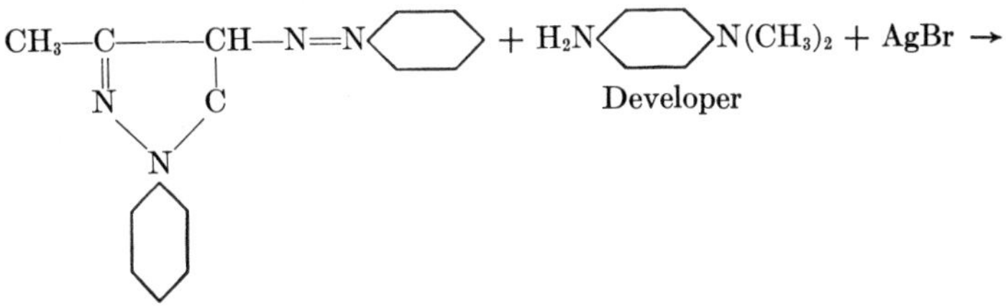 CH_3—C———CH—N=N⟨⟩ + H_2N⟨⟩$N(CH_3)_2$ + AgBr →

$\qquad$ Developer

Colored coupler

CH_3—C———C=N⟨⟩$N(CH_3)_2$

Magenta dye

The same dye is formed in both of these reactions.

This type of coupler can only be used in a color process in which the coupler is in the emulsion, rather than in the developer, and the residual coupler which does not form dye remains in the film and takes part in the final image. Couplers of this type have been described in a number of patents.[17]

[17] Can. P. 436,354; 436,847; U.S.P. 2,434,272; 2,428,054.

Chapter 15

FIXING AND WASHING

Fixing Agents. The removal of the silver halide remaining after development involves (1) the conversion of the halide to compounds soluble in water, an operation known as *fixing*, and (2) the removal of the soluble compounds and the fixing agent by washing in water.

The number of substances capable of converting the silver halides into soluble compounds, and able therefore to function as fixing agents, is rather limited. The requirements for a good fixing agent are that (1) it should dissolve silver halides without affecting the silver image, (2) the complexes formed should be readily soluble in water and yet stable, so they will not decompose during washing, (3) the agent should not cause excessive swelling or softening of gelatin. The most important are the thiosulfates—sodium thiosulfate, ammonium thiosulfate, lithium thiosulfate, and guanidine thiosulfate.[1] Sodium thiosulfate has been in general use since 1839. Ammonium thiosulfate fixes more rapidly, and acid fixing and hardening baths retain their hardening properties over a wider pH range and thus remain clear and free from sludging over a longer period of use than a fixing bath containing hypo.[2]

Potassium cyanide (KCN) has been used for fixing wet collodion, which, due to the low solubility of silver iodide, fixes slowly in solutions of thiosulfate. The use of thiourea for the fixing of emulsions with a high silver iodide content has been recommended.[3] Both tend to dissolve the finely divided metallic silver of the image resulting in a reduction in density. Ordinarily the effect is limited to the lower densities.

The silver halides are converted into soluble salts by the thiocyanates (potassium thiocyanate and ammonium thiocyanate) but these are more expensive and in no way superior to the thiosulfates for general use.[4]

Other fixing agents include sodium chloride (salt), sodium sulfite, ammonia, potassium bromide, potassium iodide, and thiosinamine. These are of theoretical interest only.

Chemistry of Fixing. The chemical reactions in fixing with the thiosulfates are still not entirely clear.[5] Thiosulfate ions undoubtedly combine with silver ions to form complex ions of varying solubility, as for example:

$$AgBr + 3Na_2SO_3 \rightarrow NaBr + Na_5Ag(S_2O_3)_3$$
$$AgBr + 2Na_2S_2O_3 \rightarrow NaBr + Na_3Ag(S_2O_3)_2$$
$$2NaBr + 3Na_2S_2O_3 \rightarrow 2NaBr + Na_4Ag_2(S_2O_3)_3$$

---

[3] Rzymkowski, *Phot. Ind.* **24**, 1251 (1926). Horgan, *Inland Printer* **78**, 785 (1927).

[4] Piper, *Brit. J. Phot.* **61**, 458, 511 (1914).

[5] Sheppard, Elliott, and Sweet, *J. Frank. Inst.* **195**, 45 (1923). Baines, *Phot. J.* **69**, 315 (1929). Orlander, *Chem. Abst.* **35**, 7852 (1941). Elvegard, *Phot. Ind.* **39**, 756 (1941). Hanson, *Amer. Phot.* **36**, 22 (1942). Ölander and Adelsohn, *Svensk. Kem. Tidskr.* **58**, 33 (1946) (In English.) Carriéré and Raulet, *Comp. rend.* **192**, 746 (1931). Schramm, *Brit. J. Phot.* **82**, 360 (1935). Luther, *Phot. Ind.* **26**, 626 (1928). Pankhurst, *Chemistry and Industry* **61**, 74 (1942). For a review of work on the complexes of silver sodium thiosulfate, see Mees, *Theory of the Photographic Process*, 1945, p. 511.

---

[1] Ham, U.S.P. 2,260,665.

[2] Alnutt, *J. Soc. Mot. Pict. Eng.* **41**, 300 (1943).

With potassium cyanide the reaction is probably as follows:

$$2KCN + AgI \rightarrow KCN \cdot AgCN + KI.$$

Acid Fixing Baths. Fixing baths of hypo alone are open to the objection that unless a stop bath is used the developing solution in the emulsion layer oxidizes and the gelatin is stained by the oxidation products. This may be prevented by the addition of sodium sulfite, which tends to prevent oxidation, and an acid to neutralize the alkali introduced by the developer.[6] Acetic acid is generally used, the reaction resulting in thiosulfuric acid which is the actual preservative.[7] A similar result may be produced with acid sulfites such as sodium bisulfite ($NaHSO_3$) and potassium metabisulfite ($K_2S_2O_5$). Fixing baths of this kind are seldom used, except in circumstances where the hardening of the gelatin is undesirable, as in the preparation of gelatin reliefs.

Acid Fixing and Hardening Baths. The acid fixing and hardening bath contains: (1) a solvent of silver halide, (2) an anti-staining agent, (3) a preservative, and (4) a hardening agent. These ordinarily are (1) hypo, (2) an organic acid, usually acetic, (3) sodium sulfite, and (4) alum. The sulfite acts as a preservative to prevent the formation of sulfur by the action of the acid on the thiosulfate and the oxidation of the developer. The acid neutralizes the alkali of the developer and thus stops development. This acid also prevents the alum from reacting with the sulfite to form aluminium sulfite and destroy the hardening produced by the alum.[8] The alum forms hydrous oxide and free acid:

$$Al_2(SO_4)_3 + 3H_2O \rightleftarrows Al_2O_3 + 3H_2SO_4.$$

The hardening is produced by the alumina oxide adsorbed by the gelatin forming a complex which is retained on washing in water.

Potassium alum ($Al_2(SO_4)_3 \cdot K_2SO_4 \cdot 24H_2O$) is usually employed,[9] chrome alum ($Cr_2(SO_4)_3 \cdot K_2SO_4 \cdot 24H_2O$) hardens gelatin more thoroughly, but the hardening properties of chrome alum fixing baths fall off rapidly unless additional acid is added from time time to time to maintain a pH from 3.0 to 3.8.[10] In used baths, there is a danger that only the surface of the emulsion layer may be hardened—a condition which in washing may lead to reticulation. Chrome alum fixing and hardening baths are preferable, however, for maximum hardening with rapid fixing baths, under tropical conditions, if the wash water is warm, and when it is necessary to dry film rapidly at a high temperature.

While acetic acid is the most widely used, propionic, butyric,[11] sulfamic [12] H_2N-SO_3H), gluconic,[13] mucic acids [14] have all been proposed. Solid organic acids, such

[6] Lancir, *Phot. Korr.* **26**, 171 (1889).

[7] Others recommended from time to time include citric, boric, lactic, maleic, tartaric, and sulfamic (Gallafent, B.P. 534,409).

[8] Sheppard, Elliott, and Sweet, *J. Frank. Institute* **195**, 45 (1923) Kieser, *Phot. Ind.* **32**, 696 (1934).

[9] Aluminium chloride was found by Muehler to have several advantages over alum as a hardener, the principal being an increase in the useful life of bath due to a longer sludge and sulfurization free period. U.S.P. 1,981,426. For the preparation of concentrated liquid fixing and hardening baths, Russell patented the use of boric acid and sodium acetate or triethanolamine (B.P. 458,050—1936) and later ethanolamine, boric and acetic acids, sulfur dioxide, and aluminium chloride hydrate (B.P. 564,271—1943). The addition of guanidine nitrate for the same purpose was patented by Ham and Barnes (U.S.P. 2,174,494; 2,260,665; 2,311,293).

[10] Crabtree and Russell, *J. Soc. Mot. Pict. Eng.* **15**, 483, 667 (1930).

[11] Russell and Crabtree, *J. Soc. Mot. Pict. Eng.* **21**, 137 (1933).

[12] U.S.P. 2,195,405.

[13] Harris, Seybold, Potter, U.S.P. 2,257,440.

[14] Webster, U.S.P. 2,214,216.

as citric and tartaric, are less suitable as they tend to unite with the alum to form complex aluminium ions which are not satisfactory hardeners. The acid sulfites do not have sufficient reserve acidity to prevent the precipitation of aluminium sulfite upon the addition of the alkali of the developer. Sodium hydrogen sulfate, obtained from the combination of sodium acetate and sodium bisulfate, has been recommended.[15]

Effect of Use on the Acid Hardening and Fixing Bath. The principal changes taking place with use in a fixing bath of this type are:

1. *The concentration of hypo is reduced and silver accumulates in the solution.* This reduces the amount of hypo available for fixing and increases the tendency toward the formation of slightly soluble, or insoluble, complexes of silver sodium thiosulfate. These are retained by negatives, or prints, fixed in the bath and are not removed by washing. In time, these complexes decompose to form a yellow-colored stain that consists chiefly of silver sulfide. Since staining of this character is more pronounced with fine grain images, prints and positive transparencies, negatives on fine-grain emulsions and high-speed, coarse-grained emulsions are more likely to stain in that order.

2. *Alkaline halides accumulate in the bath.* The accumulation of sodium bromide and silver iodide, particularly the latter, greatly retards the rate of fixing and results in the formation of insoluble complexes before the amount of silver in the bath has reached the saturation point.[16]

3. *The pH of the bath is reduced by the developer,* a sludge of aluminium sulfate forms and the bath no longer hard-

ens the gelatin satisfactorily.[17] Fixing baths of ammonium thiosulfate have the advantage over those containing hypo of hardening properly up to a pH of approximately 6.5.[18]

The limit to which a fixing bath may be used with the assurance of complete fixation depends upon the sensitive material; in the case of a negative material, one of the important factors is the amount of silver iodide present. A fixing bath which is still capable of converting silver bromide to soluble compounds may be unable to form soluble complexes with the silver iodide present. Furthermore, in a fixing bath nearing exhaustion some of the silver thiosulfate complexes are adsorbed to the silver grains, the gelatin, or the fibers of the paper so that they cannot be removed by washing and eventually discolor, causing stains which are not easily removed. This is ordinarily the limiting factor in the useful life of fixing bath used for emulsions on paper.[19]

In the case of negative materials, the time of clearance—which is a direct indication of the time required for fixing—is so greatly increased by the restraining effect of the accumulated alkaline halides that the bath is discarded before the limit of its usefulness is reached. As a rule, a fixing bath should be discarded when the time required to clear a particular emulsion is twice that of a fresh bath.

With chrome alum fixing baths, and

[15] Woolsey and Pankhurst, *Phot. J.* **82**, 12 (1942).

[16] Barth, *Z. phys. Chem.* **9**, 218 (1912). Busch and Lehrmann, *Brit. J. Phot.* **75**, 91 (1927).

[17] Crabtree and Hartt, *Trans. Soc. Mot. Pict. Eng.* **18**, 364 (1929).

[18] Alnutt, *J. Soc. Mot. Pict. Eng.* **41**, 300 (1943).

[19] On the useful life of fixing baths see: Busch and Lehrmann, *Brit. J. Phot.* **75**, 91, 105 (1927). Lumiere and Seyewetz, *Brit. J. Phot.* **54**, 138 (1907); **71**, 172 (1924). Crabtree and Hartt, *Trans. Soc. Mot. Pict. Eng.* **18**, 364 (1929). Crabtree and Russell, *J. Soc. Mot. Pict. Eng.* **21**, 137 (1933). Crabtree, Eaton and Muehler, *J. Phot. Soc. Amer.* **9**, 164 (1943).

with fixing baths containing potassium alum but without boric acid, sludge forms, or the hardening properties become insufficient, before the bath is exhausted. In general this is not true, however, of acid fixing and hardening baths containing boric acid. With these the hardening properties may show little change when the bath reaches the limit of its fixing power.

Testing of Used Fixing Baths. The amount of silver present in a used fixing bath may be determined by adding a solution of sodium sulfide to a sample of the bath. A brown precipitate is formed, the density of which depends upon the amount of silver present. The quantity of silver, as shown by the density of the solution, may be determined (1) by comparison with samples containing known amounts of silver, or (2) by measuring the density with a densitometer and converting density into silver.[20]

For practical purposes, a fixing bath may be regarded as exhausted when the addition of potassium iodide results in a precipitate of silver iodide. A few drops (3–4) of a 10% solution of potassium iodide are added to 25 cc. of the fixing bath. If a yellow precipitate forms on standing the bath should be discarded.[21]

A more critical test consists in fixing a test strip of film or paper until clear, washing in running water 15–20 minutes and then immersing the test strip in a 1% solution of sodium sulfide. The formation of a brown stain indicates the presence of silver compounds capable of combining with sulfide to form silver sulfide.

Rate of Fixing. If the fraction of silver halide dissolved is plotted against the time factor, the resulting curve (Fig. 15.1) has a short concave portion, or foot, which soon becomes a straight line. Thus, excluding the earliest stages, rate, in terms of the amount of silver halide dissolved, is proportional to the mass present.[22] The relationship is, therefore, that of an exponential function and can be represented as

$$\frac{dx}{dt} = k(a - x),$$

where a = the initial concentration
d = the diffusion factor
k = the rate factor
x = the halide dissolved in time t.

Most of the work on the time of fixing has been based on the time of clearance; i.e., the disappearance of all visible traces of silver halide from the emulsion layer. This is dependent upon:

1. *The nature and thickness of the emulsion.* In general, fine-grain emulsions, such as those employed for positive printing, fix much more rapidly than negative emulsions which are composed of larger

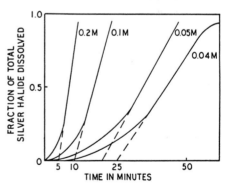

FIG. 15.1. Curve showing the fraction of silver halide dissolved in an acid fixing and hardening bath plotted against the time.

[20] A photoelectric densitometer, the *Argentometer,* for determining the amount of silver in a fixing bath has been described by Hickman and Weyerts, *Brit. J. Phot.* **82**, 739 (1935).

For other tests for fixing baths see: Huse and Atkinson, *The Chemical Analysis of Motion Picture Developers and Fixing Baths,* Motion Picture Film Division, Eastman Kodak Co., Hollywood.

[21] *Phot. Rund.* (1937) 33.

[22] Sheppard and Mees, *Investigations on the Theory of the Photographic Process,* Longmans, Green and Co., London, p. 70. Warwick, *Amer. Phot.* **11**, 585 (1917).

grains. Emulsions containing silver iodide fix more slowly than those of silver bromide and these in turn more slowly than emulsions of silver chloride. A thickly coated emulsion requires a longer time to fix than a thinly coated one, if both are of the same composition.

2. *The composition of the fixing bath.* With the thiosulfates, the time required for fixing becomes less with increasing concentration up to an optimum point beyond which the time of clearance increases with the concentration of thiosulate. At the optimum concentration, i.e., the concentration with the shortest clearing time, the time required increases in the following order—ammonium thiosulfate, lithium, thiosulfate, sodium thiosulfate. Curves representing the clearing time for wet film in ammonium thiosulfate and in hypo at different concentrations and temperature are shown in Fig. 15.2.[23] The clearing time for ammonium thiosulfate, at equivalent concentrations, is always less

than that of hypo, except at a concentration of 600 grams per liter or higher, and then only at the lower temperatures. At chemically equivalent concentrations, namely 148 grams of ammonium thiosulfate and 248 grams of hypo per liter, the clearing time for ammonium thiosulfate is from one-fourth to one-half that of hypo, depending on the emulsion.[24]

3. *The temperature.* The clearing time for a given concentration varies with the temperature, as shown in Fig. 15.2. With most acid fixing and hardening baths, however, temperatures above 70° F. (21° C.) increase the tendency of the bath to sulfurize and the gelatin is less thoroughly hardened because of the swelling which takes place before the hardening action of the bath becomes effective. Practically the useful temperature range lies between 60- and 70° F.

---

[23] Alnutt, *J. Soc. Mot. Pict. Eng.* **41**, 300 (1943).

[24] The addition of ammonium chloride to a hypo solution reduces the clearing time. See: Lumiere and Seyewetz, *Brit. J. Phot.* **55**, 417 (1908). Piper, *Brit. J. Phot.* **61**, 193 (1914).

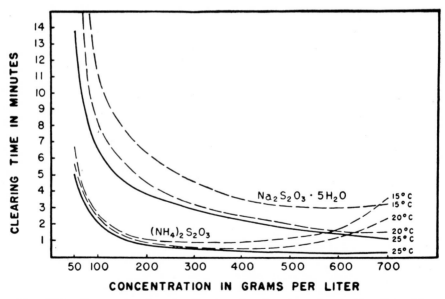

FIG. 15.2. Curves showing the clearing time in ammonium and sodium thiosulfate at different concentrations and temperatures. (Alnutt.)

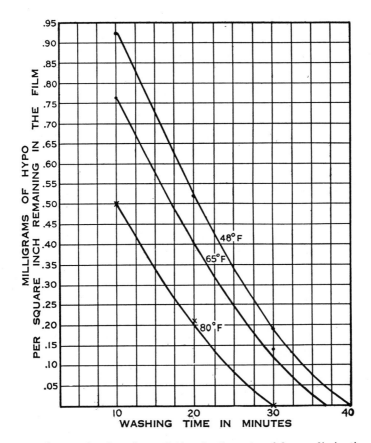

FIG. 15.3. Curves showing the variation in the rate of hypo elimination with the temperature of the wash water.

4. *Degree of exhaustion.* The time of clearing increases greatly with use as a result of: (1) reduction in the concentration of the fixing agent, and (2) the accumulation of restraining halides; sodium bromide and particularly silver iodide.[25]

5. *Agitation.* Agitation of the solution reduces the time of fixation but the effect is much less with fine-grain than with coarse-grain emulsions.

Reducing Action of Fixing Baths. Acid fixing and hardening baths have a definite

reducing action on the image.[26] The effect is slight, except with warm-tone printing papers, unless the time in the fixing bath is considerably longer than that necessary for fixation. The amount of reduction increases with the pH of the fixing bath (particularly above 4.0), with the concentration of sodium sulfite (for a constant pH), and with the temperature (particularly at high temperatures), and decreases with the exhaustion of the fixing bath. It is normally more pronounced with chrome alum fixing baths than those with potassium

[25] Strauss, *Phot. Ind.* **23**, 881, 911 (1925). Crabtree and Ross, *Amer. Ann. of Phot.* **41**, 159 (1927).

[26] Russell and Crabtree, *J. Soc. Mot. Pict. Eng.* **18**, 371 (1932).

alum. The rate of reduction is increased by the addition of potassium bromide and potassium iodide, particularly the latter.

With coarse-grain negative materials, reduction under practically all conditions is almost truly proportional, but with fine grain materials and, particularly, with papers the action is intermediate in character being generally proportional but tending toward subtractive action in the lower densities.

Silver Recovery. There are several methods by which the silver in a used fixing bath may be recovered; usually, however, the financial return is hardly sufficient to justify the time and labor involved.

Precipitation of the silver as silver sulfide with sodium sulfide is one of the cheapest and most convenient methods, but has the disadvantage of forming obnoxious odors.

While the amount of silver recovered is less, the use of zinc dust has the advantage that no obnoxious fumes are formed. About 5 grams of zinc dust (or granulated) per liter (⅔ oz. per gallon) should be added with constant stirring and the solution left for about 24 hours. The sludge which forms on the bottom is then withdrawn and dried.

Metallic units of zinc, copper, or iron on which the silver precipitates are available commercially. These do not recover as much of the silver as the chemical methods and require longer but are more convenient.

Elaborate equipment has been developed for the recovery of silver by electrolytic means. The silver is recovered as metallic silver and may be removed from the fixing bath while in use, thus lengthening its useful life. The factor of expense places such equipment beyond the resources of any but the larger motion picture laboratories.[27]

Washing. Fixing converts the insoluble silver halides into soluble compounds which are removable by washing in water. Therefore, if fixing is incomplete no amount of washing can render the image permanent and the compounds of silver sodium thiosulfate remaining will discolor with the passage of time. Washing is necessary also for the removal of the fixing agent and its oxidation products from the emulsion. These, if left, would slowly combine with the silver of the image to produce a brown-yellow stain of silver sulfide, usually with some loss in density.

In general, hypo diffuses from the gelatin layer exponentially with time. In other words, the quantity of hypo leaving the film at any moment is proportional to the quantity present at the same time. Stated differently, as time increases, the amount of hypo diffusing out from the gelatin layer decreases geometrically.[28]

Thus if, for example, in one minute, one-half of the hypo originally present in the gelatin layer is removed, one-half of the remainder will be removed during the second minute, leaving the concentration after two minutes one-fourth of that originally present. In three minutes, the amount of hypo remaining will be one-eighth and in twenty minutes 1/1,000,000 of that originally present.

[27] Hickman, Sanford and Weyerts, *J. Soc. Mot. Pict. Eng.* **17**, 568, 591 (1931).

On the recovery of silver from used fixing baths see: Arens and Eggert, *Phot. Ind.* **34**, 1011 (1936). Crabtree and Ross, *Brit. J. Phot.* **73**, 522 (1926). Holzwarth and Dupont Film Mfg. Co., U.S.P. 2,214,765. Barnes and Ham, U.S.P. 2,221,163.

[28] Elsden, *Phot. J.* **57**, 90 (1917). Warwick, *Brit. J. Phot.* **64**, 261 (1917). Hickman and Spencer, *Phot.* **62**, 225 (1922); **63**, 208 (1923); **64**, 539, 553 (1924); **65**, 443 (1925).

Time Required for Washing. The time required for washing depends upon:

1. *The efficiency of washing.* The more rapid the change of water in contact with the gelatin layer, the less the time required for washing, assuming that other conditions remain constant.

2. *The composition of the fixing bath.* Washing is more rapid if nonhardening or chrome alum baths are used than with fixing baths containing potassium alum. The time of washing varies with the pH of the fixing bath when potassium alum is used, the hypo leaving the gelatin layer more rapidly at pH values above 4.9. The hypo is eliminated more rapidly from materials fixed in fresh than in partly exhausted baths.[29]

All of these effects are more pronounced with the case of films and plates than with papers.

3. *The temperature of the wash water.* The time of washing for films and plates which have been properly hardened decreases slightly with the temperature of the wash water. The variation in the rate of hypo elimination with temperature of the wash water and a negative material is shown in Fig. 15.3. Curves for single and double weight papers are shown in Fig. 15.4[30]

4. *The pH of the wash water.* Increasing the pH value from 7 to 11 increases the rate of washing appreciably with negative materials.[31] The pH of the wash water may be raised to a pH within this range by the controlled addition of ammonia.

5. *Amount of hypo contained in the gelatin layer.* Negative materials which have not been properly hardened require longer

washing because of the increased hypo in the swollen gelatin. Negative materials require longer washing than positive materials because of the thicker emulsion coating. Although the emulsion coating of papers is thinner than that of positive film, longer washing is required because of the time required to eliminate the hypo adsorbed by the paper base.

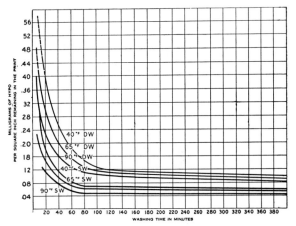

Fig. 15.4. Curves showing rate of hypo elimination from papers.

6. *Extent to which the hypo must be removed.* The time of washing, other things being equal, depends upon the amount of residual hypo which may be left in the negative or print. According to Crabtree, Eaton and Muehler,[32] the maximum concentration of hypo permissible varies in the case of negative materials from 0.02 to 0.4 mg. per square inch. In the case of archival negatives, the maximum concentration regarded as safe varies from 0.005 to 0.10 mg. per square inch.

In general, the following appear to have no appreciable effect on the rate at which hypo leaves the emulsion layer:

1. The composition of the developer.

2. The use of a stop bath whether acid or hardening.

[29] Crabtree, Eaton and Muehler, *J. Soc. Mot. Pict. Eng.* **41**, 9 (1943).

[30] Crabtree, Eaton and Muehler, *J. Frank. Inst.* **230**, 701 (1940).

[31] Crabtree, Eaton and Muehler, *J. Phot. Soc. Amer.* **9**, 115, 162 (1943).

[32] *Ibid.*

3. The concentration of hypo in the fixing bath.

4. Times of fixation beyond twice the time required to clear.

Tests For Hypo. The presence of hypo in the water draining from negatives, or prints, may be detected from the discoloration of an alkaline solution of potassium permanganate, or an iodine-starch solution.[33] The latter is the more sensitive but neither indicates the presence of hypo in the film or paper, but only in the water draining from the surface. Methods based upon the difference in the electrical conductivity of hypo solutions and hypo-free water have been recommended [34] and are more convenient but open to the same objection.

If hypo is added to a solution of mercuric chloride, preferably one to which potassium bromide has been added, it reacts with the mercuric chloride to form mercurous chloride which is relatively insoluble and renders the solution turbid.[35] This test is extremely sensitive and has the advantage over the two described previously in that samples of the material are tested rather than the wash water.

The test solution is prepared as follows:

Mercuric chloride	35 gm.	365 gr.
Potassium bromide	25 gm.	365 gr.
Water to make	1000 cc.	32 oz.

To make the test, place a piece of the washed film about 1 inch square in a test tube and add about 10 cc. of the test solution. The appearance of a milky precipitate in ten to fifteen minutes is an indication of the presence of hypo.

For papers, the silver nitrate test is more adaptable. The directions which follow are

due to Crabtree, Eaton and Muehler.[36] Process with the prints an unexposed, white sheet of paper of the same weight and kind as the majority of prints in the bath. To test for hypo, tear off a test strip and immerse a portion of it in a 1% solution of silver nitrate for three minutes. Rinse in water and compare the two portions of the test strip at once in white artificial light or in subdued daylight. The presence of hypo is indicated by a yellow-brown stain on the portion immersed in the silver nitrate solution. The presence of hydrogen sulfide in the water invalidates the test as the paper will discolor regardless of the amount of hypo present.

Hypo Eliminators. Many substances have been recommended at various times as a means of reducing the time of washing by converting the hypo into compounds more soluble in water. These include lead acetate, zinc hypochlorite, hydrogen peroxide, ammonium persulfate, potassium permanganate, potassium percarbonate, sodium carbonate and bicarbonate, ammonia, and ammonium or sodium hydroxide.[37]

Under ordinary conditions, there is no need of a hypo eliminator with plates or films as the hypo can be removed completely in a reasonable time by washing in water. However, if the water supply is limited, the negatives may be washed for ten minutes, then placed for three minutes in a

---

[33] Clark and Jelley, *Brit. J. Phot.* **76**, 714 (1929).

[34] Bender, *Brit. J. Phot.* **85**, 267 (1937). Schnoll, *Photo Trade News* **6**, 12 (July 1942).

[35] Crabtree and Ross, *J. Soc. Mot. Pict. Eng.* **14**, 419 (1930).

[36] Crabtree, Eaton, and Muehler, *J. Frank. Inst.* **230**, 701 (1940).

[37] For a bibliography of the literature on hypo eliminators, see Crabtree, Eaton, and Muehler, *J. Frank. Inst.* **230**, 701 (1940).

CARY AND WHEELER, "Quantitative Tests for Residual Hypo," *Amer. Phot.* **36**, 16 (1942).

CRABTREE, EATON AND MUEHLER, "The Quantitative Determination of Hypo in Photographic Prints with Silver Nitrate," *J. Frank. Inst.* **235**, 351 (1943).

.3% solution of ammonium hydroxide, and washed for two or three minutes.

With papers, however, the use of a hypo eliminator is necessary to insure a high degree of permanency as the last traces of hypo cannot be removed by washing in water. Experiments in the Kodak Research Laboratories have shown that alkaline hydrogen peroxide will completely oxidize sodium thiosulfate to sulfate which is not adsorbed to the paper fibers and baryta and, unlike the thiosulfate, is removable completely by washing in water. Ammonia is the most suitable alkali as, being volatile, the only residue after treatment is sodium and ammonium sulfate.

Chapter 16

DIFFUSION-TRANSFER REVERSAL PROCESSES

Diffusion-transfer reversal (DTR) is a recently developed technique that forms the basis of a distinct class of photographic silver processes. It embodies certain features or principles of a number of established photographic procedures, combined in such a manner that an entirely new image-forming system is evolved with characteristics and advantages not possessed by any other system. DTR has been described [1] as follows:

"An exposed photographic emulsion layer is developed by means of a developer that contains a silver halide solvent while it is in contact with another layer that is not light sensitive, but which is usually specially prepared. In the course of forming a negative image in the exposed layer, the developer dissolves sufficient amounts of the unexposed silver halides (representing the positive image) which are transferred to the second layer, creating a positive image on its surface by reaction of the dissolved silver halides with substances usually contained on the second support."

Thus, a positive image can be produced on a non-light-sensitive layer *simultaneously* (for all practical purposes) with development of a negative image in an exposed silver halide layer. Simultaneity of negative and positive image formation is not a limiting requirement, however, for if it is considered advantageous a distinct two-step procedure can be employed. The process is rapid and controllable, and

adaptable for many useful purposes in photographic practice.

Historical. Three workers, in as many countries, have been responsible for the various DTR processes so far evolved. Rott (Belgium), Weyde (Germany), and Land (U. S. A.) independently of one another seem to have conducted very similar investigations during approximately the same period, which since have led to the development of a number of DTR materials and applications.

Rott [2, 3] first disclosed the general scheme of the new technique and foresaw its many advantages in applications such as reflex and direct-positive printing. Because corrections for exposure errors were allowed, Rott [4] preferred a two-step procedure, i.e., one in which either the negative image layer is developed separately and then is brought in contact with the nonsensitive reception layer to form the positive image, or a material with both layers coated on a single support is processed in two steps: negative development followed by treatment in a transfer solution.[5] Technically,

[1] Varden, *P.S.A. Journal* **13**, 551–554 (1947).

[2] B.P. 614,155 (1939); U.S.P. 2,352,014; D.R.P. 764,572; B.B. 441,852; B.F. 873,507; B.I. 392,302; Ned. O. 59,365.

[3] Rott, *Science et Ind. Photo.* **13**, 151–152 (1942).

[4] Rott, *P.S.A. Journal* **14**, 108 (1948).

[5] Ned. O.A. 103,343 (1941); D.R.A. (G) 103,226; D.R.A. 103,824; B.B. 444,784; B.B. 444,785; B.F. 53,404/873,507; B.F.53,502/873,507; B.I. 399,129; B.I. 399,130; B.B. 453,209; 453,237; D.R.A. (G) 1,666; Ned. O. 60,610; 60,611; B.F. 53,513/873,-507; 513,515/873,507; B.I. 426,559; 426,560; B.F. 900,266.

l DTR processes so far proposed are re- ted to this procedure in principle to the xtent that at one stage or another a solvent issolves the undeveloped silver halides of ıe negative layer and transfers them out f the layer to form, by one means or an- ther, a positive image elsewhere.

Patents and patent applications of the G. Farbenindustrie (Agfa)[6] describe the ıvestigations done at this firm by Weyde.[7] .gain, the use of DTR for reflex and direct ositive printing was stressed. One method utlined permitted almost simultaneous ormation of the negative and positive on ıparate supports. The images required no fter-treatment, although for permanency water wash was required.

The work of Land[8, 9] came to light when ıe demonstrated a very clever adaptation f DTR for general photography. Land ıad found that methods suitable for slow hloride or bromide emulsions were unsatis- actory for ordinary fast emulsions of the ıegative type. Therefore, his investiga- ions were chiefly concerned with the chemi- al and physical requirements of DTR for ıigh-speed film materials that could be ex- ɔosed in amateur cameras. The concepts hat Land introduced enabled him to dem- ɔnstrate for the first time pictures derived

from an emulsion of the negative type ex- posed and processed directly in a camera. A wide variety of camera designs, ma- terials, and process details have been dis- closed in the patents of Land and his as- sociates at Polaroid.[10]

Actually, the history of the process was at first confusing since most findings were made during war years when patent pub- lications were delayed and periodical litera- ture was not always immediately available. This occasioned comment in the literature, but eventually the true course of events was completely clarified.[11] Disclosures before 1939 were cited that were purported to have a direct or indirect relation to the diffusion- transfer reversal process. Weyde (ref. 7) relates that her patent application was re- jected by the German examiners on the strength of a prior discovery reported in 1938 by Stevens and Norrish.[12] Attention also was called to the much earlier findings of Liesegang,[13] Colson,[14] Stenger and Hertz,[15, 16] and the firm of Schering-Kahl- baum, A. G.[17]

[10] U.S.P. 2,443,154; 2,451,820; 2,455,111; 2,455,- 125; 2,455,126; 2,458,186; 2,467,320; 2,477,291; 2,477,304; 2,477,324; 2,483,014; 2,483,389; 2,483,- 390; 2,483,391; 2,491,719; 2,495,111; 2,495,112; 2,495,113; 2,496,630; 2,497,816; 2,516,398 (1946– 48).

[11] Varden, *J. Opt. Soc. Amer.* **38**, 69 (1948); Clerc, *Science et Ind. Phot.*, No. 4 and No. 12 (1947). Introductory comment to review of Land's *J. Opt. Soc. Amer.* article, p. 206, No. 7, 1947; Clerc, *Science et Vie*, pp. 45–46, 1947; Eggert, *Camera* (Luzern) **27**, 94 (1948); **27**, 186 (1948). Also see references 1, 4, 7, 18, and 21.

[12] Stevens and Norrish, *Phot. J.* **78**, 513–533 (1938).

[13] Liesegang, *Photo. Corresp. No. 448,* 9–10 (1898).

[14] Colson, *Bull. soc. franç. Phot.* **14**, 108–111 (1898); *Phot. Rundschau* **35**, 184 (1898).

[15] Stenger and Hertz, *Phot. Rundschau* **61**, 5–9 (1924), *Zeit. fuer wiss. Photo.* **22**, 195–200 (1923); D.R.P. 382,975 (1922).

[16] Hertz, *Giessen Dissertation,* 1923.

[17] B.F. 716,428 (1931).

[6] D.R.A. (I) 68,718; (I) 68,823; (I) 69,076 (1941); B.B. 444,702; B.F. 879,995; Schw. P. 240,472; Noors. P. 66,994; 69,510; PB Report No. 34,150, *Bibliography of Scientific and Industrial Reports*, U. S. Dept. of Commerce, **3**, 822 (1946); PB Report No. 34,188, **3**, 826 (1946); D.R.A. (I) 72,638; B.B. 451,346; B.F. 896, 127; D.R.A. (I) 74,117; B.B. 457,478; B.F. 53,311/897,995.

[7] Weyde, *Foto-Kino-Tech.* **2**, No. 9, 229–232 (1948). Abridged English translation by Varden and Krause, *Photo Age* **4**, 45–46 (February 1949).

[8] Land, *J. Opt. Soc. Amer.* **37**, 61–77 (1947); *P.S.A. Journal* **13**, 370–380 (1947).

[9] U.S.P. 2,435,717; 2,435,718; 2,435,719; 2,435,- 720; 2,500,421; 2,500,422 (1944–46); B.F. 941,429; 950,235; B.B. 471,206; 471,336; 476,512; Ned. O. 60,845; B.I. 445,232; B.P.A. 1722/48; 497/48; 1972/48.

Stevens and Norrish achieved a type of positive image transfer in their investigations of photographic reversal phenomena but made no attempt to develop the method for practical use. They exposed a process emulsion behind a Chapman-Jones plate, immersed it face down in a metol developer for five seconds, and then pressed it in contact with a plain gelatin coated plate that already had been placed in the developer.[18] The plate sandwich was removed from the solution and separated two minutes later. The process emulsion was fixed in the usual manner to produce a negative. The gelatin coated plate was completely washed, then developed in an acid-metol physical developer, forming a positive image. Silver nuclei, having diffused from the unexposed parts of the process emulsion into the gelatin layer, functioned as development centers for the physical developer. This incidental observation conceivably could have marked the beginning of diffusion-transfer reversal if its possibilities had been recognized and further developed. But, as pointed out by Rott in a private communication to Weyde,[19] the citing of this discovery as an anticipation of DTR processes is unjustified since only small amounts of silver nuclei were found in the gelatin layer,

and these nuclei required subsequent physical development to bring out the image.

Liesegang coated a plate with a water solution of gelatin and gallic acid and placed over it an exposed piece of Aristo paper. The progress of development could be observed through the glass plate. After a few minutes when the paper was removed from the plate, a blue-black negative image could be seen in the gelatin layer. Apparently the silver nitrate in the paper emulsion diffused into the gelatin layer containing the gallic acid where it was reduced to metallic silver. Liesegang's findings represent a diffusion-transfer process, but he considered it of no practical value. It is unlike the contemporary methods in that silver nitrate, a water-soluble silver salt, diffuses to a layer containing a developer and not developing nuclei, the action of which was unknown in Liesegang's day.

Colson's work, cited as a reference in U.S.P. 2,500,421 to Land, appears not to be very pertinent in connection with DTR processes. He soaked an exposed plate in water, then developer, and covered the emulsion with either another plate slightly fogged or an ordinary glass plate. When a fogged plate was used the exhausted developer formed an unsharp negative image in the emulsion. This was only an incidental observation not even mentioned in his concluding remarks on the practical consequences of his researches. However, Colson and Russell[20] investigated independently the photographic action of organic and inorganic matter when placed near a silver halide layer, but not necessarily in contact with it. Volatile compounds formed or provided by the material diffused across the gap to produce a latent image by chemical action. This is a peculiar sort of image-transfer, but in no way

---

[18] A transfer procedure remotely related to that of Stevens' and Norrish's was suggested by B. Lefevre as early as 1857 (*Photographic Notes*, Vol. 2, 1857, p. 343). He prepared a gelatin coated paper sheet and pressed it in contact with a freshly developed Daguerreotype plate that had been treated in hypo and washed, but not completely dried. He stated that after a few minutes every particle of reduced silver transferred from the plate to the gelatin surface. The hue of the weak metallic negative image varied according to the density. To increase the density he suggested several methods, one being to use the silver particles as "the centre of a catalytic action, which shall group around them fresh molecules of reduced silver."

[19] Weyde, *Foto-Kino-Technik* **4**, 22 (1950).

[20] For complete discussion and references see *Psychical Physics*, S. W. Tromp, Elsevier Pub. Co., New York, 1949.

elated to the type under consideration ere.

Stenger and Hertz produced a positive image in a uniformly exposed plate emulsion by placing it in contact with an image-wise exposed plate that had been wetted with developer. The developer exhausted in proportion to the exposure at various points of the emulsion. The unexhausted developer in the lesser exposed areas diffused into the uniformly exposed emulsion, developing a positive image.

Schering-Kahlbaum, A. G. disclosed several ways for forming a positive image by diffusion, none of which involved diffusion or transfer of silver salts. A support was coated with a gelatin layer which in some instances contained a colorless compound capable of reacting with another compound to form a colored product. Over the gelatin layer was coated a photographic emulsion. Upon exposure and development in a tanning developer, the emulsion formed a negative image and hardened the layer in

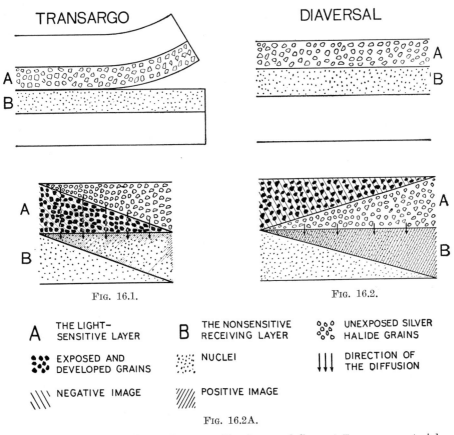

Fig. 16.1.   Fig. 16.2.

Fig. 16.2A.

FIG. 16.1. The sensitive and non-sensitive layers of Gevaert *Transargo* material are coated on separate supports. The above shows schematically how the negative image develops in one layer and the positive image forms in the other by diffusion of the unexposed silver halides to the receiving layer.

FIG. 16.2. For Gevaert *Diaversal* material the sensitive and non-sensitive layers are applied over each other on a single support. The sensitive top layer is non-hardened and washes away in processing to make the positive image visible.

proportion to the image density. The plate then was placed in a dye solution (the dye could be placed in the developer, also) which diffused into the gelatin underlayer according to the extent of tanning of the overlayer. A positive image in dye resulted when the emulsion layer was removed. By a similar technique the positive image could be formed as a colored metallic sulfide. In this case the gelatin underlayer contained a suitable colorless metallic salt, and after tanning development of the emulsion overlayer, the plate was placed in a solution containing a soluble sulfide. The diffusion of the sulfide solution was controlled by the differential tanning of the developed emulsion layer, therefore controlling the amount of metallic sulfide precipitated in the underlayer.

Processes, Materials and Equipment. As we have noted earlier, diffusion-transfer reversal involving silver halides may be carried out in several general ways:

I. The silver halide layer, after exposure, may be developed to a negative in the presence of a silver halide solvent and then placed in intimate contact with a developer soaked sheet of material which has a layer containing collodial silver or a compound capable of forming a difficultly soluble silver salt, e.g., sodium sulfide, for producing the positive.

II. The sensitive and nonsensitive layers may be brought in contact with a silver halide solvent-containing developer simultaneously and pressed together immediately so that the negative and positive images form concurrently.

III. The sensitive layer may be coated on top of the nonsensitive reception layer and removed after the transfer image has formed following a two-step processing procedure.

IV. The same as III except a one-step processing procedure may be used.

Method I was utilized by Gevaert fo *Transargo,* a process for producing photo copies on both sides of a paper suppor However, it seems that full advantage wa not taken of the process since long transfe times were required, due to the use of a rela tively low energy developer. (A highly er ergetic developer containing caustic alka was probably considered inadvisable sinc the process was carried out manually.) Fig 16.1 shows more clearly how the transfe image is formed. Layer A (upper draw ing) is a silver halide coating which is ex

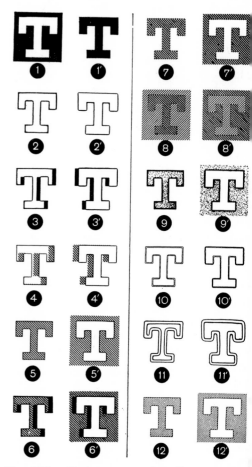

FIG. 16.3. Various types of outline and shading effects, as above, can be obtained with *Contourfilm,* a special type of diffusion-transfer material.

osed and placed in an ordinary metol-hydroquinone developer. Layer B is a nonsensitive coating on a separate support containing developing nuclei and sodium thiosulfate. This layer also is wetted with the developer and later squeezed in contact with layer A. The negative image forms in the upper portions of the exposed layer, relative to its support; therefore, the silver halides which are to produce the positive image must dissolve and diffuse through the negative image to reach the reception surface. Upon contact with the nuclei in layer B, silver or a silver compound is released, creating a comparatively weak positive image, strengthened later by selenium toning.

Fig. 16.2 shows the layer arrangement of Gevaert *Diaversal* material. This is a direct-positive printing medium, useful for contact or projection printing of color transparencies to produce monochrome reproductions. Here the emulsion layer A (upper drawing) is coated on top of the reception layer B, according to method III, both on the same support. Therefore, upon exposure and development of the material the negative image deposits in the upper strata of the sensitive layer away from the reception surface. In the transfer solution the positive forming silver halides dissolve and diffuse more or less directly to layer B. Again, the nuclei present in B act as development centers for building up the positive image. In subsequent steps of processing the emulsion layer, being nonhardened, is removed by water treatment, revealing the positive image. A final toning operation completes the processing.

Gevaert *Contourfilm* is based on variation of method III, described by Rott.[21] This is a novel material for producing contour effects which may, according to the method of exposure, consist of a simple line contour, a double-line contour, shaded contours of various types, etc., as shown in Fig. 16.3. The layer arrangement of *Contourfilm* is the same as for *Diaversal*, but the layers themselves differ in some respects. The top emulsion layer is unhardened, as in *Diaversal*, but is blue-green sensitive. The lower layer is hardened and contains nuclei, as in *Diaversal*, but is light sensitive. It is a blue sensitive silver halide emulsion. By various combinations of white and green light exposure, the image formed in the lower emulsion during processing may consist of a directly developed image, as well as a transfer image, producing an array of unusual contour reproductions.

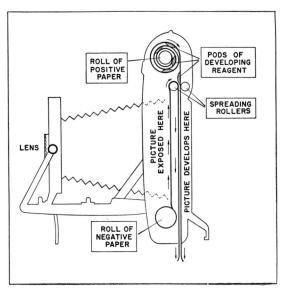

FIG. 16.4. Schematic drawing of the Polaroid *Land* Camera.

Land utilized a novel modification of method II in which the processing liquid is spread in a thin viscous layer between the sensitive and nonsensitive layers as the two are pressed together. He sought a system of photography which he characterized as follows.[22] "... a camera and a

21 Rott, *Le Procédé* **44**, 17–23 (1948).

22 Land, *J. Opt. Soc. Amer.* **38**, 69–70 (1948).

photographic process that would produce a finished positive print, directly from the camera, immediately after exposure. From the point of view of the user, the camera was to look essentially like an ordinary camera, process was to be dry; the film was to be loaded in one of the usual ways, the positive print was to look essentially like a conventional paper print, and this print was to be completed within a minute or two after the picture was taken.''

A schematic view of the Land (Polaroid) camera is shown in Fig. 16.4. The roll material consists of two paper strips, one with a high-speed, orthochromatic light-sensitive emulsion layer, the other with a nonsensitive layer containing nuclei for precipitating silver during simultaneous development of the negative and positive images. The two parts travel through the camera at first independently, but finally are brought in contact after exposure of the light-sensitive layer by passing them together between metal rollers. Pods attached at proper intervals along the nonsensitive strip, containing a viscous processing solution, are ruptured (one after each exposure) as the two strips pass through the rollers. A very thin layer of the solution is spread evenly between the sensitive and nonsensitive layers. At normal room temperatures one minute is allowed for processing, after which a special door is opened at the back of the camera for removing the positive print. The borders are predeckled and only weakly held along the edges for convenience in removing the print. The negative-bearing part is pulled through the camera and discarded.

The material supplied for the Land camera immediately following its announcement in 1947, Type 40, gave sepia colored print images. In 1950 a material for black and white images was introduced, Type 41.[23] Both of these films use fast negative

FIG. 16.5. The Land Camera finds uses in science as well as in the amateur field. The above shows its adaptation in the Fairchild-Polaroid Oscilloscope Camera for obtaining finished prints of cathode ray tube traces in one minute.

emulsions, and the pictures obtained after one minute are stable, with full tone gradation and good density. Pictures can be made over a wide range of ambient temperatures, from freezing to 115° F. The viscous processing solution that spreads between the negative and positive sheets has sufficient solid content to maintain the two sheets properly spaced during the process, giving a reservoir of known volume for metering reagent and solvent to the sheets. It serves also to hold the two surfaces in flat face-to-face relationship and acts as a reservoir for the reaction products produced during the print formation. In the Type 41 film for black-and-white images, the viscous processing solution adheres to the negative as the positive print is removed so that a completely dry positive

[23] Deschin, ''Land Prints In Black,'' *The New York Times,* July 16 (1950); Lipton, ''New Polaroid Film'' (a brief review of paper presented by E. H. Land at May 1950 meeting of New York P.S.A. Technical Section announcing Type 41 material), *Popular Photog.* **27**, pp. 24 and 26 (August 1950).

print is obtained when it is peeled from he negative-bearing part of the sandwich.

In addition to its widespread use among amateur photographers, the Land camera has found many incidental applications, primarily because of the speed with which finished prints are obtainable. Moreover, no stronger light conditions are required than for comparable high-speed negative films. For example, Hauser [24] found the camera useful for photomicrography in teaching and research. A special device for adapting the camera for scientific purposes is the Fairchild-Polaroid Oscilloscope Camera (Fig. 16.5). One end of a light-proof extension tube, which has a direct-vision side viewer, fits over the screen of the cathode-ray tube, and at the other end the camera is attached and supported. The shutter is actuated by the cable release when the desired trace pattern is seen on the fluorescent screen.

In 1949 the Agfa plant at Leverkusen introduced an automatic developing apparatus for producing positive reflex prints, called *Die Blitzkopie*.[25] The reflex material used is a new type, known as Agfa *Copyrapid*. It consists of a light sensitive layer of steep gradation and low speed on one support, and a nonsensitive layer on a separate support containing the necessary nuclei, i.e., colloidal silver and other additions to insure high image density. Contained in the layers are all the ingredients necessary for development except the alkali. When the exposed material is placed in the processing machine, electrically or manually driven rollers carry the sheet over rollers submerged in a weakly alkaline solution and press it in contact with the positive forming layer. About one minute is required for the paper to travel through the device. It is slightly damp when it

comes out. Another minute is allowed for completing the processing, whereupon the negative is peeled away from the positive. The negative may be fixed and washed for permanency. The *Copyrapid* positive material is supplied with coatings on one or both sides of the paper support.

Reaction Mechanism. The formation of the negative image in the light-sensitive layer of DTR materials is explained along classical lines, i.e., silver specks are produced on the silver halide crystals during exposure which subsequently act as an intermediary between the developer and the crystals to promote the reduction of the silver halide to metallic image silver. The unexposed silver halides fail to develop in the layer because they lack development nuclei. However, when they are dissolved and transferred to a layer containing agents that can function as development nuclei, their silver is released. The equations given by Rott [26] are typical of those that generally apply.

$$(1) \quad 2AgCl + 2Na_2S_2O_3 \rightarrow Ag_2S_2O_3 \cdot Na_2S_2O_3 + 2NaCl.$$

The silver is now contained in a complex salt which, in the presence of colloidal silver nuclei, can be reduced by an alkaline developer. Thus,

$$(2) \quad Ag_2S_2O_3 \cdot Na_2S_2O_3 + 2 \; \underset{OH}{\overset{OH}{\bigcirc}} + Na_2CO_3 \rightarrow$$

$$2Ag + 2 \; \underset{O}{\overset{O}{\bigcirc}} + 2Na_2S_3O_3 + CO_2 + H_2O.$$

Sodium thiosulfate is freed as the metallic silver is formed, and diffuses back into the

24 Hauser, *J. Chem. Educ.* **26**, 224–225 (1949).

25 Die Blitzkopie, *Foto-Kino-Technik* **4**, 25–26 (1950).

26 Rott, *Tech. Wetensch. Tijdschr.* **17**, 163–166 (1948). *Nederlands Jaarboek voor Fotokunst*, 1948/49, Hengelo, pp. 32–38.

negative layer to dissolve more silver halide. This continued dissolving action of the thiosulfate explains why such a small quantity is required.

If nuclei were not present in the receiving layer the diffusion of the dissolved silver halides would cease as soon as equilibrium was reached, i.e., when the silver halide concentration became equal in both layers. However, the nuclei prevent equilibrium, and so the reaction can continue until the positive image is fully formed.

The nuclei, or "fogging" agents, fall into two classes of substances. Colloidal silver, silver sulfide, colloidal sulfur, etc., are agents of one class which act directly as reduction nuclei for the dissolved silver halides. Substances of the second class do not function as nuclei themselves but may form such nuclei by reaction with the dissolved silver halides, either by reduction, as in the case of stannous chloride, or by the formation of difficultly soluble compounds, as in the case of sodium sulfide. Lüppo-Cramer [27] confirmed Beuker's findings that stannous chloride has no reducing power unless made alkaline. Therefore, one might expect this compound to be particularly suitable for image transfer materials since it would not reduce silver halides in contact with it until made alkaline by the developer. Also, the silver formed in alkaline stannous chloride is a yellowish-brown colloidal type which is more effective in transfer processes than the less dispersed grayish silver. However, stannous chloride, and in general substances of the second class, must not be as suitable as other agents in actual practice for they are seldom stressed in connection with the process. It seems as though colloidal silver and heavy metal sulfides are preferred, used with addition agents such

as mercaptobenzthioazole for promotin neutral tone images.

The quantity of development nucle necessary in the receiving layer is extremel small. Arens [28] studied the catalytic a tion of silver in physical development, an Eggert [29] and Rott [30] have discussed th subject as related to diffusion-transfe processes. Arens showed that when usin artificially produced colloidal silver, mor silver is deposited in subsequent physica development the smaller the size of the col loidal particles for equal total mass of sil ver. He also concluded that if the silve nuclei are present in equal numbers th same amount of silver is deposited per uni area regardless of the mass of the nucle particles. Nuclei of colloidal gold or silve sulfide acted in the same manner. Th actual mass of the silver nuclei in th shoulder region of a relatively insensitiv photographic emulsion was found to b 10^{-7} to 10^{-15} gram.

Rott showed that useful nuclei in DTI processes are smaller than those best suite for physical development. Considering th fact that the latter are found in quantitie of the order of 10^{-4} mg. per square meter the quantity present in the receiving laye of a DTR material must be very small in deed. Rott further states that the chemica constitution of the nuclei preferred fo transfer purposes is not the same as tha most adapted for physical development. Arens had found no difference in activity between silver and silver sulfide, wherea Rott found certain forms of silver sulfide nuclei more active for transfer develop

[27] Lüppo-Cramer, *Photo. Industrie*, April 26, 1939, pp. 515–516.

[28] Arens and Eggert, *Zeit. Elektrochem.* **35** 728,733 (1929); Arens, *Agfa-Veroeffentlichungen* III, 32–46 (1933).

[29] Eggert, *Helv. Chim. Acta.* **30**, 2114–2119 (1947).

[30] Rott, "Paper presented at Photographic Conferences at Liège—April 15–17, 1948," reported by Hautot, *Science et Ind. Phot.* **2**, 322–325 and by Eggert, *Camera* (Luzern) **27**, 215–217 (1948).

Chapter 17

PHOTOGRAPHIC SENSITOMETRY

EXPOSURE, DEVELOPMENT, AND DENSITY
MEASUREMENT

Definition of Sensitometry. In the beginning, photographic sensitometry was concerned almost exclusively with the measurement of the speed of a sensitive material to light. The measurement of speed is still one of the principal objectives of sensitometry; however, it is more adequately defined as consisting of the methods of measuring and expressing quantitatively the response of a sensitive material upon exposure to light, or other form of radiant energy, after development under measurable conditions. Photographic sensitometry, in other words, may be defined as consisting of the methods employed in measuring and expressing those characteristics of a sensitive material which depend on the relationship between exposure, development, and density.

Photographic sensitometry involves:

1. The exposure of the sensitive material under measurable and reproducible conditions.

2. Development of the material under standardized and reproducible conditions.

3. The establishment of standardized and reproducible methods of measuring the result of exposure and development (photographic densitometry).

4. The interpretation of the results.

Exposure and Exposure Scales. Photographic exposure is defined as the product of illumination and time: i.e., the intensity of illumination on the sensitive material multiplied by the time it is allowed to act. The unit of exposure is the meter-candle-second (m.c.s.) which is equivalent to the exposure produced by a light source of one candle power, in one second, at a distance of one meter from the surface of the sensitive material.

The instrument used to make a series of exposures on a sensitive material is termed a *sensitometer*. It consists of (1) a standard light source, and (2) a means of varying the exposure on different parts of the sensitive material by varying either the time of exposure or the illumination.

A series of exposures produced by varying the *time* of exposure, the illumination on the sensitive material remaining constant, is termed a *time-scale of exposure*. A series of exposures produced by varying the illumination, with time constant, is termed an *illumination scale of exposure*.

Light Sources for Sensitometry. If the characteristics of a sensitive material as determined from sensitometric tests are to be applicable to practice, the conditions under which the material is exposed in the sensitometer should be comparable with those existing when the emulsion is exposed in the camera (negative emulsions) or on a printer (positive emulsions).

The photographic effect produced by a given exposure depends upon the actual values of illumination and time and not simply on their product. It is highly desirable, therefore, that the illumination on the sensitive material in the sensitometer be approximately the same as in the camera or, in the case of a positive emulsion, the printer.

Since the sensitivity of photographic materials vary with the wave length, the spectral energy characteristics of the light source are extremely important. In this respect also, it is highly desirable that the light source be comparable with one which is used in practical photography. A color temperature of 5400° K. has been accepted by international agreement as a standard when the characteristics of a sensitive material to sunlight are to be determined.

In modern practice, negative materials are exposed also by incandescent tungsten lamps, fluorescent lamps, flash lamps, and gaseous discharge lamps. No standards for these have as yet been agreed upon, but a tungsten source with a color temperature of 2750° K. is widely used with positive materials. Any standard, of course, must be constant in intensity and in its spectral energy and both of these must be precisely known and reproducible.

Candles, and lamps burning liquid pentane, amyl acetate, and acetylene, have been employed as standards, but standardized incandescent electric lamps are used almost exclusively at the present time. It is necessary to calibrate such lamps accurately for luminous intensity and spectral distribution in a testing laboratory. Inasmuch as both of these factors depend upon the temperature of the filament, which in turn depends on the current flowing through the lamp, it is necessary to control with a high degree of precision the electric supply from which the lamp is operated.

Incandescent tungsten lamps of the type most suitable as a standard light source operate at color temperatures ranging from 2360° to 2800° K. It is necessary, therefore, to use a filter if radiation with the spectral energy characteristics of sunlight is required. For most purposes filters of dyed gelatin, such as the Wratten Nos. 78, 78A, 78AA, and 79, may be used; at the Seventh International Congress of Photography (London 1928), however, a tung-

sten lamp operating at a color temperature of 2360° K. and a liquid filter which has been proposed by Davis and Gibson of the U. S. Bureau of Standards was adopted.

Time-Scale Sensitometers. The usual method of producing a scale of exposures by varying the time (time scale) is by interposing, between the light source and the sensitive material, a continuously moving, opaque plate with a series of apertures whose lengths vary in accordance with the differences in exposure desired. The apertures may be longitudinal in a rectangular plate which moves in a straight line, or angular openings in a circular disc which is rotated during the exposure (Fig. 17.1). The latter is by far the more popular method.

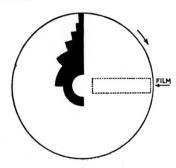

Fig. 17.1. Sector which produces a series of exposures to the power of two. The sensitive material occupies the space shown by the dotted line. The dark areas are slots in the disc.

Many different instruments of this type have been described in the literature. Practically all of these, however, have been designed by research workers, or in the laboratories of the manufacturers of sensitive materials, to meet certain specific requirements. In 1931 the Eastman Kodak Company placed a time-scale sensitometer on the market primarily for the motion picture laboratory, as the Eastman Sensitometer, Type IIb.

This instrument is shown in detail in Fig. 17.2.

ent. Mere transformation of relatively inactive silver nuclei to silver sulfide does not increase their activity. Thus, the activity of the nuclei depends upon their form and dimensions. Land [31] published electronmicrographs of metal sulfide galaxies in the receiving layer of Polaroid film and at 20,000 × the individual particles were not resolved.

Land also discussed at length the reaction mechanism of DTR as it applies to the methods he employs. Heavy metal sulfides aggregated in galaxies of chosen diameter and so maintained throughout the process are used cyclically by Land (ref. 31) to deposit silver in arrays of desired diameter and constancy of diameter. By correctly adjusting the alkali, sodium thiosulfate and developing agent to the minimum needed, and by distributing these in a viscous, thin layer of liquid agent between the negative and positive sheets, three potential "images" are established. There is a developer oxidation "image," an alkali neutralization "image," and an "image" in available silver. These are used in conjunction and in support of one another to achieve a symmetry between the negative and positive image formations, and to insure a desired extraction of silver from the negative. Cyclic use of sodium thiosulfate and sulfide, along with the preservation of the sulfide ion by the presence of an excess of metal ions, makes possible the formation of a dense image containing only trivial amounts of silver solvent and sulfide ion. As a result, images are obtained which are stable, and which have perfect homogeneity of hue in highlight and shadow.

Land studied a wide variety of over-all characteristic curves for the process and developed a preferred curve which was best suited for recording scenes in haze, sunshine and shadow, as well as by flashlight.

The contrast of the prints obtained is controllable within limits by variations in processing time, and Land has published a family of curves illustrating the effect of time on print contrast (ref. 8).

In Land's process, the less readily reducible thiosulfate transports the silver ions from the negative and gives up its silver to the heavy metal sulfide at the site of the positive to form the more readily reducible silver sulfide. The reduction of the silver sulfide completes a chain of reactions in which the thiosulfate and the sulfide ion are freed for further reaction. The sulfide is initially aggregated into clusters which insure that the deposited silver atoms are built into arrays of large enough diameter for absorbing visible light. These arrays must also have adequate constancy in diameter so that highlight and shadow of the positive are of the same hue. Migration of the sulfide ions during precipitation of silver, if permitted, will fog the negative in exposed regions, weakening the positive. It will also disarray the correct aggregation of the sulfide ion, causing silver precipitation to initiate in the positive at many points so that an erroneous number of silver grains form and thereby diminish the density of the positive and give it a yellowish hue. These dangers are avoided by introducing into the sheet carrying the galaxies of sulfide a relatively high concentration of a soluble salt whose metal ions are such that the sulfide, freed from its original site by the reduction of the silver, is at once captured before it can leave that site and be reprecipitated as the sulfide of the metal of the soluble salt.

In discussing Type 41 film, Land [32] disclosed his technique for packing silver atoms into masses less dense than the silver in mirrors and yet not insulated by long

[31] Land, *Phot. J.* **90A**, 7–15 (1950).

[32] Land, E. H., Unpublished address before the N. Y. Section, PSA Technical Division, May 2, 1950.

chain molecules of a plastic. He pointed out that in ordinary photography, each silver halide grain preempts a specific volume in the colloid binder and that development proceeds in such a way that an aggregation of silver filaments (or in some cases spheres) is then packed into this volume. Silver in this form has conductivity just right to be black and nonreflecting. His approach to the transfer problem is to create in the positive sheet a substitute for this preempted volume. The tendency in precipitating silver from solution is, of course, to form colloidal silver in which relatively small masses of silver are insulated from each other by the dispersing medium. The problem is to create a positive sheet such that the silver atoms will deposit in aggregates having high enough conductivity and large enough diameter to be black like those of ordinary positive paper and yet not to deposit the silver so densely as to create a mirror. Land solved this problem by aggregating the metal sulfides which precipitate the silver in galaxies and by preventing diffusion of the sulfide ion.

The mechanism by which Land has made his procedure operative over a wide range of temperatures is by the achievement of a symmetry between the type of reaction in the negative and the type of reaction in the positive so that changes in temperature change the rate of negative and positive image formation, increasing or decreasing both together. This symmetry is the result of forming and reducing silver sulfide to give the positive and of initially confining the processing liquid in a thin uniform layer between the negative and positive sheets.

For the print to have acceptable permanence, several mechanisms have been worked out by Land (ref. 8) and two of these have been successfully embodied in the films of Polaroid. One of these is the controlled diminution of the alkalinity of the viscous processing solution and the positive print by neutralizing agents contained within the sandwich of the positive and negative sheets, which neutralizing agents are effective only in the last stages of print formation. The other is to concentrate the reaction products of image formation in the viscous processing solution which, in Type 41 film, adheres entirely to the negative so that when the positive is peeled off, it contains only transferred silver and is free from both staining and oxidizing reaction products.

That very small quantities of developer components are necessary to process a single transfer image is clearly indicated by the data given by Land (ref. 30) for his one-step process. A viscous layer of solution only 0.0003 inch thick spreads between the emulsion and receiving surfaces, amounting to but 0.05 cc. of solution per square inch.

It can be concluded that the reaction mechanism in the development of a DTR image is a highly perfected form of physical development, with several distinct advantages over the ordinary physical development process. First, there is no loss in sensitivity in the DTR process, whereas for physical development the emulsion must be given considerably more exposure than normal. In DTR strong developers are usable, and even preferred; but for physical development only developers of weak reducing power are suitable; otherwise, the silver salt in the solution will be reduced prematurely. Therefore, DTR images form much more rapidly than physically developed images. A further advantage of the DTR process over ordinary physical development is its freedom from fog, because only the silver constituting the positive image can reach into the reception layer. Silver fog grains remain in the negative layer.

print is obtained when it is peeled from the negative-bearing part of the sandwich.

In addition to its widespread use among amateur photographers, the Land camera has found many incidental applications, primarily because of the speed with which finished prints are obtainable. Moreover, no stronger light conditions are required than for comparable high-speed negative films. For example, Hauser[24] found the camera useful for photomicrography in teaching and research. A special device for adapting the camera for scientific purposes is the Fairchild-Polaroid Oscilloscope Camera (Fig. 16.5). One end of a light-proof extension tube, which has a direct-vision side viewer, fits over the screen of the cathode-ray tube, and at the other end the camera is attached and supported. The shutter is actuated by the cable release when the desired trace pattern is seen on the fluorescent screen.

In 1949 the Agfa plant at Leverkusen introduced an automatic developing apparatus for producing positive reflex prints, called *Die Blitzkopie*.[25] The reflex material used is a new type, known as Agfa *Copyrapid*. It consists of a light sensitive layer of steep gradation and low speed on one support, and a nonsensitive layer on a separate support containing the necessary nuclei, i.e., colloidal silver and other additions to insure high image density. Contained in the layers are all the ingredients necessary for development except the alkali. When the exposed material is placed in the processing machine, electrically or manually driven rollers carry the sheet over rollers submerged in a weakly alkaline solution and press it in contact with the positive forming layer. About one minute is required for the paper to travel through the device. It is slightly damp when it

comes out. Another minute is allowed for completing the processing, whereupon the negative is peeled away from the positive. The negative may be fixed and washed for permanency. The *Copyrapid* positive material is supplied with coatings on one or both sides of the paper support.

Reaction Mechanism. The formation of the negative image in the light-sensitive layer of DTR materials is explained along classical lines, i.e., silver specks are produced on the silver halide crystals during exposure which subsequently act as an intermediary between the developer and the crystals to promote the reduction of the silver halide to metallic image silver. The unexposed silver halides fail to develop in the layer because they lack development nuclei. However, when they are dissolved and transferred to a layer containing agents that can function as development nuclei, their silver is released. The equations given by Rott[26] are typical of those that generally apply.

(1) $2AgCl + 2Na_2S_2O_3 \rightarrow$
$\qquad Ag_2S_2O_3 \cdot Na_2S_2O_3 + 2NaCl.$

The silver is now contained in a complex salt which, in the presence of colloidal silver nuclei, can be reduced by an alkaline developer. Thus,

$$(2)\ Ag_2S_2O_3 \cdot Na_2S_2O_3 + 2\ \underset{OH}{\overset{OH}{\bigcirc}} + Na_2CO_3 \rightarrow$$

$$2Ag + 2\ \underset{O}{\overset{O}{\bigcirc}} + 2Na_2S_2O_3 + CO_2 + H_2O.$$

Sodium thiosulfate is freed as the metallic silver is formed, and diffuses back into the

24 Hauser, *J. Chem. Educ.* **26**, 224–225 (1949).

25 Die Blitzkopie, *Foto-Kino-Technik* **4**, 25–26 (1950).

26 Rott, *Tech. Wetensch. Tijdschr.* **17**, 163–166 (1948). *Nederlands Jaarboek voor Fotokunst*, 1948/49, Hengelo, pp. 32–38.

negative layer to dissolve more silver halide. This continued dissolving action of the thiosulfate explains why such a small quantity is required.

If nuclei were not present in the receiving layer the diffusion of the dissolved silver halides would cease as soon as equilibrium was reached, i.e., when the silver halide concentration became equal in both layers. However, the nuclei prevent equilibrium, and so the reaction can continue until the positive image is fully formed.

The nuclei, or "fogging" agents, fall into two classes of substances. Colloidal silver, silver sulfide, colloidal sulfur, etc., are agents of one class which act directly as reduction nuclei for the dissolved silver halides. Substances of the second class do not function as nuclei themselves but may form such nuclei by reaction with the dissolved silver halides, either by reduction, as in the case of stannous chloride, or by the formation of difficultly soluble compounds, as in the case of sodium sulfide. Lüppo-Cramer [27] confirmed Beuker's findings that stannous chloride has no reducing power unless made alkaline. Therefore, one might expect this compound to be particularly suitable for image transfer materials since it would not reduce silver halides in contact with it until made alkaline by the developer. Also, the silver formed in alkaline stannous chloride is a yellowish-brown colloidal type which is more effective in transfer processes than the less dispersed grayish silver. However, stannous chloride, and in general substances of the second class, must not be as suitable as other agents in actual practice for they are seldom stressed in connection with the process. It seems as though colloidal silver and heavy metal sulfides are preferred, used with addition agents such

as mercaptobenzthioazole for promotin neutral tone images.

The quantity of development nucle necessary in the receiving layer is extremel small. Arens [28] studied the catalytic a tion of silver in physical development, an Eggert [29] and Rott [30] have discussed th subject as related to diffusion-transfe processes. Arens showed that when usin artificially produced colloidal silver, mor silver is deposited in subsequent physica development the smaller the size of the co loidal particles for equal total mass of si ver. He also concluded that if the silve nuclei are present in equal numbers th same amount of silver is deposited per uni area regardless of the mass of the nucle particles. Nuclei of colloidal gold or silve sulfide acted in the same manner. Th actual mass of the silver nuclei in th shoulder region of a relatively insensitiv photographic emulsion was found to b 10^{-7} to 10^{-15} gram.

Rott showed that useful nuclei in DT processes are smaller than those best suite for physical development. Considering th fact that the latter are found in quantitie of the order of 10^{-4} mg. per square meter the quantity present in the receiving laye of a DTR material must be very small in deed. Rott further states that the chemica constitution of the nuclei preferred fo transfer purposes is not the same as tha most adapted for physical development Arens had found no difference in activity between silver and silver sulfide, wherea Rott found certain forms of silver sulfid nuclei more active for transfer develop

[27] Lüppo-Cramer, *Photo. Industrie*, April 26, 1939, pp. 515–516.

[28] Arens and Eggert, *Zeit. Elektrochem.* **35** 728,733 (1929); Arens, *Agfa-Veroeffentlichungen* III, 32–46 (1933).

[29] Eggert, *Helv. Chim. Acta.* **30**, 2114–211 (1947).

[30] Rott, "Paper presented at Photographic Con ferences at Liège—April 15–17, 1948," reporte by Hautot, *Science et Ind. Phot.* **2**, 322–325 an by Eggert, *Camera* (Luzern) **27**, 215–217 (1948)

L represents the standard lamp which is
the source of illumination. A selectively
absorbing filter, *F*, is placed in the path
of the light coming from the lamp in order
to modify its spectral composition to the
desired quality. A plane mirror, *M*, reflects
the light at right angles, thus illuminating
the exposure plane, *EP*, in which the photographic material is placed. The rotating
cylindrical shutter or drum, *D*, having 21

photographic material is protected from the
exposing radiation by the opaque portion
of the drum, and closes as soon as the slots
in the drum have passed the exposing
plane.

Illumination Scale Sensitometers. The
illumination on different parts of the sensitive material may be varied to produce an
illumination scale of exposures by (1) varying the distance between the light source

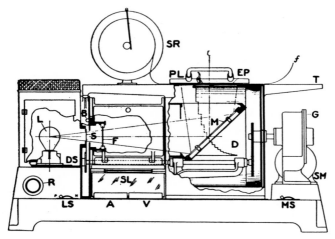

Fig. 17.2. Optical system of the Eastman IIb sensitometer (time-scale).

exposure slots of increasing length controls
the time of exposure upon adjacent steps
of the sensitive material. The platen, *PL*,
when pulled down, serves to hold the film
strips in the exposure plane during exposure.

The drum is driven at a constant angular
velocity by a synchronous motor, *SM*.
Through a reduction gear, *G*, the motor
turns the drum at 12 r.p.m. when operating
on a 60 cycle line, or at 10 r.p.m. on a 50
cycle line.

When the machine is started by throwing
the master switch *MS*, the drum revolves
continuously. Exposures are made by
means of the shutter, *S*, operated by a one-
turn mechanism. Upon pressure of the release button, *B*, this shutter opens while the

and the sensitive material for the different
exposures, (2) by the use of tubes, or cells,
with apertures of various sizes in one end,
the sensitive material being placed at the
other,[1] (3) by optical wedge methods, consisting of a stepped diagram and a cylindrical, deforming lens,[2] (4) by placing
a series of densities[3] in front of the sensitive material so that the illumination is
varied in accordance with the transmission

[1] See Eder, *Handbuch der Photographie.*

[2] Callier, *Phot. J.* **43**, 242 (1913); *Brit. J. Phot.*
60, 972 (1913). McFarlane, *J. Franklin Inst.*
228, 445 (1939).

[3] The density scales used in such instruments are
made of pigmented gelatin according to a method
devised by Goldberg (*Brit. J. Phot.* **57**, 642, 648
(1910)), or are calibrated photographic copies of
such wedges.

of the different steps, and (5) by successive exposures to the light transmitted by a condensing lens system in which the aperture is varied in accordance with the exposure difference desired.[4]

The Eastman Processing Control Sensitometer is typical in many respects of sensitometers employing a density scale. It consists (Fig. 17.3) of a 75-watt, 10-volt

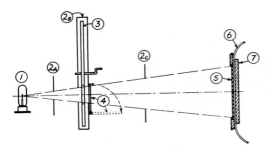

Fɪɢ. 17.3.   Eastman processing control sensitometer (intensity-scale).   1. Light source (10-v, 7.5-amp mazda photocell exciter lamp). 2A, 2B, 2C. Light baffles.   3. Pendulum disk shutter.   4. Negative-positive conversion filter mechanism (also used as manual shutter).   5. Photographic step tablet (21 steps, 0.15 density gradient; width of each step, 5 mm.; dimensions of exposure area, $1\frac{3}{8} \times 4\frac{1}{4}$ inches).   6. Film strip.   7. Film cover door.

lamp operating at a color temperature of 2850° K., a ball-bearing pendulum shutter giving an exposure of approximately 0.10 second, a filter for use with negative materials (Wratten No. 78AA producing a color temperature of 5400° K.) and a density scale ranging from 0.05 to 3.05 in steps of 0.15.   A constant voltage transformer is included and a rheostat so that the current on the lamp may be maintained.   This instrument, as the name indicates, is de-

signed to expose strips for control purpose in the processing of motion picture film

Development of the Sensitive Materia

Since the effect of exposure is measurabl only after development, and the response o a sensitive material to a given exposur varies with the degree of development, i is necessary to establish standards for de velopment as well as for exposure.   Thes involve (1) the choice of a suitable devel oper, (2) the establishment of a method o development which will result in (a) th same amount of development for all th exposures on the test strip, and (b) uni form development on different test strip

The characteristics desirable in a devel oper for sensitometry are:

1. *Freedom from fog.*   Fog, produce by the development of unexposed silver ha ide, introduces a source of error since th density due to fog is not the same for al densities on the test strip.

2. *The silver deposit should be free o selective absorption;* i.e., free from color If the deposit is stained or colored, th transmission will depend upon the color o the light in which the transmitted light i measured.

3. *Sufficient energy to produce good den sity and contrast.*

4. *Reproducibility:* i.e., freedom from variations in reducing energy due to (1 impurities in the developing agent; (2 variations in temperature; (3) sensitivit to the alkaline halides and by-products o development; (4) rapid oxidation, etc.

At the Seventh International Congress o Photography, which met at London in 1928 a paraminophenol developer was adopted a

[4] Bornman and Tuttle, *J. Opt. Soc. Amer.* **32**, 224 (1942).

Mᴇᴇs ᴀɴᴅ Sʜᴇᴘᴘᴀʀᴅ, "Instruments for Sensitometric Investigation," *Phot. J.* **44**, 200 (1904).

Rᴀᴡʟɪɴɢ, "Exposure Mechanisms," *Phot. J* **65**, 64 (1925).

Hᴀʀᴅʏ, "A Simple Non-Intermittent Sensi tometer," *J. Opt. Soc. Amer.* **10**, 14 (1925).

best meeting the requirements; [5] paramino-phenol developers, however, are not widely used and a metol-hydroquinone developer [6] was adopted in 1941 by the American Standards Association for the determination of the ASA Speed. Except for the determination of ASA Speeds, the general practice in this country is to employ a developer recommended by the manufacturer in order that development may correspond more closely with practical usage.

Whatever the developer chosen, it is of the highest importance that development be reproducible and that it be uniform on all parts of the test strip. These requirements involve (1) the standardization of (a) temperature, (b) time, (c) degree of agitation, and (2) the employment of a method of agitation which will result in uniform development. Temperature is maintained by enclosing the developing tray, or tank, in a water bath controlled by a thermostat, and the use of a stop bath prevents the continuation of development beyond the desired time.

The American Standards Association and the British Standards Institute have adopted a method of development in which the test strips are attached to a glass strip (Fig. 17.4) which is a part of the stopper of a vacuum flask, or Thermos bottle, about 2/3 full of developer. During development, the flask is tilted back and forth from a vertical to a horizontal position once each second and, at the same time, revolved on its axis about once every five seconds.

Processing machines are, of course, desirable if large numbers of strips must be processed, not only for convenience but for greater uniformity. Many such machines have been described in the literature.[7] Some of these have employed mechanical devices for stirring the solution; others have used plungers, moving up and down near the surface of the film strip, to cause the developing solution to pass rapidly back and forth across the film. Several have employed rotation of the strips in the solution and in recent years jets of air, or a gas, have been used for the agitation of the developing solution.

Density. When a photographic emulsion is exposed to light, or other form of radiant energy, some of the grains of silver halide are rendered developable and, upon development, these are reduced to metallic silver. The amount of silver formed, or what Hurter and Driffield termed the *density*, indicates the response of the sensitive material to the exposure it has received. Since the mass of a material which absorbs light is directly related to its transmission of light, the density of a silver deposit may be determined simply—and more accurately than by chemical methods—by

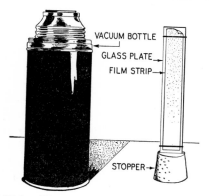

FIG. 17.4. Method of developing sensitometric strips in a temperature control flask.

VACUUM BOTTLE
GLASS PLATE
FILM STRIP
STOPPER

[5] Sheppard and Trivelli, *Proc. Seventh Int. Cong. of Phot.*, 174, Heffer, Cambridge, England (1928). For formula, see Jones, *Photographic Sensitometry*, Eastman Kodak Co., Rochester (1931).

[6] *J. Opt. Soc. Amer.* **31**, 87 (1941).

[7] Bloch and Horton, *Phot. J.* **68**, 352 (1928). Clark, *Phot. Tech.* **2** (Oct. 1940), p. 54. Davies, *Phot. J.* **84**, 185 (1944). Harrison and Dobson, *Phot. J.* **65**, 89 (1925). Sheppard and Crouch, *Proc. Seventh Int. Cong. of Phot.*, London (1928). Sheppard, Lambert, and Atkins, *Phot. Ind.* **34**, 988 (1936). Crabtree, *J. Soc. Mot. Pict. Eng.* **25**, 512 (1935). Russell, Jones, and Beacham, *J. Soc. Mot. Pict. Eng.* **28**, 73 (1937).

measuring optically the amount of light transmitted and deriving the density from this.

Thus, if I_o is the amount of light incident on the silver deposit (or layer of any light-absorbing material; e.g., pigments, dyes, etc.) and I_x is the amount emerging, then I_o/I_x is the fraction of the incident light transmitted, or the *transmission* (T), sometimes called the transparency. The reciprocal of this is termed the *opacity*; i.e., $O = 1/T$. The mass of silver, or light-absorbing material, is defined as the natural logarithm of the opacity:

$$D = \log_{10} O \text{ or } D = \log_{10} \frac{1}{T}.$$

The relationship between transmission, opacity, and density may be clearer from Fig. 17.5. In A the illumination on the

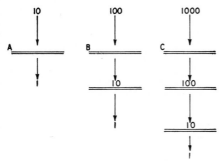

Fig. 17.5. Graphical representation of the relation of transmission, opacity, and density.

silver deposit, represented by the double lines, is 10 times the amount transmitted. The transmission, therefore, is 1/10 and the opacity 10. The density is log 10 or 1.0.

In B, the light passes through one such layer and then through a second. The transmission of the two layers combined is, therefore, 1/100, the opacity 100 and the density log 100 or 2.0.

In C, the light passes successively through three such layers. The transmission in this case is 1/1000, the opacity 1000, and the density log 1000 or 3.0.

This example shows that (1) the amount of silver has increased directly with the number of layers, (2) the opacity has increased to the power of 10, namely, 1, 100, 1000, while the transmission has decreased by the power of 10, or 1/10, 1/100, 1/1000, and (3) the increase in density, the log of opacity, is directly proportional to the number of layers of the mass of silver present.

Layers	1	2	3
Trans	1/10	1/100	1/1000
Opacity	10	100	1000
Density	1	2	3

Density Measurement and the Scatter of Light by the Silver Image. The accuracy of measurements of density optically by a densitometer is affected by the scattering of the light in passing through the silver deposit. The grains of silver which make up the image both absorb and scatter light. Suppose we consider the case of a single ray of light entering the density. That ray of light will emerge not as a single ray, diminished in intensity by the absorption of the density but scattered in all directions, as in Fig. 17.6. If only the direct, undeviated light represented by the central arrow is measured, the density will be greater (i.e., the transmission less) than if the scattered light is included. Densities determined from the direct, undeviated light are termed *specular* densities ($D //$), whereas values obtained when the scattered light is included are termed *diffuse* densities ($D \divideontimes$). The difference in the two values

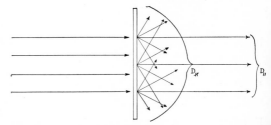

Fig. 17.6. Representation of the scatter of light by a photographic density.

depends upon (1) the amount of light scattered, which depends upon (a) the illumination on the density, (b) the degree of nonhomogeneity of the silver deposit, and (2) the extent to which the scattered light is included in the measurement. Optically it is easier to design equipment to measure specular densities; it is more desirable, however, from the standpoint of photographic practice to measure diffuse densities. In contact printing, for example, the paper receives both the direct and the scattered light. In projection printing, the lens is at some distance from the image and, therefore, cannot collect and transmit all the scattered light. In this case, the effective density lies somewhere between $D//$ and D ✳. In practice densities are measured by a diffuse source of illumination obtained by placing the density to be measured in contact with opal glass.

The ratio of the specular and diffuse density is frequently termed the Callier factor after A. Callier,[8] the Belgian who was the first to investigate thoroughly the scatter of light by photographic densities and the relation between values of the specular and diffuse density. The ratio of $D||/D$✳ increases with the density and with average grain size of the silver deposit.[9]

---

[8] Callier, *Phot. J.* **49**, 200 (1909).

[9] A standard for diffuse density and four approved methods of measurement were established as American Standards by the American Standards Association in 1946. *American Standard for Diffuse Transmission Density*, Z38.2.5—1946.

BULL AND CARTWRIGHT, "The Measurement of Photographic Density," *Phot. J.* **64**, 180 (1924).

BULL AND CARTWRIGHT, "An Evaluation of the Light Scattered by Photographic Densities," *Phot. J.* **65**, 177 (1925).

KOERNER AND TUTTLE, "Experimental Determination of Photographic Density," *Phot. J.* **77**, 444 (1937).

Densitometers. Photometers designed particularly for the measurement of photographic densities are termed *densitometers*. These may be divided broadly into two types: (1) visual densitometers and (2) physical densitometers.

FIG. 17.7. The photometric field as seen in the eyepiece.

In visual instruments, two beams of light are brought together side by side in a circular field (Fig. 17.7), or so that one beam is contained within the other. When the illumination from both beams is the same, the line of demarkation disappears and the field appears of uniform brightness. Insertion of the density to be measured in one of the beams darkens that portion of the field, and to restore equality of illumination to both parts of the field it is necessary (1) to increase the amount of light on the density or (2) reduce the other beam in such a

---

RENWICK, "How Should the Densities of a Photographic Deposit be Measured?" *Brit. J. Phot.* **71**, 65 (1924).

PITT, "A Note on the Measurement of Specular Density," *Phot. J.* **78**, 486 (1938).

TOY, "The Standardization of Photographic Density Measurements," *Phot. J.* **65**, 164 (1925).

TUTTLE, "Relation Between Diffuse and Specular Density," *J. Opt. Soc. Amer.* **12**, 559 (1926).

TUTTLE, "The Relation Between Diffuse and Specular Density," *J. Soc. Mot. Pict. Eng.* **20**, 228 (1933).

TUTTLE, "Densitometry and Photographic Printing, Illumination of the Negative and Its Effect Upon Density," *J. Opt. Soc. Amer.* **24**, 272 (1934).

TUTTLE AND KOERNER, "The Standardization of Photographic Density," *Phot. J.* **78**, 739 (1938).

way that the transmission of the density can be measured.

While many different types of densitometers have been used, those of importance may be divided into three classes:

1. *Instruments with movable light sources.* In these, the illumination produced by the comparison beam is varied in a measurable manner by moving the light source, or sources, through application of the inverse-square law. A modified Bunsen photometer of this type was employed by Hurter and Driffield in their classical investigations in photographic sensitometry but,[10] except for one recent example,[11] this type is now obsolete.

2. *Polarization densitometers.* A number of photometers have been developed in which the intensity of the comparison beam is controlled by polarization.[12] The best known densitometer of this type is an adaptation of the Martens photometer[13] and this for years was widely accepted as the standard instrument for the measurement of photographic densities. It is probably still unsurpassed among visual instruments, but in recent years has been used less and less.

3. *Density comparators.* Densitometers of this type vary the illumination from the comparison beam by means of an optical wedge, the densities of which have been measured on another densitometer. These instruments are comparatively simple optically and mechanically, relatively inexpensive and sufficiently accurate for most purposes.

The best known instruments of this type are the Eastman Densitometer (Fig. 17.8), the Kodak Color Densitometer, and [14] the the Ilford Densitometer,[15] the two last mentioned being designed primarily for the sensitometric control of three-color processing rather than for precision sensitometry.

Early attempts to use the thermopile, the selenium cell, or photoelectric cells, to measure density directly were not very successful because the cells available at the time were not sufficiently constant in their response to make them dependable. As a result a number of instruments were designed in which the cell is used in place of the eye to determine if the two beams are of equal intensity.[16]

The improvement in cells and the associated electrical circuits within the last decade has made direct-reading instruments feasible and several models are now available.

In four of these, the light, after passing through the density, falls directly upon the photocell. The current transmitted by the photocell is then amplified by vacuum tubes

---

[10] The Hurter and Driffield Memorial Volume, Edited by Ferguson and published by the Royal Photographic Society of Great Britain, London, 1920.

[11] Marshal Densitometer. See article on Densitometry, in the *American Encyclopedia of Photography* (The Complete Photographer), Chicago, 1943.

[12] See any recognized work on photometry.

[13] The most convenient sources of reference are: Jones, *Photographic Sensitometry*, Eastman Kodak Co., Rochester, 1934. Mees, *The Theory of the Photographic Process*, The Macmillan Co. Sweet, Densitometry, *American Encyclopedia of Photography*, Chicago, 1943.

"The Ilford Densitometer," *Miniature Camera Magazine* 11, 333 (1947) (Manufactured by Ilford Itd., Ilford, London, England).

GENIESSE, "Constant Illumination Densitometer," *Amer. Phot.* 39, 14 (January 1945) (Constructional details).

---

[14] The Kodak Color Densitometer, Eastman Kodak Co., Rochester, N. Y.

[15] Ilford Densitometer, *Miniature Camera Mag.* 11, 333 (1947).

[16] An instrument of this type has been made for a number of years by the National Photocolor Corp., New York City, as the National Photocolor Densitometer. See Sweet, Densitometry, *American Encyclopedia of Photography*, Chicago, 1943.

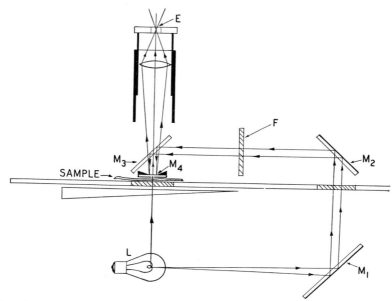

FIG. 17.8.   Optical system of the Eastman (Capstaff-Purdy) densitometer.

and read from an output meter calibrated in density units.[17]   In another example [18] the light transmitted by the density is received by an integrating sphere into one side of which the photocell is mounted so that it receives only the diffused light reflected from the inner walls of the sphere.

The Weston Photograph Analyzer employs a self-generating photocell of the type, used in exposure meters, which requires no amplification. It is intended primarily for the measurement of negative densities.

The Correction of Density for Fog. All densities of a developed image tend to be greater than the true density, since they contain some silver which is due to fog, i.e., development of unexposed grains.   Hurter and Driffield recognized the error in considering the total density as the true density and suggested that the density of an unexposed portion of the test strip be subtracted from the densities on the exposed portion. This assumes that the density of an unexposed section of the test strip is a true measure of fog.   Unfortunately it is not because the fog density depends upon the exposure and, in general, the greater the exposure the lower the fog density.   Thus the

---

[17] Ansco-Macbeth Color Densitometer, Macbeth Inc., Irvington, N. Y.   Photovolt Transmission Densitometer, Photovolt Corporation, New York. Universal Densichron, M. W. Welch Scientific Co., Chicago.

[18] Western   Electric   Densitometer,   Technical Manual RA–1100–B, Electrical Research Products Division of Western Electric Co., New York.   See, also, *J. Soc. Mot. Pict. Eng.* **35,** 184 (August 1940).

SWEET proposed a photographic method of measuring density to determine the photographic density in terms of the absorption of light as evaluated by a developing paper of silver chloride.   Exposures are made on a single sheet of paper to an illuminated opal glass and to the density to be measured.   The density is calculated from the ratio of the distances required to produce equal reflection densities on the paper.   *J. Phot. Soc. Amer.,* 126 (October 1941).   *J. Opt. Soc. Amer.* **33,** 159 (March 1943).

fog density as measured from an unexposed portion of the test strip is greater than for any of the exposed steps and, among these, the density due to fog is greater in the lower densities than in the higher.

The following formula has been proposed by Medinger [19] for the correction of densities for fog:

$$D_f = \frac{D_m - D}{D_m - F}.$$

Where D_f is the fog to be deducted, D_m the maximum developable density, D the observed density, and F the fog density on an unexposed area of the test strip.

The usual practice, however, is to plot the densities as measured neglecting any addition due to fog.

The Measurement of Spectral Sensitivity. The variation in the response of a photosensitive material with the wave length constitutes what is termed *spectral*

sensitivity or, frequently, *color sensitivity*. This is a very important characteristic, particularly of a negative material, because it determines to a large extent the tones in which colored objects are reproduced.

The Monochromatic Sensitometer. The determination of spectral sensitivity involves the isolation of comparatively narrow bands of the spectrum and determining, by one of several methods, the response of the photographic material to the radiation of each of these spectral regions. The optical system of a monochromatic sensitometer described by Jones and Sandvick [20] is shown in Fig. 17.9. In consists essentially of two quartz monochromatic illuminators, A and B. The radiation emerging from A passes into the second illuminator, B, where stray radiation is eliminated so that the radiation emerging from the exit slit of B is confined to an extremely narrow spectral range. This radiation then falls on the photographic material. As the

[19] Medinger, *Z. phys. Chem.* **114**, 89 (1924). See also Wilsey, *Phot. J.* **65**, 454 (1925) and Prichard, *Phot. J.* **67**, 447 (1927).

[20] *J. Opt. Soc. Amer.* **12**, 401 (1926).

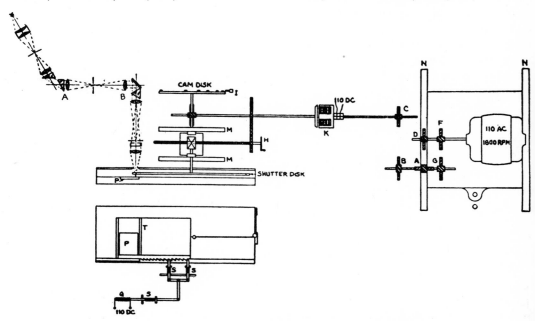

FIG. 17.9.   Optical system of the monochromatic sensitometer.

illuminated area is small, the exposure for the different steps of a sensitometric strip cannot be made at the same time but are made in succession, the time being varied to produce the range of exposures required. The exposure values, however, cannot be expressed in meter-candle-seconds as this is a unit of illumination and is measured visually. When using monochromatic radiation, exposure must be expressed in energy units, i.e., in ergs.

To compute the spectral sensitivity of a photographic material it is necessary first to determine the energy present in each of the wave-length regions at which exposure is to be made. These measurements ordinarily are made with a thermopile—galvanometer—and are both difficult and exacting. Several sensitometric strips are then made for each wave-length region developed for different times and the curves plotted. These curves are similar to the conventional *D* log *E* curve but the abscissal values are the logarithms of exposure as expressed in ergs per cm.² rather than in meter-candle-seconds. The response of the emulsion at a given gamma may be determined from the curves for the different wave-length regions from (1) the inertias, (2) the threshold exposures, or (3) the exposures for a given density. These values

ordinarily are plotted against the wave length as in Fig. 17.10 [21] to form a spectral sensitivity curve. The curve shown represents the spectral response of a panchromatic material to a light source emitting the same energy at all wave lengths (constant energy spectrum).

The Wedge Spectrograph. One of the most widely used methods of comparing the spectral-sensitivity characteristics of different photographic materials is by means of wedge spectrograms (**Fig. 17.11**).

FIG. 17.11. Wedge spectrogram.

These are made on a special type of spectrograph whose essential features are shown in Fig. 17.12. A spectrum of the light source at the extreme right is formed on the sensitive material, placed at the back of the camera by means of a diffraction grating and the optical system shown. A blackglass wedge placed directly in front of the slit varies the illumination across the spectrum logarithmically, so that the height of the exposed portion of the material at any point indicates the *logarithm* of the sensitivity at that particular wave length.

Two facts must be kept in mind when using wedge spectrograms: (1) the curve represents the relation between sensitivity and wave length only in terms of the light source used for the exposure; (2) the absorption of the glass wedge increases in the short-wave region so that the sensitivity of the film in the blue and violet is greater relatively than wedge spectrograms indicate. This is not particularly serious because there is little difference in the sensitivity distribution of different materials in

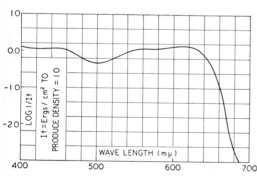

FIG. 17.10. Spectral sensitivity curve of a panchromatic material to a constant energy source of radiation plotted from data obtained with the monochromatic sensitometer.

[21] Jones, *Photographic Sensitometry*, Figs. 60 and 61.

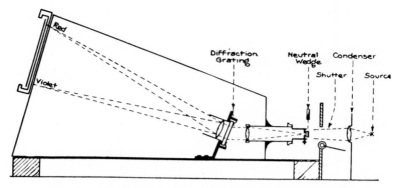

FIG. 17.12.   Optical system of the wedge spectrograph.

this region and if wedge spectrograms are used simply for comparing different materials.

Filter Methods. Sensitometric exposures made through suitable filters, rather than in the monochromatic sensitometer, provide a simple and useful means of determining spectral sensitivity although the results cannot be compared from the standpoint of completeness or accuracy. The difficulty lies in the fact that the filters available do not permit of the isolation of different parts of the spectrum equally or without overlapping. While a division of the spectrum into 5 or 6 nonoverlapping parts is possible with combinations of ex-

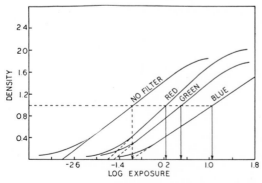

FIG. 17.13. D log E curves of a panchromatic emulsion showing the results of exposures through a typical set of three-color filters. (Wratten ABC₄.)

isting filters, in general this method has been confined to the red, green, and blue-violet filters used in three-color photography. Results of practical value may be obtained by making sensitometer test strips with each of the filters, developing to (1) the same gamma or (2) for the same time, depending upon the requirements, and determining the relative sensitivity by the exposure difference for (1) visually matched densities or from (2) D log E curves using (a) inertia speeds, (b) the exposure for a given density, or (c) fractional gradient values.

Variation of Gamma with Wave Length. Although the three sensitometric strips shown in Fig. 17.13 were developed together for the same time, the gammas are not the same. Gamma depends upon the spectral characteristics of the radiation to which the material is exposed as well as on the emulsion and conditions of development. Thus, with uniform development, the values for spectral sensitivity and the filter factor depend on the density chosen as a basis of comparison; if, however, the three strips are developed separately to the same gamma, the values are independent of the density.

Throughout the range of sensitivity of silver bromide in gelatin the variation in gamma with wave length is very nearly inversely proportional to the absorption of silver bromide.[22] At wave lengths below 250 mμ, gamma is low because of the strong absorption of gelatin. From 250 to about 310 mμ it is fairly constant. Beyond this point it rises as the absorption of silver bromide decreases to a maximum between 400 and 450 mμ. High absorption by the silver halide tends to restrict the image to the surface of the emulsion layer with a reduction in the value of gamma. Beyond the sensitivity of silver halide (approximately 550 mμ) the relationship between gamma and wave length depends upon the densitizing dye used and its concentration.

ASA Spectral Sensitivity Index. This ASA standard, adopted (1946) as a means of specifying the spectral sensitivity of photographic materials, is based upon the sensitometric determination of the response of the emulsion in three regions using a blue-violet filter transmitting from the ultraviolet to a wave length of about 520 mμ, a green filter transmitting between 520 and 600 mμ and the third transmitting from 600 to about 675 mμ, which represents the practical limit of sensitivity for the majority of high-speed panchromatic materials.

The color sensitivity of a material is expressed in two forms, a Spectral-Sensitivity Index and a Spectral Group Number.[23] The index shows the per cent contribution of each of the three spectral regions as determined by test. This gives an indication of the relative sensitivity, but in practice the degree of differentation is greater than is required for many purposes. The Spectral Group Number groups emulsion characteristics within useful tolerances so that, for pictorial purposes, any two emulsions with a given group may be expected to

show similar relative color response and to require similar filter factors for the commonly used filters.

The index values and group numbers of five typical negative film types follow:

	Index	*Group Number*
Blue Sensitive	100– 0– 0	00
Orthochromatic	89–11– 0	20
High Green Ortho	63–32– 0	50
Panchromatic	59–28–13	66
High Red Pan	41–37–22	77

II. Instruments and Methods for the Sensiometry of Developing Out Papers

Sensitometers. Since the exposure range of papers is much shorter than that of negative materials it is desirable that the exposure difference between steps be less. Sensitometers with a log E difference of 0.15 and 0.10 are in general use, and instruments with log E differences of 0.05 and 0.025 have been built for special purposes.

The time-scale instrument illustrated in Fig. 17.2, fitted with a light source of higher intensity, has been used extensively as, for a number of years, it was the only sensitometer available commercially, but the very considerable departures from the reciprocity law occurring with many papers makes intensity-scale instruments

[22] Davey, *Phot. J.* **85B**, 127 (1945).

[23] Method of Determining Spectral-Sensitivity Indexes and Group Numbers for Photographic Emulsions, ASA Standard Z38.2.4–1946.

Evans, "An Intensity-Scale Monochromatic Sensitometer," *J. Opt. Soc. Amer.* **30**, 118 (1940).

Selwyn and Davies, "A Note on the Use of Color Charts in Photography," *Phot. J.* **78**, 122 (1938).

White, "Film Color Sensitivity Identified," *Industrial Standardization* **17**, 136 (1946); *J. Phot. Soc. Amer.* **12**, 398 (1946).

White, "A Spectral Sensitivity Index for Photographic Emulsions and Calculations Based on It," *J. Phot. Soc. Amer.* **9**, 386, 585 (1943).

preferable.[24] The intensity scale instrument, shown in Fig. 17.3, may be used but is not an instrument of high precision. Special sensitometers for papers have been designed by Kinder [25] and by McFarlane.[26]

At the present time a tungsten light source with a color temperature of 2854° K. has been adopted as an unofficial standard. This is lower than that of many lamps used for projection printing, but the difference is not important with blue-sensitive paper emulsions, and the lamps available at this color temperature are more constant in their characteristics than those operating at a higher color temperature.

Processing should follow exposure immediately, because on papers the latent image begins to fade appreciably soon after the exposure. The processing of papers is less critical than negative materials because of the thinner emulsion coating and because, unlike most negative materials, papers are nearly always developed to approximate finality. For practical purposes, the developer should be the formula advised by the manufacturer and the time and conditions of development should conform closely to the recommendations of the manufacturer. An American Standard has been adopted for control and comparative sensitometry.[27] The standard provides for (1) a standard metol-hydroquinone developer, (2) a temperature of 68° F., (3) controlled agitation by tray rocking, (4) a developing time of 1½ minutes, (5) the use of a fixing bath "conditioned" before use to prevent the reduction of the image, (5) washing for fifteen minutes, and (6)

drying by air at a temperature not greater than 104° F. (40° C.).[28]

Reflection Density. In a print, the brightnesses of the subject are represented by differences in the amount of light reflected from the paper, these differences in reflectance being due to variations in the mass of silver constituting the image. Reflectance is the ratio of the reflected to the incident light or

$$R = \frac{I_r}{I_o}.$$

Where I_r is the intensity of the reflected light and I_o the intensity of the light incident on the surface.

The reflection density is defined as

$$D_r = \log I/R$$

or

$$= \log I_o/I_r.$$

The density of a sample of the paper fixed out without exposure to light or development, whatever the intensity of the reflected light, is zero. Thus a silver deposit which reflects one-half the amount of light reflected from the same paper without a silver image has a reflection density of 0.3; if ¼ or 25% of the light is reflected the reflection density is 0.6. This definition of the reflection density assumes (1) that only reflected light which is normal to the surface is measured and (2) that the sample is illuminated with diffuse light from an angle which will cause light specularly reflected from the surface to be thrown to one side and eliminated.

Densitometers for the Measurement of Reflection Density. While several types of densitometers for the measurement of reflection density have been described,[29] the

[24] See, Jones and Morrison, *J. Franklin Inst.* **228**, 445 (1939).

[25] Kinder, *Zeit. für Instrumentkunde* **10**, 393 (1936).

[26] Jones and Morrison, *J. Franklin Inst.* **228**, 445 (1939).

[27] *American Standard Z38.2.3–1947*, Sensitometry of Photographic Papers.

[28] *American Standard Z38.8.6* (Proposed), American Standard Practice for Photographic Processing Manipulation of Paper.

[29] Jones, Mees and Nutting, *Phot. J.* **38**, 342 (1914). Ferguson and Read, *Brit. J. Phot.* **81**,

instrument shown in Fig. 17.14 is one of the best known.

A part of the light from the lamp, A, reaches the surface of the paper at M. Some of this is reflected vertically and condensed by the lens system, L_1 and L_2, to form the center of the photometric field at J. Part of the light from lamp, A, passes through the wedge, W, and is re-

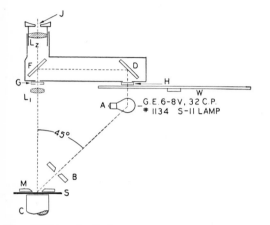

Fig. 17.14. Optical system of the Eastman reflection densitometer.

flected by the mirrors, D, F, and G, as indicated, to form the outer portion of the photometric field. The instrument is first adjusted so that photometric balance is obtained on zero density, i.e., a portion of the paper which has been fixed without exposure or development. The density to be measured is then placed in position at M and the wedge rotated until the difference in brightness in the two coincentric fields disappears. The reflection density is then read from the scale on the top of the instrument.

351 (1934). Sweet, *J. Opt. Soc. Amer.* **28**, 349 (1938). Jones and Morrison, *J. Franklin Inst.* **228**, 445 (1939). Three of the photoelectric densitometers mentioned on page 253 may be used to measure reflection density.

III. Interpretation of the Results

The D Log E Curve. The relation of density to exposure is customarily presented in the form of a curve in which density is plotted against the *logarithm* of the exposure. In Fig. 17.15 is shown such a curve for a typical negative emulsion, density being plotted against (1) exposure and (2) the logarithm of the exposure. Curves obtained by plotting density against the logarithm of the exposure are often called H and D curves after Hurter and Driffield who were the first to employ such curves although the terms "characteristic curve" and D log E curve are now used more frequently.

This method of plotting density against the logarithm of the exposure is employed (1) to reduce the length of the curve, and (2) to obtain a curve which will show more clearly the rate at which density increases *with a given multiplication in exposure.*

A considerable part of this curve is, for all practical purposes, a straight line. Throughout this exposure range, the density and log E differences are proportional. If, therefore, the darkest and the brightest portions of the subject are represented by densities on the straight-line portion of the D log E curve, the brightness ratios will be rendered proportionally as differences in density in the negative. The straight-line portion of the curve is for this reason referred to frequently as the *period of proportional representation* or as the *latitude* of the emulsion (Fig. 17.16). Thus

$$\text{Latitude} = \log E_n - \log E_m \ (\text{Log } E \text{ units})$$
$$L = E_n/E_m \ (\text{Exposure units}).$$

The value of L for any given D log E curve expresses the exposure (or log E) range over which proportional rendering is obtained and, therefore, the greatest ratio in subject brightness which the sensitive material is capable of rendering with exact proportionality.

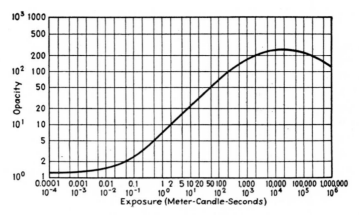

FIG. 17.15.   *D* log *E* curve.

In the straight-line portion of the curve, the gradient, or slope, *G,* is fixed by the relationship between a given log *E* interval, $\triangle$ log *E*, and the corresponding density difference, $\triangle$ *D.* Thus, the gradient may be expressed as

$$G = \triangle D / \triangle \log E$$

or

$$G = \frac{D_2 - D_1}{\log E_2 - \log E_1}.$$

This is equal to the tangent of the angle *a* formed by the straight line portion of the curve and the log *E* axis, so that

$$G = \tan \alpha.$$

The value of *G* for any particular emulsion and conditions of development varies with the time of development and was used by Hurter and Driffield as a means of expressing the degree of development

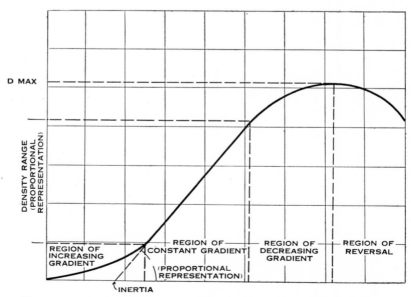

FIG. 17.16.   *D* log *E* curve showing various log *E* gradient relations.

(gamma). Thus

$$\gamma = \tan \alpha = \frac{D_2 - D_1}{\log E_2 - \log E_1}.$$

Since the gradient increases with log E, the capacity of a negative material to reproduce brightness differences in the subject photographed as differences in density increases from zero, at the beginning of the curve, to a maximum on the straight-line portion.

Beyond the straight-line portion, the gradient becomes less and less with increased exposure. In other words, the density differences for a given log E range decrease steadily. Finally, at D_{max}, the maximum density, the gradient becomes zero. Thus beyond the straight-line portion the capacity of the sensitive material to reproduce brightness differences in the subject as differences in density decreases steadily as the exposure increases.

The exposure range between the beginning of the curve and the maximum density represents the range over which the sensitive material is capable of representing exposure differences as differences in density or what is termed *the total exposure scale.*

$$\text{Total Scale} = \log E_L - \log E_c$$
or
$$= E_L/E_c.$$

The *useful exposure scale* is the range of exposure over which useful results are obtained; i.e., density differences which will produce satisfactory reproduction of brightness ratios in the print. The lower limit of the useful exposure scale may be regarded as having been established by the work of Jones and his co-workers in the Kodak Research Laboratories at the point on the D log E curve where the gradient is 0.3 of the average gradient of a log E range of 1.5. The upper limit has not yet been so definitely fixed. In practice it is probable that, for most photographers at least, the upper limit is within the straight-line portion of the curve because of the high densities involved.

The Gradient Log E Curve. For some purposes, the variation in the gradient, or slope, of the D log E curve with log E is more useful than the usual curve. A D log E curve with its first derivative, in

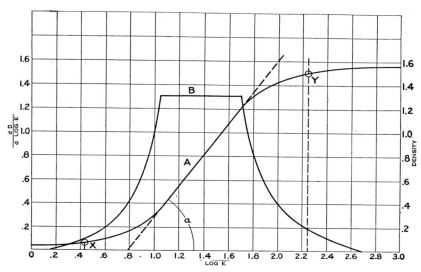

Fig. 17.17.   First derivative of the D log E curve.

which gradient is plotted against log E, is shown in Fig. 17.17. The data for this curve may be obtained in one of several ways. For example, the slope of the D log E curve at any particular point may be determined with fair precision by drawing a tangent to the curve at the point in question and determining the slope, or gradient, of the tangent line. By repeating this procedure for a sufficient number of points, the necessary data may be obtained. A second method consists in taking a number of equally spaced points along the log E axis and calculating the density difference for each log E interval.

Gamma. Gamma has been defined previously as (a) the tangent of the angle formed by the straight-line portion of the D log E curve when extended to the log E axis, and (b) as the ratio of the difference in two densities on the straight-line portion and the corresponding log E values.

$$\gamma = \tan a$$
$$\gamma = \Delta D / \Delta \log E = \frac{D_2 - D_1}{\log E_2 - \log E_1}.$$

The value of gamma for a particular curve may be determined (1) by obtaining the values for D_2 and D_1, and the corresponding log E values and solving the equation (2) by graphical methods (Fig. 17.18),

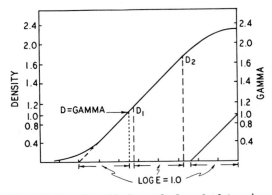

FIG. 17.18. Graphical methods of determining gamma.

and (3) by direct measurement of the gradient, G, with a transparent reading device or *gammeter* (Fig. 17.19).

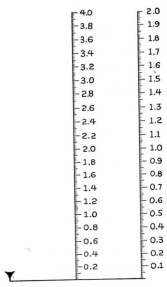

FIG. 17.19.   Gammeter.

It is clear from the equation that the value of gamma expresses also the ratio of the density differences of the negative and the log E values produced by the brightnesses of the subject. Thus, if two parts of the subject have brightnesses of 100 and 10, the log E interval, $\Delta \log E$ is log 100 — log 10 = 1.0. Then if the camera exposure is such that these brightnesses are represented by densities on the straight-line portion of the D log E curve, upon development to a gamma of 1.0, the density difference will also equal 1.0. If, under the same conditions, the negative is developed to a gamma of 0.5, then the density difference will equal 0.5. Gamma, therefore, represents the ratio of the density differences (contrast) of the negative to the brightness differences (contrast) of the subject. Thus with a gamma of 1.0, each log E interval is represented by an equal difference in density, and the negative is an exact reproduction of the brightness ratios.[30] With a gamma of 0.5 the ratio is as 1:2 (lower contrast) while with a gamma of 2.0 the ratio is 2:1; i.e., the negative contrast is twice that of the subject. It must always be remembered, however, that gamma is determined from, and applies only to, the straight-line portion of the curve; if any of the densities of the image are below or above the straight-line portion of the curve, gamma no longer expresses the contrast ratio of image and object.

The Time Gamma Curve. In Fig. 17.20 is shown a set of *D* log *E* curves representing a variation in the time of development. Plotting gamma against the time of development produces the *time-gamma* curve which represents the relationship between the

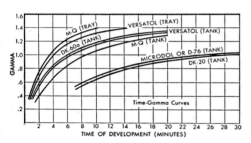

FIG. 17.20. Time gamma curves of an emulsion in different developers.

time of development and gamma. From the shape of the curve it is evident that the rate at which gamma increases becomes progressively less with increased development, or with higher values of gamma.

---

[30] In practice, the scatter of light within the lens system reduces the brightness differences of the lens image as compared with the subject by a factor of from 2 to 5 depending on the lens. See Jones and Condit, *J. Opt. Soc. Amer.* **31**, 651 (1941).

RENWICK, "An Instrument for the Measurement of Gamma," *Phot. J.* **54**, 163 (1914).
WHITE, "Gamma by Least Squares," *J. Soc. Mot. Pict. Eng.* **18**, 584 (1932).

Curves of this type are very useful. For example, the time of development for a given gamma, or the gamma produced by a given time of development is easily found by the procedure shown in Fig. 17.21. It should be noted, however, that

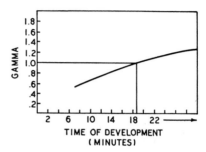

FIG. 17.21. Calculation of time of development for a given gamma.

these values may not be applied to practice unless the conditions of development represented by the curve are exactly duplicated. Values obtained, for example, from tray development cannot, in general, be applied to tank development, nor can results obtained with fresh developer at a given temperature be applied to a used developer at a different temperature nor to another emulsion.

The variation in the time of development for a given tolerance in gamma is termed

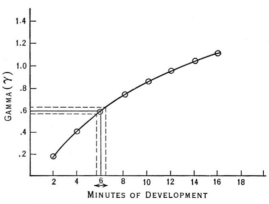

FIG. 17.22. Calculation of processing latitude.

the *processing latitude*.[31] The method of determining the processing latitude from the time-gamma curve is shown in Fig. 17.22.

For a particular emulsion, developer and conditions of development the processing latitude increases with the gamma.

The highest gamma obtainable in any particular emulsion is termed *gamma infinity*. It depends chiefly on the emulsion and to a lesser extent on the composition of the developer. Typical values for different types of emulsions are:

High-speed portrait film........	1.2
High-speed press film...........	1.7
Commercial film...............	2.0
Process film..................	3.0
Photo-litho film...............	5.0

These values are for the developers normally used with each of the emulsion types mentioned. The use of highly concentrated "process type" developers on the first three emulsions would produce higher maximum gammas than the developers generally used, whereas the substitution of a fine-grain developer would result in lower values. These differences are minor, however, as compared with the variation with emulsion type.

The value of gamma infinity for a particular emulsion may be obtained experimentally or may be calculated from the gammas of a set of $D \log E$ curves.

------

[31] The processing latitude is inversely proportional to the gradient, i,e., the differential $d\,\gamma/dt$ of the gamma-time curve at any particular point.

MEES AND SHEPPARD, "On the Highest Development Factor Obtainable on any Plate," *Phot. J.* **43**, 199 (1903).

RENWICK, "An Improved Method of Computing the Velocity Constant and Gamma Infinity," *Phot. J.* **63**, 331 (1923).

TOY AND HIGSON, "Factors Determining Gamma Infinity," *Phot. J.* **63**, 68 (1923).

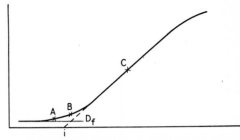

A–D$_t$ THRESHOLD DENSITY (THRESHOLD SPEEDS)
B–D$_{f+}$ 0.2 (DIN SPEEDS)
C–D = γ (WESTON SPEEDS)
i –INERTIA (H and D SPEEDS)

FIG. 17.23. $D \log E$ curve showing point from which threshold, DIN, H and D and Weston speeds are determined.

The Measurement of Sensitivity or Speed. The speed of a sensitive material may be defined as the reciprocal of the exposure required to produce a given result. Methods of measuring speed may be divided into three classes (Fig. 17.23):

1. *The exposure required to produce a given density.* In this class are included (1) the methods based on the exposure producing the first visible density (Warnerke, Scheiner, Eder-Hecht, Chapman-Jones, etc.); (2) the exposure required for a density of 0.1 above fog (the prewar German Industrial Standard method (DIN)), and (3) the exposure for a density equal to gamma (Weston).

2. The exposure at the point of intersection of the straight-line portion of the $D \log E$ curve when extended to the log E axis. (Hurter and Driffield method.)

3. The exposure at the point on the $D \log E$ curve representing the minimum useful density difference (American Standards Association Speeds (ASA)).

Methods of Speed Determination Based on the Relation Between Exposure and a Particular Density. The Scheiner speed is the best known of the methods based on the exposure just sufficient for the first visible or threshold density. The Scheiner number was obtained originally by exposing the sensitive material in a sensitometer having twenty exposure steps numbered 1 to 20; developing under certain prescribed conditions and expressing speed as the number of the step producing the first visible density above fog. A speed based upon the exposure for the threshold density is not, however, a dependable indication of the useful speed and the Scheiner method is now obsolete.

In 1931 the German photographic industry adopted a method of measuring speed which became known as the DIN method. This is based upon the exposure producing a density of 0.1 above fog. The emulsion is exposed, for 1/20 second, in a special sensitometer having a wedge of 30 steps ranging in density from zero to 3.0, developed in a standard metol-hydroquinone developer, and the step having a density of 0.1 greater than fog located on a densitometer designed particularly for the purpose. The DIN number is the density, times ten, of the exposure step in the sensitometer which produces a density of 0.1 above fog on the test strip. If, for example, the 10th step on the developed test strip has a density equal to the fog density plus 0.1, then the DIN number is the density of the tenth step of the sensitometer wedge times ten.

Weston Speeds. Weston speeds are determined by the company in its laboratories in Newark, N. J.

$$\text{Weston Speed} = \frac{1}{E} \times 4 \quad \text{or} \quad \frac{4}{E},$$

where E is the exposure for a density equal to gamma.

FERGUSON, "The DIN Speed—Marking for Plates and Films," *Brit. J. Phot.* 81, 380 (1934).

For publication, the speeds as determined by laboratory tests are grouped in classes 8, 12, 16, 24, 32, etc.

H and D Speeds. The H and D speed is determined from the exposure at the intersection of the straight-line portion of the D log E curve extended to the log E axis. The exposure at this point was termed by Hurter and Driffield the *inertia*, and H and D speeds are sometimes referred to as inertia speeds. Originally, the H and D speed was obtained by multiplying the reciprocal of the inertia by 34 or

$$H \text{ and } D \text{ Speed} = \frac{1}{i} \times 34,$$

where i is the inertia (exposure in mcs.).

Later this inconvenient multiplying factor (34) was replaced by 10 so that the H and D speed became

$$S = \frac{1}{i} \times 10 \quad \text{or} \quad \frac{10}{i}.$$

The H and D method was at one time the generally accepted method of determining speed in English-speaking countries but as time went on the speed numbers published by manufacturers became less and less reliable and changes in the characteristics of negative materials caused the H and D speed to become less and less indicative of the useful speed of the film or plate. The publication of H and D speeds was discontinued entirely about ten years ago, but inertia speeds are still useful in the laboratory for comparative purposes.

ASA (American Standards Association) Speeds. The ASA speed, adopted in 1947 by the American Standards Association, is now the recognized method of measuring and expressing negative speed in this country.[32] It is an outgrowth of the investiga-

---

[32] The British Standards Institution (BSI) speed in use in England is similar.

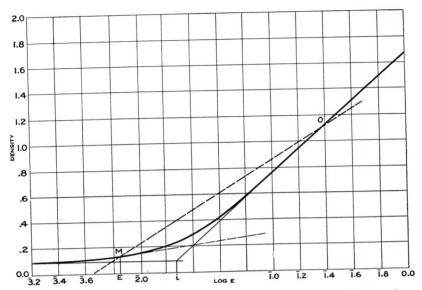

FIG. 17.24.   *D* log *E* curve showing the derivation of the ASA speed.

tions of Jones and his co-workers in the Kodak Research Laboratories and is based on the exposure required to produce a negative from which a good print can be made on a suitable paper.

This exposure was found, as a result of a lengthy series of investigations,[33] to be equivalent to the exposure, *E*, on the *D* log *E* curve at which the gradient is 0.3 times the average gradient for a log *E* range of 1.5, of which *E* is the minimum exposure (Fig. 17.24).

The ASA speed number is the reciprocal of this exposure when the exposure and development of the material conform to the standards established in the specification (Z38.2.1—1947).

The ASA method of measuring speed applies only to roll film, film packs, 35 mm. film, sheet film, and plates for general photography: it does not include infrared materials nor process-type materials.

[33] Jones, *J. Franklin Inst.* **227**, 297, 497 (1939). Jones and Nelson, *J. Opt. Soc. Amer.* **30**, 93 (1940).

The ASA Exposure Index, for use with exposure meters and calculators, is determined from the formula:

$$\text{Exposure Index} = 1/4\,E$$

or

$$= \text{ASA speed}/4.$$

The index values thus obtained are classified for publication into groups as follows:

Speed	American Standard Arithmetic Exposure Index	British Standard Logarithmic Exposure Index[34]
01000	250	35°
0800	200	34°
0650	160	33°
0500	125	32°
0400	100	31°
0320	80	30°
0250	64	29°
0200	50	28°
0160	40	27°
0125	32	26°
0100	25	25°
080	20	24°
064	16	23°
050	12	22°
040	10	21°

[34] *British Standard Specification 1380*, 1947.

Determination of the 0.3 Fractional Gradient. The point on the $D \log E$ curve from which the ASA speed is measured may be determined by (1) geometrical construction,[35] (2) by the application of a

transparent fractional gradient meter [36] to the curve, and (3) by calculation.[37]

[35] Jones, *J. Franklin Inst.* **227**, 297, 497 (1939).

[36] Tuttle, *J. Opt. Soc. Amer.* **29**, 267 (1939).

[37] Special sensitometric instruments which enable the fractional gradient to be determined directly from the sensitometric strip without the plotting of the $D \log E$ curve have been described by Tuttle, *J. Opt. Soc. Amer.* **31**, 709 (1941).

Chapter 18

PHOTOGRAPHIC TONE REPRODUCTION

Modern photography finds application in almost every field of human endeavor. Photographic materials are therefore required to perform a multitude of functions. A discussion of the tone reproduction problems involved in all these applications of photography is beyond the scope of this chapter. We shall deal here only with pictorial photography in which the end result is a two-dimensional picture in monochrome. We shall furthermore assume in this chapter that the picture is to be produced by straight-forward photographic methods without recourse to the artifices of retouching, air-brushing, masking, etc. We shall assume that the function of photography in this application is to provide the medium by means of which an excellent reproduction of an original is obtained.

An "excellent photographic reproduction" or a "photograph of excellent quality" are terms frequently used in assessing the merits of a picture made by photographic processes. These terms are often used in different senses in referring to various aspects of the appearance of a picture. In general, these aspects can be considered to fall into two categories—artistic and technical. The artistic qualities of a photograph are to a large extent determined by the lighting and composition of the scene. It is evident that the factors which control these aspects of quality are not functions of the photographic processes, but rather of the skill of the photographer in selecting and arranging his subject matter. The technical aspect of photographic qual-

ity depends upon the fidelity with which the photographic process has reproduced the light and shade and geometry of the original subject. These are the factors which determine the degree of perfection with which the photographic picture reproduces in the mind of the observer the subjective impression which he received when looking at the original. It is apparent that any attempt to evaluate this aspect of photographic quality will involve a consideration of the tonal relationships which exist between the subject and its photographic reproduction. Tone reproduction studies are concerned primarily with the derivation of these relationships and their application to a systematic analysis of problems in which quality is a factor.

In the conventional approach to the solution of tone reproduction problems there are two distinct phases—the objective and the subjective. The objective phase involves comparative measurements of light reflected from the subject and transmitted or reflected by the photographic reproduction. The subjective phase is concerned with the human factor, i.e., with the personal reactions of the observer to various visual stimuli presented in the form of photographs.

OBJECTIVE TONE REPRODUCTION

As mentioned previously, the objective phase of tone reproduction studies is concerned with quantitative relationships. Of primary interest are those which are derived by photometric methods. It is necessary, therefore, at this point to introduce certain concepts on which photometric practice is based, and to define the terms and units with which this science deals.

Photometric Terms and Units. Photometry is the science which treats of the measurement of the quantitative characteristics of light. For the purposes of photometry, *light* is radiant energy evaluated according to its capacity to produce visual sensation, particularly the brightness attribute of visual sensation. The following photometric quantities will be utilized extensively in this chapter:

Luminous Flux. Luminous flux is the time rate of flow, emission, or incidence of light. The unit of luminous flux is the *lumen.* It is equal to the flux within a unit solid angle from a point source of one candle. There are 4π lumens radiated from a source having a luminous intensity of one candle.

Luminance. Luminance is the luminous flux per unit solid angle emitted per unit projected area of a source. A convenient unit of luminance is the foot-Lambert. This is the luminance of a surface emitting $1/\pi$ candle per square foot of projected area.

Illuminance. Illuminance is the luminous flux incident per unit area of surface. The metric unit of illuminance is the meter-candle and is equal to one lumen per square meter. The foot-candle is the English unit of illuminance and is equal to one lumen incident per square foot.

The Basic Objective Tone Relationship. The basic relationship in the objective phase of tone reproduction studies is that which exists between the relative luminance and luminance differences in the original and in the reproduction. Since the luminance of the reproduction is dependent upon the illuminance under which it is viewed, and since only relative values are required, it is convenient to substitute *density* of the

print for *log luminance* of the print in the graphic representation of this basic relationship. Since density is inversely proportional to log luminance, the curve will take the same form, except that the coordinate scale will be inverted. Such a graph is shown in Fig. 18.1 in which print

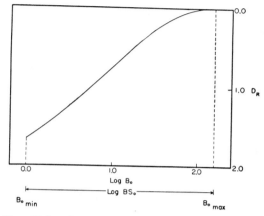

FIG. 18.1. A typical tone reproduction curve in which print density D_R is plotted as a function of the logarithm of object luminance, B_o. The log luminance scale of the object, BS_o, is indicated between the limits $B_{o\ min}$ and $B_{o\ max}$.

density D_R is plotted as a function of the logarithm of object luminance B_O. This is the so-called objective tone reproduction curve. It will be shown later that by the application of psychophysical-statistical methods, information can be obtained by means of which this curve can be interpreted in terms of the photographic quality of the print it represents.

The curve shown in Fig. 18.1, while typical, is only one of an infinite array of such curves which characterize photographic reproductions. The nature of the tone reproduction curve is dependent upon many factors, most of which will vary with each photograph. It follows, then, that these factors, because they affect the character of the tone reproduction curve, must also affect photographic quality. A careful consideration of each of these factors is essential to an adequate appreciation of the nature of the variables which are involved in the technical aspects of photographic quality. In the sections which follow these factors will be identified with:

The luminance scale of the object.
Camera flare.
Camera exposure.
The characteristics of the negative material.
Print exposure.
The characteristics of the positive material.

The objective tone reproduction curve can be considered as representing the end point of a reproduction cycle. A graphic presentation of this cycle was suggested by Jones.[1] Jones at that time did not in-

[1] Jones, *J. Franklin Inst.* **39**, 190 (1920).

corporate the curve for camera flare in his graphs since it was not until relatively recently that the importance of this function was fully appreciated. The graphical form suggested by Jones has now been modified to include the flare curve and is presented here as the four-quadrant diagram in Fig. 18.2. The tone reproduction curve in Quadrant IV is obtained by combining the separate curves for camera flare (Quadrant I), the negative material (Quadrant II), and the positive material (Quadrant III). The functions which these curves represent and the graphical procedure for combining the separate curves to give the objective tone reproduction curve will be discussed in turn.

Quadrant I—The Flare Curve. The designation of the relationship in Quadrant I of Fig. 18.2 as the *flare curve* is a matter of convenience rather than of precise no-

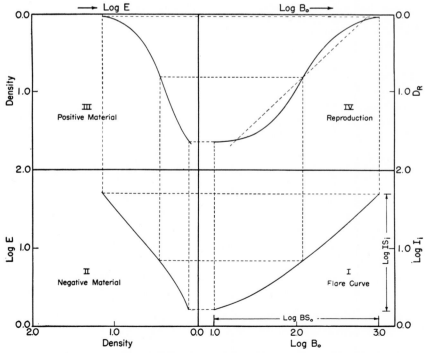

Fig. 18.2.   Complete graphical representation of the objective tone reproduction cycle.

menclature. More precisely, it is the object luminance—image illuminance curve. This relationship constitutes the first step in a complete graphical analysis of the tone reproduction cycle, because it is necessary first to establish the manner in which the luminance and luminance differences of the object are represented in the image plane of the camera. At any point in the image plane of a camera the illuminance is attributable to two distinct sources—(a) the illuminance due to "image-forming" light coming directly from a point on the object, and (b) the illuminance due to "nonimage-forming" light or flare light. The term, flare light, is used to designate the illuminance which is distributed more or less uniformly over the image plane. Nonimage-forming light arises from several sources, such as interreflections between the glass air surfaces of the lens system, reflections from the interior surfaces of the lens mount, shutter blades, and diaphragm blades, and reflections from the interior surfaces of the camera body and bellows. Although the nonimage-forming light must be considered as part of the image which acts upon the negative material, it is convenient in the subsequent treatment of the tone reproduction cycle to refer to the *camera image* as distinct from the *flare image*. In this sense the camera image may be attributed only to the light coming directly from the object by virtue of the refractive characteristics of the lens system. The flare image is not an image in the conventional sense, since it conforms to no geometrical pattern, but is a veil over the entire image plane.

The Camera Image. The illuminance of the camera image bears a simple and direct relationship to the luminance of the object. This relationship may be written in the form

$$I_o = B_o/f^2 \cdot K, \qquad (1)$$

where I_o is the image illuminance, B_o is the object luminance, f is the lens aperture ratio, and K is a constant. This, of course, is the equation for a straight line at 45° to the axes of the coordinate system.

It follows that luminance measurements made on the object can be converted directly to illuminance values of the image, provided the value of the constant K is known. Actually in most cases only relative values of illuminance are required for tone reproduction studies, and any convenient, arbitrary value can be assigned to the constant K. We are, therefore, free to describe the camera image in terms of the object itself.

Since it is not required that the flare curve relationship be based on absolute values of object luminance, it is only necessary to know the ratio of the maximum to the minimum luminance. This ratio is sometimes referred to as the "contrast" of the object. A more satisfactory term, however, is the *luminance scale of the object*, BS_o. The luminance scale of any object or scene is dependent upon two factors—the reflectance of the surfaces which comprise the scene, and the illuminance on each of the scene elements. Except for those surfaces which give rise to specular reflections, the most highly (diffusely) reflecting surfaces reflect about 98% of the incident light, while the densest black areas reflect 1 or 2% of the incident light. It is obvious then, that the maximum luminance scale that can be realized, if all surfaces of objects are illuminated to the same extent, is of the order of 90 or possibly 95. On the other hand, all of the objects composing a scene do not in general receive the same amount of illumination. Certain areas will receive illumination directly from the principal source of light while others may be shielded from it and receive only such illumination as may come, by reflection, from adjacent areas. Thus, within all scenes there are highlights and shadows. It is obvious, therefore, that the luminance scale of a scene may vary over a considerable range, depending upon the depth of the shadows and the reflectance of the surfaces receiving the direct illumination of the light source.

Such measurements of subject luminance scale as have been reported have been confined largely to exterior scenes. The most complete data are those published by Jones and Condit.[2] They made luminance measurements on about 150 exterior scenes, including a wide variety of subject types over a period of more than a year to include all seasonal conditions. In the scenes which they photometered, they found a wide variation in luminance scale, the lowest being 27, the highest 750. The average luminance scale of all the scenes was found to be 160. Experience indicates that the luminance scale of interior scenes will fall within the range measured out-of-doors.

The Flare Image. Because flare light is nonimage forming and occurs in the image plane as a uniform veil of light, its effect is to increase the illuminance of every point of the camera image and to reduce the contrast. It is exactly the same effect as is observed in a motion picture theater when extraneous light is allowed to reach the screen. The pronounced degradation of the screen image by light from the early evening sky is a familiar experience to all those who have attended outdoor theaters. The reason for this is that the presence of flare light compresses the illuminance scale of the image. This is readily explained by a simple, numerical example:

Let I_i designate the total image illuminance, I_{io} the illuminance due to image-forming light, and I_{if} the image illuminance

[2] Jones and Condit, *J. Opt. Soc. Amer.* **31**, 651 (1941).

due to flare light alone. Then

$$I_i = I_{io} + I_{if}. \qquad (2)$$

Assume that measurements of the maximum and minimum illuminance of the camera image and the illuminance due to the flare light of a typical scene give these values:

$$I_{io\ min} = 0.01 \text{ foot-candle}$$
$$I_{io\ max} = 1.00 \text{ foot-candle}$$
$$I_{if} \quad = 0.02 \text{ foot-candle}.$$

The illuminance scale of the camera image, IS_{io}, is found by the formula

$$IS_{io} = I_{io\ max}/I_{io\ min}$$

and for this example

$$IS_{io} = 1.0/0.01 = 100$$

but when flare light is added, the total image illuminance scale becomes:

$$IS_i = \frac{1.00 + 0.02}{0.01 + 0.02} = 34.$$

Thus, the presence of flare light compresses the illuminance scale from 100 to 34.

Another way of demonstrating the effect of flare light is to compare the characteristic curve of the negative material with the density-log B_o characteristic of a particular negative. Curve 1 in Fig. 18.3 is the D log E curve of a typical negative material. This curve, which was determined sensitometrically, shows the relation between density and the logarithm of the exposure incident upon the negative material, which in the camera is determined by the total image illuminance, I_i. If there were no flare light in the camera, the relationship between negative density, D_N, and object luminance, B_o, would be exactly the same as that shown in the D log E curve. This, of course, assumes that the exposure time is constant and that the exposure is therefore proportional to image illuminance.

At the top of Fig. 18.3 a scale of relative values of log B_o is shown. This scale is arbitrarily set to show values which are

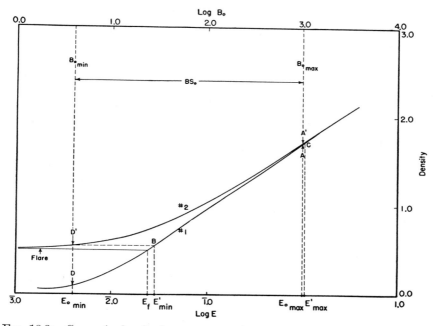

FIG. 18.3. Curve 1, density-log exposure characteristic of the *negative material;* Curve 2, between points D' and A' is the density-log B_o characteristic of a particular *negative.*

log 3.0 greater than the corresponding values of log E shown at the bottom of the figure. Let us assume that a scene is photographed for which the minimum and maximum luminance has been found to have the values indicated on the chart. These values represent the limits of the log luminance scale BS_o. For the hypothetical case in which there is no flare light in the camera, the minimum density of the negative will be that shown at point D on Curve 1, corresponding to minimum image illuminance. The maximum density of the negative will be that shown at point A on curve 1, corresponding in this case to the maximum image illuminance. Thus, for the hypothetical flare-free case, the characteristic of the negative is that shown between points D and A on Curve 1.

Let us now observe how the addition of flare light in the camera changes the charac-

teristic of the negative of the same scene. It is convenient to regard the presence of flare light in the camera as equivalent to the addition of a constant increment of exposure to the exposures of each element of the camera image. For the case illustrated in Fig. 18.3 the exposure due to flare light alone is indicated at E_f on the log E axis. The density resulting from this amount of exposure is indicated by the D log E characteristic of the negative material, as shown in Curve 1. The horizontal line labeled "Flare" corresponds to this density value. This would be the minimum density of the negative if the minimum luminance of the scene were zero. However, this is not usually the case and in this example when the exposure due to flare light, E_f, is added to the minimum exposure due to the camera image, $E_{o\,min}$, the exposure indicated at E'_{min} in the figure is obtained. The density produced by exposure E'_{min} is indicated at B on the characteristic curve of the negative material, Curve 1. This then becomes the minimum density of the negative and, when plotted as a function of minimum image luminance, we have the point D' as indicated in Fig. 18.3. Similarly the maximum density of the negative, C, will be that produced by the combined exposure E'_{max}, resulting from flare light exposure, E_f, and the exposure due to the maximum illuminance of the camera image, $E_{o\,max}$. Again, plotting this density as a function of maximum subject luminance, we have the point A'. By selecting other values of image illuminance, computing the exposure when flare light is added, selecting the corresponding density from Curve 1 and plotting this as a function of the corresponding subject luminance, a sufficient number of points can be determined to establish Curve 2, which is the density-log B_o characteristic of the particular negative selected for this example.

This procedure of deriving the density-log B_o characteristic of the negative can be greatly facilitated by the use of the curve shown in Fig. 18.4. This curve is derived from the basic relationship previously discussed.

$$I_i = I_{io} + I_{if}.$$

The log luminance, B_o, of different points in the scene, is plotted against the log illuminance, I_i, of the corresponding points in the camera image. If the image illuminance were exactly proportional to the object luminance, the data in this graph would fit a straight line having a slope of unity. This, of course, would only occur if there were no flare light in the camera, and the relationship would then take the form

$$I_i = I_{io}.$$

If, however, flare light is present in the camera and the illuminance from this source is added to the illuminance due to the camera image, the data will conform to

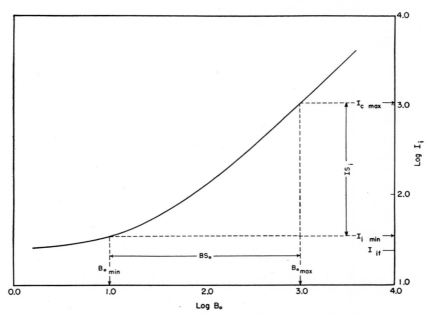

FIG. 18.4. A typical flare curve derived from measurements of $B_{o\,min}$, $B_{o\,max}$, and IS_i.

the curve of Fig. 18.4. The extent to which this curve departs from a straight-line relationship depends, of course, upon the relative magnitudes of I_{to} and I_{tf}. If there is a very small amount of flare light present in the camera, the flare curve will approach a straight line. When the illuminance due to flare light is equal or greater in magnitude than the illuminance in the camera image associated with the shadow areas of the scene, the departure of the flare curve from a straight line may be very great. In practice, the amount of flare light has relatively little effect on the gradients in the high-light region. On the other hand, flare light frequently lowers the gradient in the middle tones to 0.7 and those in the shadows to as low as 0.3 of the gradient in a flare-free image.

Derivation of the Flare Curve. As stated previously, the character of the flare curve depends upon the relative magnitudes of the illuminance due to flare light and that due to the camera image. The most straight-forward method of deriving the flare curve would therefore be to evaluate the amount of flare light in the image plane and the illuminance of the camera image itself. Instrumental methods of measuring the illuminance due to flare light are available, but they are not easily applicable to practical field work. The amount of flare light incident on the focal plane in a camera is dependent not only upon the characteristics of the camera-lens system but also upon the distribution of luminance within the scene being photographed and in its environment. One method which has been used successfully employs a modified form of photographic photometry. The procedure consists essentially of these five steps:

1. *Photometric measurements on the scene.* Values of maximum object luminance, $B_{o\,max}$, and minimum object luminance, $B_{o\,min}$, are obtained.

2. *Density measurements on the negative.* The densities of those areas in the negative corresponding to the areas of maximum and minimum luminance in the scene are determined.

3. *Determination of image illuminance scale.* From the characteristic curve of the negative material, the exposure values corresponding to the minimum and maximum densities of the negative are identified. The illuminance scale of the camera image, IS_i, which is defined as the ratio of maximum image illuminance, $I_{i\,max}$, to the minimum image illuminance, $I_{i\,min}$, is therefore equal to the ratio of these exposure values. This assumes, of course, that the characteristic curve of the negative material is derived from an intensity scale exposure in which the exposure time is constant and the ratio of exposures is equivalent to the ratio of the corresponding illuminance values.

4. *Determination of the luminance scale of the subject, BS_o.* The luminance scale of the subject is defined as the ratio of maximum object luminance, $B_{o\,max}$, to minimum object luminance, $B_{o\,min}$. This can be computed directly from the measurements of these quantities in (1).

5. *The computation of the amount of flare light.* The presence of flare light in the camera may be regarded as equivalent in its effect upon the total image illuminance to the addition of a constant luminance increment, ΔB, to all the actual luminances in the scene. Thus,

$$I_{i\,max} = (B_{o\,max} + \Delta B) \cdot K \qquad (3)$$

and

$$I_{i\,min} = (B_{o\,min} + \Delta B) \cdot K. \qquad (4)$$

In these equations, K is the constant of proportionality. Using these equations, it is possible to derive an expression for the evaluation of ΔB in terms of three quantities which can be readily determined experimentally, $B_{o\,max}$, BS_o, and IS_i. This expression takes the form:

$$\Delta B = \frac{B_{o\,max}(1 - IS_i/BS_o)}{IS_i - 1}. \qquad (5)$$

Having solved for ΔB, the flare curve can be computed by the procedure illustrated in Fig. 18.4. For this example it is assumed that the following values have been obtained from luminance measurements made on the scene and density measurements made on the negative.

$$B_{o\,max} = 1000 \text{ foot-Lamberts}$$
$$BS_o = 100$$
$$IS_i = 30.$$

By use of equation (5) we obtain

$$\Delta B = 24.1.$$

On the log B_o axis of Fig. 18.4, the measured values of maximum and minimum subject luminance are indicated. The value of total image illuminance, I_i, corresponding to any given value of B_o is computed and plotted on the graph in proper relationship to the arbitrary scale of values assigned to I_i. It is sufficient for the purposes to which the flare curve will be put to express log I_i on a relative scale. For convenience, in this illustration, the value of I_i is made equal numerically to the sum of $B_o + \Delta B$ ($K = 1$). The following is an example of the calculations.

$$B_{o\,min} = 10$$
$$\qquad\qquad I_{i\,min} = 10 + 24.1 = 34.1$$
$$B_{o\,max} = 1000$$
$$\qquad\qquad I_{i\,max} = 1000 + 24.1 = 1024.1.$$

By a similar procedure a sufficient number of points are calculated from intermediate values of B_o to establish the complete flare curve. The relationship obtained, therefore, serves as a starting point in the complete graphic analysis of the tone reproduction cycle. The ratio, BS_o/IS_i, is known as the *flare factor, FF*.

Quadrant II: The Characteristic Curve of the Negative Material

The function represented in Quadrant II of Fig. 18.2 is the D log E curve of the negative material. From the standpoint of tone reproduction, the most important feature of this curve is its shape characteristics. Shape is identified with the length of the toe and the gradient relationships in this region, the gradient and length of the straight-line portion, and the gradient relationships in the shoulder. Because of the extremely long exposure scale of present-day commercial emulsions, it is only on rare occasions that the scene luminances are recorded even partly on the shoulder portion of the negative material. The portions of the characteristic curve of most direct concern in tone reproduction problems are the toe and straight-line regions.

In general, the shape characteristics of photographic negative materials are determined largely by the way in which the photographic emulsion is made. To a certain extent, the shape of the toe and to a larger extent the gradient of the straight-line portion is affected by development. Other factors which influence curve shape, such as the time and intensity of exposure and the color of the exposing light, are of secondary importance. In Figs. 18.5 and 18.6 are shown two groups of D log E curves representing commercial emulsions differing widely in shape characteristics. In each figure there are four curves which demonstrate the change in shape characteristics with increasing development time. It is seen that the change in shape with development is small in comparison with the shape differences existing between the two types of emulsions. In Fig. 18.5 the log exposure scale interval corresponding to the toe region varies from approximately 0.73 to 1.06 depending upon the time of development, while for the

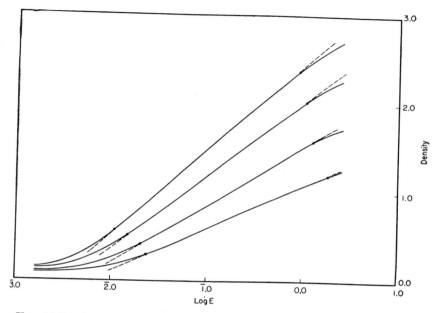

FIG. 18.5. A group of characteristic curves having a short-toe portion.

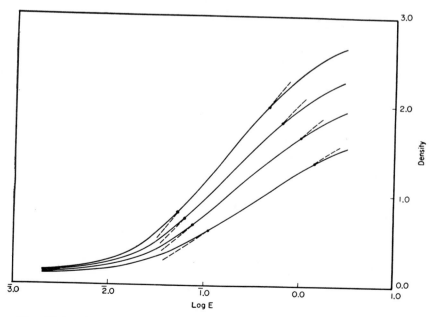

FIG. 18.6. A group of characteristic curves having a long-toe portion.

material shown in Fig. 18.6, this interval varies from 1.22 to 1.54. The same type of effect can be observed in the case of the log exposure scale interval covered by the straight-line portions of the curves. The principal effect of increasing development, as these curves illustrate, is to increase the gradient throughout the curve.

The extent to which differences in the shape characteristics of negative materials influence the tone reproduction of the final positive depends upon the portion of the $D \log E$ characteristic utilized in recording the camera image. This, of course, is determined by the magnitude of the camera exposure. It is obvious that the characteristics of a negative which utilizes the toe-portion of the $D \log E$ curve of the negative material will be quite different than those of a negative which utilizes only the straight-line portion of the characteristic curve of the negative material. In fact, the camera exposure of the negative plays as important a part in determining the characteristics of the final reproduction as the characteristics of the negative material itself.

It is important in tone reproduction studies that the $D \log E$ curve which is used in the graphical analysis be truly representative of the negative material which is used in producing the negative. It is customary to develop an exposed sensitometric strip along with the negative material which has been exposed in the camera. From the density measurements made on this developed sensitometric strip, the $D \log E$ curve is obtained. Certain precautions must be taken in exposing the sensitometric strips. The exposure should be modulated in increments of intensity. The exposure time should be approximately the same as that used in exposing the negative material in the camera. The spectral quality of the radiation should be similar to that reflected from the subject being photo-

graphed. It is also important that the density measurements made on the sensitometric strip and the negative should conform in both spectral and geometrical aspects to the characteristics of the printing process utilized in obtaining the final reproduction.

Quadrant III—The Characteristic Curve of the Positive Material

Positive materials are manufactured with the specific intent that their characteristics be such that prints of high quality can be obtained from the maximum number of different negatives. Particular importance is therefore attached to the shape characteristics of these materials. Since it is required that positive materials fit the negative rather than the converse, and since negatives vary widely in gradient and density scale, photographic printing papers are made in a number of different grades. There are also characteristic differences in the various types of papers which are available commercially. In Fig. 18.7 is a group of typical $D \log E$ curves showing the characteristics of the six grades of a commercial printing paper of the chloride type. Other papers of the bromide and chlorobromide show similar characteristics and differ from the chloride papers primarily in the rate at which they develop. Chloride papers develop very rapidly so that in thirty to forty-five seconds the curve shape has reached equilibrium. Bromide papers develop somewhat more slowly, and it is, therefore, possible to control the curve shape to some extent by adjustments in developing time. The chlorobromide papers resemble the chloride papers more closely than the bromide.

The maximum densities obtainable on printing papers of a given emulsion type are determined largely by their surface characteristics. Papers with glossy sur-

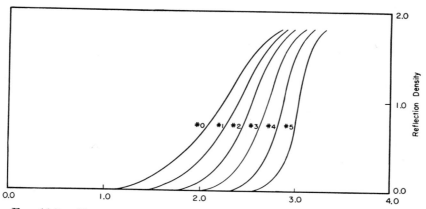

FIG. 18.7.   Six contrast grades of a commercial chloride printing paper, glossy surface.

faces which have been ferrotyped may have maximum densities as high as 1.8, whereas for semi-matte surfaces, it is about 1.55 and for matte surfaces it is about 1.3.   These values, of course, are only approximate and will vary from one type of paper to another.   The important thing to note in this connection is that the density scale of printing papers is appreciably shorter than the log luminance scale of the majority of scenes, and therefore it is impossible in such cases to obtain exact objective tone reproduction with this printing medium.   As will be discussed later, this limitation does not necessarily restrict the usefulness of printing papers in producing positives of high quality.

Before proceeding to the next phase of the reproduction cycle, mention should be made of a concept which is useful in specifying the optimum shape characteristics of both negative and positive materials with respect to their ability to yield excellent photographic reproductions.   It will be shown later that, in general, photographic quality evaluated subjectively bears a consistent relationship to the exactness with which the objective tone reproduction curve approaches a straight line having a gradient of unity.   To achieve this correct ob-

jective reproduction, it follows that the characteristics of the positive material must complement the characteristics of the negative (or vice versa) so that in combination there will be exact correspondence between the luminances of the reproduction and the original subject.   This concept has been referred to as the *mirror-image rule;* that, for perfect objective reproduction, the negative and positive characteristics must be mirror images of each other, assuming that the coordinate system, in which one of the curves is plotted, is rotated through 90° with respect to the coordinate system in which the other is plotted.

In applying the mirror-image rule some interesting and unusual relationships appear as to the shapes of negative and positive characteristics required for correct objective tone reproduction.   Such would not be the case if negative and positive materials with straight-line characteristics could be utilized, but in practice one must deal with materials having the conventional toe and shoulder properties.   The unusual shape requirements for a negative material which will give correct tone reproduction with conventional positive materials come from restrictions imposed by the characteristics of commercially avail-

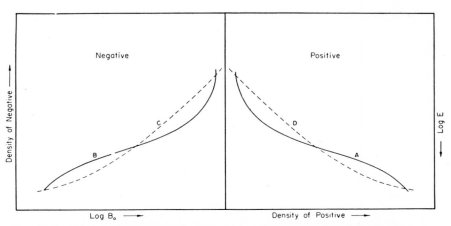

FIG. 18.8.   Mirror image reproduction curves based on a typical No. 2 paper.

able positive materials. Similarly, the characteristics of a positive material required to give correct objective reproduction with typical negatives are unusual because of the unique characteristics of available negative materials. In this connection it will be of interest to refer to the mirror-image curves in Fig. 18.8. Curve A is the D log E curve of a typical No. 2 grade photographic paper. Curve B is the mirror-image curve which represents the D log B_o characteristics of the negative which, when printed onto this positive material, will give correct objective tone reproduction. Curve C is included for comparison and represents the characteristics of a conventional negative having the same density scale and can be considered as typical of the negatives made on commercially available materials which are best printed on to No. 2 grade paper. Curve D, which is the mirror-image of curve C, represents the D log E characteristics of a positive material required to obtain correct objective tone reproduction in prints made from the conventional negative of curve C. It will be recognized that neither curve D nor B which are required for correct objective tone reproduction with conventional **negatives** or positives represent materials

which are produced commercially. They do, however, indicate the nature of curve shape changes which will be effective in improving the quality of photographic reproductions.

Graphical Construction of the Tone Reproduction Curve. Having described the functions which are represented in Quadrants I, II, and III of the graphical presentation of the complete tone reproduction cycle, Fig. 18.2, it is now possible to continue with a more detailed description of the procedure which is employed in constructing the resultant tone reproduction curve shown in Quadrant IV. Although the mechanical aspects of the procedure can be standardized, the choice and placement of the curves in Quadrants I, II, and III is determined solely by the particular requirements of each problem. The first step, therefore, is to analyze the problem, determine which of the variables in the reproduction cycle are to be studied, and select from available data or from purely theoretical considerations the desired relationships for Quadrants I, II, and III. In the majority of cases it will be found that the variables to be studied can be associated with one or more of the following factors which have been previously mentioned:

The luminance scale of the object.

Camera flare.

Camera exposure.

The characteristics of the negative material.

Printing exposure.

The characteristics of the positive material.

Before attempting a graphical treatment of the tone reproduction cycle, each of these factors must be evaluated and their influence on the characteristics of the relationships involved be taken into account. When the necessary data have been assembled, and a plan of investigation organized, the graphical construction of the tone reproduction cycle can be undertaken. The procedure can be best explained by describing each step in the graphical treatment of a typical tone reproduction problem. In the discussion which follows,

reference will be made to the four-quadrant diagram in Fig. 18.9.

Step 1. Analyze the problem. A typical problem may be stated as follows: What effect has the toe shape of the negative material on the reproduction characteristics of a negative-positive process; assuming that an average scene is photographed with a camera having an average amount of flare, that the camera exposure of each of the negative materials is the minimum which will yield a negative from which an excellent print can be obtained, that the negatives will be developed to give equal density scale, and that the negatives will be printed by contact on to a photographic paper of a suitable grade such that the shadow areas will be recorded on the shoulder portion of the characteristic curve of the positive material where the gradient is equal to the average gradient of the positive characteristic utilized?

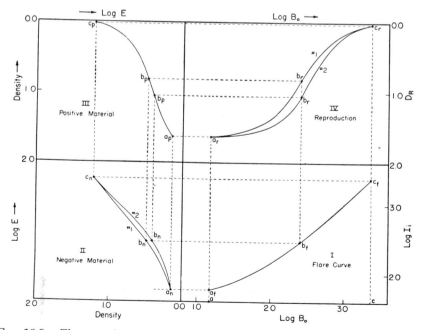

Fig. 18.9. The complete tone reproduction cycle involving negative materials having short toe characteristics (curve 1) and long toe characteristics (curve 2).

Step 2. On the log B_o axis of Quadrant I, locate points a and c corresponding to the minimum object luminance and maximum object luminance, respectively. For an average scene, these values, as reported by Jones and Condit,[3] are 14.5 and 2300, respectively.

Step 3. Construct the flare curve from measured values of IS_i in accordance with the procedure previously described. Jones and Condit report that for the average scene and camera, the flare factor is 4, which makes IS_i for the average scene equal to 40. By the use of equation (5), ΔB is calculated. For the average scene ΔB equals 44. A sufficient number of values of I_i can then be computed according to equation (3) to establish the flare curve. In Fig. 18.9, Quadrant I, three of these points are shown at a_f, b_f, and c_f.

Step 4. Locate the characteristic curve of the negative material in Quadrant II. In this example it is required that the minimum camera exposure be given which will yield a negative from which an excellent print can be obtained. Since it is known that this requirement will be satisfied if the darkest element of the scene is recorded at a point on the characteristic curve of the negative material where the gradient is equal to three-tenths of the average gradient, we have the necessary information for locating the curve in Quadrant II of Fig. 18.9. Through point a_f extend a horizontal line into Quadrant II. The curve of the negative material should then be positioned in Quadrant II so that this line will intersect the curve at a point where the gradient is equal to three-tenths of the average gradient. This locates point a_n. Points b_n and c_n are then located by extending horizontal lines from points b_f and c_f to where they intersect the characteristic curve in Quadrant II.

---

[3] *Loc. cit.*

Step 5. Locate the characteristic curve of the positive material in Quadrant III. In this example it is required that the darkest element of the scene be reproduced at a point on the characteristic curve of the positive material where the gradient is equal to the average gradient of the positive characteristic utilized. It is also required that the proper grade of paper be used in making the print. To satisfy the latter requirement, select the grade of paper for which the log exposure scale is approximately equal to the density scale of the negative. Locate the characteristic curve of this material in Quadrant III such that a vertical line from point a_n will intersect the curve at a_p where the gradient is equal to the average gradient of the curve. It should be noted that for this presentation the curve is reversed and inverted with respect to the conventional form of presentation. Vertical lines through points b_n and c_n into Quadrant III establish points b_p and c_p on the positive characteristic curve.

Step 6. Horizontal lines through points b_p and c_p into Quadrant IV intersect with vertical lines from corresponding points in Quadrant I. The intersections of these lines determine the points which establish the tone reproduction curve in Quadrant IV. This curve affords a graphic comparison between the log luminances in the original scene and the density by which they are reproduced in the photographic print.

The pair of curves in Quadrant IV show the influence of the toe shape of the negative material on tone reproduction characteristics. Curve 1 is obtained when the D log E curve of the negative material has a short toe portion, and curve 2 illustrates the case when the toe portion is long. It should be noted that the only variable in this example is that associated with the shape characteristic of the negative material. Variations in any of the other factors involved in the reproduction process will produce other changes in the pattern illustrated in Fig. 18.9. Within certain limits an almost infinite number of patterns are possible. Some of these are shown by the pairs of curves in Fig. 18.10. These curves serve to illustrate the extent to which the tone reproduction curve is affected by extreme, but not improbable, variations in certain factors operating independently. Except for the reproduction represented by curve 2, the negative material in all cases is the same. In these examples only one variable is altered between any two pairs of curves. It is assumed that all other factors which affect tone reproduction characteristics have been held constant. No attempt has been made to compensate for the effects illustrated by adjustments in negative development or in printing. In practice the large differences shown by some of these curves can be avoided by the use of two different grades of paper rather than a single grade in printing the negatives. It is the purpose of this example, however, to show the magnitude of some of these effects when no changes in procedure are employed.

Curves 1 and 2 are the same as in Fig. 18.9. Curves 3 and 4 have been selected to show the difference in appearance of the tone reproduction curves for two different scenes, one of short luminance scale, and the other of long luminance scale. Curves 5 and 6 are intended to show the effect on the tone reproduction curve of photographing a single scene with two different cameras, the only difference being in the amount of flare light which they introduce into the camera image. Curve 5 represents the case of a nearly flare-free camera, whereas curve 6 shows the results obtained when a large amount of flare light is present in the camera. It should be pointed out again that quite different tone reproduction curves would result from a differ-

ent choice of the negative and positive materials and of the camera and printing exposures. Although in this example conditions were such that the results obtained with the flare-free camera more nearly approach correct objective tone reproduction, it can also be demonstrated that when conditions are favorable, superior reproductions can be obtained with a large amount of flare light in the camera image. Curves 7 and 8 show the effect of differences in camera exposure level on the characteristics of the tone reproduction curve. Curve 7 shows the result of a camera exposure which is two full stops less than the first excellent exposure. In curve 8 the camera exposure is two stops more than the first excellent exposure. Curves 9 and 10 illustrate the effect of using two widely different grades of printing paper with the same negative, the negative in this case being properly exposed. Curve 9 is the reproduction curve for a print made on No. 0 grade paper, and curve 10 is the reproduction curve for a print made on No. 4 grade paper. In both cases the printing exposure has been such as to give the best possible prints for each grade of paper. Curves 11 and 12 show the effect of differences in printing exposure level on the reproduction characteristics. In this case a subject of wide luminance scale has been chosen so that exact objective reproduction is not possible throughout the scale. In curve 11 the printing exposure has been adjusted so that shadow detail is favorably rendered. In curve 12 the printing exposure has been reduced in order that highlight detail will be better reproduced.

The pairs of curves shown in Fig. 18.10 represent the tone reproduction characteristics of prints which differ widely in photographic quality. The next step in the solution of the tone reproduction problem is to find a method of deriving from these curves some indication of the quality

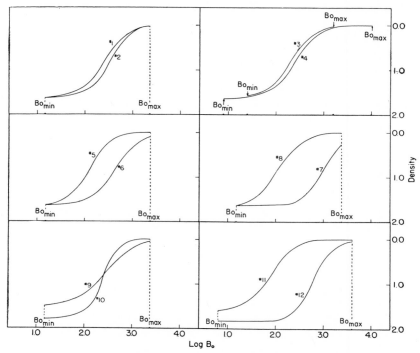

FIG. 18.10.   Tone reproduction curves illustrating effect of following variables: Shape characteristic of negative material, curves 1 and 2; Luminance scale of scene, curves 3 and 4; camera flare, curves 5 and 6; camera exposure, curves 7 and 8; contrast grade of printing paper, curves 9 and 10; printing exposure, curves 11 and 12.

of the print which they represent. This leads us into the subjective phase of tone reproduction studies.

THE SUBJECTIVE PHASE OF TONE REPRODUCTION

The subjective phase of tone reproduction studies deals with the process of evaluating the objective tone reproduction curve in terms of the quality of the print which it represents. As was suggested earlier in this chapter, it is with the technical aspect of photographic quality rather than with the artistic qualities of the picture that tone reproduction studies are concerned. It must be recognized at the outset that photographic quality is an attribute which must be appraised subjectively. It is nec-

essary to consider, therefore, the characteristics of the visual, perceptual, and other psychological processes of the human observer and the factors which determine his acceptance of a photograph as being of suitable quality.

Visual perception may be considered as having two broad aspects—form and color. The three perceptual aspects of color are brightness, hue, and saturation, but for reproductions in monochrome only the perception of brightness is involved. Through common usage the term, *tone*, has become associated with *brightness* so that the expression, tone reproduction, refers specifically to that aspect of the reproduction which gives rise to the brightness attribute of visual perception. It is to be expected that the subjective evaluation of photographic quality is determined by the exactness with which the photograph reproduces in the mind of the observer the sensations of color and form which he received when viewing the original. In general, however, the observer does not expect or demand that there be exact correspondence between the subject and the photographic reproduction in all respects, because of his awareness of the limitations of the process. In the case of photographs in monochrome, the observer is prepared to accept the reproduction of a multi-colored scene in tones of gray. He knows, furthermore, that the photograph must be a two-dimensional projection of a three-dimensional subject. He realizes also that the foreground or background of certain scenes cannot both be sharply imaged in the photograph, and therefore he does not consider that this is detrimental to photographic quality. There are other minor departures from exact duplication of color and form which the observer will tolerate and still consider the quality of the photograph to be acceptable. In one respect, however, the observer is likely to be critical. This is in regard to the exactness or inexactness with which the luminance and luminance differences in the original are reproduced in the print as viewed by the observer. An explanation for this can be found by consideration of the factors involved in the fundamental process of seeing.

From the standpoint of its role in the subjective appraisal of photographic quality, seeing may be defined as the gathering of intelligible information from the light reaching the eyes. One sees an object not by the sensation of brightness or hue or saturation produced by the light reflected from the object but by the difference in the sensations of brightness, hue, or saturation between the object and its background. This difference between sensations, which

is sometimes called the sensation of contrast, is not unique to visual experience. It is the sensation which provides the human being with a means of evaluating the quality or quantity of stimuli as they are impressed upon his consciousness, like hard, hot, sweet, loud, dark, etc. The amount of difference in the stimulus required to produce the minimum sensation of contrast is frequently taken as a measure of sensitivity. In the case of visual sensitivity measurements, one of the fundamental evaluations of sensitivity is in terms of the minimum luminance differences which produce a sensation of contrast. It follows that if the photographic reproduction distorts the luminance differences which existed in the original scene, the observer will perceive the photograph as different than the original, and in some cases may not see certain details which he saw when he viewed the scene directly. An observer's evaluation of photographic quality is intimately related with his ability to see the same detail in the photograph which he observed in the original.

This contrast sensitivity concept of human perception provides a key to the interpretation of the objective tone reproduction relationship in terms of the subjective quality of the print which it represents. It is apparent that in some way quality is dependent upon the luminance difference relationships between object and photograph which are represented graphically by the gradient characteristics of the tone reproduction curve. From the physical point of view, a perfect reproduction is one in which the luminance differences in the print are identical with those in the object or scene photographed. For such a print, the tone reproduction curve would be a straight line having a slope of unity. Although it will be shown that there is not exact correspondence between photographic quality evaluated objectively and subjectively, it can be said nevertheless that photographic quality is in some way related to the gradient aspect of the objective tone reproduction curve.

It must be recognized that there is little experimental evidence which can be brought to bear on the question: "Is the subjective impression of photographic quality related to the exactness with which the luminance and luminance differences in the subject are reproduced in the photographic print?" The reason for this is that it is usually found to be impossible with the available photographic materials to produce an exact reproduction of many objects. This is particularly true when the positive is made on a reflecting surface such as paper which must be viewed by reflected light. It has been necessary, therefore, in attempting to establish the nature of the relationship which exists between the characteristics of the objective tone reproduction curve and the subjective evaluation of photographic quality to obtain direct judgments of a large group of observers on the quality of prints in which certain compromises in tone reproduction have been made. The magnitude and character of the compromises which produce the least detrimental effect upon the final reproduction quality as established subjectively can be evaluated in terms of the measured physical characteristics of the reproduction. The problem in tone reproduction studies is therefore to identify those compromises with perfect objective reproduction which are least detrimental to the quality of the print as appraised subjectively and to establish certain limits beyond which further compromise will result in the degradation of photographic quality.

There are undoubtedly a large number of factors which condition an observer's evaluation of photographic quality in prints. It cannot be assumed that a precise reproduction of the original subjective impression will be accepted by the observer as best possible photographic quality, for he might be more pleased with a reproduction into which some distortion has been introduced. Aside from the perceptual processes involved in viewing a photograph, the human observer's appraisal of quality is almost certainly governed by his visual experience with the original subject, his photographic experience, his personal tastes, his emotional responsiveness to the mood of the picture or the nature of the subject matter, and his aesthetic standards. These may be considered strictly psychological factors which to a certain extent make human behavior unpredictable. On the other hand, if the judgments of a large number of observers are treated statistically, it will be found that there is a systematic pattern in the subjective evaluation of print quality, particularly if the conditions of viewing are controlled carefully. The conclusion which has been drawn from this is that the psychological factors are of secondary importance, and that the satisfactory reproduction of luminance differences has the most significant bearing on the resultant print quality. It follows from this that it should be possible to evaluate print quality largely in terms of the *gradient errors* found in the reproduction.

In most of the literature dealing with photographic tone reproduction, considerable attention is usually given to the psychophysiology of vision and to the psychophysical relationships which have been established in this field. Brief mention of this subject is made here, more because it helps to explain why a photographic print with its limited density scale is capable of providing an acceptable representation of an original subject than because of its practical application to the solution of tone reproduction problems.

The psychophysical relationships of most direct interest in connection with tone re-

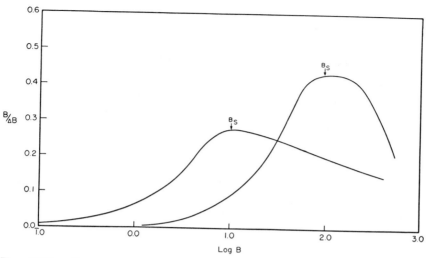

FIG. 18.11. Contrast sensitivity curves for the human eye for two different levels of sensitizing field luminance, B_s.

production studies are those between the sensation of brightness and the magnitude of the visual stimulus evaluated by photometric methods. Brightness in this case is that attribute of visual sensation which is related to the quantitative aspect of radiant energy. The early work of Weber [4] indicated that just noticeable brightness differences were produced by a fixed ratio of stimulus intensities measured in terms of luminance. This was expanded by Fechner [5] into the Weber-Fechner Law which states that "as the stimulus grows in geometrical progression, the visual sensation resulting grows in arithmetic progression." Subsequent investigators showed that the brightness-luminance relation does not follow a logarithmic equation except over a short range, and that the nature of the function is dependent upon the adaptation level of the eye, the duration of the stimulus, the area and portion of the retina

stimulated, and the magnitude and distribution of the simultaneous stimulation of other retina areas. It is obvious that brightness discrimination data, to be applicable to tone reproduction studies, must be derived from measurements made under conditions which simulate precisely those which exist in the viewing of the object or photographic prints. An effort has been made by a number of workers in this field to obtain brightness discrimination data under a wide variety of conditions. In Fig. 18.11 are shown curves based an measurements made by Lowry,[6] in which contrast sensitivity, $B/\Delta B$, is expressed as a function of luminance, B, for two levels of visual adaptation. In this case, ΔB is the luminance increment which must be added to the luminance, B, to produce a just noticeable difference in sensation. These curves apply to the specific case of a 2.5° test field surrounded by a large field of constant luminance, known as the sensitizing field. In curve A, the sensitizing field luminance is 10 foot-Lamberts, and in curve

[4] Weber, E. H., "Der Tastsinn und das Gemeingefuhl," Wagner's Handworterbuch der Psysiologie, Braunschweig (1846), *Band II*, 481.

[5] Fechner, G. T., "Elemente der Psychophysik," Leipzig (1889).

[6] Lowry, *J. Opt. Soc. Amer.* **18**, 29 (1929).

B, the sensitizing field luminance is 93 foot-Lamberts. It is assumed that the sensitizing field controls the adaptation level of the eye. The interesting fact brought out by these curves is that the contrast sensitivity of the eye reaches a maximum at approximately the luminance for which the eye is adapted and declines at higher and lower levels of luminance. The practical interpretation of this is that the human observer is not capable of detecting certain luminance differences in a scene which can be measured, and it is therefore unnecessary that a photograph reproduce such luminance differences if they cannot be seen in the original subject.

Methods have been suggested for incorporating the contrast sensitivity curves in the graphical representation of the tone reproduction cycle. The objection to doing this is that the available data can be applied strictly only to a very limited number of viewing conditions. The experimental procedures which have been used for obtaining contrast sensitivity data have few exact counterparts in normal visual experience. In the experimental procedure, the attention of the observer is directed toward a photometric field which is fixed in its position relative to the surrounding areas. In viewing a scene or photograph the observer is required to detect luminance differences in a field composed of a great variety of elements differing in luminance. The observer's attention naturally wanders from point to point within the scene. The extent to which the sensitivity of the retina is stabilized by the average luminance of these elementary areas and immediate surroundings is determined largely by temporal factors. For example, detail in the shaded area of a scene which is not detected at first glance may be readily recognized if the observer's attention is held at that point for several moments. Unless there is something of interest to the observer in that area of the scene, it is unlikely that his attention will be centered there except for a fleeting moment. He may, therefore, be unaware of measurable luminance differences that exist in the scene because they fail to contribute to his general impression of the scene as a whole. This is, perhaps, one of the fundamental reasons why an observer may consider a photographic print to have excellent quality in spite of its failure to reproduce faithfully the complete range of luminance differences measured in the original scene.

There are other factors in the human visual perceptual processes which make the use of a standardized subjective response curve in the graphic solution of the subjective phase of the tone reproduction problem of questionable value. Those factors, associated with the phenomenon of simultaneous contrast and brightness constancy, have been examined in detail by Evans.[7] Evans concluded that perfect objective tone reproduction does not give a positive assurance that the process will lead to the correct appearance in the resulting print when the illuminance of the scene is nonuniform. If a scene is uniformly illuminated, brightness will correlate with apparent reflectance. However, in scenes in which part of an object is in direct sunlight and part in a shadow the average observer will perceive that the part in the light and the part in the shadow have the same reflectance even though they differ in luminance. It is only through the knowledge that this is a shadow that the observer can reach this conclusion. It is necessary, therefore, that the reproduction of the scene be such that the observer will be aware of the uneven illumination and not mistakenly interpret the lower density of the region in the shadow as a result of a difference in reflectance rather than of a difference in illumination.

[7] Evans, *J. Opt. Soc. Amer.* **33**, 579 (1943); **34**, 533 (1944).

The magnitude of these effects is governed by such factors as whether the print is surrounded by a light border or by a dark border. There appears to be no successful way of minimizing these effects by adjustments in the reproduction characteristics of the print. They are mentioned here largely because they serve to illustrate the complex nature of the subjective phase of the tone reproduction problem.

INTERPRETATION OF THE OBJECTIVE TONE REPRODUCTION CURVE IN TERMS OF PRINT QUALITY

One of the most important advantages to be gained from tone reproduction studies is the development of an understanding of the significance which can be attached to the characteristics of the objective tone reproduction curve, and thereby to derive from the curve an evaluation of the photographic quality of the print which it represents. The accomplishment of this objective requires, first, the establishment of statistical-psychophysical relationships between print quality evaluated subjectively and certain aspects of the tone reproduction characteristic evaluated objectively. This involves the statistical treatment of the direct judgments of print quality of a large number of observers and the expression of photographic quality determined in this way in terms of the measured physical characteristics of the photographic reproduction.

As pointed out previously, it is reasonable to assume that the subjective appraisal of photographic quality is in some way related to the gradient aspects of the reproduction characteristic. From this it may be assumed that the best method of expressing quality loss lies in the evaluation of gradient errors and further that the least loss of quality is associated with the least possible average gradient error. On the basis of this assumption, the next step in the solution of the tone reproduction problem is to determine what particular distribution of gradient errors will result in the best photographic quality appraised subjectively.

This approach to the problem was taken by L. A. Jones[8] in his researches on the evaluation of negative film speeds in terms of print quality. Although print quality is dependent upon many factors involved in making the picture, Jones was concerned only with the variable of camera exposure. A series of negatives was made beginning with a camera exposure so low as to result in a badly underexposed negative. The camera exposure was then increased by fixed steps covering a wide range of camera exposure. All of these negatives were developed identically and from each negative the best possible print was made on several grades of photographic paper. These prints were then inspected by a group of observers who were instructed to make two judgments—first, the best print on each of the grades, and, finally, the grade giving the best quality. In this way the best print for each of the series of negatives was finally obtained. To secure information that would result in the establishment of the print quality-negative exposure function, Jones presented to the observer the best print from each of the negatives in the exposure series in a shuffled condition. The observer was then directed to arrange these prints on the judging easel in a horizontal series, placing the print of worst quality at the extreme left, and the remainder in order of increasing quality to the right. When he had done this once, a record of the position of the various prints in the series was made. This was continued for a large number of observers and was repeated after a lapse of time sufficient to erase possible memories of the first judgments.

[8] Jones, *J. Franklin Inst.* **227**, 497 (1939).

From such judgment data, a numerical rating of the print quality was obtained. This value was obtained by taking the number of times that a print appeared in each possible position and multiplying this by the index number of that position. The sum of these products was taken as the quality number of the print. This procedure is illustrated in Table 18.1. By plotting these quality values as a function of the log exposure of the negative of which each print was made, a curve such as that shown in the solid line in Fig. 18.12 was obtained.

This method of judgment indicated that the quality increased from a low value according to a linear relation within the group of prints from the first six negatives in the exposure series. Jones concluded that this was not valid because the method gave no indication of the quality *interval*. He therefore employed a somewhat different judging technique in order to remedy this situation. The observer was requested to lay out the prints in such a way that the space between adjacent prints represented

TABLE 18.1

Score of Print No. 12			Score of Print No. 11		
No. of Times	Position	Points	No. of Times	Position	Points
8	12	96	9	12	108
13	11	143	13	11	143
12	10	120	3	10	30
13	9	117	7	9	63
2	8	16	17	8	136
2	7	14	1	7	7
Total 50		506	50		487

his estimate of quality difference. Although this type of judgment is difficult to make, moderately good agreement between observers was obtained, and a single observer repeated his judgments with reasonable certainty. On the basis of judgments made this way Jones concluded that the print quality-negative exposure function should take the form of the dotted curve in Fig. 18.12.

The next step was to formulate an empirical relationship expressing quality in

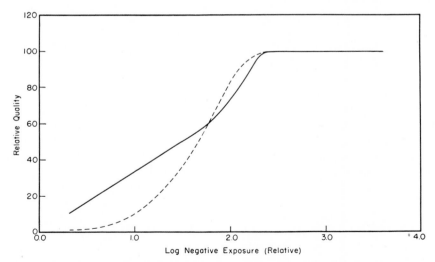

Fig. 18.12. Relation between print quality and negative exposure as determined statistically on basis of order of preference (solid curve) and on basis of estimated quality interval (dotted curve).

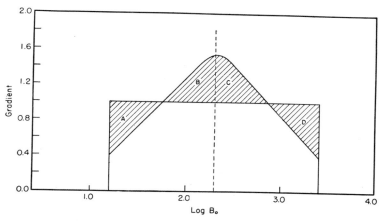

Fɪɢ. 18.13.   Typical gradient error curve.

terms of the magnitude and distribution of gradient errors and of luminance scale compression, and to compare the results obtained by this means with the psychophysical quality function for several negative materials.   Jones showed that the magnitude and distribution of gradient errors may be expressed graphically as illustrated in Fig. 18.13.   Here the values of gradient derived from the tone reproduction curves are expressed as a function of the log luminance of the object.   If it is assumed that the best photographic quality is obtained when the contrast in the object is reproduced perfectly, it is obvious that a horizontal line drawn through the point where the gradient is equal to 1.0 will represent maximum quality.   The difference between the gradient at any point on the reproduction curve and unity is the gradient error, ΔG, for that particular object luminance. From these and the reproduction curves the following quantities were evaluated:

Average gradient error, $\overline{\Delta G}$.   This was obtained by integrating the shaded areas and dividing by the log luminance scale.

The distribution of the gradient errors. This was evaluated in terms of the relative areas of the portions A, B, C, and D of Fig.

18.13.   The positive-negative balance was indicated by k_1 and the highlight-shadow balance by k_2. These quantities are defined by the following equations:

$$k_1 = 1 - \frac{(B + C) - (A + D)}{\log BS_o}$$

$$k_2 = 1 - \frac{(A + B) - (C + D)}{\log BS_o}.$$

The gradient at the extreme shadow end of the tone reproduction curve, G_s.

The gradient at the extreme highlight end of the tone reproduction curve, G_h.

The maximum gradient of the tone reproduction curve, G_{max}.

The average gradient of the tone reproduction curve, $\overline{G}_r$.

The density scale of the reproduction, DS_r.

By correlating the relationships which existed between these quantities for each print with the subjective evaluation of quality for that print, Jones drew the following tentative conclusions:

1. Prints for which the tone reproduction curve is a straight line having a slope of unity will be of uniformly high quality.

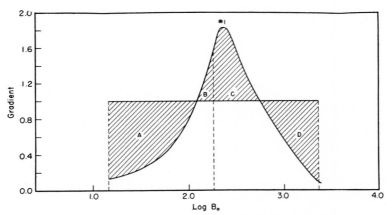

FIG. 18.14.   Gradient error curve for a reproduction from a
"short-toe" negative.

2. For prints in which there are gradient errors, photographic quality increases as the average gradient error decreases, provided:

   a. The gradient errors are properly balanced between negative and positive values and between the highlight and shadow regions.
   b. The average gradient of the reproduction approaches unity.
   c. The density scale of the reproduction approaches the log luminance scale of the object.

   d. The shadow and highlight gradients are approximately equal or the shadow gradient somewhat higher than the highlight gradient.

Although the conclusions reached by Jones are based entirely on experiments conducted to study the change in photographic quality with the exposure of the negative, there is reason to believe that they will be equally valid for those cases in which photographic quality differences have been introduced by one of the many other variables in picture-making. It must

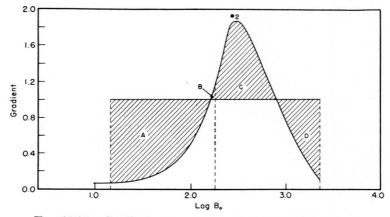

FIG. 18.15.   Gradient error curve for a reproduction from a
"long-toe" negative.

be recognized, of course, that further investigations in this field may reveal that certain of these conclusions should be modified, but it is unlikely that the fundamental soundness of the method of analysis used by Jones will be disproved. Until there is evidence to the contrary, therefore, the principles outlined above can be applied with reasonable assurance to the solution of tone reproduction problems. An example will serve to demonstrate the practical value of applying these principles in predicting photographic quality by purely physical means.

A suitable example for this purpose is one previously mentioned. The problem is to determine the effect of the shape characteristics of the negative material on the quality of the resultant print. The tone reproduction curves of Fig. 18.9 are typical of the results obtained with two negative materials, one having short-toe characteristics, the other having long-toe characteristics. From these curves the gradient-log B_o relationships shown in Figs. 18.14 and 18.15 are obtained. The areas A, B, C, and D, determined by mechanical integration, have the values shown in Table 18.2. The quantities $\overline{\Delta G}$, k_1, and k_2, which are computed as explained previously, are also shown in Table 18.2, together with measured values of G_s, G_h, G_{max}, $\overline{G_r}$, and DS_r. On the basis of these values, it can be concluded that for the conditions selected the print made from the "short-toe" negative (No. 1) will be superior to that made from

TABLE 18.2

	Negative Material No. 1 (Short Toe)	Negative Material No. 2 (Long Toe)
Area A	.553	.740
Area B	.050	.008
Area C	.237	.345
Area D	.300	.219
$\overline{\Delta G}$	.519	.598
k_1	.743	.720
k_2	.970	.916
G_s	0.13	0.07
G_h	0.10	0.10
G_{max}	1.82	1.87
$\overline{G_r}$	0.75	0.75
DS_r	1.63	1.63

the "long-toe" negative (No. 2) for the following reasons:

1. The average gradient error is smaller.
2. The positive-negative gradient error balance is nearer unity. (Unity is perfect balance.)
3. The highlight-shadow gradient error balance is nearer unity.
4. The shadow and highlight gradients are better balanced. (The shadow gradient is higher than the highlight gradient.)

Although no effort has been made here to evaluate quality on an absolute scale, the conclusions, expressed on a relative quality basis, are useful and significant in the solution of tone reproduction problems.

Chapter 19

REPRODUCTION OF COLOR IN MONOCHROME

The Fundamental Problem. In the preceding chapter the factors to be considered in accurately reproducing a uniformly illuminated gray scale are discussed. We have now to consider the photography of multicolored objects in monochrome, e.g., in terms of gray. As we have seen, one of the ultimate goals in the theory of the photographic process is to state the requirements which must be met to cause the photographic image to re-establish in the mind of the observer the same impression as created by the scene at the time it was photographed. It is apparent that in ordinary black and white photography the total visual impression created by a multicolored scene cannot be re-established. The final image consists merely of a series of gray tones ranging from a light to a dark gray. There is nothing contained within such an image to permit the chromatic qualities of the scene to be deduced. The reproduction depicts the form and position of objects in the scene primarily in terms of contrast and perspective relationships. In general, the more closely these relationships correspond to those which existed in the scene itself, the better the photographic reproduction is said to be.

In the present discussion we shall be concerned only with contrast reproduction. The subject is extremely complex. In fact, it is impossible to construct a completely adequate theory with the amount of experimental data currently available. Both objective and subjective factors must be considered, and any satisfactory theory must allow for complicated as well as simple scenes. A simple scene, such as a uniformly illuminated gray scale, exhibits tone or brightness differences by virtue of reflectance differences, i.e., a gray patch which appears lighter than some other gray patch merely reflects more light to the eye than the darker gray. On this basis the capabilities of the photographic process to record contrast relationships in terms of brightness differences becomes independent of the chromatic sensitivity of the eye, the spectral sensitivity of the film material, the spectral distribution of the illumination, and certain visual (subjective) phenomena. In the study of monochrome photography of multicolored objects, an attempt is made to derive the conditions which best apply in reproducing in terms of a single color (usually tones of gray) the contrast relationships existing between various elements of a complex, multicolored scene. The scene no longer is simplified to a series of gray tones, but rather involves a heterogeneous distribution of colors. Therefore, the spectral distribution of the illuminant, the chromatic sensitivity of the eye, the spectral sensitivity of the film, the transmittance characteristics of special filters and certain complicating subjective factors must be considered in addition to the principles discussed in the previous chapter under the theory of tone reproduction.

The Psychological Attributes of Color. Colors are perceived in the mind and, al-

VARDEN, The Visual Mechanism and Pictorial Photography (section entitled "Concerning Color Rendering in Monochrome"), *Amer. Annual of Photog.* **56**, 1–19 (1942).

though for convenience we speak of "colored objects," color per se is not a property of objects as such expressions indicate. Radiant energy within a limited frequency range has the property of stimulating the retinal system of the eye to create color sensations which the brain interprets. Radiant energy which has this property is called *light,* the physical stimulus of vision. Light can be measured in quantitative terms, but visual sensations cannot be expressed on a physical scale. As stated by Helmholtz,[1] "physical stimulus is one thing: sensation another." Nevertheless, colors can be defined in qualitative terms according to certain psychological attributes. The major attributes which so define colors are hue, brightness, and saturation. Colors possessing hue are called *chromatic* colors, whereas hueless colors (white, black and grays) are called *achromatic* colors. *Hue* is the attribute of chromatic colors which distinguishes them from achromatic (gray) colors and from each other, e.g., blue, green, yellow, etc. Brightness is the attribute of colors which allows them to be related to given tones of gray ranging in a series from white to black.[2] *Saturation* is the attribute of a chromatic color which designates the degree to which the color differs from a gray of the same brightness. These attributes are sometimes called hue, value, and chroma, respectively. Brightness and saturation can be understood in a practical sense from the following: dark and light colors possessing hue are obviously related to dark and light tones of gray respectively whereas chromatic colors of intermediate brightness are related to intermediate tones of gray. If one conceives, for example, a very vivid red (high saturation) it is easy to see that by adding either a small amount of white or a small amount of black the color will be changed, becoming lighter in one case and darker in the next. Moreover, in both instances the vividness of the. red hue will be lessened (decreased saturation). Therefore, the addition of white or black to a chromatic color affects both the brightness and saturation. However, by adding small amounts of white and black at the same time, the brightness can be held constant and only the saturation is influenced. When sufficient amounts of white and black are added, the hue of the color becomes so diluted that it can no longer be recognized, and the color is then indistinguishable from the gray tone to which it was originally related in brightness.

Since hue and saturation are possessed only by chromatic colors, a reproduction of a multicolored scene in terms of gray cannot possibly evoke the same visual impression as the scene itself. In monochrome photography, then, the brightness aspect of colors is the only attribute which can be dealt with. Unfortunately, numerous visual phenomena, and certain practical considerations, interfere with the formulation of a straightforward procedure which would result in a theoretically perfect and always usable monochrome reproduction.

---

[1] Helmholtz, *Physiological Optics,* Vols. I, II, and III, English translation published by Optical Society of America, 1924–1925.

[2] To avoid confusion the most recently adopted terminology of the Committee on Colorimetry (Optical Society of America) is not followed here. *Brightness* actually is the mental perception of light of given *luminance,* whereas the term *lightness* refers to the perception of light reflected from a surface (reflectance). A distinction must be made since two surfaces which apparently are of equal lightness often do not have equal reflectance, and vice versa. (For discussion on subject see Colorimetry Report, *J. Opt. Soc. Amer.* **33,** 544–554 (1943); **34,** 183–218 (1944); **34,** 245–266 (1944); **34,** 633–688 (1944); **35,** 1–25 (1945).

ADRIAN, *Basis of Sensation,* Christophers, London, 1934.

BIRREN, *The Story of Color from Ancient Mysticism to Modern Science,* The Crimson Press, 1941.

Spectral Sensitivity of the Human Eye. The human eye responds to radiant energy which, if expressed in terms of wave lengths in air, ranges from approximately 380 mμ to 760 mμ. Its sensitivity is not uniform for all wave lengths, nor does a curve representing its relative response at one illumination level express its relative sensitivity for all other illumination levels. However, the sensitivity of the eye is a maximum in the central region of the visible spectrum at all illumination levels, falling off rather sharply toward the blue and red extremes. But at high levels of illumination the peak of sensitivity—as well as the entire relative sensitivity curve —is shifted toward the yellow-green in comparison to the position of the curve representing the eye sensitivity at low levels of illumination where the peak is in the blue-green. The change in spectral response of the eye, according to the rather well-established duplicity theory, is due to two distinct types of receptor bodies in the retina. The receptors called *cones* function primarily at high, or *photopic,* illumination levels and are thought to be responsible for hue vision. The receptors called *rods* are responsible for vision at low, or *scotopic,* levels of illumination. The rods are incapable of creating hue sensations; thus, the adage "all cats are gray at night." When the illumination level is about 10^{-1} candles per square foot, vision is due almost entirely to the cone system. Below 10^{-4} candles per square foot, vision is due to the rod system. In between these values there is a gradual shift from cone vision to rod vision, which is the well-known Purkinje phenomenon. The ability of the eye to distinguish hue and small brightness differences is lessened as true scotopic vision is approached.

Although in photopic vision the peak of sensitivity is in the yellow-green spectral region and the relative luminosity of the blue and red extremes is considerably less, it does not follow that spectral response at the far ends of the spectrum is unimportant. It so happens that the wave lengths at the spectral extremes have a pronounced effect on hue sensation. For example, a small addition of spectral blue light can change the hue of a color appreciably although the contribution to the brightness of the color is not greatly affected.

BORING, *Sensation and Perception*, D. Appleton-Century, 1942.

CHANDLER AND BARNHARD, *Bibliography of Psychological and Experimental Aesthetics from 1864–1937,* Univ. of Calif. Press, Berkeley. Contains 1737 references, including numerous references on the psychology of color perception and other aspects of vision (1938).

FULTON, HOFF AND PERKINS, *Bibliography of Visual Literature from 1939–1944,* Chas. C Thomas, Pub. (lists 3347 references and gives names of all English and foreign periodicals that publish articles pertaining to the visual mechanism) (1945).

LUCKIESH, *Color and Colors,* D. Van Nostrand Co., Inc., 1938.

MORGAN, *Physiological Psychology,* McGraw-Hill Book Co., Inc., 1943.

PARSONS, *An Introduction to the Study of Color Vision,* University Press, 1924.

REPORT OF COMMITTEE ON COLORIMETRY, *J. Opt. Soc. Amer.* **33**, 552 (1943).

TROLAND, *Principles of Psycho-Physiology,* Vols. 1, 2, and 3, D. Van Nostrand Co., Inc. 1929–30.

ABNEY, *Researches In Color Vision and the Trichromatic Theory,* Longmans, Green and Co., London, 1913.

BIOLOGICAL SYMPOSIA, VOL. VII, *Visual Mechanisms,* Jaques Cattell Press, Lancaster, 1942.

BURCH, *Physiological Optics,* Clarendon Press, Oxford, 1912.

DUKE-ELDER, *Textbook of Ophthalmology,* Vols. 1, 2, 3, and 4, Henry Kimpton, London, 1932. Later edition published in the United States by C. V. Mosby, St. Louis, 1934–41.

Reflectance Characteristic of Colored Objects. Practically all things are seen by virtue of the reflectance of light from the surfaces of objects within our field of view. No object has 100% reflecting or absorbing properties: a portion of the incident light always is absorbed, and the remainder reflected. Some objects absorb—and therefore reflect—all wave lengths of light to the same degree and are known as *nonselective* absorbers. In white light illumination such objects appear gray, the lightness of the gray depending largely upon the fraction of the incident light reflected from the surface. Other objects absorb certain wave lengths of light more readily than others and are known as *selective* absorbers. In white light illumination such objects are said to have a hue, the nature of which depends largely upon the spectral distribution of the unabsorbed light that is reflected to the eye.

The specific color which an object appears to have is influenced by the spectral distribution of the illuminant, the nature of the surrounding objects, the level of illumination, and other factors. Therefore, one cannot predict the color sensation which an object will arouse without complete specification of the conditions under which the object will be viewed. Since most objects are viewed under similar circumstances (relatively bright white light, etc.) definite color sensations are associated with them. It is customary, therefore, to speak of object colors with reference to these more or less normal conditions of viewing.

The spectral reflectance characteristics of an object illuminated by white light can be shown by plotting the percentage reflectance for each wave length through the spectrum. Luckiesh [2] published such curves for a variety of typical pigments, numerous dyes, inks, and other colorants. In general, reds, yellow-reds and yellow pigments have high reflectance in the spectral regions characteristic of their hue. Greens, blue-greens, and blue pigments have relatively low reflectance.

Obviously, the visual brightness of an object is a function of the spectral sensitivity of the eye as well as the spectral reflectance properties of the object. By multiplying the ordinates of the luminosity curve by those of the spectral reflectance curve of the object, a curve is obtained which represents the relative brightness of the object in white light. Theoretically, a perfect white light source is one which has equal spectral distribution. However, few light sources met with in practice have equal spectral distribution; therefore, the visual brightness will depend upon the spectral emission characteristics of the illuminant. Jones and Russell [3] published useful data showing the relative reflectance characteristics of various colored surfaces

EMSLEY, *Visual Optics,* Hatton Press, London, 1936.

HECHT, "The Visibility of the Spectrum," *J. Opt. Soc. Amer.* **9,** 211 (1924).

HELSON, "Color Tolerances as Affected by Changes in Composition and Intensity of Illumination and Reflectance of Background," *Amer. J. Psych.* **52,** 406–412 (1939).

SOUTHALL, *Introduction to Physiological Optics,* Oxford Press, 1937.

VARDEN, "Aspects of Color," *Amer. Ann. of Phot.* **59,** 7–18 (1945).

WEAVER, "The Visibility of Radiation at Low Intensities," *J. Opt. Soc. Amer.* **27,** 36 (1937).

WILLMER, *Retinal Structure and Colour Vision,* Cambridge Univ. Press, England, 1946.

WRIGHT, *The Measurement of Color,* Adam Hilger, London, 1944.

WRIGHT, *The Perception of Light,* Chemical Pub. Co., 1939.

WRIGHT, *Researches on Normal and Defective Colour Vision,* C. V. Mosby, 1947.

[2] Luckiesh, *J. Franklin Inst.,* **184,** 73 (July 1917).

[3] Jones, and Russell, *Trans. Soc. Mot. Pict. Eng.* **XII,** No. 34, p. 427 (1928).

under different illuminants. Table 19.1 lists typical colored surfaces and gives reflectance data for daylight and tungsten illumination.

TABLE 19.1

Surface	Daylight	Tungsten
White Diffusing..........	0.80	0.80
Red-purple..............	0.16	0.23
Deep Red..............	0.14	0.22
Red..................	0.21	0.31
Orange................	0.38	0.48
Yellow................	0.60	0.65
Yellow-green...........	0.46	0.42
Saturated Green.........	0.32	0.24
Blue..................	0.23	0.17
Violet-purple...........	0.14	0.12

Although any two objects which are represented by identical spectral reflectance curves derived under the same conditions will match in color, it does not follow that this is a requirement for visual color identities. Objects which appear identical in color may have quite different spectral reflectance characteristics. For example, the yellow color seen in the spectrum as a result of a narrow range of wave lengths can be duplicated from a complex mixture of wave lengths consisting of all wave lengths in the spectrum except those in the blue region, or the color can be duplicated by an additive mixture of a band of wave lengths in the green region and a band of wave lengths in the red region. Accordingly, the unaided eye can give no information on the wave length structure of the light reflected to it from an object.

Spectral Response of the Eye and Typical Photographic Materials. In Fig. 19.1 the dotted curve *A* represents the relation between the wave length and photopic visual response for a light source having a color temperature of 5400 K. (the accepted standard for mean noon sunlight). The solid curves *B*, *C*, and *D* represent the relative spectral sensitivity of a blue sensitive, orthochromatic, and panchromatic material, respectively, when exposed under the same type of light source. It will be observed that whereas all three types of film materials show a maximum response to the blue-violet between 400 mμ and 500 mμ, the visual response is a maximum at a wave length of approximately 550 mμ. The shortcomings of blue sensitive and orthochromatic materials in reproducing the brightness aspects of colors to which the eye is sensitive is very evident. A film cannot record in spectral regions where no sensitivity exists; therefore, many colors, which have a high visual brightness, are reproduced as almost black by blue sensitive and orthochromatic materials. Panchromatic materials, on the other hand, respond to all wave lengths of the spectrum, but there is a considerable departure in the relative spectral response of such materials in comparison to the visual response. Thus, the use of panchromatic materials results in an improvement in the rendering of colored objects, but filters are required to

BARNES, "A Spectrophotometric Study of Artists' Pigments," *Technical Studies in the Field of the Fine Arts* 7, 120–138 (1939). Also, *J. Opt. Soc. Amer.* 29, 208–214 (1939).

EDWARDS AND DUNTLEY, "The Pigments and Color of Living Human Skin," *Amer. J. Anat.* 65, 1–33 (1939).

JONES, "The Photographic Reflecting Power of Colored Objects," *Trans. Soc. Mot. Pict. Eng.* XI, No. 31, 564–581 (1927).

MURRAY AND SPENCER, *Colour in Theory and Practice*, Amer. Photo. Pub. Co., Boston, 1939.

WRIGHT, *The Measurement of Color*, Adam Hilger Ltd., London, 1944.

WRIGHT, *"Colour,"* Science Progress 34, No. 136, 681 (1946).

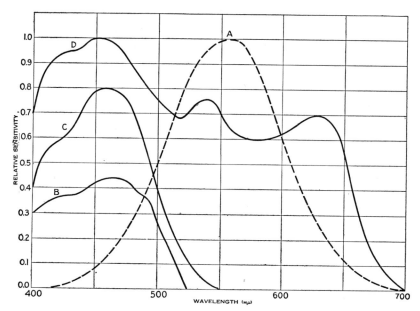

FIG. 19.1. Curves showing the spectral response of (a) the eye; (b) a blue sensitive; (c) orthochromatic; and (d) panchromatic material to light with a color temperature of 5400°K.

establish a correspondence between the film response and the visual response.

Effects of Light Sources. In Fig. 19.2 are shown spectral energy curves representing (A) average noon sunlight (5400 K.); (B) incandescent tungsten illumination (3400 K.), and (C) incandescent tungsten illumination (2360 K.). It is evident from the comparison of these curves that the spectral energy distribution of both of the tungsten sources is quite different from that of noon sunlight, the energy output of tungsten radiation being lower than that

of sunlight for the shorter wave lengths and relatively greater for the longer wave lengths. Since the *effective* distribution of spectral sensitivity depends upon the spectral energy characteristics of the light

Jones and Crabtree, "Panchromatic Negative Film for Motion Pictures," *Trans. Soc. Mot. Pict. Eng.* **X**, No. 27, 131 (1926).

Jones, Hodgson and Huse, "Relative Photographic and Visual Efficiency of Illuminants," *Trans. Ill. Eng. Soc.* **10**, 963 (1915).

Jones and Sandvik, "Spectral Distribution of Sensitivity of Photographic Materials," *J. Opt. Soc. Amer.* **12**, 401 (1926).

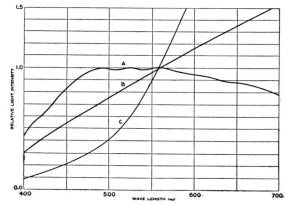

FIG. 19.2. Spectral energy distribution curves for (a) noon sunlight (5400°K); (b) incandescent tungsten illumination (3400°K) and incandescent tungsten at 2360°K.

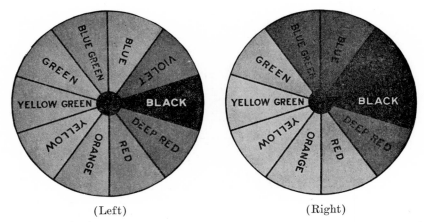

(Left)   (Right)

FIG. 19.3.   Color chart photographed on a panchromatic material.   At the left, by sunlight; at the right, by tungsten illumination.

source, as well as the spectral sensitivity response of the photosensitive material, it is clear that the use of either of the tungsten resources represented will result in sensitivity curves which are lower in the short-wave region and higher in the long-wave region than those in Fig. 19.1.

A natural consequence of the alteration in the spectral response of a photographic material brought about by a change in the spectral distribution of energy in the light source used for exposure is a difference in the relative brightnesses in which different colors are reproduced by the photographic material.   In Fig. 19.3 is shown a reproduction of a color chart photographed on a panchromatic material, at the left by sunlight and at the right by tungsten illumination.

A comparison of the relative brightnesses in which the different colors of the original are reproduced by the two light sources shows that the employment of tungsten illumination, with its greater abundance of long-wave radiation, has resulted in yellow, orange, and red being reproduced relatively lighter, and violet and blue darker, than with sunlight.   The relative brightnesses in which different colors are reproduced

depend on the distribution of spectral sensitivity with the particular light source used for the exposure.   The greater the effective sensitivity in any particular part of the spectrum, the greater the density of the negative and the lighter the tone of gray in which the corresponding color sensation is represented in the print.

Orthochromatic Reproduction.   The so-called correct reproduction of color in terms of its brightness characteristic is termed *orthochromatic reproduction.*   Orthochromatic, from the Greek roots, *ortho* correct and *chroma* color, is used here in its true sense, whereas orthochromatic films and plates were erroneously assigned this name at the time of their introduction because of the improved rendering of color as compared with ordinary, blue-sensitive materials.

IES LIGHTING HANDBOOK, Ill. Eng. Soc., New York (1947).   Gives numerous references on color nomenclature, definitions, visual phenomena, light sources, etc.

JONES, "The Use of Artificial Illuminants in Motion Picture Studios," *Trans. Soc. Mot. Pict. Eng.* No. 30, 74 (1921).

JOY AND DOWNES, "Characteristics of Flame Arcs for Studio Lighting," *Trans. Soc. Mot. Pict. Eng.* **XII**, No. 34, 502 (1928).

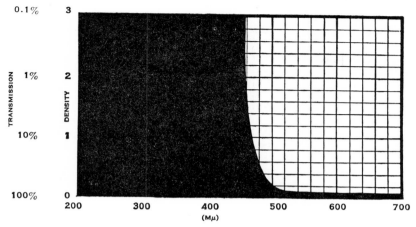

Fig. 19.4. Absorption curve of a light yellow filter.

For orthochromatic reproduction, the effective distribution of photographic sensitivity should correspond with the visual luminosity curve. Filters are required to reduce the relative blue and red response. Such filters are greenish in color but, if a perfect matching of the luminosity curve is achieved, the filters become too dense for most practical purposes. Therefore, orthochromatic correction filters are generally much lighter than theoretically required. Van Kreveld [4] arrived at results that are contrary to those which state that green filters are necessary for orthochromatic correction. He calculated by means of the addition law the improvement in color rendering by various correction filters and found that pale orange filters (hypothetically) should yield the best possible color rendering. In this work he defined the characteristics of correction filters by three improvement factors which indicated the improvement in rendering green, yellow, and red. These factors are said to be nearly independent of the color sensitivity of the emulsion, and led him to the conclu-

sion that greenish correction filters are not generally useful.

Since the relative brightnesses in which colors are reproduced by a photographic material depend upon its effective distribution of sensitivity, it is evident that the change in spectral sensitivity characteristics brought about by the use of a filter is accompanied by a similar change in the reproduction of color. The filter in Fig. 19.4, for example, absorbs violet and blue and transmits green, orange, and red. Thus, the exposure for violet and blue is reduced so that these colors are rendered darker, whereas green, orange, and red are rendered lighter in comparison. In other words, a filter causes colors of those wave lengths which it absorbs to be rendered darker while those in its transmitting band are rendered *relatively* lighter.

In Fig. 19.5A, *A* is the color brilliance curve and *B* the spectral sensitivity curve for particular panchromatic material to sunlight. In 19.5B, *C* is the curve obtained by dividing the ordinates of curve *A* at each wave length by those of curve *B* and represents the transmissions of the filter required to produce orthochromatic reproduction under these conditions. The

---

[4] Van Kreveld, *J. Opt. Soc. Amer.* **36**, 412 (1946).

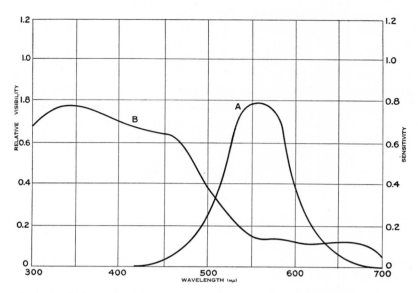

FIG. 19.5A.   (A) Color brilliance curve; (B) Spectral sensitivity curve of a panchromatic material.

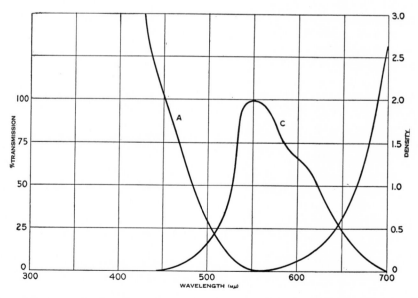

FIG. 19.5B.   C is the transmission curve of the filter required for orthochromatic reproduction with the emulsion represented by Curve B in Fig. 19.5A.

transmission values may be converted to density by the usual formula $D = \text{Log } I/T$ to obtain the density characteristics of the required filter (curve A).

As shown by Arens and Eggert,[5] it is desirable for interpreting the orthochromatic response of panchromatic films to express the wave-length sensitivity on the basis of a luminosity spectrum rather than on an equal energy or other spectrum, such as daylight or tungsten light. On this basis, a film whose sensitivity matched the luminosity curve would produce uniform density for all wave lengths if the exposure was made on the straight line portion of the film material and that gamma wave-length effects could be disregarded. In practice, this would mean that all colors of equal brightness would be reproduced with the same density. Also, when spectral sensitivity is expressed in this manner and there is a correspondence between the film sensitivity and the luminosity curve, orthochromatic reproduction is assured for all types of illumination since the brightness of colors changes under different light sources. However, if a photograph is to be made under one light source, for example, 3200 K. tungsten, so that the reproduction will appear as though it were made under daylight, then a special compensating filter is required. In general, it is customary to reproduce colors in monochrome in keeping with their brightness characteristics in sunlight. Therefore, in practice lighter filters are used in orthochromatic photography with incandescent tungsten illumination than in sunlight.

Van Kreveld [6] also considered it undesirable from a practical standpoint to express the color sensitivity of recording materials on an absolute sensitivity distribution basis. He felt that it should be expressed in comparison with the color sensitivity of the eye since Bouma [7] had shown that the addition law holds for the color sensitivity of the eye. He divided the spectrum of average daylight into four parts: I = 3500A–4800A; II = 4800A–5400A; III = 5400A–6000A; IV = 6000A–8000A. For each part the eye sensitivity is determined and expressed as O_I, O_{II}, O_{III}, and O_{IV} and the film sensitivity as S_I, S_{II}, S_{III}, and S_{IV}.

$$\text{Green sensitivity } = G = \frac{S_{II}}{O_{II}} \times \frac{O_I}{S_I}.$$

$$\text{Yellow sensitivity } = Y = \frac{S_{III}}{O_{III}} \times \frac{O_I}{S_I}.$$

$$\text{Red sensitivity } = R = \frac{S_{IV}}{O_{IV}} \times \frac{O_I}{S_I}.$$

The ideal film sensitivity is reached when G, Y, and R are equal to one; i.e., the eye and film sensitivity are equal. If G, Y, or R is less than one, the sensitivity of the film is too low for that particular color, or too high if G, Y, or R exceeds one. However, no film material has been sensitized to meet the ideal requirement without supplementary filter.

---

[7] Bouma, *Proc. Kon. Akedemie* **38**, p. 35 (1935).

ABNEY, "Orthochromatics: Colour Sensitometry," *Phot. J.* (June 1895).

BAKER, "Practical Orthochromatic Photography," *Photo Miniature*, Vol. 6, No. 67 (October 1904).

BAKER, *Correct-color (orthochromatic or isochromatic) Photography*, London, Dawbarn and Ward, Ltd., 1906.

FANSTONE, *Colour Sensitive Materials*, Pitman Pub. Corp., 1938.

GLOVER, *Photographic Filters: Their Uses and Advantages*, The Fountain Press, London (1935) (originally published as *The Photographic Rendering of Colours in Monochrome*, 1927).

HÜBL, *Die orthochromatische Photographie*, W. Knapp, Halle, 1920.

ILFORD, LTD., *Panchromatism, including Ilford Colour Chart*, London, 1919.

---

[5] Arens and Eggert, *Veröffentlichungen des wiss. zentral-lab. der phot. Abteilung Agfa*, Band I, p. 25, 1930.

[6] Van Kreveld, *Brit. J. Phot.* **72**, 388 (1935).

Instead of using a single filter for orthochromatic photography, it has been recommended to make three exposures in succession through a suitable set of tri-color separation filters. This procedure was first proposed by Lippmann (1889). L. P. Clerc [8] states that brightness values of color can be perfectly reproduced if exposures are made through the Wratten 49, 58, and 25 filters using an exposure through each filter that is one-third that necessary to obtain a fully exposed image when using any one filter alone. This is a misconception, however, since blue and red colors, especially blue, are rendered too light and green colors too dark. It has been recommended, nevertheless, to use two-thirds the total exposure through the green separation filter and one-third through the red separation filter to obtain true orthochromatic rendering.[9] This procedure is possible because the green filter transmits somewhat in the blue spectral region where all films have relatively high sensitivity. A variation of previously proposed multi-filter exposure methods is that of Rawling [10] who recommended a partial exposure through a normal orthochromatic type filter, followed by another exposure through an appropriate contrast filter.

Using Filters for Color Selection. Since the visual contrast of a multicolored scene consists of hue contrast and saturation contrast in addition to brightness contrast, a monochrome image is not satisfactory in showing tone separation of those colors which are equal in brightness contrast but which differ in either hue or saturation contrast. The brightness contrast often is of less significance than the contrast created from hue and saturation differences. Therefore, in practice it is necessary to deviate from ideal orthochromatic reproduction conditions in order to obtain tone separation in the monochrome image. For example, the visual contrast between a light red apple and a cluster of green leaves is very marked, although the brightness difference is small. When photographed on a panchromatic material with a theoretically perfect orthochromatic filter, the contrast between the red and green objects in the monochrome reproduction is negligible and the two are not properly differentiated. In such instances filters other than orthochromatic filters are necessary, or it may be possible to obtain the desired tone separation by use of a panchromatic material without any filter. Nevertheless, where filters are required the particular type to be used is largely a matter of judgment because the tone separation can be obtained by reproducing either of the two-colored objects lighter or darker than the other. In the example above, if yellow-red filter were used the red apple would reproduce in the print in a lighter tone than the green leaves, whereas a greenish filter would reverse the tone differentiation. Whichever color is to be reproduced lighter in the monochrome reproduction determines the filter to be used, because a filter of that color has a relatively higher transmittance for

[8] Clerc, *La Technique Photographique,* 4th Edition, 1947.
[9] Photography of Colored Objects, Eastman Kodak Co., 13th Edition, 1935.
[10] Rawling, *Phot. J.* **74**, 295 (1934).

MEES, *The Photography of Colored Objects,* Tennant and Ward, 1909. Subsequent editions published by Eastman Kodak Co.
ORTHOCHROMATIC PHOTOGRAPHY, *The Practical Photographer,* American Library Series, No. 17 (1905).
SCHOENFELDT, *Photographic Filters and How to Use Them; An Analysis of Color and Color Values in Photography,* VerHalen Pub. Co., Hollywood, 1927.
SCHIEL, *Tonwertrichtige Photographie; das Arbeiten mit orthochromatischen Platten und Filmen,* Photokino, Photofreund Bücherei, bd. 20, Berlin, 1931.
WILDUNG, "Panchromatic Photography," *The Photo-Miniature* **17**, No. 203 (December 1930).

the wave lengths reflected from the object. As a general rule, the warm colors such as yellow, yellow-green, orange, and red should be rendered lighter than the cool colors such as violet, blue, and blue-green. This follows from the fact that the warm colors usually have a higher brightness characteristic than the cool colors.

The Application of Color Charts. Although authorities disagree concerning the merits of color charts for use in evaluating the color sensitivity or color reproduction properties of film materials, they have been used widely for this purpose. Sheppard and Mees,[11] for example, agreed that the large amounts of white light reflected from colored pigments used for color charts simulated conditions in practice, but stated that the white light obscured the thing being measured. On the other hand, Arens and Eggert [12] were of the opinion that in attempting to evaluate the color reproduction characteristics of recording materials on the basis of response curves derived from exposures to saturated spectral colors one is often misled. This is due to the fact that colored objects met with in practice are of much lower saturation than spectral colors. For this reason, they recommended the use of color charts. Ideally, such charts consist of bands of various colors (blue, green, yellow, red, etc.) of equal saturation along side of which is placed a gray scale with one step in each scale equal in brightness to the color with which it is associated. If a film records in a truly orthochromatic manner, the color bands will reproduce in a density corresponding to the density in each of the gray scales where the luminosities of the particular color and gray patch are equal. H. W. Vogel, in the first edition

of his handbook on photography, showed a color scale consisting of 16 colored squares and noted the unsatisfactory monochromatic reproductions with the recording materials then available. Von Hübl made extensive experiments with color charts, and a table made available by him (1906) made up of four colors of equal saturation was widely used by photographers. However, it was not until the introduction of the Agfacolor chart and the Lagorio color chart around 1930 that color bands were associated with calibrated gray scales. As pointed out by Davies and Selwyn [13] one must be very careful in interpreting the results obtained by use of color charts. Using the Lagorio color chart they showed that the average ordinate of the color reproduction curve is constant irrespective of the illuminant used or the color sensitivity of the photographic material providing that the total light reflected from all the colored strips is equal in spectral quality to that reflected from the gray strips and further providing that gamma wavelength effects can be ignored. Results obtained by use of color charts have led to widely divergent views as to the best combination of film type and illuminant for most ideal orthochromatic reproduction. Olbers and Vogl [14] concluded, for example, that, although there was considerable departure from correct tone reproduction, pictures made even under sodium or mercury vapor lamps gave satisfactory rendering with both orthochromatic and panchromatic films. Their conclusions, based on tests made with a Lagorio color chart, are contrary to those of many other investigators.

If color charts serve no other purpose, they certainly indicate that the subject of orthochromatic reproduction is more complex than often considered. The values ob-

[11] Sheppard and Mees, *Investigations on the Theory of the Photographic Process*, 1907.
[12] *Ibid.*

Eastman Kodak Company, *Wratten Light Filters*, 17th Edition, 1945.

[13] Davies and Selwyn, *Phot. J.* **78**, 122 (1938).
[14] Olbers and Vogl, *Phot. Korr.* **79**, 97 (1943).

tained, even with a given film and given light source, vary appreciably when the extent of exposure or the degree of development varies. Therefore, one must not be too quick to draw general conclusions since too many factors, such as shape of the *D* log *E* curve, reciprocity law failure, gamma wave-length factors, etc., come into play.

Viewing Filters. It is difficult to determine visually how a multicolored scene will appear in a final black and white photograph. As an aid in evaluating how various colored objects will reproduce in relation to each other it has been proposed to use special viewing filters. Blue or violet glass was used for this purpose before dye sensitized materials were available in order to limit the visual response to the spectral regions to which the ordinary materials then in use were sensitive. With dye sensitized emulsions a different filter is required (theoretically) for every different type of material. Renwick [15] laid the foundations for constructing such filters and stated that the viewing filter should be complementary in color to the correction filter required to produce true brightness rendering with a given recording material. For example, he assumed that for true monochromatic reproduction with a panchromatic emulsion of uniform spectral sensitivity a greenish correction filter would be necessary. The viewing filter, therefore, would be complementary in color to green, namely, a blue-red (purple) color. Such viewing filters remain in use and are often recommended especially where it is considered desirable to distort the monochrome reproduction by use of additional filters as a means for showing tone separation between colored

objects of equal brightness.[16] The most suitable filter to use is determined by trial and error by combining various filters in turn with the viewing filter until the desired visual appearance of the scene is obtained.

A more generally applicable viewing filter is the type which transmits only in a narrow region of the spectrum, e.g., the Wratten No. 90 Monochromatic Viewing Filter. Such filters are yellow in color, transmitting principally in the visible spectrum from about 550 mμ to 590 mμ. There is another transmittance band in the deep red where the visual response is very low. In viewing a scene with this type of filter, it is possible to distinguish a red and a green, but the hue and saturation differences are so subdued that lightness judgment is not appreciably influenced. These filters can be used also for estimating what camera filters are necessary to distort the reproduction for better tone separation of colors of similar brightness.

Subjective Factors. As previously stated, in constructing an ideal theory of perfect tone reproduction it is customary to consider only the objective phases and, for purposes of simplification, the factors involved are dealt with on the basis of reproducing a uniformly illuminated series of gray tones. Such ideal conditions do not comply with conditions met in practice. Relatively minor deviations from the simplified case can cause the theory to be entirely inapplicable without even introducing further complexities arising from hue and saturation effects. For example, a white block against a dark background (Fig. 19.6) when lighted from one side contains areas which, apart from their shape, differ only in brightness. However, the object is seen in brightness differences due to differences of illuminance and not because of differences in reflectance, as in the case of a uniformly illuminated gray

[15] Renwick, *Phot. J.* **59**, 158 (1919).

[16] Meyer, ''Problems of Controlling Correct Photographic Reproduction,'' Part IV, *Agfa Motion Picture Topics*, June–July (1937).

LAGORIO, *Phot. Industrie* **28**, 629 (1930).
LAGORIO, *Phot. Korr.* **67**, 9 (1931).

scale. Under such a condition, the visual phenomenon known as approximate brightness constancy prevents a direct relationship from existing between luminance and brightness perception. As stated by Birren,[17] a gray hen in open sunlight *looks* gray, whereas a white hen in the shadow of the barn *looks* white; yet the gray hen may reflect considerably more light to the observer than the white hen.

In general, photography scenes are not illuminated uniformly, although the reproduction is viewed in uniform illumination. Because of brightness constancy we tend to evaluate the brightness of objects within a scene as though the objects were uni-

Fig. 19.6.

formly illuminated.[18] This causes dark objects to appear relatively lighter than they would appear if our visual response was dependent entirely upon the relative quantity of light received by the eye. Helson[19] has shown that dark objects may reflect as much as 1600 times the light reflected by light objects and still appear to the eye as though they were darker than the light objects which reflect so much less light. However, a photograph of two objects so illuminated would reproduce in terms of the physical quantities of light.

In addition to brightness constancy, there is a phenomenon known as chromaticity

constancy which further complicates the devising of a straightforward theory of monochrome reproduction of multicolored objects. Chromaticity applies to the total chromatic qualities of colors and is a term which combines the hue and saturation attributes of colors. It is a matter of common experience that the green appearance of grass does not change during the course of a day even thought the light from the sun may vary considerably in intensity and color temperature. Many other colors for which we have strong associations—e.g., "flesh color"—give rise to almost identical visual perceptions even under such widely different light sources such as tungsten and daylight. But, photographic recording materials do not possess similar compensating mechanisms which under normal conditions cause our world of color to appear generally the same. Constancy effects are not operative, however, except under normal illumination levels. If colored objects are viewed under widely different levels of illumination, various colors within the scene may appear brighter than others at one level of illumination and darker than others at a different level of illumination. For example, red and yellow colors appear brightest at high illuminations and blues and greens are brightest under low illuminations. A red and blue object viewed under average bright daylight illumination might appear *equally* bright, but when viewed first under a very low level of illumination and next under a very high level of illumination, the blue and then the red will appear lighter, respectively. This variation is due to the Purkinje phenomenon. The effect is more, or less, pronounced according to the particular colors under observation.

Color contrast effects introduce further difficulties in monochrome photography. These effects cause, for example, a dark color next to a light color to appear rela-

[17] Faber Birren, *Monument to Color*, p. 11.
[18] Evans and Klute, *J. Opt. Soc. Amer.* **34**, 533 (1944).
[19] Helson, H., *J. Opt. Soc. Amer.* **33**, 555 (1943).

tively darker and the light color relatively lighter than they would if viewed separately. Moreover, the hue appearance of a color is influenced by the hue of any object surrounding it and causes its hue to shift as though the complement of the surrounding hue were impressed upon it. The effect is mutual for contiguous colors and varies according to the relative size of the color areas. The overall phenomenon is known as simultaneous contrast.

Still another phenomenon, known as successive contrast, which contributes to the visual appearance of multicolored scenes but which does not enter into the photographic reproduction process must be considered. This phenomenon concerns the effects which arise when the eye passes from one colored object to another. Upon viewing one color the sensitivity of the eye is reduced for that color according to the brightness and saturation of the color and the length of time during which it is viewed. When the eye shifts its focus to a different color there is a tendency for the complementary color of the first color to be impressed upon the second.

BIOLOGICAL SYMPOSIA, VOL. VII, *Visual Mechanisms*, Jacques Cattell Press, Lancaster (1942).

BOUMA, "The Perception of Colour," *Philips Tech. Rev.* 1, 283 (1936).

BOUMA AND KRUITHOF, "Colour Stimulus and Colour Sensation," *Philips Tech. Rev.* 9, 2 (1947).

EVANS, "Visual Processes and Color Photography," *J. Opt. Soc. Amer.* 33, 579 (1943).

HELSON, "Fundamental Problems in Color Vision I, The Principle Governing Changes in Hue, Saturation and Lightness of Non-Selective Samples in Chromatic Illumination," *J. Exp. Psych.* 23, 439 (1938).

HELSON, AND JEFFERS, "Fundamental Problems in Color Vision II, Hue, Lightness and Saturation of Selected Samples in Chromatic Illumination," *J. Exp. Psych.* 26, 1 (1940).

JUDD, "Hue, Saturation and Lightness of Surface Colors and Chromatic Illumination," *J. Opt. Soc. Amer.* 30, 2 (1940).

KATZ, *The World of Colour*, Kegan Paul, Trench, Trubner and Co., Ltd., London, 1935.

MacLEOD, "An Experimental Investigation of Brightness Constancy," *Arch. of Psych.*, No. 135 (1932).

Chapter 20

STRUCTURE OF THE IMAGE, GRAININESS, IMAGE SHARPNESS, HALATION, AND RESOLVING POWER

The Structure of the Developed Image. The developed image consists of masses of metallic silver formed by the reduction of the exposed crystals of silver halide to metallic silver. To the unaided eye these appear to form a continuous deposit (Fig. 20.1); however, at a relatively low magnification a lack of uniformity becomes apparent which has received the term "graininess." With increased magnification the granular structure of the image is seen clearly. At a magnification of about 2500 times the individual grains of metallic silver are resolved. These, however, do not have the same size or shape as the crystals of silver halide from which they were formed, except in the case of special developers.[1] Studies with the electron microscope at a magnification of 25,000 times show that the grains are not solid but have a filamentary structure, the nature of which varies with the developing agent. Metol and diaminophenol produce compact masses of fine filaments; hydroquinone developers, more open masses of coarse filaments.

In general, the grains of silver halide in an emulsion develop as individual units; however, where grains are joined, or in close proximity, they develop as a group, developability of one grain being sufficient to induce development in all. This condition occurs more often with high-speed emulsions in which large grains are more numerous, and the number of grains of different sizes greater, than in slow emulsions where the grains are smaller and more nearly uniform in size. Thus the structure of the silver image varies even more with the emulsion than with the developer.

In negative emulsions the crystals of silver halide are distributed in a layer which is several grains thick. With complete development the image, assuming sufficient exposure, is distributed throughout the emulsion layer. Fig. 20.2 shows cross sections of an emulsion with a series of exposures which were developed to completion. With the shortest exposure, the image is composed of the most sensitive grains, and these are distributed throughout the emulsion layer. With increased exposure, the less sensitive grains are made developable and the mass of developed silver increases. There is, however, some variation in the depth of the image with the wave length of the radiation used for the exposure. With ultraviolet, for example, the image is confined largely to the upper portions of the emulsion layer; with x-rays, on the other hand, the distribution of the image depends almost entirely on the sensitivity of the grains of silver halide and is almost completely independent of their position in the emulsion layer.

Development begins at the surface and extends in depth with time. Fig 20.3 shows cross-sections of an emulsion receiving the

---

[1] Davidson, *Phot. J.* **65**, 19 (1925). Jelley, *J. Phot. Soc. Amer.* **8**, 283 (1942).

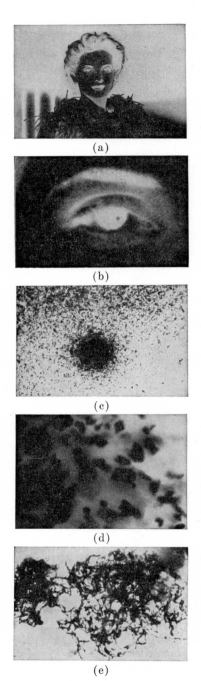

(a)

(b)

(c)

(d)

(e)

FIG. 20.1. The photographic image at five degrees of magnification: (1) exact size; (2) 25 ×; (3) 250 ×; (4) 2,500 ×; (5) 25,000 ×. (*Kodak Research Laboratories.*)

same exposure but developed for different times. It will be observed that the depth of the image in the emulsion layer increases with the time of development, also that the number of grains developed at a given depth tends to increase with the developing time. The distribution of the developed grains in the emulsion layer depends, however, on the developer as well as on the time of development; other things being equal the depth of the image, for a given density, is greater with a weak than with a concentrated developer. There are differences in this respect among the different developing agents, and the depth of the image is influenced also by the pH of the developer and other factors.

Graininess. The term *graininess* is applied to the granular appearance of enlargements and, less frequently, to the negative and is the visual effect produced by the lack of homogeneity in the silver deposit arising from the clumping of grains in the emulsion and the overlapping of developed grains in different levels. A distinction must be made between graininess and the granularity of the image. The granularity of the silver deposit refers to the degree of inhomogeneity and is measurable by objective physical methods, while graininess is the subjective sensation of inhomogeneity formed in the eye of the observer.[2]

Measurement of Graininess. Since graininess is psycho-physical, being the visual impression of a lack of homogeneity, it either must be determined from measurements made visually or, if purely physical methods are employed, the data so obtained must be correlated with the results obtained by visual methods.

The graininess of the silver image has been measured in five different ways:

[2] Jones and Higgins, *J. Opt. Soc. Amer.* **35,** 435 (1945). Selwyn, *Phot. J.* **83,** 227 (1943).

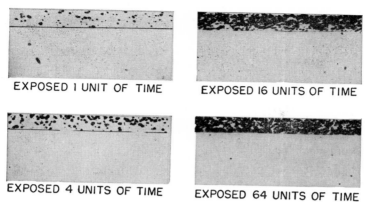

EXPOSED 1 UNIT OF TIME — EXPOSED 16 UNITS OF TIME

EXPOSED 4 UNITS OF TIME — EXPOSED 64 UNITS OF TIME

FIG. 20.2. Cross-section of the developed image showing variation in the distribution of the silver particles with exposure. (*Kodak Research Laboratories.*)

1. By determining the distance at which the deposit appears homogeneous.[3]

2. By determining the magnification at which the inhomogeneity of the density is the same as that of a standard test object.[4]

3. The Callier coefficient, i.e., the ratio of the specular to the diffuse density.[5]

4. Measurement of the variations in the density of the image with a microdensitometer.[6]

[3] Jones and Deisch, *Brit. J. Phot.* **67**, 689, 706 (1920). Jones and Hardy, *Trans. Soc. Mot. Pict. Eng. No.* **14**, 107 (1922). Lowry, *J. Opt. Soc. Amer.* **26**, 65 (1936).

[4] Conklin, *Trans. Soc. Mot. Pict. Eng.* **16**, 159 (1931) Reinders and Beukers, *Phot. J.* **78**, 192 (1938).

[5] Threadgold, *Phot. J.* **72**, 348 (1932); **79**, 524 (1939). Kuster, *Phot. Korr.* **70**, 17 (1934). Eggert and Kuster, *Kinotech.* **16**, 127, 291, 308 (1934). Hansen and Koch, *Z. wiss. P.* **37**, 86, 99 (1938). Eggert and Schopper, *Z. wiss. P.* **37**, 221 (1938).

[6] Dunham, *Die Anwenduck der Photographie in der Astrophysik.* Mees, *Photographic Plates for Spectroscopy and Astronomy,* Eastman Kodak

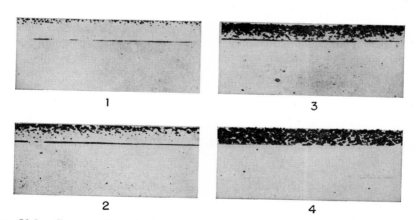

1   3

2   4

FIG. 20.3. Cross-section of the developed image showing the variation in the distribution of the silver particles with the time of development. (*Kodak Research Laboratories.*)

5. Comparison of enlargements having the same density and contrast made on the same paper and under the same conditions.[7]

Since this method is one which may be adopted by the practicing photographer for comparative tests, attention may be usefully called to the following precautions:

1. *The images must be carefully focused.* Graininess is very dependent on sharpness of the image, and any procedures that tend to diminish this sharpness, such as lack of critical focusing, movement during exposure, lens flare, or the use of a lens of low resolving power, diminish graininess, and therefore vitiate the graininess comparison.

2. *Prints must be matched exactly with regard to highlight and shadow densities since the appearance of graininess is very dependent on the density contrast of the print.*

3. *The conditions of comparison must be be held constant.* This means that the test object must remain uniformly lighted, the camera focus should not be changed, the same emulsion should be used, the developing conditions should be identical, the focus of the enlarger should not be altered, and matched prints must be obtained by similar

development of paper of the same batch number.

Factors Affecting the Graininess of the Photographic Image. In practice, graininess is of concern to the photographer in the print only. The factors involving the negative emulsion, its exposure and development are discussed,[8] therefore, in relation to their effect on the graininess of the print.

Graininess is determined by:

1. *The negative emulsion.* The primary cause of graininess is the clumping of the grains of silver halide in the negative emulsion. Important factors in the clumping of the silver halide grains would appear to be the average grain-size and the size-frequency, i.e., the relative number of grains of each size present. In general, it appears that the tendency toward clumping is at a minimum, and therefore graininess is lower, the more nearly uniform in size the grains of an emulsion and the smaller the average grain size.

Such emulsions, however, are slow and their high gamma and short exposure scale is a disadvantage in many fields of photography.

2. *The density of the silver deposit.* In the print, graininess increases up to a density of about 0.3 or slightly above; however, the graininess of an area of nearly uniform density, such as the sky, is greater than of

Company, Rochester. Goetz, Gould, and Dember, *J. Soc. Mot. Pict. Eng.* **34**, 279 (1940); *Photo-Technique* **1**, 21 (September 1939).

[7] Crabtree, *Brit. J. Phot.* **86**, 3, 19, 39 (1939).

[8] Crabtree found that graininess increases with the time elapsing between exposure and development in hot humid climates. *Trans. Soc. Mot. Pict. Eng.* **29**, 77 (1927).

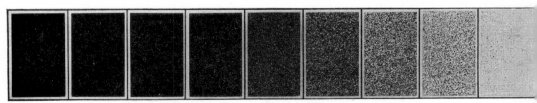

FIG. 20.4. Variation in apparent graininess with density. (*Kodak Research Laboratories.*)

areas with considerable variation in density, as trees, grass, shrubbery, etc.

The negative image likewise will appear most grainy at a density of about 0.3, but the negative density producing the maximum graininess in the print depends upon the exposure of the print, i.e., the density of the corresponding portion of the print. Thus if a series of densities is exposed so as to produce equal print densities, the negative density resulting in the maximum graininess may be considerably above 0.3. Thus although a dense negative may appear less grainy than one of lower density, the print from it will be more grainy if both prints are identical in darkness and contrast.

3. *The degree of development or gamma.* Graininess, other factors being constant, tends to increase with the negative gamma. In the motion picture industry, for example, common practice is to develop the negative to gammas of 0.5–0.7 and the print to a gamma of 2.0 or more. In general, prints with less graininess will be obtained if the negative is developed to a comparatively low gamma and a paper of higher contrast used.

4. *The composition of the developer.* The only true fine grain developing agent is paraphenylene diamine; however, a substantial improvement in graininess can be obtained with other developing agents if used at a relatively low pH and in the presence of a solvent of silver halide. Any improvement as respects graininess, however, is accompanied by a loss in effective emulsion speed and in contrast.

5. *The illumination on the negative in printing.* In general, the graininess of the print decreases with the diffusion of the illumination on the negative; however, the contrast of the image as a whole also becomes less and under certain conditions the difference in graininess may be negligible if both prints are developed to the same contrast.

6. *The degree of enlargement.* For a given viewing distance, graininess obviously increases with the degree of enlargement. Visibility of graininess at different viewing distances depends upon visual acuity and the relationship is substantially the same as that between the viewing distance and the circle of confusion.

7. *The reproduction gamma.* The greater the product of the negative and positive gammas, other conditions being identical, the greater the graininess of the positive. Thus, with a given negative, the use of a paper of higher contrast, or developing the positive to a higher gamma, will result in an increase in both graininess and contrast. Thus prints of subjects of low contrast, or made in poor light, may show more grain than those of brilliantly lighted subjects where the reproduction gamma is lower. Where the photographer has control over the lighting an improvement in graininess may be effected by lighting so the contrast of the print may be made lower than that of the original.

The Sharpness of the Image. If an object having a sharp edge, such as a razor blade, is placed in contact with the film and a brief exposure made, the line marking the boundary between the exposed and unexposed areas may appear sharp to the eye, but with slight magnification it will be seen that the granular structure of the image results in an irregular line (Fig. 20.5). With a longer exposure, the density increases and therefore the contrast between the exposed and unexposed portions, but the line separating the two now appears more diffused than granular. The diffusion is due to the scatter of light within the emulsion which causes some of the crystals of silver halide along the edge of the razor blade to be exposed by light reflected from, or diffracted by, other crys-

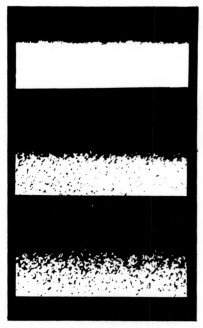

FIG. 20.5. Spreading of the image along the edge of a razor blade with fast and slow emulsions.

tals of silver halide which are within the exposed area. The greater the exposure, the more pronounced the spreading of the image. The diffusion, in most cases, is greater in rapid emulsions, which contain grains of many different sizes and varying degrees of sensitiveness, than in slow fine-grain emulsions where there is less variation in the size and sensitivity of the different grains. Thus emulsions of small grains, and little variation in grain size, tend to produce sharper images. The D log E curves of such emulsions tend to have a high gamma and a short toe or foot.

The penetration of the emulsion layer by light and the amount of scattering vary with the wave length. In general, the maximum sharpness occurs in the blue-violet, decreasing rapidly to a minimum in the blue-green and increasing again in the red, but there is considerable variation with different emulsions.

It would appear, therefore, that in most cases the highest sharpness with any particular emulsion is obtained when the developed image lies chiefly on the surface of the emulsion layer. So far as the sharpness of the image is concerned, it does not appear to matter whether the surface image is the result of low exposure, the use of a thin emulsion coating, the incorporation of a dye in the emulsion to prevent the penetration of light into the lower layers, or by development in developers which act chiefly on the surface of the emulsion layer.

Yellow dyed emulsions have been employed to secure maximum sharpness as in films designed for the duplication of motion picture negatives and in plates for spectroscopic work; however, it is necessary in such cases to use emulsions of high contrast as the incorporation of a yellow dye reduces the density and contrast by limiting the penetration of light.[9]

Halation. The halo which is sometimes observed in photographic images of bright objects, or sources of light, is known as *halation*. Halation is produced when light is reflected back into the emulsion from the rear of the support so as to form a secondary image.

The density of the halo, and to some extent its size, depend upon several factors:

1. *The amount of exposure.* The greater the exposure, or the greater the contrast between the bright object and its surroundings, the more pronounced the halo.

2. *The degree of development.* The greater the degree of development, the higher the density of the halo. Developers which act chiefly on the surface develop less of the halated image than those which develop the exposed grains next to the emulsion support.

[9] Motion Picture Laboratory Practice, Eastman Kodak Co., Rochester, N. Y., 1936.

3. *The turbidity and thickness of the emulsion.* The greater the turbidity and thickness of the emulsion coating, the less light it transmits and, therefore, the lower the density of the secondary image under given conditions. A thickly coated film or plate is much less subject to halation than a thinly coated one.

The methods employed to prevent halation may be conveniently grouped under three heads:

1. *Placing a light-absorbing layer, or backing, on the rear surface of the glass or film base.* This absorbs the light emerging from the emulsion layer and prevents its reflection from the rear surface of the film base or glass plate.

2. *Increasing the amount of light absorbed in the emulsion by double coating.* This has long been popular in the United States where the majority of cut films intended for professional use are double coated; first with a slow, blue-sensitive emulsion and then with the regular negative emulsion. The emulsion next to the support ordinarily plays no part in the formation of the image. It is designed to be as opaque as possible and its only function is to absorb light transmitted by the emulsion coated over it.

3. *Increasing the opacity of the film base.* For motion picture work, a soluble backing is not desirable and instead a grey material is incorporated in the film base. This absorbs most of the light passing through the emulsion and that reflected back toward the emulsion from the rear of the base. The increased density of the negative is compensated for by increased exposure when printing.

Resolving Power of Photographic Materials. Closely connected with the spreading of the image, although not wholly dependent upon it, is the resolving power of the emulsion. Resolving power refers to the ability of the emulsion to define sharply or "resolve" fine detail in the image, and may be quantitatively defined as the distance between two closely adjacent images, or lines, which can be rendered separately by the emulsion. It is more conveniently expressed as the reciprocal of this distance; in other words, the greater the number of lines an emulsion can reproduce clearly, i.e., the less the distance between the lines, the higher the resolving

KUSTER, "An Objective Method for the Determination of Halation," *Phot. Korr.* **71**, 65, 73 (1935); *Sci. et Ind. Phot.* (II), **6**, 363 (1935).

MAUGE, "Examination and Measurement of Halation," *Bull. soc. franç. Phot.* **14**, 12 (1927).

NEUGEBAUER, "Halation Tests," *Photofreund.* **9**, 452 (1930).

RHEDEN, "Halation and Its Prevention," *Phot. Rund.* **4**, 69 (1926).

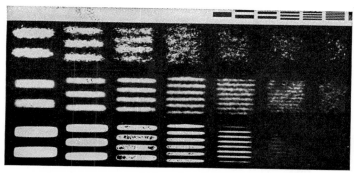

FIG. 20.6. Enlarged images of resolving power test object. (*Carl W. Miller.*)

power. Thus, if two lines are separated by a distance equal to the width of the lines, resolving power may be expressed numerically as the number of lines per millimeter.

The resolving power of an emulsion is usually determined by photographing, with a well corrected lens, a test object composed of parallel lines of different widths and examining the developed image in a microscope at a magnification of about 100 times.[10]

Factors affecting resolving power:

1. *The emulsion.* In the case of emulsions blended of fine grains for contrast and course grains for speed, the resolving power varies with the exposure and the highest resolving power for any speed is obtained with the closest approach to uniformity in grain size. The higher the maximum gamma, the greater usually is the resolving power.

So far as color sensitizing is concerned, the best sensitizer for increased resolving power is a green sensitizer whose actual color acts as a minus blue filter. Ideally, the effect of the dye would be to balance the increase in speed from the absorption in the blue and violet. Ordinarily yellow dyes improve resolution only by keeping the image on the surface and reducing image spread.

In general, resolving power increases with decreased graininess and becomes less as the thickness of the emulsion coating increases. If the emulsion coating is too thin, the grains are too scattered to form sharp image edges; if too thick, the image

spread is increased. The optimum value lies between these extremes and varies with the emulsion characteristics.

2. *The exposure.* The resolving power tends to decrease with exposure because of increased spreading of the image.

3. *The contrast of the image.* The resolving power with most emulsions, and given conditions of exposure and development, tends to increase with the contrast of the subject.

4. *The color of the light used for the exposure.* The resolving power varies with the wave length of the light in much the same way as does the sharpness of the image, showing that resolving power varies with the sharpness factor.

5. *The developer.* The work in this field is inconclusive. Early investigations indicated a variation with certain developing agents, but later work leads to the conclusion that any differences that exist are unimportant. Developing solutions which produce images of high density and contrast tend to produce higher resolving power than those forming D log E curves with long sweeping toe portions and lower gammas. Fine-grain developers do not result in higher resolving power, but on the contrary, may actually lower the resolving power, as compared with some other developers, because of the lower contrast and spreading of the image.[11]

With a given emulsion, exposure and developer, the resolving power increases with the time of development up to a certain point and then remains almost stationary until fog sets in.

Resolving Power of Typical Photographic Materials. Resolving power, like speed and many other characteristics of an emulsion, depends upon so many factors that no one value is significant except for cer-

[10] Mees, *Proc. Royal Society* **A83**, 10 (1909). Tugman, *Astrophysical J.* **42**, 331 (1915). Ross, *The Physics of the Developed Photographic Image*, D. Van Nostrand Co., Inc., New York, 1924.

Sandvick, *Proc. Seventh International Congress of Photography*, Heffer, Cambridge, 1929.

Sayce, ''The Measurement of Resolving Power.'' *Phot. J.* **80**, 456 (1940).

[11] Henn and Crabtree, *J. Phot. Soc. Amer.* **10**, 727 (1944).

tain conditions. The following values are for a test object with a brightness range of 1:30, a light source with a color temperature of 5400° K. and development in typical formulas to a value of gamma comparable with practical usage.

	Lines per Mm.
High-speed panchromatic film*	65
Fine-grain film (35 mm.)*	95
Positive motion picture film (fine grain)	120
Micro-file film	175

* Borax-type developers.

Chapter 21

NEGATIVE MATERIALS

Forms of Negative Material. *Sheet or Cut Film.* Sensitized film in cut sizes is termed *sheet film* or *cut film.* The thickness of the base is several times as great as that for roll or other film, to reduce curling and maintain flatness in the holder. American practice is to indicate the emulsion side and the type of film by notches in one side of the sheets. These are placed so as to be in the upper right hand *corner of the shorter side* when the emulsion side faces the observer.[1] The actual dimensions of sheet film are less than the nominal size, a condition due originally to the use of sheet film in plate holders, necessitating a film septum having the same dimensions as the glass plates for which the holder was designed; the film size being made smaller to fit within the septum. Sheet film marked 4×5 inches, for example, is $3\frac{60}{64} \times 4\frac{60}{64}$, the allowable limits being $\pm \frac{1}{64}$ inch.

Roll Film. The strip of film is attached at one end with an adhesive sticker to a long strip of opaque paper. Then when the film is wrapped around the spool, the end of the paper strip protruding beyond the film protects the emulsion from light so it may be placed in the camera in daylight. The strip of paper extending beyond the other end of the film strip operates in the same way to permit removal of the film from the camera in daylight.

Magazine Film. Perforated 35 mm. roll film is ordinarily supplied for use in miniature cameras enclosed in daylight loading metal magazines consisting of an inner spool and an outer shell. The film transport mechanism of the camera is threaded with the strip of film projecting from the magazine and the camera closed. With each successive exposure, the film is drawn through the narrow slit in the side of the cartridge and wound up on the take-up spool within the camera. When the last exposure has been made, the film transport mechanism is then reversed and the film wound back on the spool within the magazine which then may be removed from camera in daylight.

Film Pack. Twelve cut films each attached to an opaque, black, paper tab are placed in a metal or cardboard container. The ends of the paper tabs project from the top of the pack and by pulling out the tab the film is transferred from its position at the front of the pack to the rear section. In front of the pack is an opaque black paper "safety cover" which protects the films from light until the pack is placed in the camera, or in the lighttight adapter. This safety cover is transferred to the rear of the pack by pulling out the safety tab before the first exposure is made. When the last exposure is made, the pack is rendered lighttight by the center partition which

---

[1] The notching (1); sizes (2) of sheet film; the dimensions of roll film backing paper, etc. (3); 35 mm. film magazines (4); and film packs (5), of American manufacture are covered by ASA specifications as follows:

(1) Z38.1.42—1944
(2) Z38.1.28—1944
    Z38.1.29—1944
(3) Z38.1.7—1943 to Z38.1.24 (1943)
(4) Z38.1.47—1946
(5) Z38.1.1—1941
    Z38.1.2—1941

is now in front in the position occupied in the beginning by the safety cover.

Negative Materials Classified According to Spectral Sensitivity.

Negative materials for general photography may be divided according to spectral sensitivity into four divisions:

1. *Blue Sensitive.* The sensitivity range of emulsions of this type extends from the limit of absorption by gelatin in the ultraviolet to a wave length of approximately 500mµ.[2] In this class are included all emul-

sions not dye-sensitized such as developing papers, lantern slide and transparency materials, and some negative materials.

2. *Orthochromatic and Isochromatic.* The sensitivity of materials of this type extends to approximately 600µ. These materials are sensitive, therefore, to the yellow and green portions of the spectrum as well as the blue and violet. There is no longer any practical distinction in the terms orthochromatic and isochromatic;[3] both refer to emulsions sensitive to yellow and green but not to orange or red.

---

[2] At wave lengths shorter than 275 mµ it is necessary (1) to use emulsions made with only a trace of gelatin (Schumann plates) to avoid the absorption of gelatin, or (2) to coat a blue-sensitive emulsion with mineral oils which fluoresce in the ultraviolet producing radiation to which the ordinary gelatino-bromide emulsion can respond. Harrison, *J. Opt. Soc. Amer.* **11**, 113 (1925); *Pho-*

tographic Materials for Astronomy and Spectroscopy, Eastman Kodak Co., Rochester, N. Y.

[3] Orthochromatic from the Greek *orthos*—correct and *chroma*—color. Isochromatic, *iso*—equal and *chroma*—color, or equal color. It will be noted that both terms are incorrect as applied to sensitive materials.

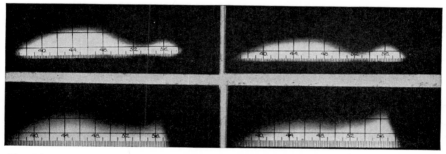

Fig. 21.1. Wedge spectrograms showing the distribution of sensitivity with wave length for orthochromatic materials, left to right in sunlight and tungsten illumination; top to bottom low-green sensitive (Type 1), high-green sensitive (Type 2).

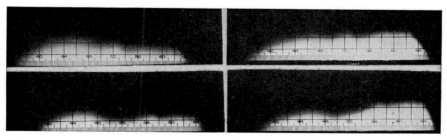

Fig. 21.2. Wedge spectrograms showing distribution of sensitivity with wave length for panchromatic materials. Left to right, in sunlight and tungsten illumination; top, Type B (orthopan); below, Type C (hyperpan).

Orthochromatic materials may be classified as (1) low green-sensitive, and (2) high green-sensitive in accordance with their sensitivity to green as compared to the blue and blue-violet region. Spectrograms of a typical example of each type are shown in Fig. 21.1.

3. *Panchromatic Materials.* Materials sensitive to the visible spectrum as a whole are termed panchromatic; from the Greek, *pan*—all and *chroma*—color, i.e., all color.

spectral sensitivity index of the American Standards Association. Z38.2.4–1946.

4. *Infrared Materials.* The range of spectral sensitivity of a typical material of this type is shown in Fig. 21.3. Normally, there is a band of sensitiveness in the violet and blue, little or no sensitivity in the yellow or green portions of the spectrum and a second band of sensitivity from a wave length of about 725 mμ to approximately 900 mμ in the infrared.[4]

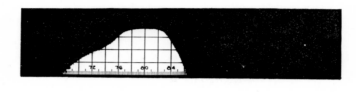

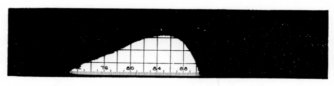

FIG. 21.3.   Wedge spectrogram showing distribution of sensitivity in the red and infrared of a typical high speed infrared material.

Commercial panchromatic plates and films show considerable differences in the distribution of sensitivity in different parts of the spectrum (Fig. 21.2) which has led to the adoption of various methods of classifications by the manufacturers, such as *orthopanchromatic* for high-green sensitive materials and *hyperpanchromatic* for high red-sensitive materials; none of these, however, is of general application and it would seem preferable in the future to adopt the

Other infrared materials sensitive to wave lengths as long as 1300 mμ are available for spectroscopy and other branches of applied photography.[5]

Sensitometric Characteristics of Typical Negative Materials. With suitable processing, the adaptability of modern emulsions is such that, except for highly specialized requirements, no more than five types need be considered. These are (1) high speed, (2) fine grain, (3) slow, (4) contrast or process, and (5) infrared.

High-speed materials may be subdivided into two subdivisions: (a) low contrast, and

American plates, like sheet film, are actually somewhat smaller than the listed or nominal size to facilitate their handling in holders. The actual size of a 5 × 7 plate, for example, is $4\frac{63}{64} \times 7\frac{31}{32}$. The thickness may vary from 0.058–0.063 inch. ASA Dimensions for Photographic Dry Plates, Z38.1–30–1944; Z38.1–31–1944.

4 Clark, *Infra-Red Photography*, John Wiley and Sons, Inc., New York.

5 *Photographic Plates and Films for Astronomy and Spectroscopy*, Eastman Kodak Co., Rochester, N. Y.

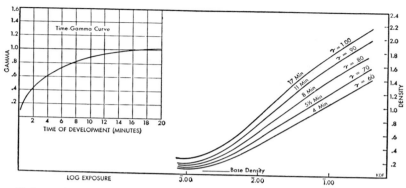

FIG. 21.4. *D* log *E* and time gamma curves of a typical high speed emulsion of low contrast.

(b) high contrast. *D* log *E* and time gamma curves for an emulsion typical of Type Ia are shown in Fig. 21.4. The maximum gamma readily obtainable with the recommended developers is usually about 1.0, and the time of development is comparatively long. These emulsions are intended primarily for portraiture and other work where high speed and low contrast are required. The sensitometric characteristics of an emulsion typical of Type Ib are shown in Fig. 21.5. The maximum useful gamma on materials of this type varies with the emulsion and the developer between 1.4 and 1.6, and the time of development in the recommended developers is generally less than for materials of Type Ia. Many of the films and plates in this class were designed originally for press photography but are now used by the commercial photographer, the illustrative photographer, and for portrait photography. In fact, emulsions of this type are now used so widely that, for many photographers, all others may be regarded as specialized materials.

Type II includes all fine-grain materials except those intended for process work which are included in Type IV. The fine-grain emulsions in this group have been developed principally for the miniature camera and for the commercial worker where a high degree of enlargement is re-

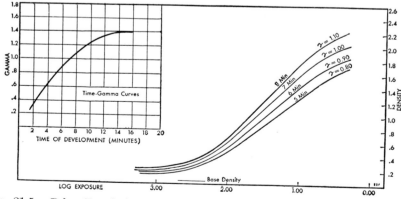

FIG. 21.5. *D* log *E* and time gamma curves of a typical high-speed emulsion of high contrast. Development under same conditions as in Fig. 21.6.

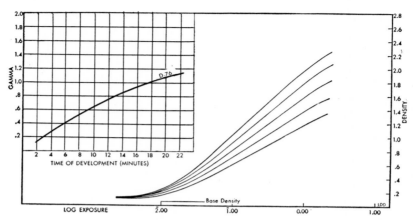

Fig. 21.6. *D* log *E* and time-gamma curves of a typical fine-grain emulsion.

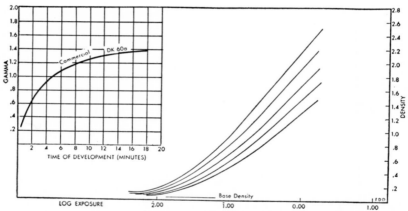

Fig. 21.7. *D* log *E* and time-gamma curves of a typical "commercial" emulsion.

quired—photomurals, etc. *D* log *E* and time gamma curves of an emulsion typical of this type are shown in Fig. 21.6. The ASA speeds of emulsions in this group range from 25 to 32. The lower speed is necessary, in the present stage of emulsion technique, to obtain the lowered graininess necessary for miniature camera use. The maximum useful gamma of fine grain emulsions varies from 1.2 to 1.6, and development is fairly rapid except where special fine-grain developers of low energy are used. The maximum useful gamma with some of these is somewhat lower than the values given.

Most of the films and plates included in Type III have been made substantially unchanged for many years. For a long time they had a finer grain, produced greater contrast, and were cleaner-working than high-speed materials. They were, therefore, definitely superior for copying and for commercial photography of machines, furniture, and still life where relatively high contrast is desirable. These materials, however, no longer have the advantage over high-speed emulsions they once enjoyed, and more and more their use is restricted to those purposes where their lower speed is a practical advantage. *D* log *E* and time-gamma curves of an emulsion typical of this type are shown in Fig. 21.7.

Type IV includes process and contrast emulsions. These materials are relatively slow, have a fine grain, high resolving power, and produce images of superior sharpness with high density and contrast.

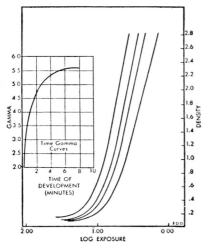

FIG. 21.8.   *D* log *E* and time-gamma curves of a typical process emulsion.

They are used in copying drawings, tracings, and printed matter in black and white. Orthochromatic and panchromatic materials are used with filters for colored copy. *D* log *E* and time-gamma curves of an emulsion typical of this class are shown in Fig. 21.8. The maximum useful gamma in the contrast developers recommended varies with the emulsion and developer from 4.5 to 6.0. The speeds of process materials are usually based upon the assumption that the meter reading will be made from white paper. Strictly speaking these emulsions have no ASA speed as this method of determining speed is not applicable to *D* log *E* curves of this character; it is usual, however, to recommend meter settings from ASA 3 to 12 for films and plates in this group when the meter reading is made from a white card and the exposure made by tungsten light.

Infrared emulsions (Type V) are used for special effects in landscape photography for photographing distant scenes to obtain detail in subjects obscured by atmospheric haze, to increase contrast on architectural subjects in hazy light or when illuminated chiefly by sky light, for photographing in darkness (blackout flash pictures), hot objects, etc., and in applied photography; e.g., documentary reproduction, criminology, medical photography, analysis of paintings, photomicrography, and spectroscopy. When exposed with the usual light sources, a deep yellow, orange or red filter is used to absorb blue and violet and restrict the response to the extreme red and infrared. Exposed without a filter, the result corresponds to that produced by blue sensitive material. In general, infrared materials are comparatively slow and have greater contrast, with less exposure latitude than other negative materials. Since sunlight varies in the ratio of infrared radiation to visible light, exposure meters are not a reliable guide to exposure. Ordinarily, exposures for open landscapes in bright sunlight vary from 1/25 to 1/5 second at f/8. Exposure meters may be used with tungsten light at settings from 5 to 8, depending on the emulsion and filter employed.

Safelights for Negative Materials. Any safelight, as its name indicates, represents a compromise between two conflicting requirements: (1) maximum illumination, and (2) maximum safety in the exposure of the film or plate to the safelight without producing fog. The efficiency of a safelight may be defined,[6] therefore, as the ratio of the visual intensity—in International candles—and the actinic intensity in terms of the time of exposure required to produce

6 Mees and Baker, *Phot. J.* **47,** 276 (1907). Chilton, *Phot. J.* **71,** 226 (1931).

objectional fogging on a particular plate or film.

Assuming a light source having a continuous spectrum, the spectral transmission of a safelight for any particular film or plate is determined by (1) the response of the eye with wave length at the level of illumination which is adopted as practical, and (2) the spectral sensitivity of the material at the same illumination level.

The maximum response of the eye with wave length shifts from the yellow-green toward the blue-green as the illumination is reduced (*Purkinje effect*), the amount of the shift depending on the intensity level of illumination and the time that the eye is given to adapt itself to the lower level of illumination. However, since, according to the Weber-Fechner law, the smallest difference in brightness recognizable by the eye is proportional to the absolute brightness of the field, a more accurate representation of the relative visual efficiencies of light from different parts of the spectrum

is obtained by plotting the logarithm of the brightness against wave length than by using the actual intensity values. Such a curve for a light source with an equivalent color temperature of 2500° K. at an illumination of 0.07 meter-candle is shown as *A* in Fig. 21.9.[7] Curve B is the spectral sensitivity curve of a typical blue-sensitive emulsion plotted on the same basis but not to the same intensity of illumination. Curve C is the transmission curve of the safelight provided by one manufacturer for use with negative materials of this type. Curves D and E are similar curves for orthochromatic and panchromatic materials respectively. In each case a 10-watt incandescent tungsten lamp has been used as the light source and the standard of safety is an exposure of 30 seconds at a distance of 3 feet from the safelight lamp. The transmission of the safelight for use with panchromatic material has been selected, it will

[7] Chilton, *Phot. J.* **71**, 228 (1931).

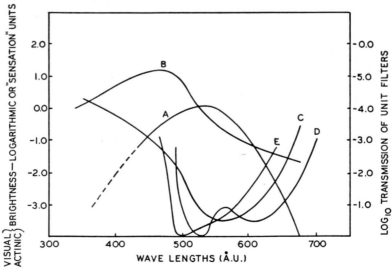

FIG. 21.9.   Curves showing the variation in the logarithm of the brightness of a light source with an intensity of 0.07 mc., the spectral sensitivity of a blue sensitive material and the transmission curve of a safelight provided for use with this material (C) and for orthochromatic (D) and panchromatic (E) materials.

be noted, to obtain the maximum illumination for a given intensity.

Storage of Sensitive Materials. The principal precautions to be observed in the storage of sensitive materials *before* exposure are:

1. *Protection from heat.* Films, plates, and papers should never be placed near radiators, steam lines, in attics where they will be exposed to the sun in summer, the glove compartment of a car, or wherever the temperature exceeds 70° F. Still lower temperatures are recommended for high-speed and color materials which must be kept from 6 to 12 months.

2. *Protection from moisture.* Negative materials should, if possible, be stored in air with a relative humidity not lower than 40% nor higher than 60% as measured with a hygrometer. Damp basements, rooms where the air is moist from the continual evaporation of water from sinks, escaping steam, water taps, etc., should be avoided. Storage in a refrigerator may lead to excessive dampness if the temperature is too low. To avoid this, the package should be enclosed in a tight jar, or a desiccating agent placed in the refrigerator to reduce the relative humidity to at least 60%.

3. *Protection from harmful vapors.* These include formaldehyde, motor exhaust, illuminating and many other industrial gases, hydrogen sulfide, lacquers, paints, and thinners, turpentine in any form and ammonia.

4. *Protection against fire.* Nearly all roll film, film pack, and sheet films are now coated on safety base which requires no special precautions in storage except that

large quantities should be kept in steel filing cabinets or metal lockers. With films on a nitrate base, the regulations of the National Board of Fire Underwriters for the storage and handling of photographic and x-ray nitrocellulose films should be observed. Films for amateur use in the original packages, however, are exempt from these regulations.

Exposed films and plates should not be wrapped in any other paper than that intended for this purpose. In the tropics, or where semitropic conditions prevail, film should be ordered in tropical packing and the packages opened directly before use. Film should not be left in holders, or cameras longer than absolutely necessary. If it is not possible to develop in a day or so, the film should first be dried out by placing it for 12–24 hours in an airtight container, such as a glass jar containing a desiccating agent—e.g., silica gel or dried rice—and sealed with adhesive tape. Silica gel is the more efficient of the two; if not in an airtight can, it must first be heated in an oven for 20–30 minutes at 300°–400° F. to discharge the water it has absorbed. If rice is used, it should be dried thoroughly over a low flame, or in an oven, until some of the grains turn brown, then sealed in an airtight container and allowed to cool before the film is placed in a moisture-proof container with it. After about 24 hours, the film may be transferred to a jar and sealed with several layers of adhesive tape. The rice may be used several times but must be dried each time before use.

If this procedure is impractical, the film package may be packed tightly in a box filled with crumpled photographic paper, which should be removed and dried daily in an oven or before a fire. Thus protected from moisture, the film will keep in good condition for several weeks.

Kreveld and van Lempt, "Measurements on Darkroom Illumination," *Physica*, **5**, 345 (1938).

Reeb, "The Concept of the 'Safety' of a Safelight," *Phot. Ind.* **35**, 278 (1937).

Chapter 22

PHOTOGRAPHIC EXPOSURE AND EXPOSURE METERS

Theory of Exposure. To obtain a satisfactory picture there are two salient steps to be taken: (1) the production of a negative, and (2) the production of a photographic print from the negative. The film, which becomes the negative after exposure and development, consists of a layer of silver halide on a transparent base such as celluloid or glass. The photographic paper, which becomes the print, after exposure and development consists of a similar layer of silver halide on a paper base. When these silver halide layers are acted upon by light the silver halide undergoes a photochemical action which after development results in black deposits of metallic silver. The extent of the black deposit is a function of exposure which is the product of light and time. Expressed mathematically:

$$E = It,$$

where E = exposure,

I = illumination expressed in either foot-candles or meter-candles, and

t = time in seconds that the illumination acts upon the photographic material.

If I is expressed in foot-candles, then E will be in foot-candle-seconds; however, it is quite common to express I in meter-candles and, therefore, E would be expressed in meter-candle-seconds. In Chapter 17 on Sensitometry, it was shown how the density of a photographic material varies with exposure, the graphical representation of these data resulting in the D log E curve of the material. An examination of this curve will show that equal increases in exposure do not always produce equal increases in density; in fact, it is only in the central portion of the curve or the so-called "straight-line portion" where this relationship is approximately true. For true brightness reproduction in the negative correct exposure would consist of working on the straight-line portion of the curve only, but in actual practice the portions of the "toe" and "shoulder" can be used without producing evident falsification of tonal values.

When a photographic material is exposed in a camera, the time factor is constant and the variation in exposure for different parts of the object or scene is proportional to the brightnesses of the corresponding parts of the subject, except for variations due to the absorption and scatter of light in the lens.

The Brightness of a Scene. The brightness of a scene depends upon two things: (1) the illumination falling upon the scene, and (2) the ability of the scene to reflect the light which falls upon it. Thus, each and every part of the scene becomes a secondary source of candlepower, or light, and it is this secondary source of light which the camera sees and, therefore, affects the film. If we assume brightness to be the criterion for photographic exposure, then the exposure time (t) in terms of the camera settings and speed of the photographic film can be represented by the following formula:

$$t = \frac{0.57f^2}{SBT},$$

where t = exposure time in seconds,

f = camera aperture setting,

S = film rating (Weston or ASA),

B = average scene brightness in candles per square foot, and

T = lens transmission.

If we assume incident light, or the light falling upon the scene, to be the criterion for photographic exposure, then the exposure time in terms of camera settings and speed of the photographic film can be represented by the following formula:

$$t = \frac{1.8f^2}{STIR},$$

where t = exposure time in seconds,

f = camera aperture setting,

S = film rating (Weston or ASA),

R = assumed reflection factor of an average scene,

I = foot-candles of illumination falling upon the scene, and

T = lens transmission.

If we assume the reflection factor to be 12.5% which is considered to be a good value, then:

$$t = \frac{14.4f^2}{SIT}.$$

Norwood, "Light Measurement for Exposure Control," *J. Soc. Mot. Pict. and Television Eng.* **54**, 585 (May 1950).

Jones and Condit, "The Brightness Scale of Exterior Scenes and the Computation of Correct Photographic Exposure," *J. Opt. Soc. Amer.* **31**, 651 (November 1941).

Jones and Condit, "Sunlight and Skylight as Determinants of Photographic Exposure," *J Opt. Soc. Amer.* **38**, 123 (February, 1948); Part II, **39**, 94 (February 1949).

The Intensity of Light on the Subject.
From the above discussion it is evident that the exposure is dependent upon the intensity of light on the subject whether we use reflected light or incident light as the criterion of photographic exposure. The intensity of sunlight is determined by the time of day, time of year, and by the presence of clouds or other atmospheric disturbances.

While with long experience the eye may acquire the ability to distinguish differences in illumination under conditions with which it is familiar, in general the eye is a poor judge of the intensity of illumination, unless aided, nor is it able to evaluate the variations in color which affect exposure. Hence, such classifications as intense light, bright light, light clouds, dull, etc., while helpful, are only approximations.

However, since the subject is not always fully exposed to the direct light of the sun or the sky, its location may have an important bearing on the illumination which it receives. In a narrow street, for example, the illumination is greatly reduced by the buildings on either side which permit light from only a small strip of the sky to reach the subject. Likewise, in heavily wooded areas or in shaded places, under porches and the like, the illumination is greatly reduced. It is extremely difficult to estimate the illumination visually under such conditions; and, while it is possible to make some allowance for the subject by classifying the more common subjects into groups, more errors in exposure probably result from the difficulties arising from this source than any other. Many exposure tables and guides have been published to assist the photographer in determining the correct exposure for a given type of scene under various light conditions, and, in addition, many types of exposure meters to measure incident light have been developed.

The Amount of Light Reflected from a Subject. The amount of light reflected from a subject differs greatly depending upon the ability of the components in the scene to reflect light. A subject containing only water and sky, for example, reflects a larger proportion of the light falling on it than does a distant landscape, and this in turn more than a landscape in which there are figures, trees, shubbery, buildings or other dark colored objects near the camera. In general, the nearer the subject is to the camera, the larger the shadow areas and less the amount of reflected light.

In evaluating the amount of light reflected, or the brightness, the quality of the light, or its color, must be considered with particular reference to the color sensitivity characteristics of the photographic material. The more nearly the color response of the film or plate approaches that of the eye, the less the difficulty experienced in evaluating the allowance to be made for the color, or colors, of the subject.

Light reflected from surfaces varies from 4% for a dead black surface to about 80% for a very white surface; hence, with perfectly flat illumination on a single plane subject, the brightness range could vary 20 to 1. However, it is very seldom that pictures are taken of a plane surface with flat lighting, and in many scenes the illumination on dark objects may be so high that the brightness of the dark objects may approach or even surpass the brightness of lighter objects which are inadequately lighted. It is because the various components of a scene do vary in reflection factors that the proponents of reflected light measurements prefer to measure brightness and use same as the criterion of photographic exposure.

Exposure Corrections when Using Lenses of Various Transmission Values. The amount of light which reaches the film is a function of the light transmission of the lenses. The more lenses used the less will be the light transmission and it is, therefore, obvious that low-priced cameras having a simple lens may transmit more light than a highly corrected lens for the same f/stop setting.

The National Bureau of Standards has recently recommended that the present f/stop system be replaced by one which considers the transmission of lenses in the calibration of the f/stop scale. If this is done, and indications are that it will; then the f/stops on a camera will be a correct indication of the light transmission of the lens and aperture setting. Most of the light is lost by surface reflection and very little in the glass itself; hence, the transmission of a lens system is largely governed by the number of glass-air or free surfaces.

Number of Free Surfaces	Approximate Transmission		f/ Stop Correction	
	Uncoated Lenses	Coated Lenses	Uncoated Lenses	Coated Lenses
2	92	97	$+\frac{1}{4}$	$+\frac{1}{3}$
4	84	94	0	$+\frac{1}{3}$
6	77	91	0	$+\frac{1}{3}$
8	70	88	0	$+\frac{1}{6}$
10	65	86	$-\frac{1}{6}$	$+\frac{1}{6}$
12	60	84	$-\frac{1}{3}$	$+\frac{1}{6}$

The above table of f/ stop corrections is based upon a lens transmission of 75% being correct and, therefore, needing no correction. For other transmissions the errors are practically negligible but if it is desired to correct the exposure the table can be used. + indicates that the f/ number should be increased and − indicates that the f/ number should be decreased. For example, if you are using a lens system having 2 free surfaces and a transmission of 92% the correction is $+\frac{1}{4}$ f/ stop. If the f/ stop for a 75% transmission lens is f/8, then the f/ stop should be set $\frac{1}{4}$ the distance between f/8 and f/11.

Exposure Meters. The problem of determining correct exposures has resulted in the development of various types of meters which may be classified in three different types: (1) those which measure the illumination on the subject by means of the darkening of a sensitized paper, (2) those in which the light reflected from the subject is observed visually through an optical wedge and the exposure is based upon the light received from the darkest shadow area, and (3) photoelectric exposure meters.

Actinometers. Among exposure meters of this type, the best known, in English-speaking countries at any rate, are the Watkins and the Wynne. Both of these utilized the darkening of sensitive paper to a standard tint which, however, differs in the two meters. The meter is held to face the light illuminating the darkest part of the subject and the time for darkening of the paper to the standard tint is determined. This time, the actinometer time as it is called, is an indication of the intensity of the light and from it the exposure required with a given lens aperture and plate or film is calculated with the aid of the movable scales which form a part of the instrument. In the case of the Watkins meter, the first visible darkening of the sensitive paper requires 1/16 of the time necessary for the standard tint; hence, indoors, or where the light is poor, the time required for making a test of the light may be reduced by using the sixteenth time as it is called.

The weak point of the actinometer is that it can measure only the light falling on the subject and not that reflected from it. However, if the proper allowance is made for different subjects, the exposure indications of an actinometer produce a high percentage of satisfactory results.

Visual Exposure Meters. Instruments of this type may be divided into two classes: (1) those in which the subject is viewed through an optical wedge, which for convenience is usually circular, and

this is revolved past the eye until details in the shadows disappear or are barely visible. The proper exposure is then determined from the scales of the instrument at this setting. Typical meters of this last class, all of which are now obsolete, are the Heyde, the Ica Diaphot, and the McMurtry. (2) Meters in which the light reflected from the subject illuminates an artificial test object, usually a transparent figure, the visibility of which may be reduced in a measurable manner by means of an optical wedge or an adjustable diaphragm. In some examples a number of figures varying in visibility are seen when the meter is pointed at the subject and the number just barely discernible is taken as a measure of the light reflected from the subject. The advantage of meters of this type over those described in class one is in the certainty with which the extinction point can be determined. On the other hand with meters of this class when used at the camera, it is the average brightness of the subject which is measured and not that of a particular part of the subject as with meters of class one. The total brightness of the subject may or may not be a satisfactory indication of the proper exposure. If, for example, a large portion of the subject is brightly illuminated and the shadow area is small, an exposure based upon the total amount of light reflected by the subject may result in underexposure of the shadow areas. All meters which measure the total amount of light are open to this objection which, however, may be overcome to some extent if the shadow area can be approached so as to exclude the remainder of the subject in making the measurement.

In all visual type meters it is the visual brightness of the subject which is measured and not the actinic brightness, which may be quite different. The eye and photographic materials differ considerably in their response to different colors; therefore, the visual brightness may not be an accurate indication of the exposure required in the case of an object involving color. In some meters, this difficulty is partially overcome by the insertion of a blue-violet screen in the field of vision. Visual measurements of brightness then correspond more nearly with the actinic brightness, but this expedient naturally fails to take into consideration the differences in photographic materials with respect to color sensitivity.

The accuracy of meters in which brightness is measured by the extinction of detail in the subject or an artificial test object is affected by the ability of the eye to adjust itself to variations in the intensity of illumination over a fairly wide range. Thus on coming into a darkened room the eye soon adjusts itself to the weaker illumination and we shortly begin to see details that were totally invisible when we entered the room. Consequently, the exposures indicated by the meter will not accurately represent the real difference in the intensity of the illumination on the two subjects. The result is that another correction factor has to be applied to the meter readings for interior work.

In the exposure photometer shown in Fig. 22.1 it is possible to measure the amount of light reflected from the different parts of the subject so that the exposure may be determined directly for any particular part of the subject.[1] The instrument consists of a small telescope in which the image is seen. A small comparison spot is formed in the center of the field by the mirror, 3, which is illuminated by a flashlight-type lamp, 9, operated from a dry battery, 10. The brightness of the comparison spot can be varied by rotation of

¹ Made by Salford Electrical Instruments Ltd. (Division of the General Electric Co. Ltd.), Salford, England. Dunn and Plant, *Phot. J.* **85B**, 114 (1945). Adams, *U. S. Camera* **12**, 56 (May 1949). Dunn, *Brit. J. Phot.* **95**, 23 (1948).

the optical wedges, 7. A color filter, 5, aids in matching by eliminating color differences. The light source is standardized, before making measurements, by means of a photoelectric cell, 9, which, through the

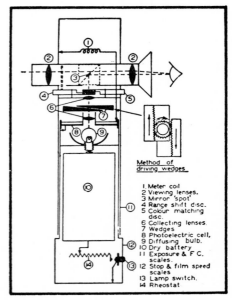

FIG. 22.1. Schematic diagram of the SEI exposure meter.

rheostat, 14, enables the intensity of the illumination on the comparison spot to be brought to a definite reading on the microammeter. Scales on the outside of the meter, not shown in the illustration, enable the exposure to be calculated from the equivalent foot-candle brightness reading.

The range of the instrument is from 1/100th to 10,000 equivalent foot-candles, and it is possible to measure the brightness of areas of approximately 0.5 degree or an area of slightly less than one foot at a distance of 100 feet.

Photoelectric Exposure Meters. In recent years, exposure meters employing photoelectric cells and sensitive microam-

DUNN AND PLANT, "The Exposure Photometer and Modern Exposure Techniques," *Phot. J.* **88A**, 230 (1948).

meters calibrated in one of the exposure factors have come into extensive use. The use of an exposure meter, in common with all tools, is largely dependent upon the skill of the user. Certain variables are definitely eliminated such as latitude, time, type of day, type of scene, etc. Also, the meter is objective; that is, it is direct reading and does not depend upon the physical ability of the eye to match brightness or to select a threshold value of brightness.

Photoelectric exposure meters may be broadly classified into two distinct types: (1) those calibrated to measure incident light and (2) those calibrated to measure reflected light. A few meters are designed to measure both incident and reflected light.

STIMSON, "The New American Standard No. Z38.2.6 for Photographic Exposure Meters," *P.S.A. Journal* **15**, 482 (August 1949).

WILLIAMS, "Characteristics of Photoelectric Exposure Meters," *Photo-Technique* **1**, 37 (June 1939).

KEINATH, "Photoelectric Exposure Meters," *Photo-Technique* **3**, 56 (January 1941).

Incident Light Exposure Meters. As the name implies, these meters measure the light falling upon the subject and utilize this value as the criterion for exposure. Some manufacturers of incident light meters recommend directing the meter at the camera from the subject position in order to measure the subject illumination while other manufacturers recommend directing the meter at the light source if a single source is used or at the mean position if two or more sources are used. To eliminate, or minimize, the problem of obtaining a mean value of illumination when more than one light source is used, one manufacturer now supplies an integrating hemisphere over the photoelectric cell so as to integrate the illumination from all angles. This integrating hemisphere has the advantage that the meter can be directed at the camera from the subject position, and the resulting meter reading is affected by the light received from all angles.

One disadvantage of the incident light meters is that the readings must be made

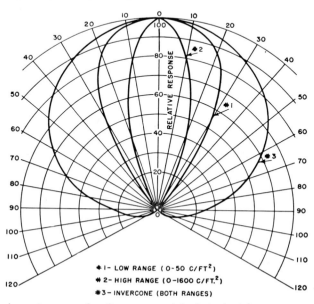

FIG. 22.2.   Acceptance angle of a commercial photoelectric exposure meter when used for reflected light and for incident light reading.

in the scene area, or the equivalent, and this is often impossible. Examples of this are pictures from a grandstand having a roof over it or a picture of a waterfall in sunlight with the camera in heavy shade and it is impossible to go out into the sunlight and measure the light falling on the subject.

Reflected Light Exposure Meters. As the name implies, these meters measure the light reflected from the subject and utilize this value as the criterion for exposure. Well-designed reflected light meters are equipped with either a mechanical or optical means of shutting off oblique light so that the acceptance angle approximates the view angle of the average camera.

An average brightness value often serves well as the criterion of exposure provided the meter is shielded from sunlight or excessive direct skylight, but in many cases the average brightness value will be either so high that the resulting exposure will cause loss of shadow details or the average brightness value will be so low that the resulting exposure will cause loss of highlight details. In fact, one of the real advantages of the reflection type of meters is that the brightness values of the shadow areas and of the highlight areas can be measured by taking the meter right up to these areas and taking close-up brightness measurements. By means of these two readings the scene brightness range is definitely ascertained, and it can be determined immediately whether the scene will reproduce well on the film being used. If the brightness range of the scene is too great for the film the exposure can be arranged to produce the shadow details and sacrifice the highlight details, or, the shadow details can be sacrificed to obtain the highlight details or, if both are desired and auxiliary lighting control is possible, then fill-in lights can be used to reduce the brightness range

so as to allow the film to reproduce the entire scene.

Incident Versus Reflected Light Exposure Meters. Some photoelectric meters are designed to measure incident light and others to measure reflected light. The question naturally arises as to which system is the better as a criterion of exposure. The fact is that good photographers use both kinds, photographic dealers sell both kinds and, therefore, irrespective of any technical arguments, it is obvious that neither system is all wrong. An exposure meter is a basic photographic tool and the answers derived from its use depend considerably upon the intelligence with which it is used. It should be self-evident that the meter should be well made so that its calibration is constant; it should have calibrated dials properly coordinated to handle all of the film speeds, aperture numbers and exposure times on films and cameras and the calibration steps on the meter scale and calculator should be small enough to indicate exposures to $\frac{1}{2}$ stop, especially if color work is anticipated.

Incident light meters are designed to have the receiving surface of the photoelectric cell exposed as much as possible so that both normal incident light and oblique light can reach its surface. The object is to measure the light, which reaches the object or scene, from all angles. Certain exposure meters, such as the General Electric and Smethurst, utilize a flat surface glass over the photoelectric cell. Light from oblique angles is highly reflected by this flat surface and, hence, the meters are not very responsive to oblique light and, therefore, give more weight to normal incident light. The Norwood meter is an incident light meter which has a hemispherical translucent dome over the photoelectric cell. By means of this hemisphere the meter gives almost equal response to light from all angles within a solid angle of 180° because the light strikes the translucent hemisphere at normal incidence, irrespective of the position of the meter to the light source or sources.

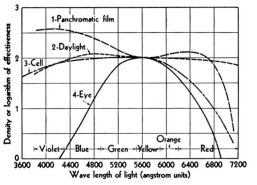

FIG. 22.3. Spectral response of the cell of a commercial exposure meter compared with that of a typical panchromatic material and the eye.

The technique of using incident light meters varies considerably as can be seen from the following typical cases.

The General Electric Company recommends that their meter, when used as an incident light meter, should be held at the object or scene position and pointed toward the camera.

The Avo Exposure Meter, which is manufactured in England, is an incident light meter having an opal diffusing glass over the photoelectric cell. This meter is apparently built according to the teachings of Smethurst, as disclosed in his patents, and when used it should be directed to the light source from the object or scene position.

The Norwood meter should be pointed directly at the camera from the subject position irrespective of how many light sources are used or where they are placed.

All incident light meters are calibrated on the basis of an average reflection factor for all objects or scenes. Some incident light meters are calibrated for a reflection factor of 10%, whereas others are calibrated for a reflection factor as high as 30%; but the average incident light meter is calibrated for a reflection factor between 10 and 20% as this is the reflection coefficient of a middle tone gray. A gray surface having a reflection coefficient of 12% has a reflection density of 0.9 which is visually midway between the white and black surface of a photographic paper.

Use of Gray Card for Exposure Determination. Many photographers use a gray card as a substitute for the object or scene when using a reflected light type of exposure meter. This is done by merely holding the gray card in the same plane as the object or scene so that it is illuminated the same as the scene and the light reflected from the card is measured by means of the meter. This should place the parts of object or scene having the same reflection density as the gray card in the center of the negative density range of the resulting negative. In many cases the gray card is convenient on scenes having a low brightness range. On scenes having a high brightness range it is often necessary to favor the shadow or highlight areas which requires that the exposure indicated by the meter must be increased to favor shadow areas or decreased to favor highlight areas.

Calculation of Exposure with Photoflash Lamps. To expose a photographic emulsion correctly by means of a synchronized Photoflash lamp source the following variables must be known and properly related:

1. Sensitivity of the film to the light emitted by the flash lamp.

2. Total quantity of light emitted by the lamp.

3. Efficiency of the lamp reflector.

4. Average reflection factor of the subject.

5. Percentage of total reflected light from the subject which is passed by the shutter.

6. f/number employed.

7. Lamp-to-subject distance.

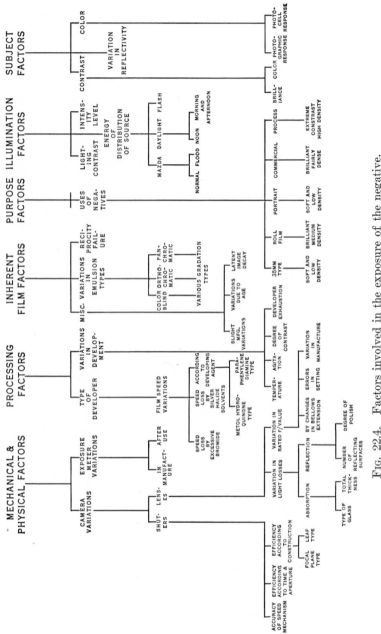

Fig. 22.4.   Factors involved in the exposure of the negative.
(Fowler and Varden, *American Annual of Photography*, 1940.)

It will be recalled that the quantity of light reaching the film varies inversely as the square of both the f/number and lamp-to-subject distance. This may be stated as follows:

$$E = k \left(\frac{1}{(f/\text{No.})^2} \cdot \frac{1}{d^2} \right), \qquad (1)$$

where E = exposure received by the film,

k = a constant whose value depends upon the sensitivity of the film the light output of the lamp, the average reflectivity of the subject, the shutter speed, and the efficiency of the reflector, and

d = lamp-to-subject distance.

From Equation 1, it will be seen that the product of the $(f/\text{No.})^2$ and (lamp-to-subject distance)^2 must be held constant if the exposure received by the film is to remain fixed, or

$$(f/\text{No.})^2 \cdot d^2 = K. \qquad (2)$$

By extracting the square root of both sides of the above equation, we may write,

$$f/\text{No.} \cdot d = \sqrt{K} = G. \qquad (3)$$

The constant G is often referred to as a Guide Exposure Number.

Both film and lamp manufacturers publish Guide Exposure Numbers which are determined experimentally by taking pictures under carefully controlled conditions at all shutter speeds and with each lamp and film combination. From the proper Guide Exposure Number, the correct f/number to use at any lamp-to-subject distance may be found by substituting in Equation 3.

Exposure Meters for Electronic Flash Photography. In flash photography the duration of the flash, and consequently the exposure time, is too short to allow the use of conventional exposure meters. The General Radio Company of Cambridge, Mass., has recently designed a light meter which is capable of indicating the product of foot candles and seconds which, of course, is exposure. Basically, the light meter consists of a vacuum phototube, a capacitor and a vacuum tube type of voltmeter. The phototube circuit is so arranged that the current flow is proportional to the illumination (foot candles) and this current is used to charge the capacitor. The voltage across the capacitor is proportional to the integral of current and time and since the current is proportional to the illumination the capacitor voltage is proportional to the integral of light and time. The voltmeter which measures the capacitor voltage can therefore be calibrated directly in foot candle-seconds.

In actual use a white card is first placed in the subject position and focused on the ground glass. The phototube assembly, or probe, is placed on the ground glass directly over the image of the white card. Rubber suction cups hold the probe in place to facilitate reading of the light meter. Although the light meter indicates exposure in terms of light and time, the user must make a few test exposures in order to calibrate the meter and camera.

NOEL AND DAVIS, "Exposure Meter for Electronic Flash Lamps," *P.S.A. Journal* **16**, Part II, 11 (January 1950).

Chapter 23

NEGATIVE PROCESSING

General Purpose Developers. In portrait, commercial, illustrative, and press photography, and in general where contact printing is employed, or the degree of enlargement is small, a developer is desired which will develop quickly to gammas of 0.8 to 1.1, produce density readily and clear, fog-free images of moderate grain size. Since in commercial practice tank development is common and the developer is used continuously, the keeping properties of the solution, the staining tendencies, and the rate of exhaustion are important factors.

While each of the developing agents has certain specific advantages and disadvantages, the trend over the last decade has been very definitely toward a combination of metol and hydroquinone to such an extent, in fact, that many developing agents, such as pyro, which were in general use a few years ago, are now almost obsolete. There has been definite trend likewise from the alkaline carbonates to the borates and metol-hydroquinone-borax, or borate formulas, which are now widely employed as general purpose developers for portrait, press and commercial work.

Fine-Grain Developers. With but few exceptions, the fine-grain developers in general use may be divided into four classes: (1) those in which an excess of sodium sulfite is used as a solvent of silver halide, (2) those employing an alkaline thiocyanate or other solvent of silver halide, (3) paraphenylene diamine developers, and (4) those containing paraphenylene diamine in combination with other developing agents, such as glycin or metol.

Metol-hydroquinone developers with an excess of sodium sulfite and with borax, or a metaborate, as an alkali have enjoyed wide popularity since 1926 when the Kodak D–76 formula was published by Capstaff and Seymour.[1]

Developers of this type produce clean, fog-free negatives of good density and contrast and with less graininess than more energetic developers of the general purpose type. The reduction in graininess is due probably to (1) an actual reduction in the size of the developed silver grain due to the solvent action of the sulfite on the silver halide during development, and (2) a more uniform distribution of the grains of silver in the developed image as a result of development becoming partly physical in character in the presence of a solvent of the silver halide.

In general, any modification of the developer which results in increased solvent action by the sodium sulfite tends to produce images of finer grain. Little can be accomplished by increasing the amount of sulfite; however, the addition of a buffer in the form of boric acid,[2] a reduction in the developing agents or the addition of potassium bromide, is effective. The slight improvement in graininess, however, involves a longer time of development, a loss

---

[1] *Trans. Soc. Mot. Pict. Eng.* **10**, 223 (1926).

[2] Crabtree and Carlton, *Trans. Soc. Mot. Pict. Eng.* 406 (1929). Abrams, *Camera* (Phila.) **49**, 233 (1934). Bowler and Varden, *Brit. J. Phot.* **83**, 523 (1936).

l effective emulsion speed, and usually some sacrifice in density and contrast.

Metol in the presence of a high concentration of sodium sulfite forms an active developer without the addition of an alkali.[3] f the activity of such a developer is reduced by the addition of an acid or an acid sulfite, such as sodium bisulfite, as a buffer n excellent fine-grain developer is obained.[4]

Other silver halide solvents which have een recommended as additions to the developer to obtain finer grain include ammonium chloride,[5] hypo,[6] an alkaline thiocyanate[7] and thiourea,[8] ethylamine, diethylamine, and ethanolamine.[9]

Developers of paraphenylene diamine or orthophenylene[10] diamine alone are not widely used despite the exceptionally fine grain of the image because of several disadvantages: (1) the loss in effective emulsion speed requiring increased exposure, 2) the time required for development, (3) he dichroic image, (4) the low density and contrast, (5) the staining of fingers, trays,

and other utensils, and (6) the highly toxic nature of the developing solution.

Developers of greater activity, with shorter times of development and higher effective emulsion speeds, may be obtained by the addition of an alkali, but the graininess increases. Of greater practical utility are the so-called "compromise" formulas in which paraphenylene diamine is combined with metol, glycin, or other developers.[11] Developers of this type are not the equal of paraphenylene diamine alone as respects graininess, but possess greater activity which reduces both the developing time and the loss in effective emulsion speed. While a number of very practical formulas have been published, many of the claims made for particular formulas have been grossly overstated and it is probable that, in most cases, equal or better results can be obtained with elon-sulfite-bisulfite developers, particularly if considerations other than graininess, such as loss in effective emulsion speed, toxicity, staining, ease of preparation, fog level, reliability, density, and contrast, etc., are considered.[12]

Developers For Use at High Temperatures.

In general, no special precautions are necessary at temperatures below 75° F. except to avoid highly alkaline developers or those requiring long developing times. Some few developers may show an undesirable amount of fog which can be reduced by the addition of potassium bromide or an antifogging agent such as 6-nitrobenzimidazole. Elon-sulfite and elon-sulfite-bisulfite formulas are well adapted for use at temperatures up to 77° F.

---

[3] Twining, *J. Soc. Mot. Pict. Eng.* **42**, 315 1944). Veldman, *Atelier* **35**, 30 (1928). Von Ehrardt, *Amer. Phot.* **28**, 466 (1934). Wiegleb, *Schweiz. Phot-Ztg.* **37**, 93 (1935).

[4] Henn and Crabtree, *J. Phot. Soc. Amer.* **10**, 27 (1944).

[5] Lumiere and Seyewetz, *Brit. J. Phot.* **51**, 630, 66 (1904). Lazenby, *Brit. J. Phot.* **81**, 663 1934).

[6] Tattersall, *Brit. J. Phot.* **91**, 434 (1944).

[7] Mees, *Brit. J. Almanac*, 1912, p. 515. Doran, J.S.P. 2,136,968. Henn and Crabtree, *J. Phot. Soc. Amer.* **4**, 1 (1938). Mayer, *Camera* (Luern) **21**, 303 (1943).

[8] U.S.P. 2,147,441.

[9] Dearing and Guell, B.P. 561,203 (1942).

[10] While paraphenylene is generally used, orthophenylene was recommended by Seyewetz as having greater stability and less tendency to stain. *Brit. J. Phot.* **83**, 487 (1936).

Wood patented (U.S.P. 2,197,017—1940) the addition of morpholine sulfite and triethanolamine sulfite to paraphenylene developers to prevent fog and increase the activity of the developer.

[11] Sease, *Camera* (Phila.) **47**, 1 (1933). Lowe, *Zeiss Magazine* **2**, 75 (1936). *Camera Craft* **43**, 558 (1936). Champlin, *Champlin on Fine-Grain*, Camera Craft Pub. Co., San Francisco, 1937. Harris, *Miniature Camera Magazine* **2**, 236 (1938).

[12] Seyewetz investigated the bleaching of developed negatives followed by redevelopment in paraphenylene diamine. *Brit. J. Phot.* **86**, 186 (1939).

With most negative materials processing at temperatures above 75° F. involves either hardening prior to development or special precautions in development to prevent (1) undue swelling of the gelatin with its attendant difficulties such as frilling, separation of the emulsion from the base, reticulation, etc., (2) excessive fog, and (3) stain resulting from the rapid oxidation of the developing agent. Most well-balanced developers may be used satisfactorily at temperatures as high as 95° F. with only a slight change in fog, graininess and emulsion speed if the material is first hardened in a prehardening bath of alkaline formaline, as for example: [13]

Solution 1

| Formaldehyde (37% Sol.) | 5 | cc. | 1½ drams |

Solution 2

Water	900	cc.	28 oz.
0.5% 6-nitrobenzimida-zole nitrate	40	cc.	1¼ oz.
Sodium sulfate (des.)	50	gm.	1 oz. 290 gr.
Sodium carbonate	10	gm.	145 gr.
Water to	1.0 liter		32 oz.

This formula contains formaline which is the hardening agent, sodium sulfate to retard swelling during hardening, and an antifogging agent—6-nitrobenzimidazole—to prevent fog from the use of formaline, and sodium carbonate to render the solution alkaline, since formaline hardens gelatin only in an alkaline solution.

Prepare directly before use:

| Solution 1 | 5 cc. | 1¼ drams |
| Solution 2 | 1.0 liter | 32 oz. |

Immerse the exposed material in the prehardening solution for ten minutes with intermittent agitation. Upon removal, drain briefly and wash for about thirty seconds before developing. The time o development as compared with that at 68 F. *without prehardening* is approximate as follows:

> 75° F.—same
> 80° F.—85% of normal time
> 85° F.—70% of normal time
> 90° F.—60% of normal time
> 95° F.—50% of normal time

Generally, however, a more practical pr cedure, where the temperature does no exceed 90° F., is to retard swelling of th gelatin during development through th addition of from 50 to 150 grams potassiu or sodium sulfate per liter of developer an harden in a chrome alum stop bath im mediately following development.[14] Unde these conditions most formulas may be use except that developers requiring more tha five to ten minutes to develop should b avoided because of the increased swellin of the gelatin on prolonged development Formulas employing a metaborate are pre ferable to those with sodium carbonate a blisters are less likely to form if the gelati should become swollen.

Regardless of the method employed i processing photographic materials at a hig temperature, it is important that the tem perature of the various solutions be kep as nearly alike as possible. Transferrin the film from a cold solution to a warme one, or vice versa, subjects the gelatin laye to strain that is likely to result in reticula tion. Recent experiments have shown tha the graininess of films processed in warn solutions is a mild form of reticulation al though not immediately recognizable a such. The effect of a sudden change in tem perature is at a maximum with swolle

---

[13] Kodak Formula SH-5. Crabtree and Russell, *J. Phot. Soc. Amer.* **10**, 397, 453 (1944).

The use of formaline and salts which have the property of retarding swelling of gelatin as a hardener was patented by Ilford Ltd., B.P. 128,337 (1919).

---

[14] The use of sodium sulfate to retard swellin of the gelatin was recommended by: Bunel, *Brit J. Phot.* **57**, 399 (1910); Lumiere and Seyewetz *Brit. J. Phot.* **58**, 137 (1911); Eastman Kodak Co *Brit. J. Phot.* **71**, 762 (1924).

gelatin, hence the desirability of preventing swelling at all stages of processing and hardening the film permanently as soon as possible.

Developers for Use at Low Temperature. The principal difficulty in developing at temperatures below normal, but above the freezing point, is the time required for development. Thus, for processing at low temperatures, highly concentrated developers are necessary if lengthy times of development are to be avoided. There is also a loss in effective emulsion speed and, while this cannot be avoided completely, it may be minimized by the use of high-energy caustic developers.

The following formula [15] is recommended for use at temperatures between 30° and 50° F.

	Metric	Avoirdupois
Hydroquinone.......	45.0 grams	1½ oz.
Sodium sulfite.......	90.0 grams	3 oz.
Sodium hydroxide....	37.5 grams	1¼ oz.
Potassium bromide...	30.0 grams	1 oz.
Benzotriazole........		
Water to............	1,000.0 cc.	1 gal.

For use down to 30° F.: Stock Solution 2 parts, water 1 part.

For use down to + 5° F.: Stock Solution 2 parts, water 1 part, ethylene glycol 1 part.

At low temperatures, the glycol should be added previous to storage.

The time of development varies, with the emulsion and the gamma required, from three to five minutes at 50° F. to fifteen to twenty minutes at 30° F.

To process at still lower temperatures, it is necessary to add an organic solvent, such as alcohol, glycerin, or ethylene glycol to prevent freezing. Of these glycol is the most suitable. Between 5° and 30° F. the

formula given above may be used with the addition of 25% ethylene glycol. The time of development will be from thirty-five to forty-five minutes at 30° and 3 to 3.5 hours at 5° F., depending on the emulsion and the gamma required.

Fixing at Low Temperatures. At temperatures below 50° F. a plain fixing bath may be used as hardening is unnecessary and the time of washing is less with materials fixed in hypo alone than in the usual acid fixing and hardening bath. Below 30° F. the addition of ethylene glycol in amounts varying from equal parts to 5 times the volume of fixing bath is advisable. The dilution caused by the addition of ethylene glycol is not an objection; in fact, at low temperatures the less concentrated solutions fix more rapidly.[16]

Rapid Developers. As used here the term *rapid developer* is applied to a developing formula designed to produce a useful degree of development within the shortest possible time. The need for such developers is rather limited but important in certain specialized applications as racetrack timing, recording radar images, and television.

High-speed processing usually involves rapid fixation and, in some cases, rapid washing and drying. So far as development is concerned, the time required to produce a given gamma on a particular film or plate can be decreased only by increasing the activity of the developer through (1) raising the concentration of the developing agents, the pH of the solution, or (2) the temperature. Increasing the concentration of the developing agents does not, in the case of most formulas, increase the rate of development sufficiently. The use of larger amounts of alkali, or changing to a caustic alkali, has a much greater effect, but fog

[15] Kodak formula D–8. Henn and Crabtree, *J. Phot. Soc. Amer.* **12**, 445 (1946).

The addition of urea to facilitate development at temperatures above freezing was recommended by Dersch, *J. Phot. Soc. Amer.* **11**, 467 (1945).

[16] Henn and Crabtree, *J. Phot. Soc. Amer.* **12**, 445 (1946).

and excessive swelling of the gelatin impose definite limits in this direction.

The rate of development may be increased considerably by raising the temperature. Excessive fog may be prevented to some extent by the addition of anti-fogging agents; however, the addition of anti-swelling agents, such as sodium sulfate, has the effect of increasing the time of development so that nothing is gained. A prehardening bath may be used, however, and decreases the time required for fixing and washing by permitting the use of higher temperatures for these operations than would otherwise be possible.

For development of high-speed negative material in 45 to 60 seconds, the following are recommended at a temperature of approximately 75° F.[17]

Solution A

Catechol (E. K. Co.)	100 grams	3 oz. 145 grains
Sodium sulfite (des.)	100 grams	3 oz. 145 grains
Water to make.....	1 liter	32 oz.

Solution B

Sodium hydroxide .	60 grams	2 oz.
Potassium bromide.	100 grams	3 oz. 145 grains
Water to make.....	1 liter	32 oz.

Add 1 part of A to 1 part of B, and add 50 cc. (1⅔ ounces) of formalin (40% formaldehyde) per liter of the final solution.

Elon or metol..............	15 grams	65.6 gr.
Hydroquinone..............	15 grams	65.6 gr.
Sodium sulfite (des.)........	50 grams	219.0 gr.
Sodium hydroxide...........	20 grams	87.5 gr.
Potassium bromide..........	1 gram	4.4 gr.
Water to..................	1 liter	10.0 oz.

Use full strength.[18]

In either case, development should be followed with an acid stop bath to prevent overdevelopment and preferably one to which sodium sulfate has been added to reduce swelling of the gelatin.

---

[17] Kodak formula, SD–10. Crabtree and Russell, *J. Phot. Soc. Amer.* **10**, 541 (1944).

[18] Charrion and Valette, *Rev. franc. Phot.* **19**, 205 (1938).

Contrast Developers. A developer for maximum contrast on process materials must produce density readily and be free from any tendency to fog within the time of development necessary for the maximum gamma. Developers of this type when used with high contrast materials produce high gammas and a short toe, or foot, on the *D* log *E* curve. At the present time, these requirements require concentrated metol hydroquinone, or hydroquinone, developers with a relatively high concentration of alkali restrained by potassium bromide. The alkaline carbonates are generally employed in metol-hydroquinone developers of this type, the caustic alkalies or paraformaldehyde with hydroquinone alone.

Hydroquinone-paraformaldehyde developers produce, on fine-grain high-contrast materials, an exceptionally high gamma and a shorter toe portion than is obtained with hydroquinone-caustic developers. This has been shown to be due to the catalytic effect of the oxidation products on development.[19] Thus development which begins after a long induction period is sudden and rapid. Areas with less than a certain critical exposure develop very slowly while the development of fully exposed areas is greatly accelerated by the oxidation products of the developer, so that a small difference in exposure produces a considerable

---

[19] Yule, *J. Franklin Inst.* **239**, 221 (1945).

Stärke claimed development in 10 seconds by a two-bath developer; the first solution consisting of a 5% hydroquinone and 2.5% sodium sulfite; the second, a 30% solution of sodium hydroxide (*Phot. Ind.* **35**, 308 (1937)). See also: Jaenieke, *Brit. J. Phot.* **87**, 184 (1940); Banfield and Baird Television Ltd., B.P. 454,749–1936. Agfa-Ansco (*Photo-Technique* **2**, March 67 (1941)) and Crabtree, Parker and Russell (*J. Soc. Mot. Pict. Eng.* **21**, 21 (1933)). Warren, "A Sensitometric Study of Five Developers for Rapid Processing," *J. Phot. Soc. Amer.* **8**, 22 (1942).

difference in density or contrast. This high contrast unfortunately is accompanied by some image spreading causing clear lines to become narrower and dense lines broader. This is due to the development of unexposed grains adjacent to heavily exposed areas and has been termed *"infectious development."* [20] For a given emulsion and exposure, infectious development with hydroquinone-paraformaldehyde developers appears to depend principally on the concentration of sodium sulfite.

From a practical standpoint, it should be noticed that hydroquinone developers should not be used at temperatures below 50° F. nor above 70° F., or dichroic stain and excessive fog may be obtained. To prevent stain, the negative should be rinsed well between developing and fixing.

Two-Bath or Divided Developers. This term is applied to methods of development in which development is begun in one developing solution and completed in another. Usually the first solution contains the developing agents and sodium sulfite and the second the alkali plus additional sulfite. Ordinarily no development takes place until the film is transferred to the second bath. In this, development proceeds until the developing agents are exhausted, or have diffused out into the surrounding solution. Developers of this type produce an almost constant gamma which depends upon the composition of the two baths—regardless of the time of development, the degree of exhaustion or the temperature. These characteristics make divided developers of this type suitable for high-speed processing

and for the development of negative records in motion picture sound recording.[21]

Two other types of divided development are possible: in one both solutions are complete developers but differ in the proportion of alkali and developing agents; in the other, both solutions are alike in composition but of different degrees of exhaustion.

In the first case, the first bath is compounded to serve as a replenishing solution for the second. Since the quantity of the first bath carried over into the second is proportional to the amount of film processed, a properly designed formula will maintain a uniform rate of development over a longer period of use than would be possible in a single solution.

Divided development in two solutions of the same composition enables the developer to be used longer, without loss in effective emulsion speed, than in a single solution as development is begun in a fresh solution and completed in a used one. Investigation has shown that this may be done without loss in effective emulsion speed.[22]

The time of immersion in the first bath is short—only long enough for the image to appear—hence the rate of exhaustion is less than if development was completed in the same solution. When the second bath is exhausted, the first is replaced with fresh solution and it in turn becomes the second bath.

Developers for Maximum Emulsion Speed. In cases of known underexposure, gradation, graininess, and other desirable requirements may have to be sacrificed to obtain as much contrast in shadow detail as possible. Any increase in effective emulsion speed obtained through the use of

[20] Yule, *J. Franklin Inst.* **239**, 221 (1945). Stauffer, Trivelli and Smith, *J. Franklin Inst.* **238**, 291 (1944).

Willcock, "Process and Contrast Developers," *Brit. J. Phot.* **90**, 384 (1943).

Southworth, "Contrast Developers," *Brit. J. Phot.* **75**, 680, 706 (1928).

[21] Crabtree, Parker and Russell, *J. Soc. Mot. Pict. Eng.* **21**, 21 (1933). Crabtree, U.S.P. 1,973,-466 (1934). Formstecher, *Phot. Ind.* **29**, 683 (1931).

[22] Dundon, Brown and Capstaff, *J. Soc. Mot. Pict. Eng.* **14**, 389 (1930).

special developers or methods of development is nearly always accompanied by an increase in fog. From a practical standpoint, however, the increased fog may be more than compensated by the greater differences in density in the shadow portions of the image.

Forcing development with concentrated metol-hydroquinone, metol-chlorohydroquinone, or catechol developers results in somewhat higher effective emulsion speeds but only when the fog values become fairly considerable. The addition of hydrazine compounds, such as semicarbazide hydrochloride or hydrazine dihydrochloride, however, produces useful increases in both speed and contrast as compared with ordinary developers.[23]

The formula which follows [24] employing hydrazine dihydrochloride and an antifogging agent—6-nitro-benzimidazole—is recommended for known cases of underexposure, particularly with subjects of low contrast.

pending upon the sensitive material. Th* maximum emulsion speed is obtained wit* a fog density of approximately 0.40. Th* time may be determined experimentally b* developing an underexposed test negativ* for different times and measuring the fo* density of an unexposed section.

If the shadows only are underexpose* and the subject one with a long range c* tones, the problem is to obtain all possibl* detail in the shadows without excessiv* negative contrast. With ordinary develop* ers, the effective emulsion speed increase* with the gamma; hence at low gamma* shadow detail is sacrificed while if develop* ment is prolonged or high energy develop* ers used to obtain maximum speed, th* contrast may be excessive. A properly d* signed two-bath developer is the simple* and most practical means of increasing th* effective emulsion speed at low gamma* In a two-bath developer of the type whic* contains the developing agents in the firs* bath and the alkali in the second, the d*

	Metric	Avoirdupois U. S. Liquid
Solution A		
0.2% solution of 6-nitrobenzimidazole nitrate.....	20.0 cc.	2½ fluid oz.
Hydrazine dihydrochloride....................	1.6 grams	96 grains
Water to make.............................	30.0 cc.	4 fluid oz.
Solution B		
Water (about 125° F.).......................	500.0 cc.	64 fluid oz.
Elon..	2.2 grams	128 grains
Sodium sulfite (des.)........................	96.0 grams	12 oz. 360 grains
Hydroquinone...............................	8.8 grams	1 oz. 75 grains
Sodium carbonate (des.).....................	48.0 grams	6 oz. 180 grains
Potassium bromide..........................	5.0 grams	290 grains
Cold water to make.........................	1.0 liter	1 gallon

For use, take one part of A to 32 parts of B *immediately* before use. The mixed solution has a useful life of only a few hours.

The time of development at 70° F. is normally between 12 and 20 minutes, de-

Some increase in effective emulsion speed i* obtainable with ordinary developers whe* used at higher temperatures than norma* The risk involved in handling the materi* in development, the increase in fog and i* graininess are, in most cases, too great t* justify the slight gain in speed. Anderso* *Photo-Technique* 1, 73 (June 1940). Long* field, *Brit. J. Phot.* 88, 348 (1941). B. J* Almanac 1942, 152.

---

23 Stauffer, Smith, and Trivelli, *J. Franklin Inst.* **238**, 291 (1944).

24 Miller, Henn, and Crabtree, *J. Phot. Soc. Amer.* **12**, 585 (1946).

eloping agents carried over in the gelatin layer from the first bath to the second are soon exhausted in the fully exposed areas whereupon development stops. The highlights, therefore, are not fully developed as they are deprived of the developer necessary to carry development to completion. The developer in the shadow portions of the image is not exhausted so rapidly and development proceeds to completion.

The following two-bath developer is recommended for a high emulsion speed at low gammas: [25]

	Metric	Avoirdupois
Solution A—First Bath		
Elon	5.0 grams	75 grains
Hydroquinone	2.0 grams	30 grains
Sodium sulfite, des. (E. K. Co.)	100.0 grams	3 oz. 145 grains
Sugar	100.0 grams	3 oz. 145 grains
Sodium bisulfite (E. K. Co.)	5.0 grams	75 grains
Water to make	1.0 liter	32 fluid oz.
Solution B—Second Bath		
Sodium carbonate, des. (E. K. Co.)	10.0 grams	145 grains
Sodium sulfite, des. (E. K. Co.)	100.0 grams	3 oz. 145 grains
Potassium bromide	0.5 gram	7 grains
Potassium iodide (0.1% solution)	10.0 cc.	⅓ ounce
Water to make	1.0 liter	32 fluid oz.

Treat the film in Solution A for five minutes at 68° F., agitating for a few seconds at one-minute intervals. Drain for ten seconds and immerse in Solution B for five minutes, agitating for a few seconds at the start and again after three minutes. After development, rinse, fix, and wash in the usual manner.

[25] Miller, Henn, and Crabtree, *J. Phot. Soc. Amer.* **12**, 585 (1946).

Lawrence recommended the use of an afterbath of potassium bromide and sodium hydroxide following development in phenylenediamine. An increase in effective emulsion speed of from four to eight times was claimed. *Miniature Camera Magazine* **7**, 121 (1943). *Brit. J. Phot.* **90**, 125 (1943). See also Harris, *Miniature Camera Magazine* **7**, 505 (1943) and Kingsbury, *Amat. Phot.* **95**, 158 (1945).

A similar result may be obtained by removing the negative from the developer after development is well under way and transferring to a tray of water. This process may be repeated several times if necessary to obtain sufficient density and contrast. A nonstaining developer not subject to aerial fog should be used.[26]

Physical Developers. The process of development mistakenly known by this term consists in the use of a solution containing a silver salt in conjunction with a suitable developing agent forming metallic silver in a colloidal state which is precipitated upon the latent photographic image. Thus the image is formed as a result of the deposition of silver from the developing solution and not, as in the usual way, by the reduction of the exposed grains of silver halide to metallic silver.

[26] Although known and practiced long before, this method of development is frequently known as the Knapp system. Knapp, *Brit. J. Phot.* **80**, 191 (1933); **81**, 422 (1934); Robinson, *Brit. J. Phot.* **82**, 728 (1935).

Smethurst adapted the Knapp procedure to time development by the Watkins method, *Brit. J. Phot.* **80**, 129 (1933); Perry (*Photo-Art Monthly* **7**, 11, 71, 131 (1939)) and Benedict (*Camera Craft* **46**, 149 (1939)) recommended that the film be removed from the developer and squeeged emulsion-side in contact with a glass plate and left for an hour or so until development was complete.

So far as negative development is concerned, physical development is of interest chiefly as a means of obtaining a fine-grain image. With physical development, the grain size of the image is largely independent of that of the emulsion.

Against these advantages must be set certain disadvantages: (1) the process is slow, (2) more than ordinary care and attention to detail are required, (3) there is less latitude in exposure, and (4) there is less control over the contrast of the negative.

The older methods were improved materially by Odell who converted the silver halide into silver iodide before development, a step which greatly reduced the tendency to fog.[27]

Forebath[28]

Potassium iodide	23.5 grams	106 grains
Sodium sulfite (des.)	51.5 grams	250 grains
Water to make	1.0 liter	20 oz.

Use full strength. The time of immersion is forty seconds. Finally rinse for twenty seconds.

Developer (stock solution)

Sodium sulfite (des.)	96.0 grams	1 oz. 403 gr.
Silver nitrate, crystal	13.7 grams	120
Borax, powdered	13.7 grams	120
Sodium thiosulfate	120.6 grams	2 oz. 180 gr.
Water to make	1.0 liter	20 oz.

The stock solution must be made up carefully by first dissolving the sodium sulfite in water at a temperature of about 120° F. (50° C.). The silver nitrate is then dissolved in about 4 ounces of water at the same temperature. The silver solution is then added, precipitate and all, slowly to the solution of sodium sulfite with vigorous stirring. The borax is then added to the

solution and finally the sodium thiosulfate after which the total volume is made up to 20 ounces or 1 liter. The solution should be allowed to stand for twelve hours before use and filtered with Whatman No. 2 filter paper.

The working solution is made up as follows directly before use:

Stock solution	250	cc.	1 oz.
Water to make	750	cc.	4 oz.
Diaminophenol	2.75 gm.		6 gr.

The time of development depends upon the sensitive material and the contrast required but varies from twelve to twenty minutes at 65° F. (18.5° C.). It is best to develop wholly by time as the image appears to be lacking in density and contrast until after it has been fixed, so that it is difficult to follow development by inspection.

Combined Developing and Fixing While it is possible to develop and fix in one operation, all methods thus far have resulted in too great a loss in emulsion speed to be practical. To prevent excessive loss in speed from the fixing out of silver halide before it can be developed, most methods thus far proposed have employed high energy developers and relatively low concentrations of hypo. Further difficulties are the occurrence of silver stains with many emulsions and the variation in the rate of development and fixing with the temperature so that a developer balanced for one temperature will not be practical for use at another. Miller and Crabtree[29] found that usable developing and fixing solutions can be prepared by adding approximately 5 grams of sodium hydroxide and from 60 to 175 grams of sodium thiosulfate per liter of conventional metol-hy-

---

[27] Odell, *Brit. J. Phot.* **84**, 310 (1937). Turner, *Brit. J. Phot.* **85**, 403 (1938). Turner, *Miniature Camera World*, Feb. 1939, p. 127.

[28] These formulas are from McQuown, *Brit. J. Phot.* **85**, 446 (1938), and **86**, 470, 483, 499 (1939).

[29] Miller and Crabtree, *Amer. Phot.* **42**, 76 (February 1948).

McLaren, "Physical Development," *Brit. J. Phot.* **85**, 464 (1938).

droquinone developers which normally develop in from 4 to 7 minutes at 68° F. The exact amount of hypo to be added must be determined for a given developer and emulsion by trial. Negatives developed in combined developing and fixing solutions of this type ordinarily have more fog and show a speed loss of about one stop as compared with separate development and fixing. The contrast and curve shape, however, are not appreciably different from normal development and fixing. The useful life of combined developing and fixing solutions is short; they soon sludge and lose activity rapidly.

The Time of Development. The time of development is determined by (1) the degree of development, or γ, desired, and (2) by the time of development required under given conditions to reach that gamma.

The degree of development, or γ, depends upon the density scale desired in the negative. This in turn depends upon

1. *The exposure scale of the paper.* The longer the exposure scale of the paper (lower contrast) on which the print is to be made, the greater the range of density required in the negative.

2. *The manner of printing.* Projection printing tends to increase the contrast of the print particularly if condensing lenses are used, so that in general negatives should have rather less contrast for projection printing than for contact printing.

3. *The brightness range, or contrast, of the subject.* As the brightness range of the subject increases, the degree of development, γ, required to produce any given range of densities in the negative becomes

less and less. Thus, assuming that the print is to be made on a particular printing paper, negatives of subjects having an extended brightness range, such as landscapes including figures beneath trees and open sky, snow scenes with dark objects or shadows near the camera, and many interiors, require a lower gamma than subjects of low contrast, as, for example, open landscapes, ordinary landscape on dull day, water and sky, old and weatherbeaten buildings in dull light, etc.

4. *The negative material.* The characteristics of a negative material, i.e., speed, latitude, curve shape, etc., vary to some extent with the gamma. Graininess likewise varies with the gamma. It is necessary, therefore, to consider the sensitometric characteristics of the material and the use to be made of the negative in determining the proper gamma.

The time of development required to reach any given gamma depends upon:

1. *The developer.* This includes (1) the formula, and (2) its previous history; i.e., whether fresh or used and, in the latter case, the degree of exhaustion. An indication of the time or development is given with most published formulas but the conditions stated (a) emulsion, (b) temperature, (c) agitation, (d) gamma, should be noted carefully.

2. *The conditions of development.* Included under this head are such factors as agitation and temperature. Agitation by removing the restraining by-products of development from the surface of the film permitting the access of fresh developer increases the rate of development and reduces the time required for a given gamma. The time of development, for example, is less in a vigorously rocked tray than in a tank; however, the relationship between the amount of agitation and the rate of devel-

On combined developing and fixing, see:
LUMIERE AND SEYEWETZ, *Brit. J. Phot.* **71**, 44 (1925). Good summary.
KENDALL, *Amer. Phot.* **41**, 15 (April 1947).
GROVES, *Amat. Phot.* **95**, 262, 313 (1945).
FOURNES AND DIAMANT, U.S.P. 2,138,486.
KING, U.S.P. 2,397,006.

opment is, apparently, a complex one [30] and must be determined for any particular set of conditions by trial and error, or by sensitometric methods.

Time and temperature tables, or charts, are now available for most published formulas.

3. *The developing speed of the film or plate.* Sensitive materials differ considerably in the time of development required to attain a given stage of contrast.

Methods of Determining the Time of Development. Development for a fixed time, based upon published data, or practical tests, is now the general practice. It is the only real practical method of dealing with high-speed panchromatic material (unless desensitized) in the processing of roll film where there is considerable variation in exposure and type of subject on the same roll, in machine processing and, in general, in large-scale processing of any kind. Development for a fixed time, however, does not allow for variation in developer, in development time of different emulsion numbers, the degree of agitation, nor for variations in the time of development required with different subjects to produce negatives suitable for a particular printing paper.

A few of the older workers still develop by inspection. Considerable experience, however, is required to recognize the density differences by the dim light of the safelight lamp and the density range desirable for a particular subject and printing paper. There is, in addition, the very real danger of fog with panchromatic materials unless desensitized.

The time of appearance of the image in development is a constant fraction of the time of development for a given gamma. Therefore, if the time of appearance of the

image is determined, the time of development can be obtained by multiplying it by a factor which is known as the "*Watkins factor.*" [31] If, for example, the time of appearance is one minute and the factor is five, the time of development is five minutes. For a constant gamma, the Watkins factor depends chiefly upon the developing agent and is not altered by temperature, the emulsion, or the conditions of development.

Factorial development has practically disappeared from modern practice because it cannot be applied to high-speed color sensitive material, as fog occurs from the exposure of the material to the safelight in the early stages of development. This difficulty is not overcome by desensitizing, since exposure of the desensitized image to the safelight results in partial destruction of the latent image, which is equivalent

Fig. 23.1. "Bromide" and developer streaks, and the silhouette effect in a print from a negative developed in a vertical position without agitation. R. N. Wolfe and R. S. Barrows, Adjacency Effects in Photography, *P.S.A. Journal* **13**, 554 (1947).

[30] Nietz and Whitaker, *Brit. J. Phot.* **73**, 630, 645, 660, 676 (1926).

[31] Alfred Watkins, *Watkins Manual.*

practically to a loss in effective emulsion speed.

Development Effects Arising from Inadequate Agitation. Development in a vertical tank without agitation, or with grossly inadequate agitation, may produce streaks.

Clear streaks, or streaks of lower density, are produced when the reaction products released from an area of high density sink down and restrain development in the parts of image directly below. The streaks are more noticeable when a high density is adjacent to, and directly above, an area of lower density.

Streaks of greater density (Fig. 23.1) are produced when the flow of fresh developer across the film from a clear, or nearly clear, area on the film, which does not exhaust the developer appreciably, accelerates the development of the image directly below the clear portion.

Similar effects may be produced by agitation in one direction only. Such conditions apply particularly to the continuous processing machines used in the development of motion picture film where such defects are known as directional development.[32]

In tray development lack of agitation results in a variation of the same effect, higher densities being surrounded by a halo or fringe of lower density (Fig. 23.1). This is commonly known as the "silhouette effect" or the "Mackie line," after Alexander Mackie of London who, in 1885, observed and explained the phenomenon. Frequently, under such conditions, the density of the dense portion of the image increases along the edge although this "border effect" is usually less noticeable than the fringe of lower density surrounding it. This halo of greater density is believed to be due to the diffusion of fresh developer through the gelatin from the surrounding area of lower density.

Eberhard in 1912 showed that, as a result of these development effects, the density of an area, if small, is increased when surrounded by a larger area of a different density. Thus, if plates were exposed behind a metal plate with openings varying from 0.3 millimeter to 30 millimeters, the densities of the exposed circles increased as the diameter became smaller. This has since been termed the "Eberhard effect."[33] The variation in density increases with the thickness of the emulsion, the difference in exposure between the two areas, the concentration of the developer—being more pronounced with dilute developers—and increases with gamma to a certain point and then decreases. All organic developers behave similarly but there is no difference in density when a ferrous oxalate developer is used.

Closely related is the so-called "Kostinsky effect" which, like the true Eberhard effect, is ordinarily of importance only in astronomical and spectrographic work. Kostinsky, in 1906, observed that the distance between two star images close together becomes greater, rather than less, as their diameter is increased by longer exposures. This apparent repulsion of the two images is due to the accumulation of developer reaction products between the two star images which restrains development along the edge and increases the distance between the two images.

Stop Baths. The primary object in using an acid bath before fixing is to stop development; however, the stop bath, by neutralizing the alkaline developer, assists in preventing developer stain and in preserving the hardening properties of the acid fixing and hardening bath.

Hardening stop baths of chrome alum (2–3%) are advisable when processing at

[32] Crabtree, *J. Soc. Mot. Pict. Eng.* **18**, 207 (1932). Luft, *Brit. J. Phot.* **81**, 73 (1934).

[33] *Physik. Z.* **13**, 288 (1912).

high temperatures to harden the gelatin more quickly and thoroughly than is possible with the usual acid fixing and hardening baths. To harden negatives which have had only a brief rinse in water, the chrome alum bath should have a pH value of 3.0 to 3.8, depending on the amount of rinsing and the alkalinity of the developer. A freshly prepared solution of chrome alum ordinarily has a pH value within this range, but sulfuric acid may be added if it is necessary to increase the acidity of the bath to obtain good hardening. The amount of acid necessary may be determined from pH measurements with suitable indicator papers or by titration with bromphenol blue.

Films placed in this solution should be kept in motion for twenty to thirty seconds; otherwise stains may be produced from the precipitation of chromium hydroxide by the alkali of the developer. Blisters may form on film processed in strongly alkaline developers, particularly in warm weather, but may be prevented by thorough agitation.

The hardening properties of the solution are reduced by the addition of developer, which increases the pH beyond the point of good hardening. The addition of sulfuric acid at intervals, in quantities sufficient to maintain the proper pH value, increases the useful life of the solution. In small-scale operations, however, the simplest and cheapest procedure is to discard the bath and prepare a new one.

At temperatures above 85°, a chrome alum stop bath with sodium sulfate is preferable to one of chrome alum alone. The sodium sulfate retards the swelling of the gelatin and enables the chrome alum to harden more efficiently and quickly.

Potassium chrome alum	30 grams	1 oz.
Sodium sulfate (des.)	60 grams	2 oz.
Water	1 liter	32 oz.

Recommended Procedures for Fixing Negative Materials.[34]

1. Use an acetic acid stop bath after development, particularly with strongly alkaline developers, to prevent change in the pH of the fixing bath with use.

2. Use a fixing bath whose pH is at least 4.9 to facilitate the removal of hypo from the emulsion layer in washing. If the pH of an acid fixing and hardening bath containing potassium alum is below 4.9 silver from the gelatin, or gelatin alumina complex, and as the bath nears exhaustion the adsorbed silver is not removed by washing in water. If the pH of the fixing bath while in use remains above 4.9, the isoelectric point of gelatin, no silver is retained.

3. Use two fixing baths, the first a used bath, the second relatively fresh with at least half the time in the second bath as in the first.

4. Discard the first bath when the silver content reaches 5 grams per liter (about 1000 square inches per liter or 4000 per gallon) and the second when the silver content reaches 0.5 to 1.0 grain per liter.

5. Use nonhardening, or chrome alum fixing baths, if the time of washing must be kept to a minimum.

Drying. Drying with air involves (a) diffusion of water to the surface, and (b) evaporation of the water from the surface. The rate of evaporation depends upon (a) the relative humidity of the air, and (b) the rate at which it is changed.

The more water the air contains (i.e., the higher its relative humidity), the less water it can absorb. Heating lowers the relative humidity and increases the capacity of the air to hold water and thus causes more rapid drying. An electric fan dries by driving away the water-laden air

---

[34] Crabtree, Eaton and Muehler, *J. Phot. Soc. Amer.* **9**, 115, 162 (1943).

and replacing it with drier air from within the room.

The aim in drying a photographic material is not to remove all water from the gelatin. Gelatin which has been dried completely (desiccated) is brittle and will crack easily; moreover, it will absorb moisture from the air until its moisture-content is in equilibrium with the surrounding air. The problem in drying is to remove the water *at a uniform rate* from all parts of the film until the gelatin contains from 10 to 15% moisture and will be approximately in equilibrium with the air in which the negative is stored and handled.

It is particularly important that the rate of evaporation (drying) be uniform over the whole surface so that every part of the negative dries at the same rate. Since the density of the image depends upon the rate of drying, any difference in the drying of the image will produce differences in density which are difficult to remove. Thus not only must the flow of air past the material be unobstructed, but neither the air velocity nor the relative humidity may change appreciably while drying.

Increasing the velocity of the air across the surface will cause the negative to dry more rapidly, as will lowering the humidity of the air by heating. The use of air which is very dry, i.e., below a relative humidity of 40–50%, may however dry the surface without evaporating water from within the gelatin layer. This may set up a strain in the gelatin and lead to a coarseness of structure which is practically equivalent to an increased graininess. Moreover, negatives which appear dry on the surface become damp as the water within diffuses to the surface with the result that they stick to one another or to the envelopes in which they are placed.

In general, where the humidity of the air is controlled by heating, the temperature should be regulated to produce a relative humidity of from 60 to 70% which may be determined by placing a hygrometer in the current of air.

Distortion of the Image in Drying. A certain amount of distortion along the edge of a plate or sheet film is inevitable as the edges dry more rapidly than the center. Negatives developed in tanning developers show some distortion on drying owing to the difference in the rate of drying of the differentially hardened gelatin. The effect, however, is small and can be ignored except where precision measurements must be made from the image as in astronomy, spectrography, etc.

Methods of Drying Photographic Negatives. A drying cabinet provides the most satisfactory means of drying negatives in quantity. The size of the cabinet and its design will depend upon the amount, size, and character of the negative material employed. The cabinet should be large enough to hold the maximum number of negatives which can come from the washing tanks in the time required for drying and allow ample space between the negatives to permit free circulation of air. A cabinet larger than absolutely necessary is undesirable as it is more difficult to maintain an adequate circulation of air in a large cabinet than in a small one. For the same reason, a long narrow shape is better than a square one.

A constant supply of warm, dry air is necessary for rapid and uniform drying. With small cabinets a good method is to force heated air by a fan through the cabinet from the top and out at the bottom, electric heating units being placed between the fan and the top of the cabinet. If other sources of heat are used, the heating unit is best placed outside the cabinet to avoid danger of fire. For this reason, metal cabinets are preferable to those of combustible materials.

The radiation from infrared lamps is

strongly absorbed by water but only slightly by gelatin and film base; consequently, the water is evaporated more or less uniformly from the whole of the gelatin layer at the same time and not progressively from top to bottom as when warm air is used. As a result, negatives may be dried more rapidly with infrared lamps than with hot air and without the same danger of surface drying mentioned in a preceding paragraph. Surface water must first be removed thoroughly to avoid water spots. In drying with infrared lamps, the lamps should be placed so as to expose the surfaces of the negative uniformly. These lamps dry by exposure to infrared radiaation; they should not be used to heat the air in contact with the film, as when drying by heat from other sources. A fan may be used, however, to remove the water vapor evaporated from the gelatin and reduce the time of drying.

The drying of negatives from which prints are required immediately (press work) may be forced by the use of heated air but only if the gelatin has been sufficiently hardened to prevent melting. An alkaline formaldehyde hardening solution (page 352) is recommended in such cases. Negatives on film, however, cannot with safety be dried at temperatures much above 100° F. (38° C.) or the film base may be buckled.

Rapid Drying. A more convenient method of drying rapidly, and the only practical method of drying at temperatures near the freezing point, is by bathing in a liquid, such as isopropyl ethyl alcohol, or acetone, which displaces water and evap-

orates more rapidly. Ordinary denatured alcohol is usually employed without dilution. If commercially pure alcohol is used it may lead to opalescence of the image, due to partial dehydration of the gelatin unless diluted with about $\frac{1}{3}$ its volume of water.

According to Crabtree,[35] opalescence rarely occurs when the gelatin is dried at temperatures below 70° F. The use of denatured alcohol containing naphtha, or insufficient fixing or washing, is a contributory cause.

The alcohol takes up water and is soon rendered useless for drying unless the water is extracted by filtering the alcohol through substances which absorb water but are not soluble in alcohol; e.g., sodium or potassium carbonate or plaster of Paris.

Concentrated solutions of certain salts which are highly soluble in water, as for example, aluminum or sodium sulfate and potassium carbonate, have the property of replacing water in gelatin and may be used for the rapid drying of negatives. Thus, if a wet negative is placed in a saturated solution of potassium carbonate for four or five minutes, the gelatin is almost completely dehydrated and, after blotting off the surplus solution and wiping the surface with a soft cloth, the negative is ready for printing.

This process affords a ready means of drying a negative temporarily so that a few prints may be made for immediate use. When the prints are made, the negative should be placed in a small quantity of the solution which should then be diluted with water and finally placed in running water for ten to fifteen minutes and dried in the usual way. If the negative is placed directly in running water, the gelatin may be disrupted and the negative ruined.

It is not necessary, of course, to dry negatives before printing. Projection prints may be made from wet negatives if the surface moisture is first removed and contact prints may be made by placing a thin sheet of acetate sheeting between the negative and the paper.

[35] Crabtree, *Brit. J. Phot.* **72**, 723 (1925). Stevens, *Brit. J. Phot.* **93**, 338, 346 (1946).

Chapter 24

IMPROVEMENT OF THE NEGATIVE

Reduction and Intensification. The removal of silver from the developed image to reduce its density is termed *reduction*; and the process of increasing density and contrast is termed *intensification*. Reduction and intensification are of value principally in correcting errors in development. Underdevelopment may be corrected by intensification and overdevelopment by reduction and, although it is better to obtain the proper contrast in development, it is possible through after treatment to obtain very nearly the same result as if the negative had been developed for the proper time. Overexposed negatives may be *improved* by reduction and the printing quality of underexposed negatives by intensification, but it is not possible to compensate completely for errors in exposure by after treatment.

There is less need for reduction and intensification in modern practice than in the past, firstly, because of improved negative materials and, secondly, because the introduction of developing papers in different grades enables good prints to be obtained from negatives differing greatly in contrast without resort to corrective treatment. No attempt will be made, therefore, to describe all of the many processes which are to be found in the literature.[1]

Considerations in the Choice of Reducers and Intensifiers. In selecting intensifiers and reducers, preference should be given to processes in which:

1. *Methods in which the change taking place is clearly evident at all times.*

2. *Dependable in action.*

3. *Free of tendency to stain or to soften gelatin.*

4. *Acts similarly on different types of emulsions.* With many processes the amount and character of reduction or intensification tend to vary with the type of emulsion.

5. *Cause little or no change in the color of the image.* A change in the color of the image increases the difficulty of determining the effective printing density and contrast of the image.

6. *Cause little or no change in the graininess of the image.* All methods of reduction or intensification affect the graininess of the image, but there is as yet little quantitative experimental data on this point.

7. *In the case of intensifiers, it should be possible to remove the intensification if carried too far, or to repeat the process if additional density and contrast are required.*

8. *The solutions should not be highly poisonous.*

9. *The result should be permanent.*

10. *The process should be convenient.*

Preparation of the Negative. If the negative cannot be replaced it is well to first make a positive from which a dupli-

[1] Wall, *Intensification and Reduction*, American Photographic Publishing Co., Boston (1924) (contains extensive bibliography). Crabtree and Muehler, *J. Soc. Mot. Pict. Eng.* **17**, 1001 (1931) (extensive bibliography at close of paper). Higson, *Phot. J.* **61**, 237 (1921) (bibliography on persulfate reduction).

cate negative can be made if anything should go wrong.

Negatives to be reduced or intensified should have been thoroughly fixed and—for most processes—thoroughly washed. If there is any doubt, it is well to refix the negative in a fresh fixing bath and wash a second time.

If the negative is dry, it should first be soaked in water for fifteen to twenty minutes. A wetting agent may be used to advantage, particularly if the negative has received much handling.

Some intensifying and reducing processes tend to soften gelatin which may lead to frilling, or reticulation, in warm weather or with negatives which have not been thoroughly hardened in an acid fixing and hardening bath. In such cases, an alkaline formaldehyde prehardening solution [2] should be employed as a safety measure:

Water...................	500.0 cc.	16 oz.
Formaldehyde...........	10.0 cc.	2.5 oz.
Sodium carbonate (des.)....	5.0 gm.	73 gr.
Water to make..........	1.0 liter	32 oz.

PART I—REDUCTION

Chemistry of Photographic Reduction. Chemically, photographic reduction is a process of chemical oxidation. The silver of the image is oxidized either to a water soluble salt or the reducing solution contains a solvent for the oxidized silver salts.

With a solution of potassium permanganate and sulfuric acid, for example, the silver is dissolved as silver sulfate, according to the reaction.

$$10Ag + 2KMnO_4 + 8H_2SO_4 \rightarrow$$
$$5Ag_2SO_4 + K_2SO_4 + 2MnSO_4 + 8H_2O.$$

In the well-known Farmer's reducer, containing potassium ferricyanide and thiosulfate, the thiosulfate dissolves the sil-

ver ferrocyanide according to the reaction:

(a) $4Ag + 4K_3Fe(CN)_6 \rightarrow$
$$Ag_4Fe(CN)_6 + 3K_4Fe(CN)_6$$

(b) $3Ag_4Fe(CN)_6 + 16Na_2S_2O_3 \rightarrow$
$$4Na_5Ag_3(S_2O_3)_4 + 3Na_4Fe(CN)_6$$

With ferricyanide and thiocyanate,[3] the reaction is:

1. $4Ag + 4K_3Fe(CN)_6 \rightarrow$
$$Ag_4Fe(CN)_6 + 3K_4Fe(CN)_6,$$

2. $Ag_4Fe(CN)_6 + (x + 4)NH_4CNS \rightarrow$
$$XNH_4CNS \cdot 4AgCNS + (NH_4)Fe(CN)_6.$$

With iodine and cyanide: [4]

$$2Ag + I_2 + 4KCN \rightarrow 2KAg(CN)_2 + 2KI.$$

With quinone,[5] which is of interest as being the only reducer employing an organic substance, the reaction according to Seyewetz is:

$$C_6H_4O_3 + 2Ag + H_2SO_4 \rightarrow$$
$$C_6H_4(OH)_2 + Ag_2SO_4.$$

With ferric ammonium sulfate,[6] the reaction is probably,

$$2Ag + Fe_2(SO_4)_3 \cdot (NH_4)_2SO_4 \rightarrow$$
$$Ag_2SO_4 + FeSO_4 + FeSO_4 \cdot (NH_4)_2SO_4.$$

There is still some uncertainty regarding the exact reactions in reduction with a persulfate. The simple equation

$$2Ag + (NH_4)_2S_2O_3 \rightarrow Ag_2SO_4 + (NH_4)_2SO_4$$

is obviously incomplete as the solution grows more acid during reduction and the rate of reduction is accelerated by the hydrogen ion and silver.

---

[2] Kodak formula SH–1.

[3] Haddon, *Brit. J. Phot.* **39**, 49, 60 (1892).

[4] Becker and Winterstein, *Brit. J. Phot.* **65**, 81 (1918). Iodide and cyanide: Eder, *Handbuch* 1903, **3**, 559. Iodide and hypo: Lanier, *Photo. Korr.* **31**, 64 (1894).

[5] *Brit. J. Phot.* **76**, 775 (1929).

[6] Crabtree and Muehler, *J. Soc. Mot. Pict. Eng.* **17**, 1001 (1931).

Sheppard [7] gives the following equations as representing the probable reactions more completely:

1. $S_2O''_8 + H_2O \rightarrow 2HSO'_4 + O$
2. Atomic oxygen from (1) forms oxides —Ag_2O_2, Ag_2O
3.
4. Oxides, Ag_2O, etc., react with acid
$$Ag_2O + 2H^+ \rightarrow 2Ag^+ + H_2O$$
$$2HSO_4^- \rightarrow 2H^+ + 2SO_4^{--}$$

Higson [8] gives a similar equation:

1. $S_2O'' + H_2O \rightarrow 2HSO'_4 + O$
2. Nascent oxygen from (1) forms peroxide, probably Ag_3O_4
3. Silver peroxide oxidizes gelatin and is reduced to Ag_2O
4. Ag_2O reacts with acidic ion—HSO_4^-.
$$Ag_2O + 2HSO_4^- \rightarrow$$
$$2Ag^+ + 2SO_4^{--} + H_2O$$

Types of Reducers. Reducers are classified as *proportional* if the amount of silver removed is proportional to that originally present; *superproportional* if the degree of reduction is greater in the higher densities than in the lower; and *subproportional* if the degree of reduction is greater in the low densities than in the higher. These differences are shown in Fig. 24.1 in which the top curves represent the D log E curve before reduction and the lower curves the D log E curve after reduction.

A *proportional* reducer should be used to correct excessive density and contrast resulting from overdevelopment. A proportional reducer, by removing silver from all densities in the same ratio, produces a result similar to that obtained by developing to a lower gamma.

A *superproportional* reducer should be used when it is necessary to remove silver from the higher densities to a greater de-

gree than from the lower as, for example, a negative in which excessive contrast is due to the nature of the subject and not to overdevelopment alone. It should be noted that both proportional and superproportional reducers lower contrast as well as density: the proportional reducer

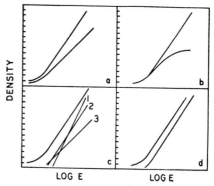

FIG. 24.1. D log E curves showing the effect of reduction in (a) a proportional reducer; (b) a superproportional reducer; (c) a subproportional; and (d) a subtractive reducer.

is used when it is necessary to reduce contrast proportionally throughout the entire density range, i.e., in correcting overdevelopment; the superproportional reducer when it is necessary to reduce the density of the highlight areas of the negative with little reduction of the shadow portions, i.e., negatives of subjects of high contrast.

Proportional Reducers. These include potassium permanganate and potassium persulfate, ferric ammonium sulfate, quinone, and ferricyanide-hypo when used as two separate solutions.

Of these permanganate-persulfate is generally the most useful.[9] Ferric ammonium sulfate has the disadvantage of softening gelatin, necessitating a prehardening solution, and, in addition, the rapid oxidation usually results in the staining of the image. Almost true proportional reduction can be obtained by using the familiar ferricyanide-hypo reducer as two separate solutions

[7] *Phot. J.* **61**, 450 (1921); **62**, 321 (1922).
[8] *Phot. J.* **62**, 98 (1922).

[9] Huse and Nietz, *Brit. J. Phot.* **63**, 580 (1916).

immersing the negative for two to three minutes in the ferricyanide solution and then transferring to a solution of hypo, but the degree of reduction cannot be determined until the process is complete.[10]

Proportional reduction may be obtained also by bleaching the negative in a solution of potassium ferricyanide and bromide followed by redevelopment to the desired contrast in a dilute, slow-acting developer containing only sufficient sodium sulfite to prevent excessive oxidation. A developer containing a high concentration of sodium sulfite, or any solvent of silver halide, will tend toward greater reduction of the lower densities. After development, the negative should be washed briefly, fixed to remove the silver halide remaining, and washed as usual.

Superproportional Reducers. The persulfates are the only reducers of this type in general use although under certain conditions superproportional reduction is obtained with benzoquinone.[11]

Unfortunately, reduction with persulfate usually entails some risk. With some emulsions reduction is more nearly proportional than superproportional, and in other cases the action of the reducer is uneven. Moreover, the reduction, after a slow start, becomes faster and faster and the negative may be reduced too far before the process can be stopped. Many workers hesitate to use persulfate preferring either to employ one of the redevelopment processes to be described later, or to make (1) a duplicate negative of lower contrast, or (2) a photographic mask for use over the negative in printing (page 361).

Ammonium persulfate (c.p.)..	60 gm.	260 gr.
Sulfuric acid..............	3 cc.	15 mm.
Water to.................	1,000 cc.	10 oz.

Prepare immediately before use with distilled water. The use of water containing salts of iron or soluble chlorides, bromides, sulfates, and nitrates is one of the most frequent sources of difficulty in using the persulfate reducer.[12]

Watch the action carefully and when reduction is complete, place the negative immediately in a fresh, acid fixing. After fixing for 3–5 minutes, wash and dry as usual.

Redevelopment Processes of Reduction. These methods of superproportional reduction, originally suggested by Eder,[13] consist in converting the silver image to a halide (*rehalogenizing*) and redeveloping.

There are several methods:

1. Bleach the image in an acid solution of bichromate, wash out the free bi-chromate, redevelop in a diluted nonstaining developer until the proper contrast is obtained and finally remove the undeveloped halide by fixing in hypo. This procedure results in intensification of the lower densities and reduction of the higher.

2. Bleach the image in a solution of potassium ferricyanide and bromide as used for sulfide toning until the lower densities only are bleached. Dissolve the silver remaining in a solution of potassium permanganate, made acid with sulfuric acid, clear with a 10% solution of sodium bisulfite and redevelop in any non-staining developer except one containing a high concentration of sodium sulfite or a solvent of silver halide.[14]

3. Bleach in a solution of potassium ferricyanide and bromide as before, wash well and convert bleached image to silver sulfide, as in sulfide toning. Wash five to ten minutes and reduce in ferricyanide-

[10] Crabtree and Muehler, *J. Soc. Mot. Pict. Eng.* **17**, 1001 (1931).

[11] Lumiere, *Brit. J. Phot.* **57**, 625 (1910).

[12] Sheppard, *Brit. J. Phot.* **65**, 314 (1918).

[13] Eder, *Phot. Korr.* **18**, 111 (1881).

[14] Namias, *Il. Prog. Fot.* **36**, 74 (1929).

hypo until the desired density and contrast are obtained.[15]

4. Bleach in a solution of potassium permanganate and hydrochloric acid until the lower densities have been bleached, wash two to three minutes in water, remove the silver remaining in a solution of potassium permanganate and sulfuric acid, clear the manganese stain with a 10% solution of sodium bisulfite and redevelop in a non-staining developer.[16]

The great difficulty with all of these methods is that considerable experience is required in order to obtain the result desired. The first method is perhaps the most straightforward and dependable. The intensification of the lower densities is an advantage if the shadow detail is lacking in contrast, a disadvantage if the contrast of shadow detail and the negative as a whole is to be reduced.

Subproportional Reducers. These include ferricyanide-hypo, ferricyanide-thiocyanate, cupric chloride-thiosulfate, permanganate, ferric chloride-thiosulfate.

Ferricyanide-thiosulfate (Farmer's Reducer) is perhaps the most widely used of all reducers. As generally employed, it is subproportion in action but it becomes more and more nearly proportional as the dilution is increased. Reduction is also more strongly subproportional with fine grain than with coarse grain emulsions.

Ferricyanide and thiocyanate have the advantage of being stable in solution.

Cupric chloride and thiosulfate form a strongly subproportional reducer that is recommended for the reduction of line negatives and process work. It keeps well and may be used over and over.

Permanganate reducers are more nearly proportional in action than the methods previously discussed and become more so as the acidity of the solution decreases.

For practical purposes a slightly acid, permanganate solution may be considered a proportional reducer. A brown deposit of manganese oxide is formed which may be removed by placing the negative in either a fixing bath or a 5% solution of sodium bisulfite.

Ferric chloride and thiosulfate (Belitzski) form a reducer which is intermediate in character between subproportional and proportional reducers. The slope of the $D \log E$ curve is lessened, but a greater proportion of silver is removed from the lower densities. This reducer, furthermore, has the advantage of keeping well in solution.

Methods of Intensification. 1. *Methods based upon the addition of silver to the image.* This method employs a so-called physical developer which deposits metallic silver on the image from a developing solution containing a silver salt, and a developing agent in either an acid or alkaline solution. The developing agent reduces the silver salt to silver and the silver grains of the image, acting as nuclei, cause the reduced silver to deposit on the image, thus increasing its density.

2. *Methods based on the addition of a compound of silver or another metal; e.g., chromium or mercury.* Intensification with chromium, for example, involves bleaching with a solution of an acid bichromate, the reaction probably being: [17]

---

[17] Piper and Carnegie, *Amat. Phot.* **40**, 336, 397 (1904); **41**, 453 (1905). *Brit. J. Phot.* **53**, 367 (1906). Lumiere and Seyewetz, *Brit. J. Phot.* **66**, 709 (1919).

For formulas and directions for these reducers, see *British Journal Photographic Almanac,* Henry Greenwood and Co. Ltd., London; *The Photo Lab Index,* Morgan and Lester, Publishers, New York; Wall, *Intensification and Reduction,* American Photographic Publishing Co., Boston and the formulas published by the principal manufacturers.

---

[15] Fripp, *Gallery 1,* **66** (1933).

[16] Fripp, *Brit. J. Phot.* **91**, 433 (1944).

$2 \ Ag + K_2Cr_2O_7 + 2HCl \rightarrow 2AgCl +$ a reduction product of the bichromate, probably CrO_2 or Cr_2Cl_2.

Development with an ordinary developer reduces the silver chloride to silver and the density is increased by the amount of the chromium compound added to the image.

With mercury, the image is first bleached with a solution of mercuric chloride or mercuric bromide,[18]

$$2HgCl_2 + 2Ag \rightarrow Hg_2Cl_2 + 2AgCl$$

then blackened with

(1) *Sodium sulfite*

$$Hg_2Cl_2 + Na_2SO_3 + H_2O \rightarrow$$
$$2Hg + Na_2SO_4 + 2HCl,$$

(2) *Ammonia*

$$Hg_2Cl_2 + 2NH_3 \rightarrow$$
$$NH_2Hg_2Cl + NH_4Cl,$$

(3) *Ferrous oxalate*

$$Hg_2Cl_2 + 2AgCl + 4FeC_2O_4$$
$$+ 2K_2C_2O_4 \rightarrow 2Ag + 2Hg$$
$$+ 2Fe_2(C_2O_4)_3 + 4KCl,$$

(4) *Silver cyanide*

$$Hg_2Cl_2 + 2AgK(CN)_2 \rightarrow$$
$$2Ag + 2Hg(CN)_2 + 2KCl.$$

Blackening with sodium sulfide results probably in silver sulfide and a mercury sulfide but no analytical determination of the compounds formed seems to have been made.

Mercuric iodide forms a single solution intensifier. The reaction is probably:

$$2HgI_2 + 2Ag \rightarrow Hg_2I_2 + 2AgI,$$
$$Hg_2I_2 + 2Na_2SO_3 \rightarrow$$
$$Hg + HgI_2, 2Na_2SO_3.$$

3. *Methods in which the mass of the deposit remains substantially unchanged but its opacity is increased.* For example, if

a negative is bleached in an oxidizing solution, as for example, one of ferricyanide and bromide, and redeveloped in sodium sulfide (e.g., sulfide toned), its printing opacity and contrast are increased because the yellow-brown color transmits less of the blue-and-violet light to which papers are sensitive. This is sometimes referred to as *optical* intensification.

The ratio of the visual density to the photographically effective density is known as the *selectivity coefficient* or as the *color index*. The greater the difference in the visual and photographic densities the higher the color index. If the ratio of the visual and the photographic densities is constant over a log E range which is sufficiently great for the gammas of the two curves to be determined, the ratio of the two gammas is the *color coefficient* (Jones and Wilsey).

Nearly all methods of intensification result in some change in the color of the image, the amount of the change depending upon (1) the method of intensification, (2) the grain size of the image, and (3) the degree of intensification. The change in color is generally negligible with silver intensification (color coefficient 1.0) and with chromium or mercuric chloride when redeveloped in a metol-hydroquinone developer (color coefficient 1.01 and 1.05 respectively). The color of the image becomes more brownish, however, if the process is repeated. Intensifying processes with marked change in color include sulfide toning (color coefficient 1.60); mercuric iodide followed by redevelopment in paraminophenol (1.40) and uranium (2.52).[19]

It is difficult, without experience, to determine the degree of intensification from the appearance of the image when using a process having a high color coefficient and

---

[18] Chapman Jones, *J. Soc. Chem. Ind.* **12**, 983 (1893).

[19] Nietz and Huse, *Phot. J.* **58**, 81 (1918); *Brit. J. Phot.* **65**, 179, 191 (1918). Crabtree and Muehler, *J. Soc. Mot. Pict. Eng.* **18**, 1001 (1931).

preference should be given to processes which are free from this disadvantage.

Sensitometry of Photographic Intensification. A number of studies have been made (1) of the degree of intensification produced by the different methods, and (2) the relation of the added density to the original density, but the most complete are those of Nietz and Huse.[20]

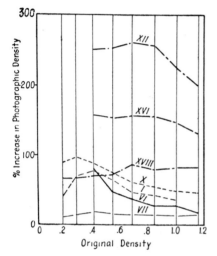

FIG. 24.2 Curve I. Mercuric chloride and ammonia. VI. Chromium and diaminophenol. VII. Mercuric bromide and diaminophenol. X. Mercuric iodide and diaminophenol. XII. Uranium. XVI. Mercuric iodide and Schlippe's salts. XVIII. Cupric chloride and sodium stannite.

In Fig. 24.2 the percentage increase in density is plotted as the ordinate against the original densities as abscissae. A line parallel with the base would thus indicate proportional intensification. No intensifier reaches absolute perfection in this respect, although several approach it closely. The distances of the lines above the base indicate approximately the degree of intensifi-

[20] Abney, *Phot. J.* **44**, 457 (1897). Janko, *B. J. Almanac* (1898), 899. Bennett, *Phot. J.* **53**, 214 (1913). Clerc, *Brit. J. Phot.* **59**, 215 (1912). Nietz and Huse, *Phot. J.* **58**, 81 (1918); *Brit. J. Phot.* **65**, 179, 191 (1918).

cation produced with the corresponding methods of intensification.

Most methods of intensification in general use produce approximately proportional intensification. Only two processes —uranium and quinone—are definitely subproprotional in character.

Superproportional intensification is obtained only when solvent action prevents the lower densities from increasing in the same ratio as the higher, as when the image bleached in mercuric chloride is blackened in sodium sulfite or in silver cyanide; or in chromium intensification when a developer with a high concentration of sodium sulfide, or thiocyanates, is employed for redevelopment.

Intensifiers. Intensification with silver has the advantage of being permanent, proportional and progressive so that the growth in density and contrast is directly visible. It demands greater care and attention to detail, however, and in practice is less reliable than some of the other methods. Many of the older formulas are unstable; the best in this respect is that of Crabtree and Muehler.[21]

Intensification with chromium is one of the most popular of all methods as it is simple and reliable, the color of the image is not materially changed, and the result is fairly permanent. Furthermore, the operation may be repeated if the increase is not sufficient after one application.

The rate of bleaching and the degree of intensification vary with the acid content of the solution. Strongly acid solutions bleach more rapidly and produce less intensification. Subproportional intensification, i.e., relatively greater intensification of the lower densities than the higher may be obtained by bleaching the lower densities completely, the higher only partially.

Developers containing a high concentration of sodium sulfite should not be used

[21] *J. Soc. Mot. Eng.* **17**, 1001 (1931).

for redevelopment of negatives bleached in chromium because solvent action of the sulfite on silver halide may result in reduction of the lower densities.

Negatives intensified in chromium may be reduced in dilute solutions of hydrochloric (5%) or sulfuric (2%) acid which remove the addition product responsible for the increase in density. Only film which has been hardened in formalin should be so treated or the gelatin may reticulate.

There are several methods of intensification with mercury. One of the most widely used consists of bleaching the negative in mercuric bromide followed by blackening (redevelopment) in (1) ammonia, (2) sodium sulfite (10%), (3) sodium sulfide (2%), (4) sodium sulfantimoniate (10%), (5) a nonstaining developer, and (6) silver-cyanide (Monckhoven's intensifier).

The gain in density with both ammonia and sodium sulfide is slight and is not increased by repetition of the process. Sodium sulfide produces a brown image and requires a prehardening bath to prevent softening of the gelatin. Sodium sulfantimoniate, although little used, is quite satisfactory and produces approximately proportional intensification.

Alkaline developers containing sulfite exert a solvent action which results in a lower degree of intensification of the lesser densities; with fine-grain developers containing a large concentration of sodium sulfite, the lower densities may actually be reduced. Diaminophenol is therefore preferable since no alkali is required; however, paraminophenol or metol-hydroquinone developers may be employed if the concentration of sodium sulfite is not excessive.

Silver-cyanide results in a high degree of intensification with a reduction of the lower densities and is used principally for process work. The solution is extremely poisonous and must be handled with care.

Mercuric iodide forms a very convenient, single-solution intensifier which may be used repeatedly until exhausted. Intensification is progressive and may be stopped when the required density and contrast have been attained. The intensifier may be prepared with either thiosulfate or sodium sulfite; a suitable formula for the latter consists of 2 grams each mercuric iodide, potassium iodide, and sodium thiosulfate to a liter of water.

Intensification may be removed if necessary in a 40% solution of sodium thiosulfate.

If the yellowish color of the intensified image is objectionable, or greater permanency is desired, the negative should be placed in a 1% solution of sodium sulfide until the image becomes brownish black when viewed from the rear. Negatives so treated cannot be reduced in hypo.[22]

For the maximum intensification of the lower densities without a corresponding increase in the higher (subproportional intensification) either uranium or quinonethiosulfate [23] should be used. The latter is recommended where the maximum increase in contrast of shadow detail is required on underexposed negatives, particularly on high-speed emulsions with which other methods of intensification are less effective.

A preliminary alkaline-formaldehyde hardening bath *must* be used. Graininess of the image is increased considerably and, as with silver, greater care in mixing and use is necessary than with most methods of intensification if streaks and stains are to be avoided. In addition, the image is

BOUCHER, "Study of the Contrast Variation Obtained with the Chromium Intensifier," *Amer. Ann. of Phot.* 49, 59 (1935).

22 Shaw, *Brit. J. Phot.* 80, 348 (1933).
23 Kodak In–6. Miller, Henn and Crabtree, *P.S.A. Journal* 12, 585 (1946).

not permanent. Despite these disadvantages, it is the best method of treating underexposed negatives in which detail is present but with insufficient contrast for printing.

Miscellaneous Methods of Intensification. A negative developed in a nonstaining developer, such as metol-hydroquinone, may be intensified by bleaching in a solution of potassium ferricyanide and bromide and redeveloping in a pyro developer. The increase in density and contrast depends upon the intensity of the stain image which is controlled by the amount of sodium sulfite in the developer. The less sulfite used the greater the increase in density upon development. Intensification is approximately proportional, except for the highest densities, and may be increased by repeating the process.[24]

If the bleached image is sulfide toned (page 359) a moderate degree of intensification is obtained, but the process cannot be repeated if increased density is required. Images of silver sulfide, however, may be intensified by exposure to light, after treatment in a solution of sodium sulfite and silver nitrate, but the process is not as simple as those in general use.[25]

Toning the developed image with ferrocyanides of copper, or uranium, increases density and contrast by increasing the printing density. For a long time, toning with uranium was the best method of intensifying negatives with weak shadow detail but quinone-thiosulfate is preferable

because: (1) the degree of intensification is greater; (2) the change in color of the image is less marked visually, and (3) the image is more permanent.

The density and contrast of a negative can be increased by making a duplicate negative, or reduced by making a positive, and using this as a mask in printing.

A number of methods of intensifying based on the conversion of the silver image into a mordant for basic dyes and substituting a dye image for the original silver image have been described but have not come into general use.[26] While the claim has been made that such methods have the advantage of producing finer grain than other methods of intensification, this claim has not been supported with quantitative experimental data.

Local Intensification and Reduction. If the negative is dry, it should first be soaked in water until thoroughly wet. The surface water is then removed with cotton, chamois, or a viscose sponge and the negative hung up for three or four minutes. This tends to avoid the danger of streaks and the spreading of the reducing or intensifying solution into adjacent areas where it is not wanted.

The solutions may be applied to small areas with a brush; for larger areas, a tuft of cotton may be used. The action should be watched carefully and the negative rinsed with water to stop the action of the solution. It is better to repeat the process rather than to run the risk of too great a change in density.

If a small area of uniform density is to be reduced, the ferricyanide hypo reducer

---

24 Wilsey, *Brit. J. Phot.* **66**, 721 (1919).

25 Hickman and Weyerts, *Brit. J. Phot.* **80**, 482 (1933).

Formulas and working directions for these methods of intensification will be found in the *Photo Lab Index,* Morgan and Lester, New York; *The British Journal Photographic Almanac,* American Photographic Publishing Co., St. Paul, and the formulas published by principal manufacturers.

26 Ives, *Brit. J. Phot.* **68**, 186 (1921). Lumiere and Seyewetz, *Brit. J. Phot.* **73**, 147 (1926). Wiegleb, *Atelier* **39**, 45 (1932). Ashton, *Brit. J. Phot.* **91**, 330 (1944).

The use of coupler developers for redevelopment has been suggested by Friedman, *Amer. Phot.* (February 1943), p. 44.

is satisfactory. If a larger area, with important density differences, is to be reduced, the reducer should be chosen to produce the type of reduction required, subtractive, proportional, or superproportional, exactly as if an entire negative is to be reduced.

Mercuric iodide is one of the best intensifiers for local intensification, as the growth of density can be watched and stopped when it has reached the proper point.

Retouching with Dyes. A most useful method of increasing the density of small areas is by the addition of a dye. A reddish dye known as crocein scarlet, or as coccine, is recommended but the yellow, orange, and red of the more transparent water colors employed for the coloring of prints and lantern slides may be used. Naphthalene black [27] also may be used and has the advantage of being a neutral black, thus enabling the added density to be estimated more accurately. The well diluted dyes are best applied to the dry negative with a small water color brush. As soon as the area to which the dye has been applied has been completely covered, the surplus dye is removed by blotting with clean lintless blotting paper. With the brush in one hand and the blotter in the other, apply successive washes of the dye, blotting each off a moment later until the desired result has been produced. Should too much of the dye be applied, it can be removed by soaking the negative in water. In the case of neo-coccine, it may be necessary in some cases to soak the negative for a few minutes in a weak solution of sodium sulfite or carbonate. The effect of the dye may be determined by examining it through a blue-green filter which causes it to appear gray.

Retouching Portrait Negatives. Portrait negatives usually require some re-

[27] Wakefield, *Brit. J. Phot.* **89**, 254 (1942).

touching to remove skin blemishes and other imperfections, to improve the modeling and soften harsh lines and features. The face and other areas which have to be retouched are first covered with retouching *medium,* using a tuft of cotton, to retain the pencil work. A hard (2H or 3H) retouching pencil, sharpened to a fine point, is used to fill in each freckle or spot with a fine network of strokes until its density matches that of the surrounding area. When all the spots due to freckles, pimples, and other skin blemishes have been filled in, harsh lines may be softened by crosshatch strokes or, if very narrow, by penciling directly along the line. In all retouching the density of the area must be built up slowly by repeated application. A soft pencil, or hard pressure, will lead to coarse, scratchy work. Care must be taken to avoid over-retouching, which may give the skin a marble-like smoothness, or to removing, or even unduly softening, character lines.

The etching knife is used to reduce the density of small areas by scraping away some of the silver deposit. The knife must be *sharp* or it will not be possible to cut away the silver deposit without scratches. Any etching required on a negative must be done before applying the retouching medium.

Removal of Backgrounds. Where a white background is desired, the area surrounding the subject is painted out with a black or red water-soluble paint known commercially as "opaque." The operation is commonly termed "blocking-out" by commercial photographers. The negative should be supported on a sheet of glass,

HAMMOND, *The Art of Retouching and Improving Negatives and Prints,* American Photographic Publishing Co., Boston.

ANDERSON, *"The Theory and Practice of Portrait Negative Retouching,"* American Photographic Publishing Co., Boston.

illuminated from below. It is helpful to be able to see the surface of a negative as well as to see through it. If the subject contains many straight lines, some workers prefer to begin by ruling these in with a draftsman's ruling pen and a straight edge. Many curves can be ruled in with a draftsman's curve. Other workers, however, prefer to use a one-eighth to one-quarter inch brush, freehand. A free, rather flowing, motion of the hand from left to the right, and away from the body, holding the brush as when writing, moving the entire arm from the elbow as a pivot, will, with some practice, enable one to follow the lines of a subject quite accurately. The negative must, of course, be shifted as required so that the lines of the subject may be followed without changing the direction of the strokes.

If a black background is required, the simplest method is to cover the subject with a waterproof varnish, or collodion and immerse the negative in a concentrated reducer until the background is clear. An alternative method is to apply a solution of potassium bichromate, as used for chromium intensification, to the areas to be removed with the brush, working right up to the outline of the subject. If the bleaching solution runs over on the subject, its action may be arrested immediately by placing the negative in a 1% solution of sodium carbonate. The operation may then be continued after washing for three to four minutes. If portions of the subjects are bleached accidentally, the negative should first be thoroughly washed and the areas touched up with a brush containing developer. When the background is thoroughly bleached, the negative is washed two or three minutes, fixed to remove any traces of the image which may remain, and then washed and dried as usual.

Masking. Masking, although widely used in three-color printing, seems largely

unknown in black and white. Masking may be the means of (1) reducing the density range of a negative to the printing paper, (2) increasing the apparent sharpness of the image by increasing detail contrast without a corresponding increase in the contrast of the print as a whole,[28] and (3) to eliminate gradation and resolve the image into areas of contrasting tones (posterizing).

The earlier methods of masking were designed as a means of controlling the tone values of the image rather than to correct the negative and employ sharp masks. In the Persson process, for example, a number of masks are made from the original

FIG. 24.3. Portion of an unsharp mask. (*Graphic Arts Bull.*)

[28] "Consider a negative containing fine, but not perfectly sharp, details which are completely lost in the print. It is a well-known fact that an increase in contrast by increasing the density gradient at the edge of detail, will increase its apparent sharpness. The contrast is limited, however, by the density range of the reproduction process. The unsharp mask may reduce the contrast and total density range of the negative to half their original values. Nevertheless, it does not reduce the contrast of fine details since these are not resolved by the mask. When the density range is brought back to normal to compensate for the flattening effect of the mask, the contrast of the fine details may be doubled; hence, they are sharper." Yule, *J. Phot. Soc. Amer.* **11**, 123 (1945).

Fig. 24.4. Example of the use of an unsharp mask. At the left is a direct print; at the right is the masked print, exposed with the mask in register with the original negative. (*Graphic Arts Bull.*)

negative by printing on film. The exposure is varied so that one mask includes only the shadow portions; a second, the shadow and middle tones; and the third, all but the highlights of the image. The masks are registered with the negative and one edge fastened down to the glass of the printing machine with adhesive tape, so that one or more masks may be placed over the negative in register for the exposure. Then, if the paper is attached along one side of the glass, it is possible, by multiple exposures using different masks and combinations of masks, to exercise considerable control over the tone relations of the image. The process has not been widely employed, however, because of the labor involved and the difficulties experienced in registering the masks and the image.

Unsharp masks, made by placing a sheet of celluloid or a glass plate between the negative and the film and exposing to diffused light, largely avoid the difficulties of registration which are encountered with sharp masks and afford a useful method of modulating the illumination on the negative for the control of tone values of the print.[29]

An emulsion of relatively low contrast should be used for making unsharp masks. The separation between the negative and the emulsion used for making the mask depends upon the subject, the size of the negative, and the result desired. Masks

Peterson, G.P. 529,370 (1930).
Persson, *Bild. Massige Leica-Photos Neuer Tone-Trennung*, Bechhold, Frankfurt (1935). See also *Phot. J.* **75**, 569 (1935).

[29] Johnson, *Amer. Phot.* **37**, 15 (March 1943).

Modifications of the Persson process to produce poster effects by reducing the tone differences of the original to three or four sharply contrasting tones have been described by Wade (*Amer. Phot.* **36**, 8 (November 1942), by Jorgenson (*Amer. Phot.* **40**, 476 (1946)).

made with thin spacing materials, such as .003 acetate sheeting, are comparatively sharp and may result in edge or contour effects with subjects of strong contrast. In general, the thickness of the spacing material and, therefore, the unsharpness of the mask must increase with the contrast of the subject.

To avoid contour effects, the mask should be exposed by diffuse light. If a printing machine is used the light should be well diffused with opal or ground glass, tracing cloth, tissue paper, or other good diffusing material. If a printing frame is used, the diffusing material should be placed over the frame at least one inch from the negative, or the exposure made by light reflected from a white wall or screen.

While the use of unsharp masks tends to hide errors of registration, registration marks are advisable, as it is at times difficult to register the blurred mask accurately with the sharp negative.

Exposure and development of the mask are determined by the requirements of the negative and explicit directions cannot be given. In general, the mask will be low in density and contrast. If it is to include the full density range, however, care should be taken to avoid underexposure and there should be no clear areas. If the mask is intended to affect only a part of the image then it must be exposed accordingly. The contrast of the mask, other things being equal, is determined by the time of development; the higher the contrast of a positive mask, the lower the contrast of the negative and positive when combined.

Chapter 25

PRINTING PROCESSES.
I. SILVER DEVELOPING PAPERS

Developing Papers. The emulsions employed for developing papers differ from those employed for negative materials principally in the lower concentration of the reactants used in making the emulsion, resulting in lower dispersity (finer grain) and in containing less silver, per unit area.[1] The amount of silver per 100 square centimeters is given by Sheppard as being of the order of 0.018 grams as compared with 0.10 grams per 100 square centimeters of the average negative emulsion. According to the same authority [2] the grains of silver halide in a developing paper seldom exceed 0.01 to 0.02 micron and are mostly below the resolving power of the microscope.

In general, emulsions for developing papers are not washed to remove the extraneous salts, nor digested or ripened, except for the cold ripening which may take place in storage before or after coating. Various substances, the nature of which is largely a commercial secret, are added to paper emulsions, these additions being necessitated by the properties of the paper base or to control the color of the image.

Papers in which the sensitive halide is silver chloride develop rapidly and are used for both contact and projection printing.

Bromide papers in which the sensitive halide is silver bromide develop slowly producing a black image and are used almost exclusively for projection printing.

Chlorobromide papers contain both silver chloride and silver bromide and are used for both contact and projection printing. The speed and image color of these papers vary with the proportions of one halide to the other. In the faster papers producing black images, silver bromide dominates, whereas in the slower papers designed to produce warm black or brown black images, there is a larger proportion of silver chloride.

Paper Base. This is always made especially for photographic purposes. It must be free from all foreign substances which would affect the emulsion, cause discoloration of the paper stock with time, and must have the physical strength to withstand the action of the various processing solutions. While pure rag paper stocks were formerly regarded as absolutely necessary for photographic purposes, paper base made from wood pulp is now used and is, in some respects, superior to the rag stocks formerly employed.

Paper stocks for photographic papers differ in three particulars: (1) in weight or thickness, (2) surface, and (3) color.

Depending upon the thickness of the base, photographic papers are usually classified as (1) light weight, (2) single weight, (3) medium weight, and (4) double weight. Single weight paper is ordinarily used for small prints or for prints to be mounted to solid mounts. Double weight papers are preferred for those left unmounted or if not to be mounted solidly. Light weight papers are used where weight

---

[1] *Photography as a Scientific Implement*, p. 162, D. Van Nostrand Co., Inc., New York.

[2] *J. Chem. Ed.* **4**, 298, 465, 749 (1927).

is a consideration and more particularly when a high degree of flexibility is required.

In most cases, a paper is obtainable in several surfaces, the more common being: (1) glossy, (2) semi-matt, sometimes called "velvet," (3) matt, (4) rough, and occasionally (5) very rough. All other surfaces may be regarded as variations of these. The semi-matt, matt, and rough papers may or may not have a "sheen" or luster.

The usual colors are (1) white, (2) natural or cream white, (3) buff, also known as old ivory, and (4) pensé or pink. Blue, green, and other paper stocks have been supplied for special effects.

The selection of a particular surface and color is largely a matter of personal preference; however, the use to be made of the print is, at times, an important factor. Glossy papers, for example, are preferred for prints for reproduction or where fine detail and a brilliant image are required. Semi-matt papers are used where the glossy surface is not desirable but a surface with a decided texture would obscure fine detail. Matt, or fine-grain papers, result in a softer, less brilliant, image which is regarded by many as more "artistic." Rough papers are used chiefly for large prints where the general effect desired is one of breadth, with broad masses rather than detail.

The selection as to color depends upon the subject, the color of the image, and the effect desired. In general, for subjects with cold colors and for reproduction, a white paper stock is preferred. For pictorial work, sunshine effects, portraits, landscapes with foliage, the greater warmth of a cream

white, or "natural" color base may be preferable. Buff colored paper stock is preferred by many for toned prints, for portraiture, and other subjects for which a warm, colored image is suitable.

The D Log E Curve of Developing Papers. The D log E curve of the typical developing paper either does not have a true straight line portion or only a short one [3] (Fig. 25.1). The toe portion is

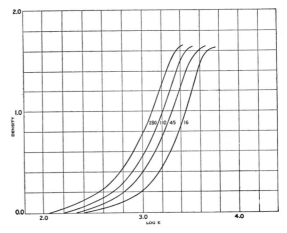

Fig. 25.1. D log E curves for chloride paper.

longer and the shoulder more abrupt, i.e., flattens out more quickly than with negative materials. The curves of bromide papers (Fig. 25.2) ordinarily have a more clearly defined straight line portion than chloride papers. In development (Fig. 25.1), the shape of the curve of a typical silver chloride paper changes rapidly at

[3] For sensitometric data on other printing processes: Jones, Mees and Nutting, *Phot. J.* **38**, 342 (1914). Curves are given for platinum, gelatin P–O–P, and carbon. Hardy and Perrin, *J. Franklin Inst.* **205**, 97 (1928) (bichromated gelatin). *Keilich, Zeit. Wiss. Phot.* **37**, 195 (1938). *Richter, Zeit. Wiss. Phot.* **23**, 61 (1924) (carbon transparencies). *Heigl, Dentscher Drucker,* **48**, 449 (1942).

WANDELT, "Modern Developing Papers," *Phot. Ind.* **32**, 1350 (1934); *Sci. et Ind. Phot.* II, **6**, 121 (1935).

CHARRIOU AND VALETTE, "Photographic Emulsions for Printing Papers," *Chemie et Ind.* **36**, 888 (1936).

POTTER, "Effect of Surface on Print Quality," *Defender Trade Bulletin,* May–June 1936, p. 3.

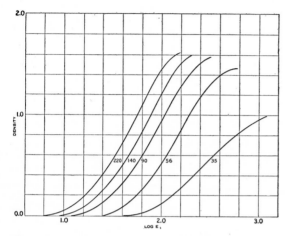

FIG. 25.2.   *D* log *E* curves of a bromide paper.

characteristic differences. These are shown in Fig. 25.4 where the three curves, ABC represent chloride, chlorobromide and bromide papers, respectively, each of which has the same exposure range and maximum density. It will be noted that the curve of the chloride paper shows little, if any, straight-line portion and that the portion most nearly approaching a straight line is in the upper density range. The shoulder portion of the curve is very short. On the other hand, the toe portion is long and sweeping. Curve C, representing a bromide emulsion, shows a more clearly defined straight line portion, a more gradual shoulder, and a less sweeping toe portion. Curve B, representing a chlorobromide emulsion is of an intermediate character as might be expected. The curves of both chlorobromide and bromchloride emulsion vary in character with the halide which predominates and the extent of predominance.

first but soon reaches a stable shape and, upon continued development, shifts to the left without any appreciable change in shape, slope, or in the maximum density. With bromide, chlorobromide and brom-chloride papers (Fig. 25.3) the changes occurring in the early stages of development are more pronounced but these two reach, in a comparatively short time, a *stabilized* curve shape which is characteristic of the emulsion and does not change importantly with further development.

The *D* log *E* curves of chloride, chloro-bromide and bromide papers show certain

Density Scale. The total density scale of a paper is the range in density available or the difference in D_0 and the maximum density. The maximum density and, therefore, the density range, depends upon the emulsion and the surface of the paper. In Fig. 25.5 are three *D* log *E* curves for the same silver chloride emulsion coated on (A) a glossy paper stock, (B) a semi-matt paper and (C) a matt paper. The density range for the glossy paper is approximately 1.7; for the semi-matt 1.5, and 1.2 for the matt. Since the reflection density is equal to log $1/R$, the brightness range (ratio of the amount of light reflected from the white paper and the maximum density) is $1:50$ for the glossy paper as compared with $1:30$ for the semi-matt, and $1:16$ for the matt paper.

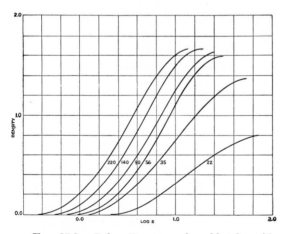

FIG. 25.3.   *D* log *E* curves of a chlorobromide paper.

Of greater practical concern is the *useful density scale*. A lengthy investigation of the subject by Jones and Nelson of the Kodak Research Laboratories has shown that in practice the full density range of

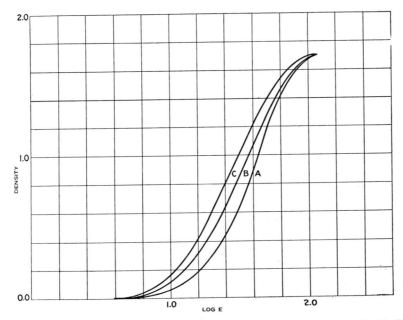

FIG. 25.4.   *D* log *E* curves showing the characteristic differences of chloride, bromide, and chlorobromide emulsions in curve shape.

the paper is rarely, if ever, used. Usually the maximum print density is much closer to the upper end of the straight-line portion of the curve than to the maximum density. This would seem to indicate that, to most printers, sharp, distinct differences in density (tone) in the shadows of the print are

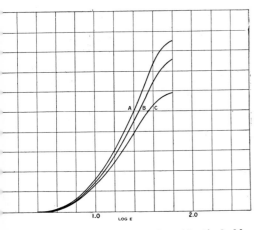

FIG. 25.5.   *D* log *E* curves of an identical chloride emulsion coated on glossy, semi-matt and matt surface papers.

more important in good reproduction than the increase in the brightness range which would result from the use of the full density scale of the paper. At the other end of the *D* log *E* curve, the variation is greater. Usually the brightest highlight of the subject is represented in the print by a density very near the end of the toe portion of the curve, but in some cases the brightest highlight is represented by white paper. This, when it occurs, does not appear to be from deliberate choice but from the impossibility of fitting the exposure scale of the paper to the density scale of the negative but, since even in this case the maximum density of the paper is not used, it indicates that in practice most printers prefer to sacrifice tonal differences in the highlights rather than in the shadows. They conclude that the useful limit of the toe portion of the curve is a function of gradient and have suggested the point at which the gradient is 0.1, the gradient of a line from that point which is tangent to the shoulder of the

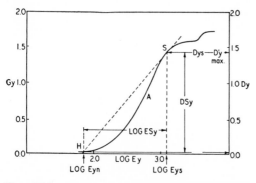

FIG. 25.6. *D* log *E* curve showing limits of useful density and exposure as defined by ASA specification Z38.2.3—1947.

curve (Fig. 25.6). The density at *S* in this case represents reasonably well the maximum useful density. Thus the useful density range of the paper lies between these points on the *D* log *E* curve or

$$DS = D_S - D_L.$$

Exposure Scale. As with negative materials, the total exposure scale is the range of exposure, or more conveniently log exposure, over which differences in reflection densities are produced. The total exposure scale, however, is of less interest than the useful exposure scale. This, in accordance with specification Z38.2.3—1947 [4] of the American Standards Association, is defined as the difference in log *E* corresponding to the useful density scale or the difference in log *E* values for the points *S* and *L* [5] on the *D* log *E* curve in Fig. 25.6.

Thus:

$$ES = \log E_S - \log E_L.$$

Average Gradient. Gamma, as measured in the usual manner from the slope of the straight-line portion of the curve, is not a very significant characteristic of a developing paper because the straight-line portion,

[4] American Standard Z38.2.3—1947, Sensitometry of Photographic Papers.
[5] For instrumental methods of determining these points, see Swift, *Phot. J.* **86B**, 71 (1946).

if one exists, includes only a small part of the useful density scale. The gradient of the useful portion of the curve is more completely defined as the slope of a straight-line connecting points *H* and *S* (Fig. 25.6). The gradient of this line, *DS*/log *ES*, is termed the *average gradient*.

Speed. Speed has been variously defined in terms of the exposure necessary to produce the threshold density and by others as the exposure producing the maximum density. The American Standard defines speed as a function of the exposure producing the maximum useful density

$$S = 10^4/E_S$$

where E_S is the exposure for the point *S* (Fig. 25.6).

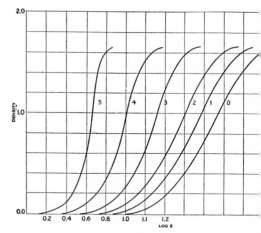

FIG. 25.7. *D* log *E* curves of the six grades of a contact paper of silver chloride.

The Contrast of a Printing Paper. *D* log *E* curves of six contrast grades of a typical silver chloride paper are shown in Fig. 25.7. The curves have been shifted laterally along the exposure axis to avoid the overlapping and confusion that would result if all were plotted on the same exposure scale.

SOUTHWORTH, "Print Exposure and Paper Speed," *Brit. J. Phot.* **83**, 641 (1936).

The contrast of a printing paper depends on a number of factors the proper evaluation of which is exceedingly difficult. The problem may be approached from two points of view: (1) the measurement and evaluation of the inherent contrast of the paper as a function of the gradients of the $D \log E$ curve and the density range, and (2) the evaluation of contrast in terms of the relationship of the sensitometric characteristics of the paper and the contrast of the print from a given negative. The first of these has been studied in detail by Jones,[6] and the second has been stated by Romer and Rajeski [7] as follows:

"The definition of gradation should characterize those qualities of the paper which, whatever the shape of its characteristic curve and its type of surface, enable it to produce the best possible print from a negative of given contrast. It should allow the numerical expression of this quality, and the figures obtained should bear a simple relation to the densitometric data of the negative for which the paper is most suited."

Bontenbal,[8] Romer and Rajeski,[9] and Chilton [10] all came to the conclusion that, for practical purposes, the contrast, or printing capacity, of a paper may be defined in terms of its useful exposure scale but differ in the method of fixing the limits of the useful exposure scale. Bontenbal preferred densities of 0.25 and 0.09, but he was concerned only with the reproduction of straight-line negatives. Romer and Rajeski suggested a gradient 0.2 of the maximum gradient (γ) in the highlights, and 0.5 γ as the limit in the shoulder. Chilton suggested gradients of 0.1 γ and 0.5 γ.

None of these take into consideration the changes in subjective contrast which may

[6] Jones, *J. Franklin Inst.* **202**, 117, 469, 589 (1926); **204**, 41 (1927).

[7] Romer and Rajeski, *Phot. J.* **82**, 66 (1942).

[8] Bontenbal, *Phot. J.* **78**, 76 (1938).

[9] Romer and Rajeski, *Phot. J.* **82**, 66 (1942).

[10] Chilton, *Phot. J.* **82**, 151, 232 (1942).

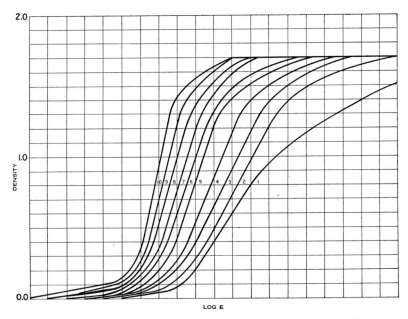

Fig. 25.8. $D \log E$ curves of Varigam paper with filters 1–10.

arise from differences in the shape of the *D* log *E* curve within the useful exposure scale.

Variable Contrast Papers. Developing papers, in which the contrast of the image may be varied over a wide range by changes in the color of the exposing light, have been introduced commercially in both England and America. With these papers it is possible by the use of filters to duplicate, on one paper, the range of contrast obtained on the different contrast grades of other papers.

In one of these (*Multigrade*),[11] is a blend of two emulsions, one of low contrast sensitive only to blue and violet light, the other of high contrast sensitive to green as well as to blue and violet light. The other (*Varigam*)[12] is a single emulsion to which a green sensitizer has been added. It is believed that the sensitizer is adsorbed to the larger grains in greater amounts than to the smaller with the result that the larger grains are made more sensitive to green. Thus with an emulsion in which the contrast varies with the average size of the silver halide grains utilized in the exposure, the use of a yellow filter will confine the exposure to the larger grains, producing a soft print, while a blue filter will cause only the smaller grains to be affected, producing a print of higher contrast. If a single exposure is made through a filter transmitting both green and blue, an intermediate degree of contrast is obtained, depending upon the proportion of each transmitted.[13]

Variable contrast papers of a different type have been introduced for printing from amateur negatives on a roll for continuous processing (*Monodex, Unicontrast*, etc.). These are not true variable contrast papers, however, but simply emulsions with a characteristic curve of such shape that the contrast of the print may be adjusted to the requirements of the negative by exposing so as to use the proper part of the paper curve. The principle is shown in Fig. 25.9.

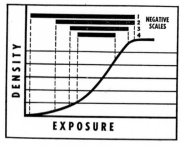

Fig. 25.9. *D* log *E* curve of a typical single contrast paper for photofinishing.

Safelights for Developing Papers. Since the darkness and contrast of the print must be determined by its appearance in the illumination provided by the safelight lamp, this should

1. Permit the best possible judgment of print contrast and color as compared to subsequent white light examination.
2. Provide maximum visibility with sufficient safety; i.e., freedom from fogging the sensitive material.
3. Cause minimum visual discomfort.

The sensitivity of chloride papers ends at approximately 450 to 480 mμ. They

[11] Renwick, *Phot. J.* **80**, 320 (1940).

[12] Potter, *J. Phot. Soc. Amer.* **8**, 507 (1942); *Phot. J.* **83**, 296 (1943); *Phot. Tech* **2**, 59 (1940).

[13] For patents on papers of this type: U.S.P. 2,384,598, Carroll, Assigned to Eastman Kodak Co. B.P. 552,368 (1941), Kodak Ltd. B.P. 580,173 (1943), Stevens and Kodak Ltd. B.P. 541,510 and 541,515 (5 patents), Davey, Robinson, Amor, and Kodak Ltd. See also, *Brit. J. Phot.* **89**, 62 (1942).

Chilton, "Some New Techniques for Multigrade," *Phot. J.* **83**, 151 (1943).
Turner, "Further Data on Multigrade," *Miniature Camera World*, Sept. (1940), p. 448.
Meister, "Multigrade and Varigam," *Camera* (Lucerne **27**, 149 (1949).

re, in other words, sensitive to ultraviolet, violet, and blue. A yellow filter absorbing all wave lengths of less than 500 mμ (Fig. 25.10 is quite satisfactory. The sensitivity of typical nonsensitized chlorobromide and bromide papers extends to between 500 and 520 mμ. Generally, these papers are considerably faster and for these reasons a yellow-green safelight absorbing all wave lengths of less than 525 mμ affords sufficient safety with good visibility (Fig. 25.11). Safelights of the type shown, with appreciable absorption beyond 600 mμ, are much to be preferred over orange or orange-red safelights, as careful tests [14] have shown that (1) it is difficult to judge the quality of the print in orange or orange-red light because of the increase in apparent contrast, (2) for equal visibility, the yellow-green light has less tendency to fog than an orange or orange-red, and (3) it is less tiring on the eye.

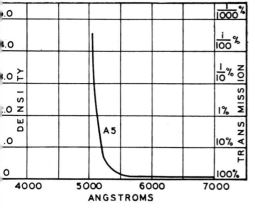

FIG. 25.10. Spectral transmission characteristics of a typical yellow safelight for slow chloride papers.

For various reasons a number of papers are now dye sensitized to the blue green and green. These include the variable contrast papers, photocopy papers, and several papers for projection printing. The sensitivity of these papers extends to about 540

14 Centa, Amer. Phot. **39**, 20 (1945).

mμ (Fig. 25.12). Safelights transmitting principally between 550 mμ and 600 are satisfactory for such materials and are preferable for the reasons given in the preceding paragraph to the orange and orange-red safelights which have been recommended.

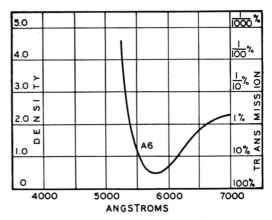

FIG. 25.11. Spectral transmission characteristics of a yellow-green safelight for chlorobromide papers.

Determination of the Printing Exposure.
Usually, two interrelated problems are involved in the determination of the exposure: (1) the selection of the proper contrast grade of paper for the negative, (2) the exposure required to produce a print of the required density. Both of these are ordinarily determined by trial and error based upon the judgment of the printer from past experience, or from test strips.

The determination of printing exposures from the measurement of negative density has received considerable study in recent years, particularly in connection with the design of printing equipment for photofinishing, where elimination of losses from errors in judgment is an important factor in production. Printers employing photocells to control the exposure of the print were patented as early as 1902 and are now

VARDEN AND KRAUSE, "Printing Exposure Determination by Photoelectric Methods," *Amer. Ann. Phot.* **64**, 30 (1950).

widely used in large-scale photofinishing. In these, the total (integrated) density of the negative is measured. The studies of Tuttle,[15] Jones and Nelson,[16] as well as practical experience, have shown that measurements of the integrated density correlate very well with the printing exposure, but that the minimum density of the negative is a more dependable indication of exposure with negatives having an unusual distribution of density. The maximum density, often recommended, has been found almost valueless as a means of determining the proper exposure.

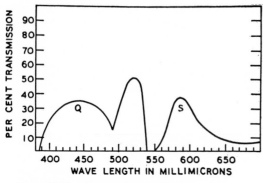

Fig. 25.12. Spectral sensitivity curve of a green-sensitive printing paper (Q) and the recommended safelight (S).

Photoelectric exposure meters may be used in projection printing to determine exposures by measuring the light at a point directly below the lens; or a selected portion of the projected image may be measured with a small spot photometer of which several types are available commercially. In most of these, the brightness of a portion of the image, received on a white field, is measured by comparing it with the illumination on a small spot which is illuminated by an electric lamp controlled either by a rheostat or a density wedge.

---

[15] Tuttle, *J. Franklin Inst.*, 1937, p. 315; *J. Soc. Mot. Pict. Eng.* **18**, 172 (1932).

[16] Jones and Nelson, *J. Opt. Soc. Amer.* **32**, 558 (1942): **38**, 897 (1948).

Developers for Black Tones. A factor of major importance in the development of prints is the color of the image. Excluding the effect of the paper base, the color of the image depends upon the dispersity of the silver deposit; i.e., the average size of the particles of metallic silver comprising the image.[17] The smaller the average particle size, the warmer the color.

With chloride, bromchloride and bromide emulsions designed to produce black or blue-black images, the purest black the paper will yield is obtained when the solvent effect of the developer is at a minimum, i.e., when a relatively large proportion of alkali is employed with only sufficient restrainer to prevent fog and when the image is developed to finality, i.e., until the latent image is completely developed.[18]

Developers for Warm Tones. To obtain warm tones on chloride or chlorobromide papers, the alkali is reduced and the amount

---

[17] Jones, *Phot. J.* **51**, 151 (1911).

[18] The production of blue-black tones is facilitated with many papers, particularly those of the slow silver chloride type, by the addition to the developer of nitrobenzimidazol, benzotriazol, nitroimidazol, nitrosoquanidine, thiosemicarbazide, thiosemicarbazone, thioglycollic acid, 5-amidoquanide, quinone chloride, iodosobenzine, quinoline, and potassium sulfocyanate.

A very important factor in the production of good black tones is the use of a fresh developer. Chloride papers are very sensitive to soluble bromide, and, since the amount of bromide in the developer increases with every print developed, the developer must be renewed frequently to obtain good blacks. Very small traces of hypo have a marked effect on the color of the image, changing it from a good black or blue-black to a degraded color.

Schwartz, "Substances Affording Development of Bluish-Toned Images on Gelatino-Silver Chloride Papers," *Sci. et Ind. Phot.* (II) **7**, 113 (1936).

Seyewetz, "Constitution of Substances Giving Bluish Images with Silver Chloride," *Proc Ninth Int. Cong. of Phot.*, Paris, 1935. *Sci. et Ind. Phot.* (II), **6**, 300 (1935).

of bromide or other restrainer increased in order (1) to increase the solvent action during development, and (2) to prevent the complete development of the exposed grains of silver halide before an image of satisfactory gradation and quality is obtained. The use of developing agents of low potential, such as chloroquinol and glycin, alone or in combination with metol and hydroquinone, is favorable toward the production of warm-colored images. If these are heavily restrained with potassium bromide, the color of the image may be controlled to a considerable extent with many chlorobrom papers, by varying (1) the amount of restrainer, (2) the dilution of the developer, and (3) the time of development. Warm-tone chloride papers, in general, are less adaptable than chlorobromide to manipulation because they develop more rapidly.

Control of Contrast by Modification of the Developer. The contrast of the image is, for practical purposes, determined by the emulsion used and can be controlled only within narrow limits by variation in the time of development or the composition of the developer. Slight changes in image contrast may be obtained with a metol-hydroquinone by varying the proportions of the two developing agents. Increasing the amount of metol and decreasing the hydroquinone tends to produce softer results, whereas increasing the amount of

hydroquinone and alkali, and the addition of glycin,[19] tend to increase contrast. The usefulness of these methods of control is limited, in many cases, by the degradation of the higher densities, with a reduction in contrast or by an image of unsatisfactory color.

Fixation of Developing Papers. The fine-grain emulsions of silver chloride and silver bromide used for printing fix much more rapidly than negative materials.

Chloride papers have been shown by Lumiere and Seyewetz [20] to fix completely in a fresh fixing bath within twenty to thirty seconds. The customary five to ten minutes is justified, however, when prints are fixed in quantities and in a used fixing bath. Prolonged fixation is undesirable, however, because (1) the image may be reduced causing the print to appear bleached, (2) the color of the image may be changed, particularly with warm-tone papers, by partial sulfiding of the image, and (3) longer times of fixing increase the adsorption of hypo by the paper base and require longer washing.[21]

It is often assumed that since paper emulsions contain less silver than negative materials, a fixing bath will fix more prints than film. Crabtree and Eaton have shown,[22] however, that the insoluble complexes of silver-sodium-thiosulfate formed in fixing are strongly adsorbed by the paper base, and the fixing bath becomes incapable of fixing prints thoroughly long before its capacity to dissolve the silver halide of the emulsion is reached. If a single fixing bath is used, the safety limit is reached with about 30 8 × 10 prints per

---

BURKI AND JENNY recommended (*Camera* (Lucerne) 22, 3 (1943)) a pyrocatechol developer with the addition of ammonium sulfate for reddish to red chalk tones on chlorobromide emulsions.

WIEGLEB described (*Camera* (Lucerne) 10, 151 (1931)) the addition of selenium salts to the developer for brown, red, purple, and blue tones on chlorobromide papers.

WILLIAMS, "Toning by Direct Development," *Camera* (Phila.) 64, 20 (1942).

HOWELL, "Brown Blacks by Direct Development," *J. Phot. Soc. Amer.* 10, 155 (1944).

[19] Varden, *Photo-Technique* 2, 32 (October 1940). Kett, *Brit. J. Phot.* 92, 306 (1945).

[20] Lumiere and Seyewetz, *Brit. J. Phot.* 71, 103 (1924).

[21] Crabtree, Eaton, and Muehler, *J. Phot. Soc. Amer.* 9, 115 (1943). Weyde, *Brit. J. Phot.* 82, 326 (1935).

[22] *Ibid.*

gallon of the typical acid fixing and hardening bath containing potassium alum. Beyond this point there is danger that the insoluble complexes adsorbed to the paper base may be sufficient to result in noticeable staining in the course of time. If two fixing baths are used, the second relatively fresh, it is possible to fix about 150 8 × 10 prints per gallon. However, for maximum stability three fixing baths should be used in succession. Under these conditions, it is possible to fix about 150 8 × 10 prints, or their equivalent, per gallon. At least two fixing baths should always be used if the permanency of the image is of importance.

Washing. It is necessary to remove hypo more completely from prints than from negative materials because (1) the nature of a print is such that changes in color or density are more apparent, and (2) because such changes are more likely to occur due (a) to the finer grain of the reduced silver and (b) the retention of hypo and silver by the base. Because of this, the time of washing is much longer for papers than for films or plates.[23] Crabtree, Eaton, and Muehler found [24] that prints cannot be washed entirely free of hypo within a reasonable length of time, i.e., in less than two to three hours, unless a hypo eliminator is used.

The following eliminator was found satisfactory (Kodak formula HE-1):

	Metric	Avoirdupois
Water	500.0 cc.	16 oz.
Hydrogen peroxide (3% solution)	125.0 cc.	4 fl. oz.
Kodak ammonia (3% solution)	100.0 cc.	3¼ fl. oz.
Water to make	1.0 liter	32 oz.

[23] The time of washing may be reduced approximately one-half by placing the prints, after rinsing, in a weak alkali, such as a 2% solution of Kodak Balanced Alkali, for 2 minutes and then washing as usual.

[24] Crabtree, Eaton, and Muehler, *J. Phot. Soc. Amer.* **6**, 6 (1940).

To make 3% ammonia, dilute 1 part of 28% ammonia with 9 parts of water.

After washing for about thirty minutes transfer prints, one at a time, to the hypo eliminator. Turn prints over and over in the eliminator to insure free access of solution to both sides. After 5 minutes (70° F.) remove and wash for an additional ten minutes before drying.[25]

Tests for the presence of hypo can be made by any of the usual methods, but for prints the silver nitrate test is the most reliable.

Temperature has considerable influence on the washing time. While raising the temperature will result in more rapid removal of hypo, temperatures above 70–75° F. are inadvisable owing to softening of the gelatin and the greater danger of damage to the print or sticking to blotters, or squeegee tins, when drying. The use of a hypo eliminator is advisable when it is necessary to use water for washing at a temperature below 50° F., because the time of washing at low temperatures becomes inconveniently long.

Permanency of Prints. The fading of silver images is the result of the partial conversion of the silver of the image to silver sulfide from (1) the decomposition of hypo left in the image from insufficient washing, (2) insufficient fixation which results in the formation of complex silver sodium-thiosulfates which decompose to form silver sulfide, or (3) to attack by hy-

[25] With some papers this solution may lead to a slight change in tone. If this is objectionable add 15 grams of potassium bromide to each 32 oz. (1 gram per liter). The slight yellowing of the highlights may be minimized by placing the prints, upon removal from the hypo eliminator, in 1% acetic acid for two minutes. The eliminator should be discarded after treating 50 8 × 10 prints or their equivalent per gallon.

CRABTREE, EATON, AND MUEHLER, "Fixing and Washing for Permanence," *P.S.A. Journal* **9**, 115 (1943).

drogen sulfide, sulfur dioxide and other gases generally present in the atmosphere, particularly in industrial localities. Fading from all sources, but particularly the last named, is greatly accelerated by high temperature and by moisture.

Prints made for historical or other records should be fixed in three successive fixing baths and thoroughly washed using a hypo eliminator to insure the complete removal of hypo.[26]

Fading, due to external agents, may be reduced (1) by sulfide or gold toning, (2) by covering the print with a waterproof lacquer, and (3) by drymounting rather than the use of water-miscible adhesives. The latter, being hygroscopic, tend to contribute to facing by attracting moisture to the image. Gold toning is generally preferable to sulfide toning, as the change in the color of the print is so slight with many papers as to be unimportant. In using a lacquer, care should be taken to use only those which have been tested and found to be free of any deleterious effect on the image.

Reduction and Intensification of Prints. Generally speaking, the action of the various reducers is the same as with negative materials.[27] The permanganate reducer acts nearly proportionally, whereas iodine-cyanide is perhaps the best subtractive reducer because it is nonstaining. For superproportional reduction, persulfate alone appears suitable. In practically all cases, it is necessary to use a diluted solution to keep the process under control.

For local reduction it is much simpler usually to work on the dry print with a iodine-thiocarbamide reducer in alcohol.[28]

Solution A—Iodine	20 grains
Methyl alcohol	1 oz.
Solution B—Thiocarbamide	40 grains
Water to	1 oz.

For use, take equal parts of A and B. Control rate of reduction by dilution.

The dry print is pinned down by the corners to a board and the reducing solution applied with a water color brush of appropriate size or, on larger areas, a tuft of cotton. In the other hand must be a larger brush, or a tuft of cotton, charged with methyl alcohol. This is applied immediately without waiting to see if the reduction has gone far enough to prevent further reduction. The excess alcohol is then blotted off and the operation repeated if further reduction is desired. As soon as the area has been reduced sufficiently, dip the print in hypo (without previous washing) for two minutes and then wash and dry as usual.

Intensification sometimes results in an improvement, but frequently the color of the image after intensification is displeasing. The chromium intensifier produces good results with some papers. Certain toning processes, such as copper and uranium, are also intensifiers and may be used if warm tones are desired.

Spotting Prints. Even with the utmost care in avoiding dust, most prints will require some spotting. Clear spots may be removed with spotting (water) colors, dyes, or spotting pencils. These are obtainable in at least two colors—black and sepia; if dyes or colors are used, these two may be mixed to match warm-black prints.

With spotting colors or dyes, the first essential is a brush that can be brought to a fine point; the second, is a steady hand and a fair amount of patience. Using spot-

[26] Crabtree, Eaton, and Muehler, *J. Phot. Soc. Amer.* **6**, 6 (1940).

[27] Jones and Fawkes, *Brit. J. Phot.* **68**, 275 (1924).

FREYTAG, "Factors Influencing Permanency of Prints," *Phot. Chron.* **44**, 401 (1937).

[28] Greenall, *Brit. J. Phot.* **73**, 383 (1926).

ting colors, the brush is first moistened and then rotated on the color slab to take up the color and at the same time maintain a fine point on the brush. Dyes usually need to be diluted. Either a very dilute solution should be prepared and the spot built up to the proper density by repeated applications, or solutions of different dilution prepared (and labeled) for use as required.

The brush should be held almost vertical and brought down on the spot so that the fine-tipped point just touches the spot. If the first application does not darken the spot sufficiently, another application should be made. It is not necessary to take up more color or dye on the brush each time; in fact, as long as the brush is applying color it should not be renewed. With spotting colors moistening the brush slightly from time to time will keep the color flowing. Start with the spots in the denser portions first and work down to those in the lighter areas as the color on the brush weakens. Large spots should be filled in with a stippling motion but still using only the tip of the brush.

Spotting pencils are easier to use but cannot be used on glossy papers and have the disadvantage of showing on the surface when the print is viewed at an angle.

Methods of Finishing Photographs. In artistic hands, prints may often be improved by the addition of a pigment of suitable color to darken areas which lack depth. The pigment is first reduced to the proper consistency by dilution with the thinning medium using a palette knife and a clean glass plate for mixing, finally spreading out in a thin layer when mixed. The print is then covered with the medium (Megilip) and the pigment applied, using a tuft of absorbent cotton. If an excess is applied, rub down with clean cotton. Small areas may be touched up with a brush and heavier pigment. Details which have been

covered may be lightened by applying the thinning medium with a brush or a tuft of cotton on the end of a toothpick or a match. If a serious error is made, the pigment may be removed entirely with the thinning medium, or turpentine and a soft cloth.

The finishing of prints with crayons is not as popular as in past years, but a modification known as "abrasion-tone," developed by Mortensen, has been used by him and his students with great success. The process employs a "toning powder," made by powdering Faber "Castell" Polychromos crayons, black and brown, and for added emphasis a carbon black drawing pencil (Wolff BB). The toning powder, prepared by rubbing the crayon on sandpaper, is applied evenly and thinly to the areas to be darkened with absorbent cotton. Any excess is removed by rubbing lightly with a wad of clean cotton. The powder is removed from the highlight areas with a kneaded rubber eraser, no attempt being made to blend the highlights with the surrounding areas. This is done by sprinkling a small amount of powdered pumice on the print and rubbing lightly with clean cotton. If this leaves the highlights smudged, they are cleaned with an eraser a second time and the margins blended as before. Finally add any clear highlights required with a stiff pencil eraser.

The carbon pencil is used on areas which cannot be darkened sufficiently with the powder crayon. Large areas are crisscrossed with the pencil in broad, sweeping strokes and blended with a little pumice on a wad of cotton. Highlights are introduced by removing the deposit with a pencil eraser.

As in all processes of this kind, the re-

JORDAN, "The Mediobrom Process," *Amer. Phot.* **36**, 12 (October 1942).

SANCHEZ, "Mediobrom," *Minicam* **7**, 38 (August 1944).

sults depend upon the imagination and the artistic judgment of the user.

The coloring of prints is an art in itself and as such outside the scope of this work. Either oil colors or dyes (water colors) may be used but dyes are more suitable for commercial work on gloss papers. Coloring with oil has the advantage that errors are easily removed by the application of the thinning medium, or turpentine on absorbent cotton. The transparent colors sold for coloring photographs should be used rather than the opaque pigments of the artist. The colors are mixed and applied with cotton, as described in the first paragraph under this heading.

When dyes are to be used, the print should first be placed for ten to fifteen minutes in a 2 to 5% solution of ammonia, then washed five minutes in running water. When ready for coloring, the print is placed on a sheet of glass, or other smooth, waterproof surface, and surface water blotted off with lintless blotting paper. Prepare much diluted solutions of the required colors and apply with a sable, or camel's-hair, brush, blotting off the surface solution after each application. Use only light washes of color, building up to the color required through successive application. Concentrated colors,

however, can be used for touching up small, brilliantly colored details.

The airbush is used extensively by commercial artists for the retouching of prints for reproduction. The airbrush is a spray gun, similar to those used in painting walls, buildings, machinery, etc., but much smaller, being little larger than a pencil. It is designed to produce a fine spray of color which may be used to build up the density of a part of the print or, using a white pigment, to lighten an area that is too dark. In working on small areas, or to produce sharp lines, the portions which are not to be sprayed are covered with protecting (*frisket*) paper. This is stripped off when the work is finished. The airbrush produces a uniformity of tone that is next to impossible to duplicate with a brush and by going back and forth over the area it can be built up gradually to exactly the tone desired. If a gradation of tone from dark to light is required, this can be obtained by repeated spraying much more directly and simply than in any other way. Thus, it is possible for a retoucher who is skilled in the use of the airbrush to make extensive changes without the work showing in the reproduction.

Paper Negatives. Duplicate negatives on paper have become quite popular with pictorialists in recent years because of the broad effects obtainable by printing through the paper and because of the ease

---

The term "Brometching" was applied by Luellyn (*Amat. Phot.* **80**, 349 (1935); *Brit. J. Phot.* **83**, 4 (1936)) to a process in which a bromide or chlorobromide print is given from two to eight times normal exposure, developed as usual but much darker than usual, rinsed in water, and then partially reduced in a permanganate reducer. On matt and rough papers, reduction increases the brilliancy of the image and produces a granular texture which, for many subjects is quite pleasing, resembling superficially the texture of a bromoil print. See also Martz, "Silver Etching," *Minicam*, March 1935, p 29.

MORTENSEN, "Print Finishing," Camera Craft Publishing Co., San Francisco.

DURHAM, *Coloring Photographs*, F. Weber & Co., New York.

LEHART, *Coloring Photographs in Oil and Water Colors*, American Photographic Publishing Co., Boston.

MARSHALL, *Photo Oil Coloring*, American Photographic Publishing Co., Boston.

TOBIAS, *The Art of Coloring Photographic Prints*, American Photographic Publishing Co., Boston.

TOBIAS, *A Manual of Airbrush Technique*, American Photographic Publishing Co., Boston.

with which local retouching may be done on the back of the paper.

Any smooth, single-weight paper, free of objectionable differences in transparency of the proper contrast for the negative may be used. Some workers prefer a glossy paper, others a smooth semi-matt surface. Transparency papers of the type having an emulsion on both sides are more transparent but generally produce too much contrast except with soft negatives. Generally, the paper-negative process is employed only for fairly large prints; i.e., 11 × 14 inches or larger; however, smaller prints can be made if the proper technique is employed and critical definition is not required. Prints from paper negatives are not necessarily coarse or grainy. With the proper technique, paper negatives can be made which are only slightly inferior in this respect to those on film.

Some workers make an enlarged positive on paper, retouch this, and made the duplicate negative by contact printing. Others make the positive on film and the paper negative from this. The use of film results in a sharper image with better reproduction of detail and is the favorite method of many for this reason. In this case, simple retouching is done on the positive while major changes are made on the paper negative. It is possible, of course, to make the positive on paper, retouch this, and make a negative on film. This, however, is not as popular as the other methods.

When paper is used, whether for the positive or the negative the graininess of the image—by transmitted light—is greatly reduced if the exposure is made through the paper base; i.e., with the back of the paper toward the positive, or the original negative, as the case may be. The exposure must be increased from ten to twenty times, depending upon the transparency of the paper, and a sheet of black paper

placed against the emulsion to absorb any light which passes through the emulsion and prevent its reflection back into the emulsion from the white surface of the easel, or the back of the printing frame. Exposure and development must be regulated to produce an image of the proper density and contrast when viewed by transmitted light. If properly exposed, the highlights of the image will appear veiled by reflected light and the deeper shadows will be much darker than for a good print, but usually not so dark as to completely obscure shadow detail.

Instead of exposing through the paper, some workers prefer to expose the paper in the usual way, after which the emulsion side is placed in contact with black paper and a second flash exposure made through the back. The purpose of this exposure from the rear is to expose the emulsion so that upon development the densities produced by the flash exposure will compensate for the differences in the transparency of the paper stock. In this way an image almost free of graininess can be obtained. The proper exposure is found by exposing a sheet of paper in steps, dividing this to obtain a number of test strips, and developing these for different times. Upon examining these strips by transmitted light, the exposure and development producing the most uniform density can be selected readily.

Both the paper negative and positive can be retouched easily on the back. On the positive, a black, carbon pencil, or for larger areas a crayon, or crayon sauce applied with a stomp, may be used to accent shadows, tone down light areas, and soften harsh lines. Small highlights which are obscured by this treatment can be introduced with a sharp-pointed rubber eraser. On the negative, the same materials may be used to accent highlights, soften contrast of lines, and increase the density of highlights and halftones. Local areas may also be reduced with a ferricyanide-hypo reducer or with thiocarbamide. Oil paints, dyes, and substances such as black stove polish may be used but are not as easily controlled.

Naturally the usual methods of shading and dodging may be used in exposing both the positive and the negative.

It is sometimes recommended that the paper negative be oiled or waxed to increase its transparency and reduce the time of exposure. However, the tendency of the negative to pick up dust and grit is increased and if the proper paper is used the reduction in exposure hardly seems worthwhile.

PEEL, "How to Make and Use Paper Negatives," *Camera* (Baltimore) **65** (March), 32, 91 (1943).

WIGHTMAN, "Making Pictorial Photographs from Paper Negatives," *Amer. Phot.* (Jan. 1931) 3.

THOREK, "Paper Negatives Simplified," *Photo Art Monthly* **8**, 505 (1940).

WARD, *Picture Making with Paper Negatives*, American Photographic Publishing Co., Boston.

McMASTER, "Print Control by the Paper Negative Method," *Phot. J.* **80**, 124 (1940).

GIBBS, "Pictorial Prints from Paper Negatives," *Popular Phot.* (March 1939) 16.

Ward, "Paper Negative Possibilities in Architecture," *Photo-Technique* **2**, April, 32 (1941).

FASSBENDER, "The Paper Negative," *Amer. Ann. of Phot.* 55, 1941.

MORTENSEN, "The Paper Negative," *Popular Phot.* **17**, November 21 (1945); **18**, 34, 110 (1946).

ATWATER, "Paper Negative Process," *Camera* (Baltimore) **66**, 41 (1944).

Chapter 26

TONING OF DEVELOPED SILVER IMAGES

Toning Processes. The process by which the color of a print or transparency is changed through the conversion of the silver image into a silver compound, or the replacement of the silver image in whole or in part by another metal or a dye is known as toning. The conversion of the silver image into silver sulfide, for example, produces brownish-black to brown (sepia) colored images depending upon the process used and the dispersity of the silver deposit in the developed images. Colors ranging from blue, purple, brown-black, sepia, green to red are obtained by depositing on the image colored compounds of iron, gold, copper, uranium, selenium, lead, nickel, tin, vanadium, or cobalt. A still wider range of color is possible by dye toning. The silver image is first converted into a compound which acts as a mordant for the dye and then placed in the dye solution. The dye is precipitated on the mordant to produce a dye image.

The following tabulation indicates some of the more important toning methods employing inorganic compounds and the range of colors available. Not all of the colors mentioned, however, are obtainable on every paper.

In some toning processes—for example, practically all of those employing sulfur compounds—the toning action proceeds to completion and then stops. With others, as for example copper, uranium, and lead, the action is progressive; various colors follow one another in a definite order and the color of the image depends upon the time of toning.

TONING PROCESSES AND COLORS

Sulfur	warm black-sepia
Hydrosulfite	warm brown-sepia
Gold (black prints)	blue-purple
Gold (sulfide toned prints)	red
Tin (stannous salts)	purple-black, sepia-brown
Selenium	purple-brown to red-brown
Copper	warm black-red chalk
Uranium	warm black-brick red
Vanadium	yellow (with iron produces greenish tones)
Nickel	red and red brown
Dye	depends upon dye used.

Some processes of toning (sulfur) reduce the density of the black and white print; others, such as mercury, copper, uranium, and lead, intensify the image.

The color of the image obtained by any process of metallic toning depends upon the dispersity of the silver image, which in turn depends upon the emulsion and the conditions of development. The smaller the average size of the silver grains which compose the image, the greater the range of colors obtainable with most metallic toning processes and particularly with sulfur processes. Conditions of development which tend to produce images composed of finer grains—as, for example, the use of developers highly restrained with a soluble bromide—increase the range of tones obtainable by most toning processes (except dye toning).

In general, matt or semi-matt papers tone more readily and produce more pleasing effects than glossy or other papers with a decided luster.

It is essential for most toning processes that the print be thoroughly fixed and thoroughly washed. The use of fresh fixing baths for fixing and hypo eliminators in washing is recommended. Prints which have been dried should be soaked in water before toning. Some processes soften gelatin but in general no difficulty will be experienced with prints which have been well hardened in an acid fixing and hardening bath, particularly if dried before toning.

Sulfur Processes. The sulfur processes are probably the most widely used of all methods of toning. The range of colors extends from purplish-brown to a yellowish-brown depending upon the emulsion, the development of the image and the toning process. The toned image in every case consists of silver sulfide, the difference in color being due to differences in particle size.

With a given emulsion, a blue-black developer with a high alkaline content and the minimum of soluble bromide will tend to produce cold, i.e., more purplish colors while the use of a warm-tone developer, restrained with potassium bromide, tends to warmer (more yellowish) colors. With a warm-tone developer, the color of the toned image varies with the time of development; the shorter the time of development the warmer the color of the image after toning.

The most popular of all sulfur processes is undoubtedly *sulfide toning*. In this the image is first bleached in a solution containing (1) an oxidizing agent, such as potassium ferricyanide,[1] bichromate,[2] permanganate,[3] persulfate, quinone or quinone-

sulfonic acid,[4] mercuric or cupric chloride,[5] and (2) a soluble halide, such as potassium bromide, which converts the image into compounds which are reduced to silver sulfide in a solution of sodium, ammonium [6] or barium sulfide,[7] sodium orthothiostannate, sodium thioantimonate, sodium thiomolylbdate,[8] pentasulfide, organic sulfur compounds such as thiourea in strongly alkaline solutions, sulfuretted hydrogen,[9] sulfoxyphosphate,[10] or sodium sulfantimonate alone or in conjunction with a pyrocatechin developer.[11]

The reactions which take place in the case of a bleaching bath composed of potassium ferricyanide and bromide are probably as follows:

Bleaching:

(1) $4Ag + 4K_3Fe(CN)_6 \rightarrow$
$$3K_4Fe(CN)_6 + Ag_4Fe(CN)_6$$

(2) $Ag_4Fe(CN)_6 + 4KBr \rightarrow$
$$K_4Fe(CN)_6 + 4AgBr$$

Sulfiding:

$$2AgBr + Na_2S \rightarrow Ag_2S + 2NaBr$$

[4] Lumiere and Seyewetz, *Bull. Soc. franc. Phot.* **7**, 267 (1920); **9**, 331 (1922).

[5] Bennett, *Brit. J. Phot.* **68**, 25 (1921).

[6] *Brit. J. Phot.* **54**, 523 (1907).

[7] Namias, *Brit. J. Phot.* **58**, 324 (1911).

[8] Smith, *Phot. J.* **48**, 267 (1908).

[9] Tripel, *Brit. J. Phot.* **58**, 657 (1911); B.P. 24,378 (1911).

[10] Lumiere and Seyewetz, French Patent 507,332.

[11] Valenta, *Phot. Korr.* **49**, 279 (1912).

[1] Bullock, *Brit. J. Phot.* **68**, 442, 447 (1921).

[2] *Brit. J. Phot.* **56**, 233 (1909); **64**, 173 (1917).

[3] Greenall, *Brit. J. Phot.* **63**, 659 (1916); **62**, 353 (1915).

CURRENT, "Some Factors Effecting Sepia Tone," *P.S.A. Journal* **16**, 684 (1950). This paper utilizes spectrophotometric curves for the first time instead of the usual term, warm black, brown black, olive brown, black, etc.

WALL, "Sulfide Toning," *Amer. Phot.,* 620, 696 (1927); 22 (1928) (excellent summary).

The following papers deal with the effect of the composition of the bleaching solution on the color of the toned image: Bullock, *Brit. J. Phot.* **68**, 447 (1921); Backstrom, *Phot. J.* **76**, 607 (1936); Asloglou, *Phot. Revue* **48**, 49 (1936); Jelley, *Phot. J.* **72**, 480 (1932); Nitze, *Brit. J. Phot.* **79**, 486 (1932); Schweitzer, *Brit. J. Phot.* **75**, 169 (1938).

In hypo-alum toning, a solution of hypo and alum is heated to a temperature of 100° to 125° F. (40°–50° C.) at which point free sulfur is liberated and this attacks the silver image, converting it into silver sulfide.[12] The reactions may be represented as follows:[13]

$$Al_2(SO_4)_3 + 3Na_2S_2O_3 \rightarrow$$
$$Al_2(S_2O_3)_3 + 3Na_2SO_4$$
$$Al_2(S_2O_3)_3 + 3H_2O \rightarrow$$
$$Al_2(OH)_3 + 3SO_2 + 3S$$

or possibly,

$$Al_2(SO_4)_3 + 3H_2O \rightarrow Al_2(OH)_3 + 3H_2SO_4$$
$$Na_2S_2O_3 + H_2SO_4 \rightarrow Na_2SO_3 + SO_2 + S$$
$$Ag_2S + S \rightarrow Ag_2S$$

The addition of gold chloride results in darker and colder (more purplish) colors. The toned image in this case consists of gold sulfide and silver sulfide, the latter predominating. Nelson, U.S.P. 1,849,245.

A variation of the hypo-alum process consists in the addition of an acid, such as sulfuric or hydrochloric, to a solution of hypo. The collodial sulfur formed reacts with the silver of the image to form silver sulfide.[14]

There are several other methods which, for various reasons, are not in general use.[15] The use of a hot solution of ammonium or ammonium polysulfide or, more commonly, "liver of sulfur," which is a mixture of potassium sulfide and potassium sulfate, converts the silver of the image into silver sulfide according to the following reaction:[16]

$$S + H_2O \rightarrow H_2S + O$$
$$Ag_2 \rightarrow Ag_2O$$
$$Ag_2O + H_2S \rightarrow Ag_2S + H_2O$$

Another method is based upon the use of an oxidizing agent such as potassium ferricyanide, ammonium thiocyanate,[17] potassium persulfate,[18] ferricyanide and thiocarbamide,[19] sodium meta-nitrobenzene sulfate,[20] and sodium or barium sulfide in one solution. The silver image is attacked by the oxidizing agent and converted into silver sulfide by the sodium sulfide present. With nitrobenzene, which is one of the most successful of these methods, the reaction probably is as follows:[21]

$$C_6H_5NO_2 + 4Ag + 2NaSH \rightarrow$$
$$C_6H_5 \cdot NH \cdot ONa + NaOH + 2Ag_2S$$

Gold Toning. Toning in gold produces blue or blue-purple images on warm-tone prints on chloride or chlorobromide papers; bromide and bromchloride papers show little change, or at best bluish-gray tones, and sulfide-toned prints a brilliant red.

The brilliant purple-blue images which have become so popular with salon exhibitors in recent years are obtained by developing chlorobromide, or chloride, papers in warm-tone developers and toning in a solution of gold chloride. The warmer the color of the developed images, the more brilliant the color of the toned image. Thus, developers heavily restrained with potassium, or ammonium bromide, are gen-

[12] According to Wall, this method of toning is due to Baekeland sometime prior to 1896.

[13] Sheppard, *Photography as a Scientific Implement*, D. Van Nostrand Co., Inc., New York. Seyewetz and Chicandard, *Eder's Jahrbuch* **10**, 488 (1896). Southworth, *Brit. J. Phot.* **74**, 166 (1927).

[14] Lumiere and Seyewetz, *Brit. J. Phot.* **59**, 972 (1912). Soar, *Brit. J. Phot.* **60**, 156, 185 (1913). Hoel, *Brit. J. Phot.* **69**, 73 (1922). Rawling, *Phot. J.* **62**, 3 (1922).

[15] Fenske, *Brit. J. Phot.* **60**, 674 (1913). Rawkins, *Brit. J. Phot.* **61**, 218 (1914). Bullock, *Brit. J. Phot.* **68**, 450 (1921). Underberg, *Brit. J. Phot.* **71**, 50 (1924). Steigman, *Brit. J. Phot.* **71**, 661 (1924) (sodium hydrosulfite).

[16] Lumiere and Seyewetz, *Brit. J. Phot.* **70**, 733 (1923).

[17] Punnett, *Brit. J. Phot.* **56**, 571 (1909).

[18] Kropf, *Brit. J. Phot.* **57**, 837 (1910).

[19] Triepel, B.P. 24,378 (1910).

[20] Shaw, *Brit. J. Phot.* **70**, 267, 759, 591 (1923).

[21] Sheppard, *Brit. J. Phot.* **70**, 679 (1923); Seyewetz, *Brit. J. Phot.* **87**, 116 (1940).

erally used, but some exhibitors favor special warm-tone developers containing glycin or catechol.

The toned image consists of gold precipitated on the silver particles. The red obtained by toning sulfide-toned prints with gold consists of a double sulfide of gold and silver.[22]

Selenium Toning. As an element selenium is related to sulfur and many of its compounds are analogous to those of sulfur. Sodium thiosulfate ($Na_2S_2O_3$) and sodium polysulfide (Na_2S_2) are toners converting the silver of the developed image into silver sulfide, and the corresponding seleno sulfate (Na_2SeSO_3) and seleno sulfide (Na_2SeS) are toners also, converting the image into silver selenide (Ag_2Se) which forms a dark brown image with a high degree of permanency.[23]

With sodium selenosulfate, the reaction is probably:

$$Na_2SSeO_3 + 2Ag \rightarrow Ag_2Se + Na_2SO_3.$$

As with other toning processes, the colors obtained depend upon the emulsion, the developer, and the time of development. On warm-tone chloride and chlorobromide papers, selenium towers produce reddish brown to purple brown images. Little or no change occurs with bromchloride and bromide papers. Toning is progressive and can be stopped at any stage without double toning.

Selenium-toned prints may be reduced in ferricyanide hypo and other reducers. The reduction in density results in a warmer color.

Miscellaneous Toning Processes. The combination of cupric sulfate and an oxidizing agent, such as potassium ferricyanide, forms a single-solution toner which is capable of producing a wide range of colors from warm black through various shades of brown to red chalk, depending on the emulsion, the developer, and the time of toning, as the various colors follow one another in a definite order as the reaction proceeds.

The chemical reactions taking place according to Mees are probably as follows:

$$4K_3Fe(CN)_6 + 2CuSO_4 + 4Ag \rightarrow$$
$$2Ag_2SO_4 + Cu_2Fe(CN)_6 + 3K_4Fe(CN)_6.$$

The last two stages in ionic notation, are:

$$Fe\overline{(CN)_6} + Ag \rightarrow Fe\overline{(CN)_6} + Ag.$$
$$2Cu^{\cdot\cdot} + Fe\overline{(CN)_6} \rightarrow Cu_2Fe(CN)_6.$$

The range of colors obtained by toning with uranium extends from warm black through various shades of brown to plum colors and various shades of red, terminating in a bright brick red. As with copper, the toning action is progressive, the various colors proceeding in a definite order, as the action proceeds.[24]

As the image is intensified in toning with either copper or uranium, the black and white prints should be lighter than normal.

Processes of toning with tin,[25] cobalt,[26] lead, nickel, cadmium, tellurium, molybdenium, mercury, and vanadium are of greater interest from an experimental standpoint than practically. With some exceptions, these processes either offer no real advantage or are less reliable and more complicated.

Purplish black to warm black tones are obtainable by toning in an alkaline solution of stannous chloride, but the results vary greatly with the emulsion.

[22] Lumiere and Seyewetz, *Brit. J. Phot.* **70**, 331 (1923).

[23] Asloglou, *Brit. J. Phot.* **85**, 599, 629, 643, 662 (1938). Formstecher, *Phot. Ind.* **34**, 1014 (1936). Seyewetz, *Brit. J. Phot.* **77**, 718 (1930).

[24] Sedlaczek, *Amer. Phot.* **19**, 4 (1925).

[25] Druce, *Brit. J. Phot.* **69**, 433 (1922). Gamble and Wolley, *Brit. J. Phot.* **60**, 978 (1913). Formstecher, *Brit. J. Phot.* **68**, 759 (1921).

[26] Namias, *Rev. Gen. Sci.* 1916, p. 72. Strauss, *Das Atelier* **30**, 66 (1923). Strauss, *Phot. Ind.* 1924, p. 282. Schommer, *Atelier* **33**, 91 (1926). Harris, *New Photographer* **1**, 308 (1923).

A wide range of colors ranging from violet to red may be obtained with cobalt, but the processes generally are unreliable and the results frequently leave much to be desired, the colors being muddy and the highlights degraded by staining.

Methods of toning with nickel are of interest chiefly in three-color photography. A magenta suitable for three-color printing is obtained by toning silver images in nickel dimethylgloxine or *p*-dimethylamino-benzylidenerhodanine and the yellow with nickel ferrocyanide, cadmium sulfide, or lead chromate.[27]

Several methods of toning with mercury have been described by Sedlaczek.[28] Bleaching in a solution of mercuric chloride and potassium bromide followed by toning in one of the following (a) hypo and ammonium thiocyanate, (b) hypo, barium chloride, and ammonium thiocyanate, or (c) hypo, ammonium thiocyanate, and silver nitrate produces yellowish-brown to sepia images, depending upon the emulsion. The permanency of the images is open to question.

Silver telluride (Ag_2Te) is analagous to silver selenide (Ag_2Se) and like it forms a dark-brown image. Tellurium dissolved in sulfide forms a sulfotelluride which, like the seleno-sulfate, is a toner for warm-tone silver images.[29]

Vanadium alone produces deep yellow to orange-colored images but when combined with an iron salt, such as ferric oxalate, the yellow image of the vanadium ferrocyanide and the blue image of ferri-ferrocyanide form a brilliant green.[30] The green is rather brilliant for landscapes but is suitable for some purposes.

Dye Toning. The range of colors obtainable by toning with metallic compounds is rather limited; a much broader range is possible by dye toning. Dye toning should not be confused with tinting or staining. A dye-toned image consists of a colored dye image in uncolored gelatin; in a tinted image the gelatin is more or less uniformly stained by the dye.

To produce the preferential deposition of the dye to form a dye image, it is necessary to convert the silver image into inorganic compounds which will cause the dye to come out of solution and precipitate on the compound. Such a substance is called a *mordant* and the dye is said to be mordanted. Silver ferrocyanide is a typical mordant; consequently, if a silver image is converted into an image of silver ferrocyanide and immersed in a solution of a basic dye, the dye is precipitated upon the silver ferrocyanide, producing a mordanted dye image.

A comparatively large number of inorganic compounds may be used as mordants; among them silver iodide, various ferrocyanides and sulfocyanides, silver sulfide, lead and iron.[31]

Dye toning is used chiefly for transparencies, although methods involving the application of the dye solution by brushes, or cotton, to the surface of prints on paper have been described.[32]

27 Nilsson, *Brit. J. Phot.* **83**, 503 (1936). Snyder, B.P. 469,133 (1937).

28 Sedlaczek, *Brit. J. Phot.* **72**, 635 (1925).

29 Kieser, *Phot.-Korr.* **55**, 9 (1918). Bullock, *Brit. J. Phot.* **68**, 442 (1921). Thorne-Baker, *Brit. J. Phot.* **48**, 827 (1901). Schering, G.P. 290,720. Spitzer, G.P. 292,382.

30 Namias, *Eder's Jahr.* 1901, p. 171; 1903, p. 158. Smith, *Brit. J. Phot.* **60**, 416 (1913).

31 *Tinting and Toning of Eastman Positive Motion Picture Film*, Eastman Kodak Co., Rochester, N. Y., 4th Edition, 1927. Clerc, *Photography, Theory and Practice*, Pitman, New York, 2nd Edition, 1937, p. 387. Wall, *History of Three Color Photography*, American Photographic Publishing Co., Boston, 1925, pp. 364, 385. *American Encyclopedia of Photography* (*The Complete Photographer*), article on Toning, p. 3411, Chicago, National Education Alliance.

32 Lumiere and Seyewetz, *Brit. J. Phot.* **73**, 135 (1926), *Brit. J.* **74**, 31 (1927). Garnotel, *Brit. J. Phot.* **75**, 153 (1928).

Chapter 27

PRINTING PROCESSES. II.

(1) Pigment Processes
(2) Processes Employing Iron and Other Metallic Salts
(3) Diazo Processes

Pigment Processes. The pigment processes are based upon the hardening of a colloid (gelatin, glue, gum arabic, etc.) in the presence of (a) a chromate, (b) a ferric salt, (c) a dye, or (d) the oxidation products of certain developers. The hardening of chromate-gelatin may be produced either by exposure to light or, in the presence of silver oxidizing agents such as a ferricyanide, by finely divided silver.

Chemistry of the Tanning of Colloids by Chromates. The reactions involved in the tanning, or insolubilizing, of a chromate-colloid upon exposure to light are still not definitely known. The neutral chromates, with the exception of ammonium chromate which decomposes in solution into ammonium dichromate, do not sensitize gelatin and the dichromates are not light-sensitive appreciably except in the presence of organic matter. The investigations of Eder, Lumiere, Seyewetz, and others, suggest that the dichromate, or chromic acid, is reduced to chromium sesquioxide, Cr_2O_3, which then reacts with excess bichromate to form a chromium chromate, which may be Cr_2CrO_6, and is the actual tanning or insolubilizing compound.

$$2H_6CrO_6 + light \rightarrow Cr_2O_3 + 6H_2O + 3O$$
$$Cr_2O_3 + CrO_3 \rightarrow Cr_2CrO_6 \rightarrow (3CrO_2)_1$$

Even less is known of the exact reactions taking place in the tanning of colloids containing a chromate by finely divided silver. In the carbro process, for example, pigment tissue is sensitized by immersion in a solution of potassium ferricyanide, potassium bichromate, and potassium bromide. The tissue is then placed in contact with the wet bromide print. The sensitizing solution diffuses into the gelatin layer containing the silver image, bleaches the silver image, and the reaction products diffusing back into the pigmented tissue result in the insolubilization of the gelatin. It is probable that the bleaching of the silver image results into the formation of halide and potassium ferrocyanide. This is reoxidized by the bichromate back to ferricyanide, the reduction of the bichromate resulting in the insolubilization of the gelatin. With copper salts, the reaction is presumably the same, the cupric salt and silver halide reacting with the silver image to form cuprous halide which is reoxidized by the bichromate into a cupric salt, the reduction of the bichromate resulting in the insolubilization of the gelatin.

BULLOCK, "Theory of the Carbro Process," *Phot. J.* **67**, 213 (1927).

MURRAY AND SPENCER, "The Hardening of Gelatin by Means of Copper Dichromate Solutions," *Phot. J.* **73**, 497 (1933).

In the bromoil process, a bromide print is bleached in a solution containing a bichromate, or chromic acid, potassium bromide, and either potassium ferricyanide or a cupric salt, usually the chloride or the sulfate, which results in the tanning of the gelatin in contact with the grains of silver, thus producing an image in differentially hardened gelatin. The bromide print is then soaked in water which is repelled by the hardened gelatin. An oil pigment applied with the brush adheres to the shadow portions of the image but is repelled by the highlights which have taken up the water. Thus, there is built up a pigment image on one of differentially hardened gelatin. From a chemical standpoint, bromoil and carbro are essentially the same; the mechanism of the two processes, however, is somewhat different as in bromoil the insolubilization of the gelatin takes place in the gelatin layer containing the image, while in the carbro process the insolubilization has to be produced in another layer of gelatin by diffusion.

Classification of Pigment Processes. The processes of printing based upon the insolubilization of colloids by chromates may be classified as follows:

I. Processes requiring exposure to light.
II. Processes in which the colloid is rendered insoluble, without exposure to light, by the conversion of metallic silver to silver halide in the presence of a chromate.

Each of these may be subdivided as follows:

A. Processes in which the pigment, or dye, is present during exposure.

1. Processes without transfer; e.g., gum-bichromate, Fresson, etc.

2. Processes requiring transfer; e.g., carbon.

B. Processes in which a pigment, or dye, is applied to a relief in a hardened colloid.

1. Processes based upon the repellency of a water-charged colloid; e.g., oil, bromoil, photolithography, powder processes.
2. Dye processes; i.e., processes in which (1) the unhardened colloid is dyed to produce a reversed image, and (2) the unhardened colloid is removed and the colloid relief image which remains is dyed.

The Carbon Process. Carbon is a process of pigment printing perfected by J. W. Swan in 1865. It is the oldest of the pigment processes and has long been recognized as one of the finest of printing mediums. The term *carbon* arose originally from the use of finely divided carbon as a pigment but many other pigments are now used to obtain images in different colors.

Carbon tissue consists essentially of a layer of soft gelatin, containing an inert pigment, coated on a thin paper support. About 30 different colors are available from the Autotype Company of London, the principal producer of materials for the process. These tissues must be sensitized by the user immediately before use as the sensitized tissue becomes insoluble within a few days.

There are two methods of carbon printing; single and double transfer. In single transfer, the carbon tissue is first sensitized in a solution of ammonium bichromate, dried and exposed.[1] It is then soaked for a few minutes in water until soft and

SCHIEL, "Chromic Acid Bleach and Its Reaction Product," *Phot. Rund.* **63**, 120, 138 (1926).
TRITTON, "Theory of the Carbro Process," *Phot. J.* **66**, 126 (1926).

[1] The use of wet tissue, exposed through a transparent, plastic sheet, to avoid the delay and the variations in sensitivity caused by drying the tissue before exposure, was patented by Symmes, U.S.P. 2,381,234 (1943). See also: *Autotype Color Printing Processes; Carbro, Contact Carbon, Projection Carbon, Wet-Printed Carbon*, The Autotype Company Ltd., London, 1948.

the pigmented layer squeegeed onto a sheet of *transfer paper,* which is a paper coated with a somewhat harder gelatin. After remaining in contact for several minutes under slight pressure, the carbon tissue and the adhering transfer paper are placed in warm water. In this the soluble gelatin becomes soft, permitting the tissue to be stripped off leaving the pigment layer adhering to the transfer paper. The soluble gelatin is removed by washing in warm water until an image of pigment in the hardened gelatin remains. Finally the image is hardened in a solution of alum, washed briefly to remove the alum and dried. With single transfer, the image is reversed from left to right unless the negative is printed from the back side.

Reversal of the image is avoided by double transfer. In this, the pigmented layer is sensitized and exposed as for single transfer but is placed first on a temporary support of celluloid, glass, waxed paper, or cellophane. It is developed on this temporary support; i.e., the soluble gelatin is dissolved to produce the image, and finally the pigmented image is transferred to sheet of gelatin-coated transfer paper.

The carbon process has been almost completely replaced by carbro which is not limited to contact printing and does not require exposure to light.

The Gum-Pigment Process (Gum-Bichromate). This process, now practically obsolete, was formerly a great favorite of salon exhibitors. It is a flexible process permitting considerable control and is noteworthy for the rich, deep shadows. It is, however, a tedious process as, for a full scale of tones, three separate printings, one for the shadows, one for the halftones, and a third for the highlights, are generally necessary, and for each of these the paper must be sensitized, exposed, the soluble pigment removed, and the image cleared and dried.

The coating mixture consists of gum arabic, or a similar colloid, a pigment of the color desired and a bichromate. The three coatings differ principally in the amount of the pigment, the shadow coating containing the most, the halftone coating less, and the highlight coating still less. The amount of the pigment in each coating may be varied to meet the needs of the negative, the subject, or the effect desired. As each coating reproduces only a part of the tone scale of the subject and the contrast of each coating may be varied by the relative proportions of colloid, pigment and sensitizer, the possibilities of control are very great.

The coatings are applied with a large brush, dried, and the exposure made by daylight or a strong source of artificial light. An enlarged negative is necessary if the print is to be larger than the original negative as the sensitivity of the coating is too low for projection printing. After the exposure, the paper is placed face down in a tray of water at room temperature and left for about half an hour. In this time, if the exposure is correct for the coating mixture, the soluble gum will have dissolved, leaving behind the pigment image in the hardened gum. This image is then cleared in a solution of alum, washed, and dried. It is then ready for the second printing which is a repetition of the first except for the composition of the coating mixture.

ANDERSON, "The Gun-Pigment Process," *Amer. Phot.* **7**, 504, 584, 700, 707 (1913); **8**, 8, 12, 76 (1914).

STARNES, "The Gum-Bichromate Process and a New Colloid," *Phot. J.* **58**, 287 (1918); *Brit. J. Phot.* **66**, 50 (1919).

LIBBY, "Multiple Gum," *Amer. Ann. of Phot.,* 1922, p. 124.

AUTOTYPE CARBON AND CARBRO PROCESSES, The Autotype Company Ltd., London.

Gum Bromide and Gum Platinum.
Multiple printing may be avoided by combining gum printing with bromide or platinum, using a print made by one of these processes as a foundation to supply the necessary depth to the shadows and middle tones and a superimposed gum pigment image to secure the characteristic appearance of a gum pigment print.[2]

Miscellaneous Gum Pigment Processes.
The processes which follow are now obsolete. Each in its day attracted a small following of salon exhibitors chiefly in Europe.

Glue Print. This is a modification of the gum-pigment process due to the German pictorialist, Heinrich Kuehn, in which paper coated with pigmented glue and sensitized with potassium bichromate is exposed through the paper and the soluble glue removed by washing in warm water.[3]

Fresson. This process of Belgian origin is similar to gum pigment except for the method of removing the excess pigment from the image. In the Fresson process the print is placed in water after the exposure until the gelatin is "tacky" after which the excess gelatin is removed with a mixture of sawdust and water. The image has a pronounced grain which is not displeasing for certain effects.[4]

Sury Process. In this process a fine, colorless powder is added to the coating mixture of gelatin or gum arabic. The paper is sensitized with ammonium bichromate, exposed, and the soluble gelatin removed by washing in water as usual. When dry, pastel colors are applied by hand, the roughened portions take up the colors to form an image.[5]

Artigue Process. In this process, developed by Artigue about 1894, paper coated with gelatin and a pigment and sensitized in potassium bichromate was exposed as usual and the excess pigmented gelatin removed by alternately immersing the print in a solution of sodium hypochlorite, followed by washing in water.[6]

Resinopigmentype. In this pigment process, developed by Namias of Milan,[7] a gelatin-coated paper is sensitized in potassium or ammonium bichromate, dried and exposed under a positive transparency. It is then placed in cold water for several hours to eliminate the excess bichromate and transferred to water at 50° C. (122° F.) to produce an image of differentially hardened gelatin. The surface moisture is removed and a resinous pigment, such as gum dammar, shellac, bitumen, or dragon's blood with a suitable pigment, is applied with a brush.

Oil Process. The oil process is based upon the work of Poitevin but was developed practically by Rawlings (1903). It was taken up by others and for some time was quite popular among salon exhibitors but has been superseded by the Bromoil process. Paper coated with a thick layer of gelatin is sensitized in ammonium bichromate and dried. After exposure to daylight, or strong artificial light, the paper is soaked in water in which the gelatin swells producing a relief image in differentially hardened gelatin. The surface moisture is then removed and a rather stiff, lithographic ink applied with a brush.

[2] Davis, *Amer. Phot.* **15**, 53 (1921).

[3] Richter, *Amer. Phot.* **17**, 38 (1923).

[4] Mauret, *Amer. Ann. of Phot.* **43**, 179 (1929).

BATTY, "A Simplified Method of Gum-Bichromate," *Phot. J.* **63**, 398 (1923).

LEIGHTON, "A Method of Working the Gum-Bichromate Process," *Amer. Ann. of Phot.*, 1924, p. 40.

KILMER, "The Gum Print," *Amer. Ann. of Phot.*, 1947, p. 145.

HALFORD, "Gum-Bichromate, Some Recent Experiments," *Phot. J.* **83**, 292 (1943).

[5] *Phot. J.* **46**, 239 (1916).

[6] Durham, *Brit. J. Phot.* **90**, 21 (1943).

[7] Namias, B.P. 205,092 of 1922; *Brit. J. Phot.* **72**, 220 (1925).

The shadow portions of the image, which have absorbed very little water, accept the ink more readily than the halftone and highlight portions which contain more water, and in this way a pigment image is built upon a gelatin relief. Since the ink is applied locally by brushes, it is obvious that there is considerable control over the final result.

Bromoil. The Bromoil process consists in making a bromide print in the ordinary way, bleaching this in a solution which produces an image in differentially hardened gelatin, and finally applying pigment with a brush to form an image. Since an ordinary bromide print is used, neither daylight nor an enlarged negative is necessary as with the oil process.

The bromide print should be made preferably on a paper without a super coating, although Symes [8] has described methods of using such papers. Special bromide papers without a super coating for use in bromoil and carbro are obtainable on special orders from dealers in materials for these processes.

Prints for the bromoil process should be correctly exposed and developed for slightly less than normal. The shadows should be a deep gray and the highlights a trifle darker than usual. Either diaminophenol, or metol-hydroquinone developers, may be used, but in any event a fresh developer should be employed as a used developer may result in partial tanning of the gelatin. An acid fixing bath without alum or other hardening agent is preferable.

The usual method is to fix, wash, and dry the print before bleaching; some workers, however, prefer to bleach directly after development.[9] The usual bleaching solution contains a bichromate, or chromic acid, potassium bromide, or sodium chloride, and a cupric salt, usually the chloride or the sulfate. Bleaching of the image and hardening are usually accomplished simultaneously in a single solution, but separate bleaching and tanning operations have been recommended by Venn.

A typical bleaching solution follows:

Solution A

Copper chloride..	36.6 grams	160 grains
Sodium chloride..	265 grams	2 oz. 290 grains
Hydrochloric acid	0.6 cc.	3 minins
Water..........	1,000 cc.	10 oz.

Solution B

Potassium bichromate........	12.5 grams	55 grains
Water..........	1,000 cc.	10 oz.

For use, take one part of each, A and B, and two parts of water. Within four to five minutes the silver image is converted into a faint brownish color. When fully bleached, the print is washed in running water for about fifteen minutes to free it from yellow stain and then fixed in hypo. After which it is washed for about one-half hour.

Before pigmenting, the print is soaked in water, temperature between 70 and 80° F. (21–27° C.) The time may vary from fifteen to thirty minutes, depending upon the temperature of the water and the requirements of the paper used.

If the degree of relief is correct, the print will accept the pigment from the brush readily and in doing so will differentiate between the highlights and shadows. Ordinarily, pigmenting is begun with ink as it comes from the tube until the image is distinct and the shadows well-

---

8 Symes, *Brit. J. Phot.* **70**, 103 (1923).

SINCLAIR, *How to Make Oil and Bromoil Prints*, Iliffe and Sons Ltd., London.
TILNEY AND COX, *The Art of Pigmenting*, Henry Greenwood and Co., London.
MORTIMER AND COULTHURST, *The Oil and Bromoil Process*, Iliffe and Sons Ltd., London.

9 Sattler, *J. Phot. Soc. Amer.* **10**, 294 (1944).
10 Venn, *Brit. J. Phot.* **71**, 427 (1924).

defined. Then, it may be necessary to change to a softer ink to which either linseed oil, Robertson medium, or Meglip, have been added. It is easy to tell when more pigment is needed because the brush will begin to pick up the pigment instead of depositing it.

The method in which the brush is used to apply the pigment varies greatly with different workers. Some employ a pressing, smudging action, while others simply dab the brush on the surface. With practice, one will develop a distinctive method of his own.

Particular care is necesary, especially in the case of large prints, or where a long time is required for pigmenting, to keep the paper thoroughly wet. The usual practice is to place the print on a wet blotter during pigmenting, however, if the print tends to dry before pigmenting is complete it should be removed and carefully floated on water until the unhardened gelatin has absorbed sufficient water to repel the ink.

The advantage of the bromoil process, of course, is that the gradation of the image may be varied at will to conform to the pictorial conceptions of the worker.

Bromoil Transfer. Transfers are made by transferring the pigment from the bromoil to another sheet of paper under pressure thus producing an image in pigment on plain paper without a gelatin coating. The bromoil is made in the usual way, except that it is usually necessary to employ softer pigments than would otherwise be used. Since the transfer of the pigment is proportionally greater in the highlights than in the shadows, the contrast and depth of the transfer image is lower than that of the bromoil. This is overcome by making the pigmented image darker and more contrasty than that for a bromoil print.

For the transfer, the pigmented bromoil and the moistened water color, or drawing

paper of suitable surface, are placed together and passed through the rollers of a press of the type used for copper plate printing. A corner of the transfer paper may then be lifted and the image examined. If the pigment is not transferred completely, and the shadow portions are too light, the bromoil print may be removed and inked more heavily for a second transfer. Registration marks will be necessary, of course, to enable the second transfer to be accurately superimposed on the first.

Flexichrome. This process of making prints in color, introduced by the Eastman Kodak Company in 1949, employs a gelatin relief to which dyes are applied with brushes.

A print is made from the negative, by contact or projection printing, on Flexichrome Stripping Film, the exposure being made through the film base. After exposure, the film is developed in a tanning developer which hardens the gelatin to produce an image in tanned gelatin corresponding in thickness with the densities of the silver image. The film is then placed in water at a temperature of about 110° F. in which the unhardened gelatin washes away, leaving the silver-gelatin, relief image. The silver image is then removed by bleaching, leaving a clear gelatin-relief image. This relief image is immersed in a special black or "modeling" dye which it absorbs differentially to produce an image that is not greatly different in appearance from the original silver image. At this point, the gelatin relief image is stripped from the film base and transferred to paper and dried.

JORDAN, *Photographic Control Processes*, American Photographic Publishing Co., Boston.

HAWKINS, *Pigment Printing*, Henry Greenwood Co. Ltd., London.

When the special Flexichrome colors are applied with a brush, they are absorbed by the image differentially in proportion to the thickness of the gelatin layer. Thus highlights and white areas accept little color and remain clear. The applied color, however, acts on the modeling dye as a cutting reducer, replacing it in the light and middle tones before affecting the deeper shadows. In addition, any Flexichrome dye applied to the relief image replaces any dye present as well as the modeling dye. Thus, if through error an area has been colored blue which should be yellow, the first light application of yellow dye will produce green, the second yellow-green, and so on until a pure yellow is obtained. This makes corrections in color possible at any time during the coloring process.

The Carbro Process. The *carbro* process is used chiefly for three-color photography.[11]

Prints for carbro should be made on bromide paper without a supercoating, preferably one of the special papers supplied for the carbro process. The prints should receive a full exposure and development in a diaminophenol or a metol-hydroquinone developer. After fixing in an acid, but nonhardening fixing bath, and washing, it is well to immerse the print for about five minutes in a 3% solution of hydrochloric acid, followed by ten minutes washing in running water. This is especially advisable if hard water is used for washing; otherwise the highlights may not bleach completely with the result that they will wash away when the pigment image is developed.

A typical sensitizing solution is:

Concentrated Solution No. 1:

Potassium bichromate.......	10 grams	1 oz.
Potassium ferricyanide......	10 grams	1 oz.
Potassium bromide........	10 grams	1 oz.
Water to make............	200 cc.	20 oz.

Concentrated Solution No. 2:

Glacial acetic acid.........	10 cc.	1 oz.
Hydrochloric acid (pure).....	10 cc.	1 oz.
Formaldehyde 40%........	220 cc.	22 oz.

The addition of 1¼ oz. or 12 cc. of water to the above will prevent precipitation in cold weather.

For use take:

First Bath:

Concentrated No. 1 stock solution	100 cc.	6 oz.
Water to make...............	300 cc.	18 oz.

Second Bath:

Concentrated No. 2 stock solution	10 cc.	1 oz.
Water to make...............	320 cc.	32 oz.

The normal time of immersion is from twenty to thirty seconds. The actual time, however, is determined by the degree of contrast required, the brand of paper employed for the print, the hardness of the water and, to a minor degree, the number of carbro prints.

After sensitizing, the tissue is placed in contact with the bromide print, squeegeed, and allowed to remain for fifteen minutes. The two are then separated and the pigment image developed in warm water, exactly as in the carbro process. The bromide print is washed in water for fifteen to twenty minutes, and then redeveloped in the usual developer. It may then be used for making a second carbro.

BRAHAM, "The Carbro Process," *Phot. J.* **62**, 16 (1922); *Brit. J. Phot.* **69**, 4 (1922).

FARMER, "The Carbro Process," *Amat. Phot.*, p. 285 (1919); *Brit. J. Phot.* **66**, 583 (1919); *Amer. Phot.* **14**, 92 (1920).

GARON, "Revised Formulae for Carbro," *Brit. J. Phot.* **68**, 327 (1921).

LIGHTON, "Sharpness of Reproduction in the Carbro Process," *Phot. J.* **66**, 545 (1926).

---

11 On the theory of the carbro process: Namias, *Phot. J.* **42**, 57 (1912); *Brit. J. Phot.* **59**, 217 (1912); Eder, *Handbuch* **4**, 279 (1917); Venn, *Brit. J. Phot.* **71**, 427 (1924).

Chemistry of Processes with Iron Salts.
Ferric salts, such as the oxalate, tartrate, citrate, etc., are reduced to ferrous when exposed to light. Potassium ferricyanide likewise is reduced to the ferrocyanide upon exposure to light.

Conversion of the salt from the ferric to the ferrous state, in most cases, is accomplished without any important change in color and without appreciable darkening. Substances which differentiate between the ferric and ferrous salts and form a colored reduction product with one or the other include potassium ferricyanide, potassium ferrocyanide, tannin, gallic acid, silver salts, platinum and palladium salts, and β-naphthoquinone sulfonic acid. If one of these forms a dark or colored precipitate with the ferrous salt only, it may be combined with the ferric salt when sensitizing the paper. A typical example is the well-known blue print process in which paper coated with ferric ammonium citrate and potassium ferricyanide is exposed to light reducing the ferric salt to the ferrous state. When the print is placed in water, the compound ferric ferrocyanide $Fe_4(FeCy_6)_3$ (Prussian Blue) is formed.

If the substance combines with the ferric salt only, it is applied as a developer after exposure. The reaction then takes place in the areas not exposed to light, so that the result is a positive from a positive. A typical example is cyanotype, the so-called positive blueprint process, in which paper is coated with ferric chloride and tartaric acid, exposed to light, and then developed in a solution of potassium ferrocyanide which with the ferric salt forms the compound ferrous ferricyanide, $Fe_3(FeCy_6)_2$ (Turnbull's Blue). Thus the print of a tracing consists of blue lines on a white background.

Ferrous salts are able to reduce salts of platinum, palladium, silver, copper, mercury, gold, and other metals. The most important processes based on this property are those employing salts of platinum, palladium, or silver. In printing with platinum, the paper is coated with ferric oxalate and potassium chloroplatinite. Upon exposure to light, the ferric salt is reduced to the ferrous, forming a pale image. The print is then placed in a solution of potassium oxalate which dissolves the ferrous salt and at the same time reduces the platinum salt to the metallic state to form an image of finely divided platinum.

$$Fe_2(C_2O_4)_3 + light \rightarrow 2Fe(C_2O_4) + 2CO_2,$$
$$6FeC_2O_4 + 3K_2PtCl_4 \rightarrow$$
$$2Fe_2(C_2O_4)_3 + Fe_2Cl_6 + 6KCl + 3Pt.$$

Lastly, ferric salts possess the property of rendering gelatin and other colloids insoluble. Thus, if a gelatin-coated paper is sensitized with ferric chloride, exposed to light and placed in water, the portions acted on by light are reduced to the ferrous state—and made soluble while those not exposed become insoluble.[12] If a pigment is included with the gelatin an image will be produced as in the well-known carbon process, or a greasy ink may be applied to the gelatin relief to produce an image as in the oil process. These processes have the disadvantage of producing a negative from a negative; the ferric-gelatin reaction is not, therefore, as useful as the corresponding chromate gelatin reaction.

Ferrous salts also possess the property of combining with carbonyl compounds, particularly quinones, to form a colored image. Thus, if paper is coated with a ferric salt and β-naphthaquinone-sulfonic acid, on exposure to light the ferric salt is reduced to the ferrous which combines directly with the quinone to form a visible

---

[12] Spencer, *The Ferro-Gelatin Process*, International Congress of Photography, Heffer, Cambridge, 1928.

image. Washing in water prevents further action by light.[13]

Plan-Copying Processes with Compounds of Iron. The processes which follow are suitable only for the reproduction of plans and tracings:

The Blueprint or Ferroprussiate Process. The blueprint process (white lines on a blue background) is the most widely used process for the reproduction of plans and tracings primarily because of its low cost and general suitability. It is, however, meeting increased competition from diazo papers which have a number of advantages.

Blueprint paper is obtainable commercially in rolls in a number of different speeds from slow to extra fast.[14] In general, the slower papers have the advantages of higher contrast; i.e., deeper blue background and better keeping properties. However, like all papers containing iron salts, blueprint papers are extremely sensitive to moisture and should be kept in tightly sealed metal cans. They are exposed in a heavy vacuum printing frame to sunlight or, in commercial establishments, by an electric arc or mercury vapor lamps. Most commercial printing, however, is done with continuous machines. An endless belt carries the tracing to be printed and the band of paper around a curved glass surface which is illuminated from the inside with a mercury arc. After exposure, the paper is drawn through water, or a solution of potassium bichromate, then washed and dried on a circular drum drier.

Positive Blueprint Process. There are two variations of this method of printing. In one, paper is coated with a sizing and ferric salts and after exposure developed with a solution of potassium ferrocyanide.[15] In the other, the paper is coated with ferric ammonium citrate and ferric chloride in the presence of gum arabic, exposed and developed by washing in water as in the usual blueprint process.

The Ferrogallic Process. In this process,[16] the paper is coated with a ferric salt, usually the chloride alone, or with the sulfate and tartaric acid, exposed and developed in a solution of gallic acid producing rather weak purplish-blue lines on a white ground.

The Iron-Silver or Sepiatype Process. This process is used chiefly as a negative process for making copies of tracings from which blueprints are to be made. It produces white lines on a rather dense, brownish-black background.[17] The paper is coated with a ferric salt, usually ferric ammonium citrate, and silver nitrate. Upon exposure to light the ferric salt is reduced to the ferrous and, upon washing in water, this reduces the silver salt to metallic silver. The silver nitrate remaining is removed by fixing in hypo and washing.

True-To-Scale Process. This process of offset printing, or duplicating, invented by F. & J. Dorel (1900) is based upon the insolubilizing action of ferric salts on gelatin and is used for making copies of tracings, etc., from blueprints.[18] A duplicating surface is prepared by spreading a mixture of gelatin, glycerine, and a wetting agent over a smooth surface to a depth of about 1/8th inch. When this has set to a jelly,

[13] Kogel, B.P. 302,282 (1927): *Brit. J. Phot.* **76**, 763 (1929).

[14] Formulas for blueprint sensitizing: Wall, *Amer. Phot.* **16**, 677, 766 (1922); **17**, 4 (1923). Willcock, *Brit. J. Phot.* **82**, 456 (1935). Kivich, U.S.P. 1,877,246; 2,126,504.

[15] Pellet, B.P. 4632 (1877).

[16] Suggested by Poitevin (1859) but frequently termed the Colas process (1883).

[17] Arndt and Troost, D.R.P. 6317 (1894.)

[18] For detailed working directions see: Brown, *Brit. J. Phot.* **86**, 719 (1939).

SPENCER, "The Ferro-Gallic Process," *Proc. Int. Cong. of Phot.*, Heffer, Cambridge (England) (1928).

the exposed blueprint is placed, without washing, face down on the gelatin surface for one to two minutes. It is then removed and a duplicating ink applied to the gelatin layer with a roller. The ink adheres to the insolubilized portions of the gelatin which correspond to the lines of the image, but is repelled by the soluble portions; thus there is produced an image in ink which corresponds with that of the blueprint. If a light, absorbent paper is applied to the inked surface under slight pressure the ink is transferred from the gelatin to the paper, thus producing an ink copy of the original tracing. From 25 to 50 copies may be made by repeating the process of inking and proofing.

The process is now seldom used in this country.

Kallitype, Platinotype, Palladium, and Related Processes. Unlike the processes described, which are restricted to the copying of tracings, these processes are suitable for pictorial work and are in fact among the most beautiful of printing processes. All, however, are practically obsolete because of the high cost, as in the case of platinum and palladium, or to the poor keeping properties of the sensitized paper which make ready-sensitized products impractical commercially.

Kallitype. This is a silver-iron process producing either black or brown images of excellent gradation and richness of tone.[19] There are two methods: in one, the paper is coated with a ferric salt and silver nitrate, exposed and developed in a solution of borax and Rochelle salts; in the other,

the paper is sensitized with a ferric salt, exposed, and developed in a solution of silver nitrate. The first is the more popular method. This really beautiful and inexpensive process has become obsolete because (1) it is a printing out process suitable only for contact printing, and (2) the paper must be prepared by the user.

Platinotype. This is one of the most permanent of all photographic printing processes. The image consists of finely divided particles of platinum, which is one of the most stable of metals, so that the platinum prints are as permanent as the paper on which they are made. Manufacture of platinum printing papers ceased about twenty years ago due to the high cost of platinum and the process is now obsolete except for a very few who are willing to go to the expense and the difficulty involved in sensitizing their own papers.

The usual method is to coat the paper with ferric oxalate and potassium chloroplatinite, expose, and develop in a solution of potassium oxalate. This results in a pure black image. Warmer tones may be obtained by adding mercury to the developer. After development the ferric salts remaining in the paper are removed in a weak solution of hydrochloric acid. The print is then washed and dried.

A variation of the above method is to sensitize the paper with the ferric salt and develop in a solution of potassium oxalate and potassium chloroplatinite. While less common, this is the simpler method for the beginner.[20]

[19] Thomson, "Kallitype," *Amer. Phot.* **17**, 422 (1923). Valenta, "Kallitype," *Das Atelier* **27**, 10 (1920), with extensive bibliography.

JUNIPER, "Early Days of True-To-Scale," *Brit. J. Phot.* **86**, 752 (1939).

SPENCER, "The Ferro-Gelatin Process," *Proc. Int. Cong. of Phot.*, 1928, Heffer, Cambridge (England).

[20] Hubl, *Platindruck*, Knapp, Halle a/s.

CANDELARIO, "The Platinum Process," *Minicam Phot.*, **8**, 60 (1944).

KOSEL, "The Platinum Printing Process," *Camera* (Lucerne) **5**, 225 (1927).

ANDERSON, *The Technique of Pictorial Photography*, Lippincott, Philadelphia.

ANDERSON, "Palladium vs. Silver for Photographic Prints," *Photo-Technique* **2**, 58 (August 1940).

Palladiotype. Palladium may be substituted for platinum and the results are indistinguishable except in color, the palladium image being a warm black. Palladium has the advantage of being much less expensive than platinum and the preparation of the paper is simpler.

Silver-Platinum. A silver-platinum paper was placed on the market under the trade name *Satista* by the Platinotype Company of England in an effort to produce a paper yielding results similar to platinum or palladium but less expensive.[21] Manufacture of the paper ceased when the company suspended operations a few years after the close of World War I.

Diazo Processes. These processes are based upon the light sensitivity of diazonium (diazo) compounds. Only a few types are useful and these are decomposed into colorless compounds upon exposure to light, particularly of the shorter wave lengths and the near ultraviolet. The light sensitivity varies both with the particular compound used and with the amount present; the sensitivity increases as the amount present in the coating decreases.

The second essential component in the diazo process is the coupling compound. These are phenol, naphthol, or amino compounds which combine, or *couple*, with the

diazonium compound to form an azo dye which is colored. The color of the dye depends on the chemical structure of the coupler and, to a lesser degree, on the diazonium compound. Since the effect of light is to decompose the diazonium compound, coupling takes place with the unexposed portions of the image so that the result is a positive from a positive or a negative from a negative.

The two variations of the diazo process in commercial use differ essentially in the way in which the coupler is used. In the Dry Process, the coupling component, together with stabilizing substances to maintain an acid condition, are coated together on the paper or film base. After exposure the image can be developed merely by exposure to an alkaline atmosphere such as that produced by the volatilization of aqua ammonia. In modern equipment both steps are extremely rapid, and, in a completely automatic machine, finished prints may be produced in as little as five seconds. In the Moist or Semi-Wet modification of this process only the diazo salt with a small amount of stabilizing material is coated on the base stock. Following exposure, a solution of the coupling component is applied by means of a metering roller to the sensitized surface of the product. If the developing solution is of the proper alkalinity, a practically instantaneous coupling forms the azo dye. After a brief drying, a finished print is obtained.

Diazo papers at present find their widest usage in the copying of plans and tracings for which they are tending to replace the long-established blueprint. For this purpose they have the advantage of (1) speed, as exposure and coupling require only two or three minutes and, with the dry process, the print does not require drying, (2) of producing a positive image and (3) of being true-to-scale, as there is no expansion or contraction, as in the blueprint and

[21] Willis, B.P. 20,022 (1913); *Brit. J. Phot.* **61**, 777 (1914).

SCHUMPELT, "Palladium Printing Process," U.S.P. 2,267,953.
CLERC, *Photography, Theory and Practice*, Pitman, New York.
HENNEY AND DUDLEY, *Handbook of Photography*, McGraw-Hill Book Co., Inc., New York.
ANDERSON, "Hand Sensitized Palladium Paper," *Amer. Phot.* **32**, 457 (1938).
SAUNDERS, *The Aromatic Diazo Compounds and Their Technical Applications*, Longmans Green, London, 1937.
GROGGINS, *Unit Processes in Organic Synthesis*, McGraw-Hill Book Co., Inc., New York.

similar processes, from the wetting and drying of the paper. While many different colors are possible, the most important commercially are the black line, blue line, and sepia line papers.

Continuous tone materials producing black, sepia, or blue prints are available commercially. These, however, have a limited exposure scale as compared with conventional printing papers and at present are employed chiefly where a large number of prints are required at low cost.

Red, blue, and yellow diazo materials on thin film base (Ozachrome) are available for making color prints from three-color positives. These are used principally in proofing three-color positives for photo-mechanical printing.

SPENCER, "Photographic Applications of Diazo Compounds," *Phot. J.* **68**, 490 (1928).

MURRAY, "Diazo Compounds in Photography," *Phot. J.* **73**, 6 (1933).

BROWN, "Basis and Practice of the Diazotype Process," *Chemistry and Industry No. 16*, 146 (1944).

PERDUE, "Ozalid Light-Sensitive Materials," *J. Soc. Dyers and Colorists* **63**, 24 (1947).

MURRAY, "The Diazotype Process," *Chemistry and Industry* **69**, 769 (1940).

WOLFE, "Continuous-tone Diazo Printing," *Photo-Technique* I, December, 44 (1939).

The decomposition products of some diazonium compounds in the presence of a chromate possess the property of tanning gelatin and other colloids. Printing processes based on this observation have been patented by Kalle & Co. B.P. 296,008 (1927); B.P. 401,898 (1931).

Chapter 28

PRINCIPLES OF THREE-COLOR PHOTOGRAPHY

Trichromatic Theory. All practical methods of three-color photography are based upon the theoretical investigations of Wunsch and Young (1802) on the wave theory of light and the trichromatic mechanism of color vision. Clerk Maxwell was the first to point out (1855) and demonstrate (1861) how these principles might be applied to reproduce a colored scene by means of photography. Maxwell stated that the visual appearance of any color could be matched by a proper mixture of

green produces yellow; green and blue produce cyan; and all three together produce white. Various other colors may be produced by the combination of these primary colors in varying proportions. Thus, the addition of green to red will produce orange, yellow, or yellow-green, depending upon the relative intensity of the green to the red; in like manner, the combination of green and blue produces various blue-greens, and combinations of red and blue can produce all variations of magenta.

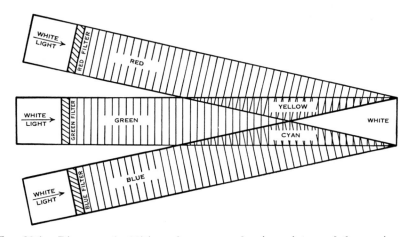

FIG. 28.1.   Diagram of additive color process showing mixture of three primary colors producing white light.

three differently colored light sources. The three chosen colors were red, green, and blue, the so-called "primary colors," whose additive mixtures will match all but a few very saturated colors.

If, for example, beams of white light are directed upon a screen but pass first through red, green and blue filters as shown in Fig. 28-1, the combination of red and

It is possible to determine the proportions in which each of three monochromatic lights must be mixed in order to produce the same color sensation as obtained when examining any part of the spectrum. In Fig. 28-2 are shown three color-mixture curves, one for each primary color. The heights of these curves at any particular wave length indicate the proportions in which the primary colors must be combined to produce the color sensation corresponding to that wave length of the spectrum.

The eye is not an analytical instrument, and the range of colors observed when examining a spectrum from sunlight is continuously variable—the gradual alteration of hue being due to the changing activation of the three color-sensitive elements of the eye. The eye is not able to identify the

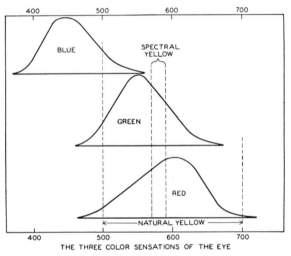

FIG. 28.2.   The three color sensations of the eye.

origin of colors. Thus, the visual sensation produced by a monochromatic yellow from the spectrum, an additive mixture of limited red and green regions, and a mixture of the whole of the color range from dark red through green might be identical. Mixtures of monochromatic light of wave lengths 640, 532, and 464 mμ were found to be satisfactory for matching most natural colors.[1] It is also possible to obtain similar results with broad mutually adjacent bands of color instead of single wave lengths. The greatest range of colors can be matched, however, by using highly saturated red, green, and blue colors as sources.

Maxwell's development of the theory of color photography is best expressed in his own words: "Let it be required to ascertain the colors of a landscape by means of impressions taken on a preparation equally sensitive to rays of every color. Let a plate of red glass be placed before the camera, and an impression taken. The positive of this will be transparent wherever the red light has been abundant in the landscape, and opaque where it has been wanting. Let it now be put in a magic lantern along with the red glass, and a red picture will be thrown on the screen. Let this operation be repeated with a green and violet glass, and, by means of three magic lanterns, let the three images be superimposed on the screen. The color of any point on the screen will then depend on that of the corresponding point of the landscape; and, by properly adjusting the intensities of the lights, etc., a complete copy of the landscape, as far as visible color is concerned, will be thrown on the screen. The only apparent difference will be that the copy will be more subdued, or less pure in tint, than the original."[2] This method of combining the color records (positives) is called *additive synthesis,* since color is obtained by adding colored lights together on the screen to produce the various color combinations.

Color may be produced also by subtracting light of certain wave lengths from white light. Yellow transmits red and green and absorbs blue. In other words, yellow is minus blue; it contains all the colors of the spectrum except blue. If a yellow filter is placed on a white paper and then over this a magenta filter which absorbs green light, as in Fig. 28-3, only red light will be reflected to the observer. Similarly, a combination of cyan and yellow filters produces green (Fig. 28-3) as

[1] *Bull. Phot. J.* **75**, 257 (1935).

[2] Maxwell, *Trans. Roy. Soc. Edinburgh* **21**, 275 (1855).

the yellow absorbs the blue and the cyan the red, leaving only the green. A blue image may be obtained through a combination of magenta and cyan filters.

Thus, the three "primaries," red, green, and blue,[3] may be produced by subtracting color from white light by means of cyan, magenta, and yellow colorants. This is known as *subtractive synthesis.*

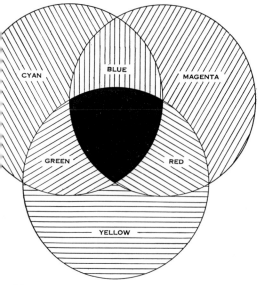

FIG. 28.3. Superimposed color filters yield mixture colors by subtraction.

Additive and Subtractive Processes. It has long been the custom to divide color processes into two main groups—additive and subtractive. Such a division is convenient as long as it is clearly recognized that the grouping is valid only when considering the synthesis of the color picture. The method of analysis is the same no matter which type of reproduction is employed. Furthermore it can be shown that, optically, ideal subtractive printing colorants are equivalent to the red, green, and blue used in an additive synthesis. A more logical exposition is possible, if color processes

[3] The blue primary is often designated by the term *blue-violet.*

are considered as a color analysis and an additive or subtractive synthesis.

If a photograph is made using a red filter, the negative will record, in terms of density, the amount of red light reflected from the subject; in other words, the greater the amount of red reflected from any particular part of the subject, the greater the density of the corresponding parts of the black-and-white negative. Areas which do not reflect red light are completely clear, whereas colors reflecting only a small amount of red are of low density.

A second negative made with a green filter will record the green, and a third negative made with a blue filter will record the blue reflected from the various parts of the subject. Hues that may be formed from two or more of these colors will be recorded on two or more negatives in accordance with the amount of light of each primary color reflected. Thus, the three negatives collectively will record, in terms of silver densities, all the colors of the subject.

If black-and-white positive transparencies are made from these negatives, color will be indicated by *lack of density.* In the positive from the red separation negative, for example, areas corresponding to red parts of the subject will be almost clear, those containing some red represented by a low density and those without red by a relatively high density. This positive is therefore a photographic record, in terms of silver density, of the absence of red in the subject photographed. The greater the silver density, the less red present in the subject.

This transparent positive, when viewed by red light, will inform the observer of the red component present in the various parts of the subject. In like manner, positive transparencies from the other two negatives will reproduce the corresponding

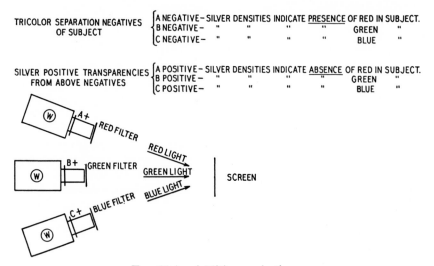

TRICOLOR SEPARATION NEGATIVES OF SUBJECT
{
A NEGATIVE– SILVER DENSITIES INDICATE <u>PRESENCE</u> OF RED IN SUBJECT.
B NEGATIVE– "   "   "   "   GREEN   "
C NEGATIVE– "   "   "   "   BLUE   "
}

SILVER POSITIVE TRANSPARENCIES FROM ABOVE NEGATIVES
{
A POSITIVE– SILVER DENSITIES INDICATE <u>ABSENCE</u> OF RED IN SUBJECT.
B POSITIVE– "   "   "   "   GREEN   "
C POSITIVE– "   "   "   "   BLUE   "
}

FIG. 28.4.   Additive projection.

green and blue color components of the subject when illuminated by light of the same color as used in making the negatives.

It is now only necessary to combine the three images to produce a representation in full color of the subject photographed. This may be done in one of two ways: (1) the three positives may be placed in a specially designed triple projector (Fig. 28-4) which is so arranged that the three images can be made to coincide upon the screen, or (2) the three positives may be placed beneath filters and the images superimposed with the aid of mirrors in an instrument known as a *Photochromoscope* (Fig. 28-5). A modern form of this instrument is available as the Curtis Color Analyst.

There have been many attempts to utilize this system of making colored pictures. As will be shown later, the color fidelity of such methods is quite high, but because of expensive and inconvenient viewing or projecting devices, they have never attained widespread popularity. The widest field for these methods has been in color motion pictures [4] and screen processes.

Color Screen Materials. Screen plates, discussed in Chapter 31, have been widely used and illustrate one type of additive synthesis by color photography. In just the same way that a painter may secure a certain color by the admixture of dabs of pigment of two or more colors which, at a suitable viewing distance, are no longer seen individually but combine to form a single color, so it is possible to secure all three color-sensation records on a single

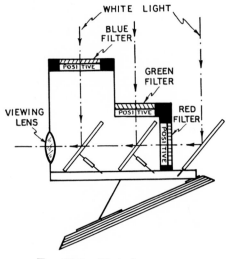

FIG. 28.5.   Photochromoscope.

[4] Klein, *Colour Cinematography.*

plate by exposing the plate behind, and in contact with, a screen composed of a large number of red, green, and blue filters so small as to be indistinguishable to the unaided eye.

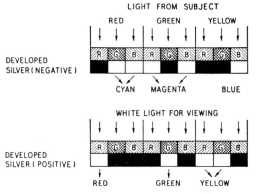

Fig. 28.6. Principle of screen plates.

In Fig. 28-6, beams of red, green, and yellow light are represented as falling on a screen composed of small filters designated R (red), G (green), and B (blue). Red light is transmitted by the red filter (R) and renders the emulsion beneath it developable. Green light is transmitted by the green filter and the emulsion beneath is rendered developable. Yellow light is transmitted by both the green and red filters, rendering the emulsion beneath both filters developable.

The deposits of silver produced upon development are shown by the darkened portions.

If the negative image is reversed to form a positive, or a positive is made from the negative and placed in register with the screen, red light is reproduced by the light transmitted by the red filters, since the green and blue filter elements are covered with the silver of the positive image. In the same way, yellow is reproduced by the light transmitted by the green and red filter elements, only the blue being obstructed by the positive silver image.

If the screen material is developed to a

negative, not only will the subject values be reversed but the colors will all be complementary to those of the original. A silver negative and a color negative will be obtained. The red will be represented by a mixture of green and blue (cyan), the green by a mixture of red and blue (magenta), and the blue by a mixture of red and green (yellow).

Subtractive Processes of Color Photography. Negatives for subtractive printing are prepared in exactly the same manner as negatives for additive color processes. Any of the following systems may be used: (1) by making three separate exposures with an ordinary camera, changing the sensitive material and filters between each exposure; (2) by means of a repeating back which enables these changes to be made automatically in a much shorter period of time; (3) by using a separable tripack in which three emulsions, each recording only one of the primary color sensations, are placed in a single holder and exposed; (4) by using a tricolor camera in which all three negatives are exposed at the same time through the same lens; and (5) by making use of a screen or integral tripack positive or negative material to record the separations. These may later be re-separated to obtain the color records as three separate negatives, if desired. All of these methods will be described at greater length in the following chapters.

To obtain a positive color reproduction from negatives produced by any of the above methods, it is necessary to superimpose three positive images of the proper colorants made from the negatives. As discussed earlier, each negative is a record, in terms of silver density, of the presence of one of the primary colors. The higher the density on the red filter negative, for example, the greater the quantity of red in the subject. A positive made from this negative indicates, by silver densities, where red was not present in the subject. Such a positive, if placed in a projection lantern with a red filter, prevents red light from reaching the screen in the appropriate areas of the picture. Or, stated differently, the positive acts as a light valve for red, allowing red light to reach the screen in the proper parts of the picture. This is additive synthesis since red light is added to the screen onto which the other two colors, green and blue, are projected sepa-

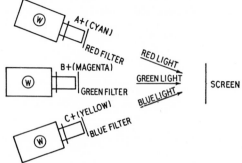

FIG. 28.7.   Substitution of three colorants for silver images.

rately. Since the addition of lights by projection requires considerable equipment, other methods of obtaining the same color information (reproduction) are desirable.

The only requirement is that three images be prepared that will furnish the same information as the three projected images of the additive processes (Fig. 28-4). This can readily be done by transforming the black silver of the positive prepared from the red filter negative into a cyan colorant. This cyan colorant (dye, ink, pigment, or metallic material) is one

which absorbs red light. If it is a good cyan it will absorb just as much red light as a black silver image. A positive cyan image may therefore be substituted in the projection lantern for the silver image. The appearance of the projected image will be the same in both cases. This explains why cyan is often termed "minus-red." In a similar manner, magenta (minus-green) and yellow (minus-blue) may be substituted for the black silver in the positives made from the green and blue filter negatives, respectively.

The cyan, magenta, and yellow images are not only equivalent to the three silver positives when used as shown in Fig. 28-7, but they have a further advantage in that they may be superimposed in a single projector without any filter and supply similar information to the observer. In this case, Fig. 28-8, the cyan image subtracts red from the white light of the projector in the proper areas, the magenta image subtracts green, and the yellow image subtracts blue. This is the same information as supplied by the additive process; i.e., areas in which each primary color was and was not present in the subject and how much in each area. This information is all the eye requires to form a color reproduction of the original scene. Such a process using superimposed cyan, magenta, and yellow images in a projector or on a reflecting white surface, such as paper, is a subtractive color reproduction.

The great majority of color reproductions are made today by means of a sub-

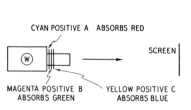 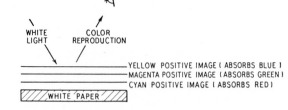

FIG. 28.8.   Subtractive schemes.

tractive color synthesis. A discussion of the production of suitable cyan, magenta, and yellow colorant images includes the techniques of almost every practical color process today.

Subtractive Printing Processes. The methods employed in making the color images for subtractive printing processes may be divided into six classes:

1. Toning Processes
2. Relief Processes
3. Selectively Hardened Gelatin Processes
4. Dye Coupling Processes
5. Chemical Dye Destruction Processes
6. Dye Bleaching Processes

The details of these processes are discussed in Chapters 30 and 32.

Subtractive Processes Based upon an Integral Tripack. Ducos du Hauron, who seems to have anticipated almost every possible process of color photography, suggested the use of three superimposed emulsions, each separately sensitized to one of the three primary colors, as a means of making three-color negatives. The simplest method of making such a tripack is by superimposing suitable emulsions coated on three separate films.

Tripacks in which the three emulsions are coated over one another on the same base are termed "integral tripacks." The first tripack of this type to be introduced commercially for camera use was developed in the research laboratories of the Eastman Kodak Company and introduced as Kodachrome, first for amateur cinematography, then as 35 mm., and finally as sheet film for amateur and professional use.

The trend in modern color photography is definitely toward the integral tripack type of material for reversal, negative-positive, and paper print processes. For a detailed discussion of integral tripacks, see Chapter 32. Typical widely used commercial processes are Kodachrome,[5] Ansco

Color Positive Film, Kodacolor, and Ektachrome.

Two-Color Processes. Pleasing, although obviously incomplete, pictures in color may be obtained of certain subjects by using but two (orange and cyan) analysis colors. Two-color negatives can be made with one exposure, in an ordinary camera, by using a bipack, and printing processes employing two images are naturally simpler than those employing three colors. The complications of the three-color processes have led numerous investigators to attempt to perfect two-color processes, particularly for making motion pictures in color. There is at present a declining interest in two-color processes except in professional motion pictures, and it is probably safe to say that such processes will soon be chiefly of historical interest except for motion picture uses.

In two-color processes, the spectrum is either divided into approximately equal parts by the taking filters, the orange and red being recorded on one negative and the green and blue on the other, or one of the tricolor primaries is ignored altogether, the choice depending upon the type of subject and illumination for which the process is designed.

When the spectrum is divided into two approximately equal parts and prints made with colorants complementary to those of the taking filters, flesh values are reproduced quite well.

Yellow and purplish-blue are not included, nor neutral tones, although, as du

---

[5] Eastman Kodak Company names its color products in such a way that the name is descriptive of the type of process. Thus, *Koda-* indicates a color material processed by the Eastman Kodak Company (*Koda*chrome, *Koda*color, *Koda*chrome prints); while *Ekta-* means a color product that may be processed by the user (*Ekta*chrome, *Ekta*color). The designation, *chrome*, indicates a reversal process, while *color* indicates a negative-positive process.

Hauron pointed out, the yellow sensation is produced if the results are viewed in a yellowish light and the degraded whites produced by two-color processes frequently appear practically white due to the contrast of the other colors. Suggestions have been made that the usual three-color prints be made, the yellow image being exposed partly from the blue-green and partly from the red negative. While such methods, under certain circumstances, produce pleasing results, it is impossible to reproduce a wide range of colors satisfactorily in this manner.[6]

---

[6] Ives, *Camera* (Phila.) (1933) 33.

Chapter 29

THREE-COLOR SEPARATION NEGATIVES

Requirements of Color-Separation Negatives. The purpose of a set of three color separation negatives is to record, as variations in their silver deposits, the relative amounts of the three primary colors, red, green, and blue-violet, present in the subject being photographed. The three records obtained, after development, are then used as light valves to control the intensities of red, green and blue-violet light that will finally make up the reproduction—whether in the form of an additive mixture of lights or a subtractive mixture of dyes, pigments, or inks.

Since the color images must be superimposed in the final result, the three images should be:

1. The same size,
2. Made from the same position, and
3. Equally sharp in all portions.

Since each negative must represent in terms of density the amount of light of a particular primary reflected from the different parts of the subject:

1. The filters and emulsion-sensitivities should divide the spectrum into three approximately equal parts with some overlapping to insure complete coverage, and
2. The rendering of a scale of grays should usually be the same in all three negatives in order to obtain color-free rendering of white and grays, and to insure the proper balancing of the color records when making the reproduction.

Filters for Three-Color Photography. The filters used to limit the range of wave lengths recorded on each separation nega-

tive have been well standardized in practice. Suggestions put forward to the effect that the transmission ranges of the filters should correspond to the color mixture curves have been extensively debated since the turn of the century.[1] The filters giving the most satisfactory color reproductions with the practices in common usage, however, were found to be much more abrupt in their division of the spectrum. At one time it was thought that the ideal filters would be the type shown in Fig. 29.1. The spectrum is divided by these filters into three

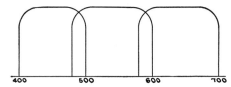

Fig. 29.1. Curves of the ideal three-color filters. (*Photography of Colored Objects.*)

broad and two narrow bands. The region from 600 mμ to 700 mμ is recorded in the red filter negative only, the region between 580 mμ and 600 mμ through both the green and red filters and is reproduced as yellow, since yellow results from the admixture of red and green light. The region between 500 mμ and 580 mμ is recorded only in the negative made through the green filter, whereas the region between 480 mμ and 500 mμ is recorded in both the green and blue filter negatives and, therefore, is reproduced as cyan. The region

[1] Bull, *Phot. J.* **75**, 257 (1935). Spencer, *Phot. J.* **75**, 337 (1935). Murray and Spencer, *Phot. J.* **78**, 474 (1938). Geoghegan and Smethurst, *Brit. J. Phot.* **85**, 339 (1938).

between 400 mμ and 480μ is recorded only on the blue filter negative and is reproduced as blue. While it is not possible by using these filters to produce a distinction between hues which lie totally within any of these spectral regions, in practice this deficiency is not serious, since naturally occurring colors reflect light of nearly all visible wave lengths, their hue being due to a reflection peak in some region of the spectrum.

These "ideal" filters would not, of course, enable one to distinguish between two pure blues, for example, at 430 mμ and 450μ, both being recorded only on the blue record negative. A photograph of the spectrum, therefore, would record only as a five-colored band of light, there being no separation of hues within the five divisions. Fortunately, subjects generally photographed do not respond as monochromatic lights, the distribution of reflected light from all common objects being selective through the spectrum to give the object

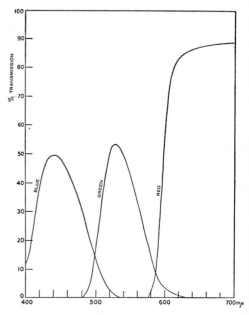

FIG. 29.3.   Transmission curves for a set of standard tricolor filters.

its color. However, there is usually some reflection at all wave lengths (Fig. 29.2). The dyes and coloring materials available for the manufacture of color filters necessitate some departure from the generally accepted ideal transmission curves (see Chapter 33). Spectrophotometric curves showing the transmission of a well known set of three color filters (Wratten, No. 25-red, No. 58-green, and No. 47-blue-violet) are shown in Fig. 29.3. The transmission curves of the red and blue filters approximate the ideal very closely; the transmission of the green filter ends less abruptly at the long wave region than that of the ideal. Although this characteristic can be overcome by increasing the red-absorbing component of the green filter, such a procedure is not practical because of the increase in the filter factor, necessitating greatly increased exposure.[2]

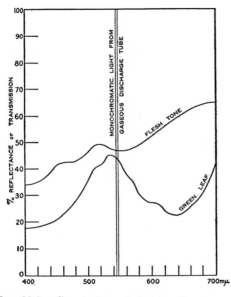

FIG. 29.2.   Comparison between the general spectral reflectance of natural colors and the single wave lengths from monochromatic light sources.

---

[2] While color separation filters may not be efficient (transmit 100% of the light of their own color), they do give excellent color separation.

It is possible to obtain good results with No. 47B or other than standard tricolor filters. For example, the darker Wratten No. 49 (C4) blue filter can be substituted for the Wratten No. 47 filter if conditions permit the necessarily longer exposure time. Some slight improvement in color reproduction may thus be obtained. With other than the panchromatic emulsions, yellow, violet, or other color filters may be required.

Exposure of Color Separation Negatives. Color separation negatives may be made in a variety of ways as indicated in the following table. In this chapter, we shall consider in detail only the records made with a lapse of time between each exposure or instantaneous exposures of the physically separable type. Any of the following methods yields records of the primary colors present in the subject in terms of silver deposits.

I. *Successive Exposures.*
  A. Direct successive exposures.
  B. Repeating backs.

I. *Simultaneous Exposures.*
  A. Physically separable records.
    1. Bipacks and tripacks.
    2. Beam splitters.
  B. Physically inseparable records.
    1. Lateral separation—one emulsion.
      a. Screen processes.
      b. Lenticular processes.
    2. Vertical separation—integral tripacks and bipacks.
      a. Differently sensitized emulsions.
      b. Emulsion layer sensitization.
  C. Miscellaneous combinations.
    1. Screen bipack.
    2. Lenticular bipack.

ow efficiency is of no significance as long as the xposure times may be adjusted to compensate for he light losses.

Direct Successive Exposures. For still objects an ordinary camera may be used, the three negatives being made by successive exposures, the filters and the sensitive material being changed between each exposure. The exposure must be adjusted, of course, in accordance with the multiplying factors of the filters. Care must be taken that the lighting does not change during the time the three exposures are being made and that a rigid camera and tripod are used to prevent any danger of shifting position when changing plates and filters. Neither portraits nor landscapes in which movement is likely can be photographed in this way.

Repeating Backs. An improvement over the ordinary camera with separate emulsions and holders is provided by a repeating back. The holder of the repeating back takes a plate long enough for the three exposures, or three separate small plates, and the filters are placed in front of each plate so that filter and plate are changed together for each exposure. With repeating backs, all three exposures may be made in the space of three or four seconds.

Bipacks and Tripacks. A bipack consists of two separate emulsions held face to face in one holder, both being exposed at the same time. A red recording emulsion is generally used as the rear element of the bipack, preceded by an orthochromatic film with a red filter surface coating. This combination is not essential as other pairs may be used. A bipack may be employed as the negative material for two-color processes or it may be used with an appropriate filter as a means of recording two of three color separations for a three-color process. A separable tripack consists of three different films. The front film is coated with an ordinary (blue-sensitive) emulsion and then with a layer of gelatin, containing a yellow filter dye. The second film is coated with an orthochromatic emulsion sensitive to green and on the back with a gelatin layer containing a red dye. The first and second films are exposed with their emulsions in contact. The rear film (third) is coated with a panchromatic emulsion. Thus, with one exposure in the camera, a blue-violet record is made on the front film, a green record on the second and a red record on the third, or rear, film. Other emulsion combinations and orders may also be used.

There are several drawbacks to the widespread use of the separable tripack as a means of obtaining three-color negatives. The middle, and especially the rear, emulsion records are somewhat unsharp because of the scattering of light in passing through the first and middle emulsions. To minimize scattering the emulsions are kept thin and relatively transparent, resulting in a limited exposure latitude. Separable tripacks have been quite slow for studio color photography even though the red filter dye coating (Fig. 29–4)

allows more orange light to pass than is considered advisable for the optimum color analysis.

For work not requiring the delineation of fine detail or color accuracy, the separable tripack is quite satisfactory. Its special field of usefulness lies in portraiture where the diffusion of the red record is usually of no concern.

An improved form of separable tripack has recently been described by Defender.[3] This material, called *S–T Tripack*, gives sharper images in the rear emulsions and considerably higher speed than formerly attainable. This emulsion assembly consists of a double support tripack, the front film coated with the blue and green recording emulsions separated by a soluble stripping layer. The second film is red sensitive. The two films are exposed, emulsions in contact, in a single pressure holder. After development and fixation, the uppermost emulsion on the front support (green record) is stripped from the base and blue record. The stripped emulsion is transferred to another support. Three negatives may thus be obtained of acceptable sharpness.

Tricolor Cameras. Tricolor cameras are designed to divide optically the light transmitted by the lens in such a manner as to produce two or three separate images in different planes. Such devices are sometimes called *beam-splitters*. A great number of methods of dividing the light from the lens have been developed; but the only types of interest here are those in which the whole area of the light cone transmitted by the lens affects each separation. The tricolor cameras in present usage may be divided into (1) the single-mirror type,

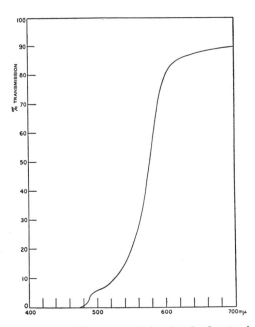

FIG. 29.4. Wide transmission band of a typical tripack red filter.

3 *J. Phot. Soc. Amer.* **14**, 49 (1948).

CAPSTAFF, *J. Soc. Mot. Pict. Eng.* **54**, 448 (1950).

and (2) the double-mirror type. In the single-mirror camera, two images are formed, one transmitted directly through the mirror, the other reflected from the front surface of the mirror. In this type of camera, a bipack is exposed at one negative position and a single film at the other. In the double-mirror camera, one image is formed after passing through both mirrors, the other two after a reflection.

The design of the optical system in one-exposure color cameras is limited by the requirement that each emulsion must be evenly illuminated. Lack of observance of this requirement leads to what is known as "color wedging"—a variation in negative density across the image but not the same on each separation negative. The change in ratio of reflected and transmitted light with varying angles of light incident on the mirrors makes this condition difficult to satisfy. In Fig. 29.5, three representative camera constructions are illustrated. In Type A, the two mirrors are parallel and there is some color wedging on the second and third images. In Type B, the two mirrors are at right angles to each other, so that one reflected image is either above, or to the left, of the direct image, the other below, or to the right. The advantage of this arrangement over some others is that the tendency toward uneven illumination of the direct and second reflected image is exactly corrected by having the mirrors at right angles. In Type C, the mirrors are not at 45° to the optical axis of the lens. This type of construction yields negatives, when the camera case is properly constructed, that are quite free from color wedging and is the most common type of present day construction.

The optical construction of the single mirror camera is shown in Fig. 29.6. In single-mirror cameras, sometimes called "bipack and singles," there are three possible separation combinations. The single film may be either a red, green, or blue record

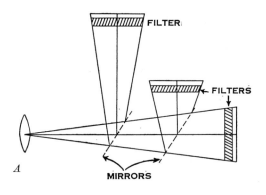

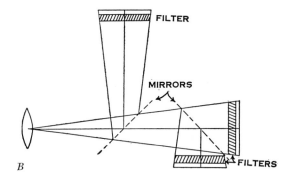

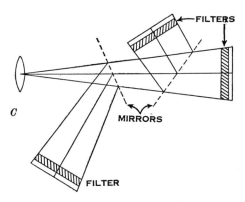

FIG. 29.5. Three types of double mirror color camera construction.

COOTE, *Phot. J.* **81**, 293 (1941).
KLEIN, *Colour Cinematography.*
WALL, *History of Three-Color Photography.*
FRIEDMAN, *History of Color Photography.*

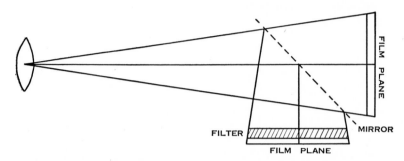

FIG. 29.6. Single-mirror color camera using a bipack. Mirror angle may be
increased over 45° to obtain more even illumination.

in which case the bipacks will record blue and green, blue and red, or red and green respectively. There are many emulsion filter combinations that can be used to obtain the three types listed. In the first example the single film would be a panchromatic emulsion exposed behind a red filter, and the bipack a combination of a yellow-dyed, blue sensitive film and an orthochromatic film. In the second case, the single film may be an orthochromatic emulsion behind a yellow or a green filter and a bipack of blue-sensitive or orthochromatic front film with a red filter layer and a panchromatic rear film, the pair being exposed behind a magenta filter. The third combination consists of a blue-sensitive emulsion without a filter, or with a magenta or violet filter, and a bipack of orthochromatic and panchromatic emulsions in contact behind a minus blue filter. The orthochromatic film requires a red filter layer over its emulsion. The arrangement chosen depends upon the emulsion combinations available and the reflection-transmission ratio of the mirror in the camera. The performance of the single mirror camera depends upon the quality of the negatives produced by the bipack, i.e., on (1) the color separation obtained, and (2) the sharpness of the image obtained on the rear negative of the bipack. The single-mirror camera, being much simpler

than the double-mirror camera, is less expensive and usually permits shorter exposure. With suitable subject matter a single-mirror camera yields very satisfactory results.

The modern tricolor camera is generally of metal construction. The partially reflecting mirrors are made either of glass or are thin membranes of collodion stretched over an optically flat metal frame. These latter are called *pellicle* mirrors. Whichever form of mirror is used, it may be clear or colored and its surface may be partially metallized to obtain the desired reflection-transmission ratio. Pellicle mirrors have rapidly replaced the glass mirrors formerly found in one-shot cameras. Because of the thickness of glass mirrors, unless special precautions were taken, a double image was obtained on the reflected beam due to reflection from both the front and rear surfaces of the glass. This drawback was sometimes overcome by making the mirror serve as a filter so that the back surface reflection would be minimized. The color of the filter was usually complementary to the separation negative filter. Such an arrangement, of course, would not allow of any alteration in position of the separation negatives for different type illuminants. A further disadvantage of glass is the refraction of the light passing through the thickness of the glass mirror.

Due to this refraction, one-half the image is expanded, the other half contracted. This makes registration difficult, and no really satisfactory compromise can be reached for the distortion produced.

All these disadvantages are readily overcome by the use of pellicle mirrors, which are so thin that the refraction and double-image errors are small enough to be negligible. These membrane mirrors may also be dyed if necessary, although this is not common practice at present except in single mirror cameras. The only drawback to the thin membrane type mirror is its susceptibility to mechanical damage. It has been proved conclusively, however, that, under normal atmospheric conditions, no difficulty is experienced if reasonable care is exercised. Present color cameras have speeds approximately the same as current reversal color transparency materials. The recent development of interference filters that may be incorporated in the camera mirrors may make possible the manufacture of color cameras of higher efficiency in the future.

Sensitive Materials for Three-Color Photography. For three-color separation work, one requirement is that three negatives finally be obtained which are records of the red, green, and blue in the subject. The following combinations may be used:

three exposures, it has been stated that the sensitometric characteristics of the three records will be the same and that, upon keeping, the relative speeds and gradations for each color record will change in a similar manner. The arguments in favor of separately sensitized emulsions revolve about the desire for speed. Because of the low light efficiency of the standard green and blue tricolor filters, a much faster combination is obtainable from a yellow filter on the green record and a violet or no filter for the blue record. Some observers find that the sensitometric characteristics can be matched about as closely with different emulsions as with a single panchromatic one.[4] The emulsion recording the red separation should be of the medium red sensitivity type. Since accurate color reproduction necessitates the use of the straight portions of the emulsion's characteristic curve and a wavelength-gamma variation as small as possible, these factors should be considered when choosing emulsions for color separation.

Most manufacturers of photographic emulsions have one or more materials especially suited to the production of color separation negatives. All panchromatic emulsions of adequate speed are not equally satisfactory since the tricolor characteristic

Red Record	*Green Record*	*Blue Record*
Panchromatic emulsion Red filter	Panchromatic emulsion Green filter	Panchromatic emulsion Blue filter
	Orthochromatic emulsion Green filter	Orthochromatic emulsion Magenta filter
	Orthochromatic emulsion Yellow filter	Non-color sensitized emulsion without filter or with blue-transmitting filter

The combination chosen depends on many factors such as availability, speed, and the characteristics of the various sensitizings. In favor of using one panchromatic emulsion with the appropriate filters for all

curves may not be similar or the length of the straight-line portion of the curves may

---

[4] Housekeeper, *Photo-Technique* **2**, No. 2, 26 (1940); Colton, *Photo-Technique* **2**, No. 7, 54 (1940); Coote, *Brit. J. Phot.* **87**, 15 (1940).

not be adequate. The manufacturers should be consulted for the latest recommendations.

For three-color photography, glass plates have the advantage of being free from unequal expansion or contraction in processing which would disturb the registration of the three-color images. Experience has shown, however, that films may be used if all three are on the same type of base, receive the same treatment in processing, and are dried slowly and uniformly while oriented in the same manner. The emulsions on films are generally much more evenly coated than on the same size plate, and less difficulty is experienced from local variations in color due to such unevenness. The material used in the various tricolor cameras is generally prescribed by the manufacturer of the camera. For a given set of mirrors and color quality of incident light, the negatives give equal gray scales with proper development. Any alterations in the color temperature of the light used, the characteristics of the emulsions, or the conditions of development, will necessitate some form of compensation to secure balanced negatives. When a single-mirror camera employing a bipack is designed, the mirror reflectivity is chosen for some commercially available emulsion materials, and their use is essential for a satisfactory balance in the three separation negatives.

Lighting in Color Photography. In tricolor photography, both the quantity and quality (color temperature) of the illumination are of great importance.

The quantity of illumination required in color photography is generally somewhat greater than that necessary for black-and-white work due to the light losses involved in the exposure of the sensitive materials. The quantity of illumination must also be considered in respect to the different areas of the picture. Color processes are more limited in regard to exposure latitude than

black-and-white processes, and, therefore, precautions should be taken to avoid inadequately illuminated areas that might reproduce as dark areas without detail. Subject matter of unduly varying luminosity and color may require some adjustment in the relative quantity of illumination since a fairly dark green and a bright red cannot be given any single exposure under constant illumination that will make them both appear correctly in a modern color transparency. Separate illumination is often necessary to bring the various hues and values in the subject up to light levels that will give a satisfactory reproduction. The judicious use of an exposure meter is indicated for accurate color work (see Chapters 22 and 32).

In black-and-white photography, the modeling and contrast are supplied by the subject matter and its lighting. In color photography a great deal of both is supplied by the color of the subject. It is, therefore, unnecessary, indeed unwise, to use lightings of very high contrast for color photographs unless special effects are desired. Harsh highlights tend to be devoid of color, and poorly illuminated shadows will be black. The lighting should be soft, although not necessarily flat.[5]

The second attribute of illumination, its quality, is of very real importance to the color photographer. The light sources commonly used differ widely in their energy distribution throughout the visible spectrum (see Chapter 1). These differences, even though not apparent visually, may seriously affect the reproduction of color. As in black-and-white photography, the quality of illuminants may be divided into two general classes—those whose color is approximately similar to average sunlight plus skylight (so-called daylight illumina-

---

[5] Haskell, *Camera Craft* **110** (1938); 550, 601 (1940). Baker, *J. Soc. Mot. Pict. Eng.* **29**, 471 (1937).

tion) and those sources approximating the studio-type incandescent lamp. The exposure ratio for color separation negatives, or the materials to be used with integral tripacks, is determined by the quality of the illumination. The following rough classification serves to differentiate between the two types of light sources:

"Daylight" Types

Sunlight
Arc lamps
Speed flash tubes
Blue flash lamps
Daylight fluorescent lamps
Blue photoflood lamps

"Tungsten" Types

Photoflood lamps (3300° K.–3450° K.)
3200° K. lamps
Clear flash lamps (3300° K.–4000° K.)
High intensity tungsten lamps (3000° K.–3200° K.)
White fluorescent lamps

When three color separations are made individually, the exact quality of light is not important so long as the distribution of energy from the source is reasonably continuous, since the exposure ratio may be adjusted to yield balanced negatives. In the case of tripack materials, or a one-shot color camera, where the sensitivities are adjusted for a given source of light, that source must be approximated either directly or by filtration to yield satisfactory color negatives or positives.

Light sources which emit radiation approximating that of a black body radiator may be assumed to give satisfactory color reproduction. Several "daylight-type" sources, such as high speed flash lamps and fluorescent lamps, have an energy distribution which is a combination of a line spectrum and a continuous spectrum. A few colors may reproduce improperly when photographed with such a source, but in the vast majority of cases, no difficulty is encountered with these illuminants. A

color temperature meter [6] may be used successfully in studio photography where variations in the applied voltage cause considerable changes in the quality of the light emitted by tungsten lamps. It is necessary that the applied voltage be within one or two volts of that for which the lamp was designed, if the proper quality of light is to be obtained from the lamp. Voltage regulation equipment is advisable in most locations where professional color photography is practiced on a large scale.[7]

Lenses. A good color-corrected lens should be used when making three-color negatives. It is essential that the lens produce images of the same size and sharpness on all three negatives. For the highest quality work, where accurate registration is required, the use of an apochromat is advisable (see Chapters 7 and 8). The lens to be used may be tested by carefully photographing on a reversal integral tripack color material a subject consisting of white threads against a black background. If the transparency shows color fringes along the images of the white thread, then the three separations would not be suitable for making high-quality color reproductions. It is also possible to test the lens by making a red separation negative on a glass plate from which a contact positive is prepared. This contact positive may be visually registered with the green and blue separation negatives to check the size equivalence of the three-color images. A simple, but less precise, check can be made by examining the image of the above-mentioned test subject in the space normally occupied by the camera ground glass. This can be done with a color-corrected magnify-

---

[6] Lowry and Weaver, *J. Soc. Mot. Pict. Eng.* **32**, 298 (1939). Miller, *J. Soc. Mot. Pict. Eng.* **54**, 435 (1950). Crandell, Freund and Moen, *J. Soc. Mot. Pict. Eng.* **55**, 67 (1950).

[7] Forsythe, *Photo-Technique* **1**, No. 6, 20 (1939). Dudley, *Photo-Technique* **1**, No. 10, 8 (1939).

ing glass. Serious color aberrations can be quickly detected in this way.

Scattered light can lead to serious desaturation of colors. A coated lens is advisable along with an adequate lens hood. If color filters are used, they should be clean and so placed that the subject illumination does not fall directly on the filter or lens surface. For the longer focal length lenses, optically flat glass filters or sheets of gelatin should be used.

Reference Object. It is helpful to include in the scene a reference object consisting of a scale of neutral tones. This reference object is useful (1) to insure proper balance of density and contrast in the three separation negatives, and (2) to aid in the determination of exposure times for the positives and in the judgment of the best print quality. The reference object should consist of a scale of gray tones from white to black and each step should be large enough when recorded on the negatives to be read with a densitometer. The range of reflectances included in the steps of the gray scale should include all reflectances of the subject in which accurate color reproduction is desired. The gray scale should be placed in the picture area so that it will receive the same illumination as the important parts of the subject. Any variations in illumination will lessen its value as a reference object. Care should be taken to see that no colored areas are reflecting light onto the reference object so that it will appear colored to the photographic materials. A gray scale should be placed so that its image on the separation negatives is slightly away from the edge to avoid any emulsion or processing variations along the margins of the negatives. Wherever small reference objects are required, they may be obtained commercially along with registration lines and color patches to identify the separation negatives. When larger scales are required, such as in photographing landscapes, a suitable scale of grays may be prepared by exposing sheets of matte photographic paper and processing so as to obtain a neutral image. The number of steps prepared may vary from two, a white and a black, up to about 10. The more steps provided, the more complete, useful and accurate the information available.

If possible, the densities of the various steps in the gray scale should be measured in a reflection densitometer. These values may then be plotted against the densities measured on the separation negatives for the same steps. In such a manner, the characteristic curves for a set of separation negatives may readily be plotted (see Fig. 29.7). Such data are not conclusive because of the effects of lens flare and other

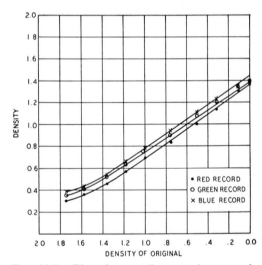

Fig. 29.7.   Plot of separation records on graph.

factors, but they are of great value in checking the various stages in the process of color reproduction. They are also helpful in determining what adjustments of exposure and processing should be made to obtain an optimum set of color separation negatives.

HENDERSON, "The Densiscale," *Photo-Technique* **I**, No. 3, 34–36 (1939).

Filters and Filter Factors. Filters used in making separation negatives are of two types—*tricolor* filters used to divide the spectrum into three parts, and *color compensating filters,* used chiefly with the one-shot color cameras and integral tripack materials to alter the quality of the light reaching the sensitive material. In general, one can say that the filter factor of a filter used in making separation negatives indicates the amount of exposure increase necessary when using that filter to reproduce a gray scale with the same densities as would have been obtained without a filter. With most panchromatic materials recommended for color separation work, the filter factors for the recommended set of triclor filters are determined by tests and printed on a card which is packed with the films or plates. While these factors are accurately determined, they should not be accepted as final since the multiplying factor of a filter depends upon a number of considerations (see Chapter 4), for which it is difficult to make accurate allowance. Slight alterations in the color quality of the light source, development to different gammas, duration of the exposures, or even the age of the sensitive materials, may necessitate revisions of the filter factors.

For all but the most precise work, it is sufficient to make a set of trial exposures under conditions similar to those to be employed later, using the factors submitted with the sensitive material. When properly developed, the gray scales on the three separation negatives may be compared visually, or with a densitometer. Suitable exposure and development adjustments are then made if necessary to insure that the scale densities are recorded alike on each negative. Plotting the results of a set of trial separation negatives in a manner similar to that shown in Fig. 29.7 gives a graphical picture of the quality of the separation negatives. Necessary adjust-

ments of exposure and development can be readily estimated from such a set of curves. For most types of work, it is of greater importance to have the negatives of identical contrasts rather than of the same densities. If the subject is one of long brightness range so that the recording of all the tones in the subject barely fits on the straight-line portion of the characteristic curve, then the densities should be closely matched on each of the three negatives. If such a match is not obtained from a set of negatives from a long-scale subject, some colors in the original will be recorded beyond the correct reproduction region of one or more of the negatives, and inaccurate color reproduction will result. For work requiring high precision, account must be taken of the failure of the reciprocity law, and the filter factors should be determined under approximately the exposure duration conditions to be used in practice. If the filter ratio for a set of tricolor filters at exposure times of around three seconds are determined accurately, the same ratio may not apply for separation negatives made with the same filters on a subject requiring exposure times of approximately three minutes. This is one of the reasons why the tricolor filter recommendations for a given negative material may differ somewhat from the filter factors given for black-and-white photography.[8]

Exposure Determination. The factors affecting exposure are essentially the same in color photography as those discussed in Chapter 22. The generally shorter latitude of color processes, however, makes accurate determination of exposure of greater importance for satisfactory results. In black-and-white photography, the practice has been to determine exposure by means of some estimation or measurement of the brightness of the darkest part of the subject be-

---

8 Tupper, *Photo-Technique* **2**, No. 5, 29 (1940).

ing photographed. The effectiveness of such a procedure is due to the long exposure scale of black-and-white negative materials, and to the fact that the toe regions of their characteristic curves may be employed successfully. In color photography, the highlights of the subject are of more importance in the reproduction since color errors in this region of the brightness scale are much more apparent. This is especially true with reversal materials such as integral tripacks, but it applies on a somewhat lesser scale to direct separation negatives.

Reflected light readings from a subject by integrating type exposure meters can readily lead to exposure errors unless considerable judgment is employed in deciding how to make the exposure reading. More consistent results may be obtained, however, by making incident light measurements at the subject or by making reflected light readings from a standard object of known reflectance, such as the Kodak Neutral Test Card. A reflected light reading from such a standard object yields results similar to those obtained by incident light readings. When making separation negatives, the exposure should be adjusted so that the brightest parts of the subject are recorded on the upper region of the straight line portion of the D log E curve.

Development. It is important that the three color-separation negatives have not only approximately the same density levels but also that their contrasts be alike so that each step on the gray scale of one negative finds an equal density on the other two negatives for the same step. Contrast for color separation negatives is generally indicated by the term "density range" rather than "gamma." The density range is simply the difference in density readings of the black and white portions of the gray scale reference chart, assuming that the

chart range includes all densities present in the subject.

Due to the variation in gamma with wave length (see Fig. 29.8), it is generally necessary to develop the three separation negatives for different times to obtain satisfactory balance. Panchromatic emulsions have lately appeared in which the gamma-wavelength variation is relatively slight, but it

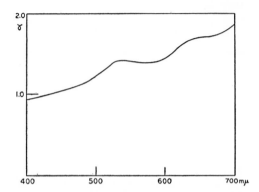

Fig. 29.8. Wave-length-gamma curve for a typical panchromatic emulsion.

is not uncommon to have to increase the development for the blue separation record about 30% over that necessary for the red and green records. A typical wave-length-gamma curve for a panchromatic emulsion is shown in Fig. 29.8. The variations in developing time must be borne in mind when determining the filter factors for the three color records. A given panchromatic emulsion may also show varying shaped characteristic curves when exposed to radiation of different wave lengths. This unfortunate condition may only be overcome by the choice of appropriate emulsions and developers.

The contrast to which the negative should be developed depends upon the process to be used in making the three-color print. If the printing process increases contrast, the contrast of the negatives must be correspondingly lower, whereas if the contrasts obtained in the positive stage are low, then the negatives must be developed to a higher degree of contrast. In general, soft, well-graded negatives with slightly less contrast than would be employed in black-and-white work are desirable. A successful set of negatives depends to a large extent on the care taken in developing. Uneven development will result in color patches when the negatives are printed, and it is practically impossible to cover up such deficiencies in the printing. Since the eye is much more sensitive to variations in color than it is to variations in black and white, extreme precautions must be observed to avoid any unevenness.

It is advisable to develop separation negatives in a developer that gives a neutral image deposit, since (1) a colored image would have a somewhat different visual and photographic contrast, and (2) negatives that may later be masked with other negatives or positives should have neutral images on both emulsions to avoid anomalous sensitometric curves when used together.

Development may be carried out in either a tray or a tank. In the latter case, it is essential that each image be oriented the same way to avoid color wedging. In tray development, a rather large volume of solution should be used in a tray at least one size larger than the negative being developed. Local variations in development are difficult both to avoid and to trace to their source. Continuous irregular agitation or brush development is advisable unless automatic developing machines are employed. Negatives developed under varying conditions of agitation may show a series of sensitometric curves similar to those found upon small variations in developing time (Fig. 29.9). Precautions must also be taken to keep the temperature of the developer constant to within 0.5° F., since small temperature changes produce decided differences in negative contrast. To help keep development conditions constant, it is advisable to use a fresh volume of developer solution for each color record or set of separations. The importance of satisfac-

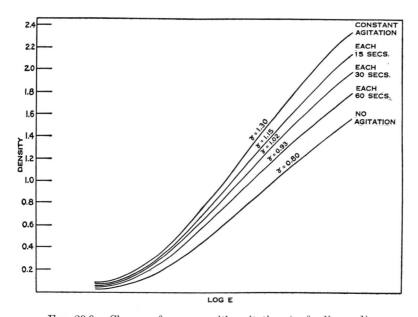

FIG. 29.9. Change of gamma with agitation (agfa diamond).

tory negative balance and even development cannot be overemphasized, because the success of the color print is entirely dependent upon the quality of the separation negatives used to produce it.

Separation Negatives from Integral Tripacks. When a color print is to be made by means of a process requiring separation negatives, these negatives may be obtained by the procedures previously discussed, or they may be made from an integral tripack color film (positive transparency or color negative) which has previously been exposed to the subject. Separation negatives are not generally required when working from a color negative, such as Kodacolor, but are usually necessary when printing from a reversal color transparency, such as Ansco Color Positive, Ektachrome, or Kodachrome.

The color filters generally used are of the analysis type (sharp cutting filters without appreciable overlap), such as Wratten No. 29, No. 61, No. 49. The most satisfactory filters for any given film are specified by the manufacturer. There are two important requirements that these filters have to fulfill. The first is that each filter must have a narrow region of transmission with its maximum transmission at approximately the wave lengths where one of the dyes of the color film has its maximum absorption. The second requirement is that the contrast of a neutral scale as reproduced in the transparency be the same when recorded on each of the separation negatives through the chosen filters. This second requirement is necessary if a silver gray scale is to be used in controlling the contrast and density relationships in the three separation negatives.

The panchromatic emulsion should have a long, straight portion in its characteristic curve since the density range of the average reversal color transparency is approximately 3.0. Such a long range requires a

negative material with a more extended straight-line portion of its characteristic curve than is normally found in negative materials. Whether one panchromatic emulsion is used for all three negatives or whether different type sensitizings are used for the three separations, the shape of the characteristic curve should be the same for each color separation. The exposure of the separation negatives may be made either by contact or projection, depending upon the size of the original transparency and final print. Except from 35-mm. color transparencies and possibly the smallest sheet film size, it is generally more desirable to make the separation negatives by contact and then make the color prints by projection. If large prints are desired from miniature transparencies, the grain of the negative material itself may become objectionable if contact separation negatives are made which are subsequently printed by projection. When exposing the separation negatives, a silver gray scale with a density range as great as that of the transparency being reproduced is generally included beside the transparency, so that it is recorded on each of the separation negatives. The reproduction of this

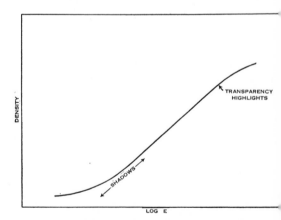

FIG. 29.10. Placement of transparency highlights at negative characteristic curve's shoulder may enable shadow areas to record on straight line.

scale on the separation negatives gives complete information as to the correctness of the separation negative technique and indicates what changes should be made, if any are necessary. A neutral scale made by photographing a gray scale on the same material as the color transparency film is often more useful than a separate silver gray scale.

Since accuracy of highlight detail is most important, the exposures of the separation negatives are adjusted so that the highlight densities of the transparency fall near the break between the straight line and shoulder of the characteristic curve of the separation material employed, as in Fig. 29.10. Even with such placement, the shadow regions of many long-scale color transparencies will be incorrectly reproduced because they are recorded on the toe portions of the separation negatives. Development to a low gamma of approximately 0.7 is necessary to keep the reproduction scale within the range of the negatives and the printing process to be

subsequently employed.[9] The density range of the color transparency may be reduced and so minimize this difficulty by preparing a low contrast black-and-white negative mask, to be bound in register with the color transparency when the separation negatives are being made. This negative mask is contact printed from the color transparency, using a panchromatic emulsion and white light.[10] After development to a low contrast and drying, the mask is bound in register with the transparency. This combination is used when exposing the separation negatives. The decreased density range of the transparency-mask combination may now be readily recorded on the straight region of the separation negative's characteristic curve. Color correction may also be obtained from such a mask with a suitable choice of exposing light and mask material (see Chapter 33).

[9] Color Separation and Masking—Kodak Color Data Book (1951).

[10] Such a procedure is not the same as reducing the contrast of the separation negatives by development since the mask maintains color separation but reduces the achromatic scale.

Chapter 30
SUBTRACTIVE PRINTING PROCESSES

Introduction. Additive systems of color synthesis have several advantages over subtractive synthesis as used in three-color reproduction on paper (see Chapter 33). The additive processes are not suitable, however, for prints on paper and are therefore of little practical interest to the professional photographer. Even in motion picture work, the difficulties with additive processes in projection and cost make the subtractive printing methods of more general commercial interest.

Types of Subtractive Printing. All three-color subtractive processes use the colorants, cyan, magenta, and yellow, in printing from the red, green, and blue separation negatives. The exact shades of cyan, magenta, and yellow used in the various processes vary widely, although the ideals would be optically equivalent to the additive synthesis colors. The cyan and magenta are the poorest colorants and are often, in reality, almost blue and red. The color of most yellow colorants is quite satisfactory. The procedure for all subtractive processes is to superimpose in register the three-colored positive images made from the appropriate color separation negatives. A classification of photographic subtractive printing processes on the basis of their method of forming the colored images shows six distinct types of process. The lines of demarcation between the various methods cannot be drawn too clearly

SUBTRACTIVE PRINTING PROCESSES

	Process	*Image Colorants*
I.	Toning Processes	
	A. Metallic Toning	Colored Metallic Salts
	B. Dye Toning or Mordanting	Dyes (usually basic)
II.	Gelatin Relief Processes	
	A. Tanning Development	Dyes or Pigments
	B. Dichromated Colloids, Hardening Brought About by:	
	1. Light	Pigments
	2. Silver	
	a. Carbro	Pigments
	b. Hardening Bleaching	Dyes
	c. Dyebro	Dyes
	C. Etching	Dyes
III.	Differentially Hardened Colloids—Relief Formation not Essential	
	A. Differential Staining	Dyes
	B. Differential Water Absorption	Inks
IV.	Dye Coupling	Dyes
V.	Dye Destruction	Dyes
VI.	Dye Bleaching	Dyes

since some commercial processes are in reality combinations of the basic types listed.

This chapter will be devoted to a discussion of the various processes involving the superimposition of three separate positives to produce the final print, leaving integral tripacks for a following chapter.

Metallic Toning. The three-color toning processes make use of the principle common to toning, the replacement of a black silver image by an image of another metallic compound which gives the desired color. The procedure for three-color prints is similar, although more complicated, to that employed in obtaining a sepia print by redevelopment. Successful three-color metallic toning processes are relatively new in color photography because (1) a satisfactory magenta color was not available until recently, and (2) a satisfactory balance of density and contrast in the three images was difficult to obtain.

A satisfactory metallic cyan has been available for some time from the standard iron toning formulas. Many variations of this toner have been in common use, especially for two-color motion picture processes and for making blue-toned prints in monochrome photography. Yellow images are readily obtainable by the conversion of a silver image to yellow lead chromate, cadmium sulfide, or nickel ferricyanide. Of these three, the first two produce the best hues. The search for a satisfactory magenta metallic image was fruitless until 1930. Between 1930 and 1936, several British and United States patents were granted for obtaining the magenta image with nickel dimethyl-glyoxime or p-dimethylamino-benzylidenerhodanine. Previous toning methods had made use of uranium and copper toners which, although rather useless for three-color photography, were quite successful in two-color processes

since the image color was red rather than magenta.

With the availability of a satisfactory magenta toner, the remaining difficulty was in the compounding of the three toners so that satisfactory control of density and contrast was obtainable for each color. The successful conclusion of this investigation led to the introduction in 1936 of a convenient positive stripping film on a removable paper support. The Defender *Chromatone* process successfully made use of these techniques. It has not been available since 1941.[1]

In brief, the Chromatone process necessitated the making of three black-and-white positives on a special collodion stripping paper. Considerable opportunity for the control of contrast was afforded by variations in the processing of the positive images. The stripping paper was available in two grades of contrast and several developers were suggested. Exposure and development were altered until equal gray scale neutrals were obtained on each of the three positives. After development, the three positives were fixed in a nonhardening fixing bath and washed thoroughly before toning. During washing, the water soluble adhesive layer securing the emulsion-coated collodion to the paper base was softened enough to permit removal of the image-bearing collodion film from the paper backing. The three positives were next toned to the proper colors. The magenta image was obtained by bleaching the silver in a bath of a nickel salt, potassium ferricyanide, and various other reagents to control the conversion to nickel ferrocyanide. After washing, the white image was converted to nickel dimethyl-glyoxime and treated with hypo to remove the silver ferrocyanide, the desired transparent magenta image remaining. The cyan image was ob-

---

[1] *The Chromatone Process*, Defender Photo Supply Co., Rochester, New York.

tained in a similar manner, being converted to an iron instead of a nickel compound. The yellow image was obtained by bleaching in a lead nitrate bath to lead ferrocyanide and then converting to yellow lead chromate. After toning and a final washing, the three colored films were ready for assembly. If required, a slight reduction in the intensity of the various images could readily be made since the yellow and magenta images were somewhat soluble in acid, and the cyan in alkali. Caution had to be exercised in controlling any such reduction since the highlights were reduced rapidly, and all alkali and acid had to be removed before the films were assembled. The yellow image, being the most opaque of the three, was squeegeed to a wet gelatin-coated paper and the other two images superimposed in register, the whole assembly being taped to a glass support and dried. The surface of the print could be altered during assembly or before mounting.

Dye Toning. The dye toning process involves the replacement of the positive silver image by a compound having an affinity for dyes. These methods are sometimes called dye mordanting processes since the compound replacing the silver image acts as a mordant for the coloring matter. The most commonly used mordants are silver iodide, several metallic ferrocyanides and sulfocyanates as well as various complex compounds composed of two or more substances of the above types. Mordants for color photography should, of course, be as transparent and colorless as possible, and several of the above mentioned possibilities are satisfactory.

In general, basic dyes are more readily attached to the available mordants than the acid dyes and are used for most dye toning. The usual procedure is to make three thin, low-contrast positives on film and then, after fixation and washing, treat

them with the chosen mordanting bath. After the silver image is converted to the mordant, the films are washed and dyed in weak solutions of the appropriate basic dyes. A final washing clears the nonimage portions of dye. The three images are then registered either as a transparency or stripped from their supports and superimposed to form a print on a white support.[2]

The dye mordant processes are capable of yielding highly accurate color pictures due to the brilliance and desirable hues of the basic dyes. The chief disadvantages of processes of this type are the difficulty in holding clear whites and the lack of permanence of the dyes used. Little commercial color photography is practiced today with the dye toning processes.

Relief Processes. Several methods of making color photographs may be classified as relief processes. A relief process is one in which, instead of an image composed of silver in gelatin, there is a layer of material, usually gelatin, of variable thickness —the thickness varying in the same manner as the quantity of silver in the usual print. It might be said in describing such a film that, instead of having a variable density (silver image), it has a variable thickness (gelatin relief image) (see Fig. 30.1).

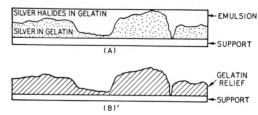

Fig. 30.1. A normal photographic image (A) composed of silver grains which give the photographic density. A similar relief image of gelatin (B) may be clear or contain some coloring material.

---

[2] Friedman, *History of Color Photography*, Chapter 21.

WALL, *History of Three-Color Photography*.

Under the heading of Relief Processes are included two of the most common color print processes: Carbro and Relief Imbibition printing. The cross mixtures of relief formation and coloring materials testify to the thorough search that inventors have made for practical methods of making color prints. Thus, there are relief processes in which the relief is colorless gelatin, which is later dyed, the final print made by imbibition, and those in which the reliefs are permanently colored with pigments which themselves compose the final image. The production of the relief itself, no matter how used later, may be carried out by a variety of methods as indicated in the process classification table.

Tanning Development. Gelatin relief formation by means of tanning development depends on the fact that the oxidation products of certain developing agents, notably pyrogallol, pyrocatechin, and hydroquinone, exert a tanning action on gelatin. This reaction occurs wherever the silver image is formed, the remainder of the gelatin being unaffected. The tanning action depends on the composition of the developer. Preservatives, such as sodium sulfite, retard the oxidation of the developer and, if present in large amounts, may prevent any tanning of the gelatin. Most formulas compounded for tanning development contain a minimum of, or no, preservative. A typical developer, for example, is:

Solution 1:

Citric acid	16 grams	234 gr.
Pyrogallol	140 grams	4¾ oz.
Ammonium bromide	40 grams	1 oz., 147 gr.
Water to make	1 liter	32 oz.

Solution 2:

Sodium hydroxide	30 grams	1 oz.
Water to make	1 liter	32 oz.

Take one part each to 25 parts of water. Develop five minutes at 18° C.

The production of gelatin reliefs by means of tanning development must be carefully standardized since the insolubilization of the gelatin may go on after the film is removed from the developer. A constant wash followed by fixation and bleaching is sometimes carried out before the removal of the unhardened gelatin by hot water.

The *Duxochrome* process for color prints, available in Europe before World War II, made use of a tanning developer, pyrocatechin, in the production of three relief films. The Duxochrome films were sensitized with the usual silver halides but in addition contained coloring pigments suspended in the gelatin. These films, colored cyan, magenta, and yellow, were exposed through the film base to the proper negatives and developed in the tanning developer which tanned the gelatin wherever silver halide was reduced. The films were then "developed" in hot water, which dissolved the soluble gelatin, and bleached in a reducer to remove the developed silver. The colored gelatin relief positives were then placed in register for a transparency or dried in succession onto a paper base to make a paper print. This process allowed considerable latitude and control of the various color images but was never very popular in the United States. The pigments composing the final image were not as brilliant as dyes and the images were somewhat grainy.[3]

Reliefs made by tanning development have also been used widely for imbibition dye printing. The Technicolor Corporation has produced many color motion pictures by printing from such matrices. The hardness of the relief after suitable tanning development is an important factor where many successive printings are desired from a single set of matrices.

Two recently introduced processes of color printing making use of tanning de-

---

[3] *Phot. Ind.* **38**, 558 (1940).

velopment are the Kodak *Dye Transfer* Process and the Curtis *T-D* Process. These processes are quite similar except for the mechanics of transferring the dye images from the matrices.

Dye Transfer. The Kodak Dye Transfer process, introduced in 1946, is an improvement on the older Kodak Wash-Off Relief Process. Separation negatives of a rather wide variety of density ranges may be satisfactorily printed with the new process and the operator has control over the contrast and density of the individual dye images up to the moment of transfer to paper. Duplicate prints are readily made from the same set of printing matrices.

Briefly, the process consists of making exposures from each of the separation negatives on three sheets of matrix film. This is a yellow-dyed emulsion of bromide paper speed and it is exposed through the film base. Contrast is controlled by adjusting

the composition of the developing solution. The matrices are processed in a tanning developer for two minutes, rinsed in water, and placed in a nonhardening fixing bath. They are then treated with hot water to remove the untanned gelatin, rinsed, and dried. After drying, the matrices are dyed in the appropriate dyes, cyan, magenta, and yellow, and superimposed in register over an illuminator. This allows the matrices to be trimmed so that each of them has a common pair of sides which can be used in placing them on a transfer blanket (Fig. 30.2) in such a way that the transferred images will superimpose. After registration is complete, the matrices are redyed, the excess surface dye removed in an acetic acid rinse and the dye images transferred to paper one after the other (Fig. 30.3). The matrices may be redyed for subsequent prints.

The Dye Transfer process will success-

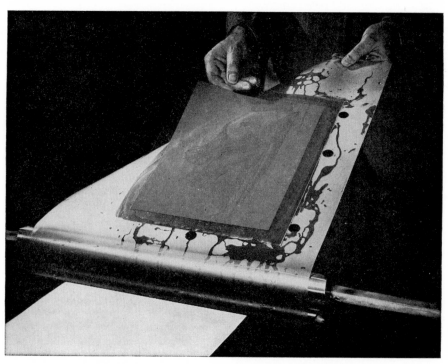

Fig. 30.2.   Cyan dyed matrix on transfer blanket.

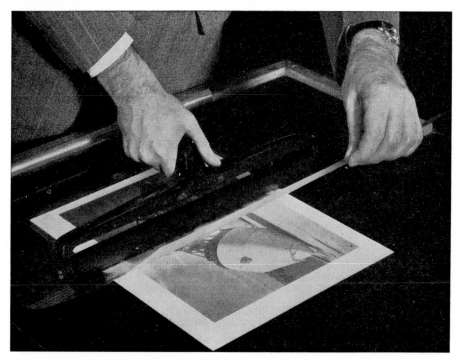

Fig. 30.3.   Magenta dyed matrix being rolled down over cyan image.

fully print from negatives with density ranges from a minimum of 1.0 up to a density range of 1.8. Such a variety of

speed slightly so that the exposure time must be adjusted as shown by the exposure adjustment column.

For Development to	Stock Solution A	Stock Solution B	Exposure Adjustment*	Negative Density Range
Very low contrast	1 part	1 part	130%	1.8
Low contrast	1 part	1½ parts	115%	1.6
Normal contrast	1 part	2 parts	100%	1.4
High contrast	1 part	4 parts	85%	1.2
Very high contrast	1 part	6½ parts	70%	1.0

* Assuming normal exposure at 1:2 development to be standard.

negatives can be printed because of the contrast control available. By changing the ratio of the developer components it is possible to adjust for the different permissible density ranges of the separation negatives. Within the limits shown in the following table, the greater the proportion of 'B' developer component the higher the dye image contrast. Changing the composition of the developer affects the film

To make this contrast control table applicable to the various types of contact and enlarging equipment, it is possible to make use of color filters or adjustments of the optical quality of the light source. Since the matrix film emulsion is dyed yellow to control the penetration of the exposing light, changing the color of the light from violet through white to yellow gives increasing penetration and therefore a thicker relief and higher dye image contrast. Adjustments may also be made in the specularity of the light in some projection systems. The above table is based on the use of a diffuse type enlarger and some condenser type enlargers may require additional diffusion to use the table as given. As with most tanning developers, the working solution is relatively unstable and is mixed fresh just before use and discarded after processing a set of matrices.

If the separation negatives have been carefully prepared so that the three negatives will register, reasonable precautions must be taken in the exposure and handling of the matrices to insure that the three dye images will also register. The most important factor is that the three matrices of a set be handled identically during the processing and drying operations. Matrices should be dried carefully with their images oriented in the same direction. The operation of edge registering a set of matrices over the illuminator is a simple and rapid procedure. The matrix made from the red separation negative, dyed cyan, is taped to a plate of glass so that two edges of the matrix project over the edges of the glass plate. The magenta matrix, and then the yellow, are successively taped down in register with the cyan matrix. A trimming board is then used to trim off the projecting edges of the matrix films. Such a procedure makes it possible to have all three matrices with two common edges when the images superimpose. This method of registration allows the use of a transfer blanket on which the matrices can be placed with their trimmed edges in contact with a set of thin buttons. The cyan dyed matrix is rolled into contact with the paper first to allow the dye to transfer to the gelatin-coated surface (Fig. 30.2). With a properly trimmed set of matrices,

FIG. 30.4. Pin-register board on enlarger easel.

the same operation can be carried out with the magenta and yellow matrices, and their dye images will register on the paper with the already transferred cyan dye image. It is also possible to perforate the three superimposed matrices with a punch so that their dye images can be transferred in register on a board containing two or more pins of the same size and spacing as the matrix perforations.

Before transferring the dyed matrix images to paper, the operator can again make adjustments of contrast and density. After the matrices are thoroughly expanded and dyed, they are handled in succession through two rinse trays containing dilute acetic acid. The purpose of the first rinse bath is to remove nonimage dye on the surface of the matrix film while the second rinse tray serves to hold the dye in the gelatin until ready for transfer. The density of the dye image to be transferred to paper may be reduced by the addition of a control solution (Highlight Reducer) to the first rinse bath. Either increased time in the bath, or increasing the quantity of reagent added, will lead to more dye being removed from the matrix. It is also possible to add to the first rinse solution a measured quantity of sodium acetate which will effectively lower the contrast of the transferred dye image. By the use of these two controls, the operator has the possibility of adjusting the dye images at the printing stage.

The gelatin-coated paper to which the dye images are transferred is mordanted by the manufacturer and merely needs soaking in a conditioning solution before the transfer operation. If the matrices are carefully cleaned between transfers, they may be used to make a number of prints which will be identical if the same manipulative steps are carried out each time a print is made. The dye solutions

may be replenished in order to maintain their ability to dye the matrix properly.

Panchromatic Matrix Film. Late in 1949 the Eastman Kodak Company made available a panchromatic matrix film for making prints from Ektacolor negatives by the Dye Transfer procedure. Kodak Pan Matrix Film is used to obtain prints from color negatives, such as Ektacolor and Kodacolor, by making three exposures, by contact or projection, onto three separate sheets of film. One film, exposed when using a red filter over the light source, is dyed cyan after the formation of the gelatin relief image. The other two films are exposed by green and blue light, respectively, processed by tanning development and the resulting relief images dyed magenta and yellow. The Kodak Pan Matrix Film contains a neutral pigment instead of the yellow dye of Matrix Film to limit the penetration of the exposing light. Dye image contrast is controlled with Pan Matrix Film by adjusting the developer composition using various quantities of water. The exposed films are bathed in water before development, but the processing is essentially similar to the procedure followed for Matrix Film processing-development, rinse, fixation, hot water relief formation, cool water rinse and drying.

Since the three color records are in register in a single film (color negative), it is only necessary to secure the three panchromatic matrix films in the same position at the time of exposure to obtain three relief images which will register during transfer. This is accomplished by perforating the matrix film during manufacture. The perforated film is placed over two pins of the Kodak Vacuum Register Board which is fixed in position relative to the color negative (Fig. 30.4). After the three matrix films are processed and the relief images dyed, the images are successively transferred to mordanted gelatin using the same or a similar pin board for the transfer operation. The contrast and density of the transferred dye images may be controlled in essentially the same manner as discussed under Dye Transfer.

Flexichrome. This process, announced by Kodak in 1949, makes use of a tanning developer to obtain a positive gelatin relief image on Kodak Flexichrome Stripping Film from a single black-and-white negative. Processing and contrast control are carried out in essentially the same manner as discussed under Dye Transfer. The gelatin relief image is dyed with a neutral dye. The dyed relief is removed from its base and dried in contact with a white final support paper. The dyed gelatin relief image is on the upper surface and the neutral dye may be replaced with other dyes by brushing over the relief image with a brush containing the desired color. A number of suitable dyes are available and the operator may make any adjustments of color desired. This process has extreme flexibility and makes possible a colored print having any desired colors and yet maintaining the photographic gradation of the original relief image.

Hardening Action of Light on Dichromated Colloids. One of the most important photographic reactions is the hardening [4] action of light on dichromated colloids, discovered by Ponton in 1830. The colloid used in color photography is usually gelatin which may be either clear or contain some coloring pigment in suspension. If such a gelatin film is bathed in a solution of a dichromate and dried in the dark, it becomes light sensitive. When exposed under a negative to a strong light the gelatin becomes insoluble in proportion to the intensity of the exposure. If the film is placed in warm water, the unaffected gelatin may be dissolved and removed.

The *Carbon* process, which has largely been superseded by carbro, employed this procedure for making three-color prints. *Belcolor* and *Dufaytissue* are modern adaptations employing the same basic reactions with new techniques and materials. In general, both of the last processes are alike in that pigmented gelatin films are sensitized in bichromate solutions and dried in the dark before exposure to the proper separation negatives. After exposure through the film base under strongly actinic light, the films are developed to reliefs in hot water.[5] Some local control may be exercised with very hot water in areas requiring reduction. When a satisfactory balance is secured the films may be dried. The three-colored films may be either combined to form a transparency (if the contrasts are sufficiently high) or superimposed on paper to form a paper print. By using a suitable cement the pigmented gelatin may be secured to the paper and the transparent films removed. As transparencies, these processes have found acceptance in the graphic arts fields for use as color guides because of their simplicity and the rapidity with which they can be prepared.

Hardening Reaction Between Silver and Dichromate Colloids. The result considered in the previous section may be duplicated in a simple manner by means of a reaction discovered by Howard Farmer in 1899. If a developed image consisting of finely divided silver is treated with a suitable dichromate solution, the gelatin sur-

[4] For the purposes of color photography, tanning and hardening give the same result—the insolubilization of the gelatin. Strictly speaking, tanning is a reversible reaction, whereas hardening is not reversible. Grutzne, ''Gelatine,'' *Leim und Klebstoffe* (January 1939).

Kodak Dye Transfer Process—Kodak Color Data Book (1951).
Kodak Flexichrome Process—Kodak Color Data Book (1950).

[5] Beale, *Phot. J.* **81**, 108 (1941).

rounding the silver grains is hardened in a manner similar to the hardening of a dichromated colloid by light. This interesting reaction is the basis for two widely used color processes, a form of relief imbibition printing and carbro printing. In appearance these two processes are dissimilar, but in reality they are dependent on a similar chemical reaction. The exact reactions are not known, but it will suffice to say that the dichromates are reduced and the reaction products are capable of hardening gelatin. In the relief imbibition process, the hardening action takes place around the individual silver grains; whereas in carbro, the hardening action is transferred to an adjoining layer of pigmented gelatin. In both processes the unaffected gelatin is washed away with hot water, leaving a positive relief image of gelatin. In imbibition printing the relief is of clear gelatin which is later dyed, the dyes being transferred to a paper base. In carbro, the gelatin reliefs contain pigment, and the final print is composed of a combination of the three pigmented relief images on a single paper support. Since these two processes are widely used for

commercial and amateur color printing, it would seem advisable to review briefly the procedures employed.

Relief Imbition Printing. The introduction, in 1934, of Wash-off Relief Film by the Eastman Kodak Company and their presentation of an outline of procedures made this type of relief process generally available. This method of color printing was not new, but satisfactory materials for its production were not previously obtainable. Since the publication of the method under the name of the Eastman *Wash-off Relief Process*, other manufacturers have introduced similar emulsions for relief production and dyes for printing. Eastman Wash-off Relief Film has now been replaced by Kodak Matrix Film which is essentially similar, and the techniques used in the making of the matrices have been largely replaced by the previously discussed Dye Transfer process. The Wash-off Relief technique is still used to a limited extent for color printing and also for making color transparencies by binding together the three dyed matrices.

Wash-off Relief or Matrix Films are exposed to color separation negatives through

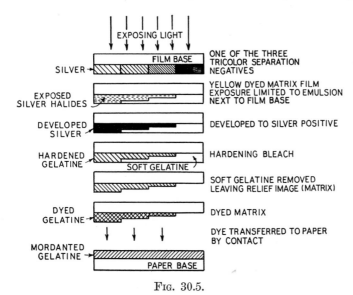

Fig. 30.5.

the base of the film with white or colored light, depending upon the contrast desired. The exposed films are developed in a black and white developer and, after development, the films are washed thoroughly and then bleached in an acid dichromate bath containing a halide salt. The bleaching of the silver image is accompanied by the hardening of the gelatin by the reduced chromic salts. The silver is converted to a silver chloride. When all the silver is bleached, the films are treated with hot water to remove the unhardened gelatin. As the hardening reaction only occurs at positions containing a silver image, the layer of gelatin remaining shows, as variations in thickness, what the silver image formerly showed as changes of density. After fixation, the relief films are washed and dried before dyeing. It is also possible to remove the unhardened gelatin by treatment in a cool 20% solution of ammonium thiocyanate. The relief films are often treated with a solution of formalin before drying to help harden the gelatin image. The relief image obtained by this procedure is not as resistant to abrasion as a gelatin relief obtained by the tanning development process.

The dyes used for printing from these matrices are similar to those used for dye transfer. They are generally of the acid type, and the choice of a satisfactory set is quite critical as regards their hues and transfer characteristics.[6] The general practice in printing with this process is to work for negatives of fixed density range (about 1.0) and to make most of the adjustments of contrast that are required with the dye solutions themselves. The addition of acetic acid to the dyes, for example, increases the dye absorption and therefore the contrast of the dye image

transferred from a given matrix. If the dyes are to be transferred to a gelatin-coated paper, the matrices are rinsed first in acetic acid and the dye that is slowest to transfer is placed on the paper first. The mordant generally used is ammonium hydroxide, and the paper is usually treated with buffering solutions which leave it at the proper pH for the transfer operation.[7] The second and third images are registered with the first dye image on the paper and transferred in succession. This registration may be done visually or with some pin registration system. Both heat and pressure tend to accelerate the transfer of the dye to the paper.[8]

Three-Color Carbro. The carbon process was for a long time the only really practical means of printing from three-color negatives. In recent years, it has largely been superseded by three-color carbro. Three-color carbro, while more exacting in its technique than other processes in general use, is capable of producing excellent prints. The procedure, in general, is the same as monochrome carbro (see Chapter 27) except that three-color pigments are employed and several image transfers are required.[9]

Bromides. The basis for a satisfactory three-color carbro rests on the bromide prints made from the color separation negatives. The emulsions employed are usually specifically coated for carbro printing and do not have the gelatin anti-abrasion overcoat generally placed on light-sensitive photographic papers. The emulsions are of projection speed and are obtainable both in cut sheets and rolls. Care must be taken to have the paper grain run

---

[6] Friedman, *Amer. Phot.* **34**, 529, 609 (1940). Colton and Thronson, *Photo-Technique* **2**, No. 11, 54 (1940).

[7] *Brit. J. Phot.* **86**, 435 (1939); **87**, 611 (1940).

[8] *Color Printing with Eastman Wash-off Relief Film,* Eastman Kodak Co.

[9] Alexewicz, *J. Phot. Soc. Amer.* **16B**, 99 (1950). Coppin and Spencer, *Phot. J.* **88B**, 78 (1948).

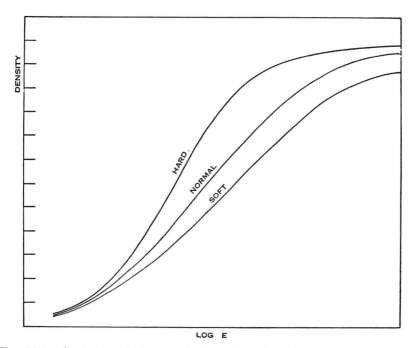

Fig. 30.6.   Contrast variations obtainable with various developers on a common carbro printing paper.

in the same direction on each print of a color set to avoid unequal expansion and later registration difficulties. The cut sheets available for carbro come with the same paper grain orientation throughout a package.

The production of a three-color carbro print does not offer as much opportunity for photographic corrective measures as is available in relief imbibition printing. The two stages where corrections are possible, however, offer enough variation to enable considerable adjustment to be made. The first, and most reliable, stage of control is in making the bromide prints where variations in both density and contrast of any of the images may be made by exposure and development. Exposure determinations are generally made from the cyan printer. The safest criterion is a slight veiling-over of the highlight portions of the image in subject areas containing little or no cyan color. A gray scale, if properly

illuminated when the subject was exposed, may also be used. When a tentative exposure has been determined for the cyan printer bromide, the magenta and yellow printers are exposed and developed so that identical gray scales are obtained on each print. Such a result will be obtained with equal exposures and developments, given negatives of equal densities and density ranges. If the maximum density of the negatives is different, compensation of exposure may be calculated from the density readings. If the contrasts of the three separation negatives are different, all possible steps should be taken to adjust exposure and processing of the bromide prints so that their gray scales appear identical. Sizeable adjustments are possible by making use of variable contrast developers or using two or three different developers (Fig. 30.6). The use of a reflection densitometer is quite helpful, but not essential, since gray scales on paper may be compared visually with considerable accuracy. The inclusion of a gray scale in the original scene is of inestimable value when corrective work is necessary.

Development of the bromide prints must be carefully standardized as to time and temperature to make possible reproducible results. Slight variations that would be of no importance in black and white will give an unsatisfactory color print. An acid stop bath rinse is advisable for the bromides, followed by fixation in a nonhardening fixing bath. With occasional agitation in a fresh fixing bath, five minutes fixation should be sufficient and all prints should be treated alike. A thorough wash in water, at least an hour, will leave the bromides ready for pigment printing. The acidity of the paper determines to some extent the density of the pigment image obtained from a given point. Since wash water varies in alkalinity in various geographical locations, it is advisable to bring bromides to a definite pH value after washing. A number of buffer solutions may be prepared which will enable the operator to hold the bromides to the desired pH value. A value of roughly 6.5 seems to be a happy medium. The bromide prints, after washing, are swabbed with a 2% acetic acid solution to remove any surface alkali. They are then briefly washed and brought to the proper pH value by soaking in a tray of appropriately buffered water. The bromides are then ready for pigment printing or they may be dried before use. If dried, the prints must be suspended from two corners with the images oriented in the same manner.

Some of the difficulties in the tricolor carbro process may be traced to the incomplete removal of hypo from the bromide prints. Treatment of the bromide prints with potassium iodide instead of a fixing bath has been suggested as one means of

eliminating such chemical contamination.[10] Another source of trouble has been the use of pigment papers in which the gelatin bearing pigment has hardened on the surface. This has recently been corrected by the introduction of stripping tricolor pigment papers. With such a stripping pigment paper, an extra operation is involved in the stripping of the pigment from its support before combining with the bromide print. In this manner, the "fresh" under surface of the pigment layer is placed in contact with the bromide print.

Pigment Supports. It is necessary to develop pigment images on some transparent material to which they will adhere before being transferred to a final support. Celluloid sheets have been used in the past but require careful waxing before use. Sheets of other plastic material, such as Vinylite, have been used without the necessity of prior waxing.

Sensitizing. The three sheets of pigment paper must be treated in a sensitizing solution before being placed in contact with their respective bromide prints. The sensitizing solution may take several forms, although the so-called single bath sensitizer is generally used in the United States. The most widely used sensitizers are combinations of dichromate, bromide, and ferricyanide, although copper chloride is sometimes used. The formula to be used should be that recommended by the manufacturer of the pigment paper. Contrast may be controlled to some extent by the proportions of the sensitizer components.

The cyan, magenta, and yellow pigments whether of the stripping variety on a plastic base or on "paper support," are wet thoroughly and then placed in the sensitizing solution. Sensitizers should be kept at approximately 18° C. to prevent excessive swelling of the pigmented gelatin

---

[10] Perskie, *Defender Trade Bulletin,* **26,** No. 1 (1942).

Each pigment sheet is left in the sensitizer the required time and when the cyan pigment is ready to be removed, the proper bromide print is placed on a glass plate and covered with a pool of water. The sensitized pigment is lowered onto it and rapidly squeegeed into contact to remove all water and air between the two surfaces. This sandwich is then laid aside. The same operations are then carried out for the magenta and yellow pigments and their respective bromide prints. Several types of apparatus, similar to a clothes wringer, are available for combining bromides and pigments with ease and certainty. When the bromides and pigments have been in contact for approximately ten minutes, the bromides are separated from the pigments and placed aside for re-development if desired. Each pigment is then squeegeed, after being wet, to one of the celluloid or plastic sheets. All air bubbles must be removed and intimate contact obtained between the pigment and support.

Carbro pigments are somewhat affected by the temperature of the surroundings during the sensitizing and bleaching operations. Modern gelatin pigments are less susceptible than the older types but precautions should be taken to keep the pigment papers between 18° and 20° C. Higher temperatures may lead to veiled highlights and trouble with blisters on the pigment images.

Hot Water Development. After approximately ten minutes, the pigment and support may be placed in a tray of hot water with the pigment uppermost. When the pigment commences to ooze out from the edges, the paper or plastic pigment support may be lifted from the lower support. The pigment image is then developed by agitation in a succession of baths of hot water until no further pigmented gelatin can be removed, rinsed in cold water and set aside to dry.

Transfer to Soluble Support. A piece of soluble support paper (coated with gelatin soluble in water at about 45° C.) is expanded in water for about ten minutes and the cyan image, when dry, is also soaked for several minutes in water at room temperature. The two are then removed from the water, image in contact with the gelatin surface of the support paper, and squeegeed firmly together. When dry, the paper will leave the film support and carry the cyan image with it. If there is any wax on the surface of the cyan image it must be removed with successive swabbings of turpentine, and polished dry. The soluble support bearing the cyan image is then re-soaked in cold water with the magenta bearing film support and the two removed together and lightly squeegeed into contact. The magenta and cyan images must then be carefully registered, bending the sandwich if necessary, and then squeegeed firmly in contact before drying. A similar operation is carried out for the yellow image.

Transfer to Final Paper. A piece of single transfer paper, somewhat larger than the temporary support, is soaked for ten minutes in hot water and then placed in contact with the soluble support bearing the three images. This operation is carried out in a tray of water at room temperature. The two are withdrawn, squeegeed firmly together, and placed aside between blotters under pressure to dry for thirty minutes. The sandwich of soluble and final support papers is then placed in a tray of hot water at 50° C. for about three minutes, when the soluble support may be stripped away. The final support bearing the three images is washed with

The Tricolor Pigment Process, McGraw Colorgraph Co., Burbank, Calif.
Making Color Prints with 3-Color Pigment Paper, National Photocolor Corporation, New York.

hot water until all the soluble gelatin is removed. The final color print is then briefly rinsed in cold water and taped to a glass plate to dry.

Dyebro Process. *Dyebro* is a hybrid process which makes use of the carbro method of producing a set of gelatin reliefs and then uses the relief imbibition method of dye transfer to form the final print on paper. In practice, a set of bromide prints is made from the color separation negatives using the same procedure as for the carbro process. The pigment papers for Dyebro come with a very slight pigmentation, just enough to make the image visible after transfer to the celluloids. These pigment papers are sensitized in the normal manner and contacted with the bromide prints. After bleaching is complete, the pigments are squeegeed onto plain celluloids and then developed in hot water in the usual manner. The absence of any wax coating on the celluloids enables the gelatin relief image to adhere firmly to the celluloid. When fully developed, the three celluloids bearing their relief images are hardened briefly in a formalin solution before drying. When dry, the films are dyed in a manner similar to that employed for imbibition matrix material. The dye images may then be transferred to a prepared gelatin surface in the usual manner.

Etching Processes. A dye-absorbing, gelatin-relief, positive image may be obtained by chemically etching a silver negative. This process makes use of nascent oxygen from the etching solution to attack the colloid surrounding the finely divided silver grains. R. E. Liesegang observed in 1897 that the gelatin surrounding a silver image was softened and could be removed with hot water after the film was treated with a solution containing ammonium persulfate. This method was improved by M. Andresen,[11] who used hydro-

gen peroxide with a halogen acid, and by Wall.[12] This process necessitates the use of a negative image to obtain a positive relief. *Defender Pan-Chroma* Relief Film (not available at present) was produced for making positive relief images directly from positive color transparencies by this method. Three sheets of film containing a neutral light absorber to restrict the penetration of the exposing light were exposed from the emulsion side through tricolor analysis filters. After development to negative silver images, fixation and drying, they were treated with the cool etching bath. The reaction removes the negative silver image and adjoining gelatin, leaving a positive gelatin relief. After fixation, washing, and drying, the three films are ready for dyeing. Transfer of the dye images was carried out in the usual manner.

Differential Hardening of Dichromated Colloids. The dichromate-colloid reaction may be used in several other ways to form a useful image. In contrast to the previously considered relief processes, use may be made of the hardening action of light or silver, on a dichromated colloid to form images in which the distinguishing characteristic is the hardening, to which various parts of the colloid (gelatin) have been subjected. A slight relief image may be formed in some of these processes, but it presence is incidental and none of the colloid is removed. It may be said that these processes are distinguished by the *differential hardening* of certain colloids, generally gelatin. Such processes are practical since certain water-soluble dyes and greasy ink react differently to hard and soft gelatin. For purposes of classification, it is possible to distinguish between those processes employing dyes and those using inks as the coloring medium.

---

[11] *Phot. Korr.* 260 (1899).

[12] Wall, *History of Three-Color Photography* American Photographic Publishing Co., Boston 1925.

1. Dye processes employing the differential hardening of colloids are generally, although not always, of the imbibition type. Edwards in 1875 and Cros in 1880 discovered that a gelatin layer could be made to absorb some water-soluble dyes differentially by properly hardening parts of the gelatin. This idea was further developed by Didier and developed commercially as the *Pinatype* process. The dyes used in Pinatype were capable of staining soft gelatin in preference to hardened gelatin. If a gelatin layer contained an image of hardened gelatin, the dye would be absorbed by the reverse image—i.e., by the soft gelatin. Thus, if the printing plate image was made from a positive, a positive dye image was created. The original process made use of the standard color separation negatives from which three positive transparencies were made. These transparencies were then used to expose three sensitized colloid layers. The colloids, usually gelatin, were treated with dichromate and dried before their exposure to light. The gelatin is hardened by exposure in proportion to the transparency of the positive, thus giving a negative image of hardened gelatin. If such a plate is immersed in a Pinatype dye, a positive dye image is obtained. The film might be used either as a transparency, or the dye transferred to a final support of soft gelatin as in the relief imbibition processes. It must be borne in mind that the printing plates made by this procedure are smooth and contain all the original gelatin, various parts of which absorb certain dyes. As discussed under relief processes, there are many ways of obtaining an image of hardened gelatin and other methods could be used as satisfactorily as the one described.

2. A second type of process employing a differentially hardened colloid is based on a somewhat different property of the colloid. If a layer of gelatin containing hardened and soft portions is placed in a water bath, the water will be freely absorbed by the soft gelatin and not by the hardened gelatin. If such a film is then inked with a greasy ink, the hard gelatin surface will absorb the ink while the water-soaked soft gelatin will reject it. Such an ink image may be transferred to any paper surface. The photo-gelatin processes, such as Collotype and Bromoil, make use of such a procedure and are capable of the highest quality reproductions of mediums employing inks as a coloring material. In this process again, the method of obtaining the differential hardening of the colloid is not limited.

Dye Coupling or Color Development. Dye coupling processes are undoubtedly one of the most logical methods of obtaining color prints. Aside from the three separate films required, the procedure is exactly the same as that employed for normal black-and-white production. Color development involves the conversion of a latent image to metallic silver and the simultaneous formation of a dye. As the production of the dye is directly connected with the reduction of metallic silver, the dye alone will give a positive image proportional to the intensities of the exposing light. By the proper choice of developers, a set may be found producing the necessary subtractive colors—magenta, cyan and yellow. If three such films are prepared from a set of color separation negatives and if, after removing the silver image, they are superimposed, a color print results. Color development processes for paper prints put together in this manner have not as yet achieved any widespread commercial success.[13] There are several difficulties such as instability to light, stained highlights, and unsatisfactory spectral re-

[13] Wilson, *Amer. Phot.* **33**, 161 (1939). Friedman, *Amer. Phot.* **34**, 851 (1940).

flectance of the colorants available. For the present, the greatest use of dye coupling development lies in the integral tripack transparency reversal and negative-positive processes discussed in Chapter 32.

Dye Destruction Processes. The dye destruction processes date back to the early years of this century and are based on the chemical destruction of dyes in an emulsion containing a silver image. The emulsion is dyed fully and after the silver image is developed, the film may be treated with solutions which destroy either (1) the dye in contact with the silver image, or (2) the dye in contact with the remaining silver halide. In either case, the color remaining after the removal of the silver and halides is a pure dye image in gelatin. Of the two methods of dye destruction, the first is the more useful, being the basis for the successful commercial processes. Since the only commercial use of dye destruction processes at present is in connection with integral tripacks, this process will be discussed in Chapter 32.

Dye Bleaching. In a photochemical system, the only effective radiation is that absorbed by the medium itself (Grotthus-Draper Law). Most dyes fade when exposed to visible or ultraviolet radiation, and many are known that fade so rapidly as to be useless for many commercial purposes. Since any coloring agent transmits its own color and absorbs the remainder of the visible spectrum (its complementary color), a magenta dye, for example, is most effective in the absorption of green light, a red dye in the absorption of blue-green light, etc. Now if, for example, a layer of gelatin containing a fugitive yellow dye is exposed to a colored positive, the dye will be bleached wherever blue light reaches the layer of gelatin. The blue radiation will be absorbed by the yellow dye and produce a photochemical change which results

in the bleaching of the dye, while red and green are transmitted freely and, therefore, will not cause any appreciable alteration of the dye. Consequently, if three such layers, dyed with light-sensitive subtractive printing colors, are exposed to a positive image in color, a positive color picture will be obtained directly.

Such an apparently simple solution to the problem of obtaining color photographs has naturally been extensively investigated. At least two such processes have been exploited commercially; *Utocolor* paper produced by Smith in 1912 was an early commercial process,[14] and *Vitachrome* paper was available in 1938. There are a number of serious obstacles to be overcome in a successful bleach-out process, among them being the difficulty of obtaining sufficient sensitivity to permit reasonably short exposures and to fix the image after the print has been made. It has also been very hard to obtain clean whites by means of the bleach-out process. In contrast to the success achieved to date, a very great amount of effort has gone into the development of bleach-out processes. The obvious simplicity of the system attracts so strongly that developments are still being made, and future improvements may reasonably be expected.

Since most usable dyes are so slowly bleached by light as to be useless for practical work, various sensitizers, or accelerators, have been added to the different dyes to increase their light sensitivity for use with this process.[15] The sensitizer may take the form of the dye carrying material (collodion or gelatin) or be present as added ingredients (other dyes, thiourea derivatives, oxides, and salts of various metals with acids).[16] A study of the reactions of

---

[14] *Phot. J.* **50**, 141 (1910).

[15] *Amer. Phot.* **32**, 821 (1938).

[16] *Brit. J. Phot.* **87**, 455 (1939).

the various light-sensitive dyes has indicated both photochemical oxidation and photochemical reduction as taking place when the dyes are bleached, the exact reaction depending on the dye. A somewhat analogous method employs, as the sensitive system, dyes or leuco derivatives that will react as dyestuff generators when exposed to light.[17] In all these processes, the sensitizers are destroyed, or are removed by chemical treatment or by washing, after the light reaction is completed. The final dye images are thus left relatively insensitive to light after the accelerating agents are removed.

---

[17] *Brit. J. Phot.* **88**, 624 (1940).

Chapter 31

SCREEN AND LENTICULAR PROCESSES

Introduction. Screen and lenticular processes are similar since they both contain in a single layer of emulsion the three color separation images. The three color records, as silver images, are physically separated laterally instead of vertically as in the integral tripack processes considered in the next chapter. In general, color is obtained by additive synthesis.

The screen plate process was originally suggested by du Hauron in 1868 and has slowly developed since its first commercial use by Joly in 1894 to the present *Dufaycolor* screen films. The lenticular process, on the other hand, is a relatively recent addition to color processes, as the earliest mention of such a method was in 1908. The lenticular method enjoyed a meteoric rise to prominence and, during the 1920 to 1930 period, it was probably the most widely investigated color process. Since the introduction of integral tripacks, interest has waned.

Screen Plate Processes. The screen plate processes are comparatively simple to work and, until recently, were virtually the only processes of natural color photography practical for the average amateur or professional photographer. Screen materials suffer from low resolution and an objectionable screen pattern if appreciable enlargement is attempted. The screen itself involves a large loss of light, and the image brightness is quite low unless special high intensity sources are used for viewing the transparencies.

Screen plates may be divided into two main classes: (1) separable, and (2) inseparable screen processes. The separable screen is generally geometric in character and coated on a separate plate from the emulsion. The chief advantage of the separable screen lies in the possibility of producing duplicates simply and at low cost. The inseparable processes have their screen and emulsion coated onto a single support. The screen may be either of the geometric regular type or an irregular mosaic. Each of the above types has achieved commercial success.

The Requirements of a Screen Plate. The following factors determine the performance of a screen plate:[1]

1. *The Size of the Color Elements.* These must be below the resolution of the eye (visual angle of one minute, corresponding to 0.02 mm. at the average distance) but above the resolution of the emulsion. If too large the elements are perceived individually; if too small, the color rendering cannot be true, since the emulsion is unable to record accurately the result produced by the screen.

For geometric screens, the color elements should not be larger than 1/300 of an inch or much smaller than 1/600 of an inch; for mosaic screens, the size should not exceed 1/900 of an inch or be less than 1/2000. The color elements may be larger in geometrical screen than in a mosaic because in the latter it is virtually impossible to avoid a certain amount of clumping on the part of color elements of the same color thus giving rise to areas producing dominant color.

[1] Mees, *J. Chem. Ed.* **5**, 1578 (1928).

2. *The Transmissions of the Color Elements.* The requirements of the three-color taking filters have been discussed previously. The transmissions of three-color viewing filters, unlike the taking filters, should not overlap and should be relatively narrow so as to produce brilliant, sharply defined colors (F. E. Ives). In a separate screen process, the transmission of the filters of the taking and viewing screens need not be the same, although, of course, the color elements must be of the same size in both screens and must conform to the same pattern. In a combined screen plate process, such as *Dufaycolor, Autochrom,* etc., the same screen must serve both for taking and for viewing; the transmission of the color elements must represent the best compromise possible under the circumstances.[2]

The average transmission of the screen elements for a typical screen process is as follows:

	Transmission Range	Maximum Transmission
Red Element	570–690 mμ	615 mμ
Green Element	480–620 mμ	535 mμ
Blue Element	400–530 mμ	470 mμ

3. *The Relative Area Covered By Each Color.* This must be adjusted so that the screen appears neutral. Any dominant tint in the screen will result in a color shift in the direction of the dominant color of the screen.

4. *The Interstices.* These, if they exist, must be filled to prevent irradiation, which would greatly reduce the ability of the emulsion to reproduce the pattern of the color elements sharply and lead to color dilution.

5. *Thickness of the Screen.* The screen must be as thin as possible to prevent parallax. The thickness should not in any case exceed the smallest dimension of the color elements.

6. *The Emulsion.* This must be panchromatic, highly and as evenly sensitive as possible. Its resolution must be equal to the color elements of the screen, and it must be able to produce a relatively high density in order that, where necessary, the color elements which should not function in the formation of an additive color can be stopped out. In the case of a screen plate in which the screen and the emulsion are inseparable, the emulsion must be adaptable to the requirements of the reversal process.[3]

Construction of Color Screens. The irregular mosaic screens are made from a mixture of small colored particles. The particles may be of colored glass, powdered enamels, gelatin, resins, starch, flours, corpuscles, or various gums. A mixture of appropriate amounts of the three-colored particles may be obtained mechanically by sifting or by the use of ultrasonic vibrations. Certain types of particles are emulsified in various media, or atomized, and allowed to settle onto a properly prepared plate. Whatever method is employed, the particles colored red, green, and blue-violet are mixed so that the finished screen is nearly neutral. If the screen particles do not completely cover the plate, an opaque material, such as carbon or dye, must be employed to fill the interstices.

The geometrical screens, whether of the separable or inseparable type, are generally produced either photographically or mechanically. The basis of both types was laid by du Hauron in 1897 and Joly in 1894. The photographic procedure employs most of the methods used in the production of color prints, such as the dichromate-light or silver hardening reactions, the differential staining by certain types of dye, as well as chemical toning

---

[2] Mees, *Brit. J. Phot.* **55**, 41 (1908); **58**, 45, 52, 62, 68 (Col. Suppl.) (1911). Sproson, *Photo. J.* **9B**, 108 (1949).

[3] Thorne-Baker, *Phot. J.* **72**, 109 (1932).

and dye coupling. In the mechanical methods, the film base or an over-coat is dyed and then ruled with a greasy protective resist. The unprotected film is bleached, redyed another color, and the resist lines removed. This procedure is repeated for the third color.

Over the completed screen, whatever its nature, a protective layer is placed before the panchromatic emulsion is coated. This layer must be thin to avoid parallax, waterproof to prevent the processing solutions from affecting the screen, and adhesive enough to hold the emulsion firmly and also adhere to the screen layer below.[4]

The Lumière Filmcolor. The first commercially successful screen plate was the Lumière *Autochrom* introduced commercially in 1907. This plate was of the inseparable screen type.

The screen (Fig. 31.1) was composed of grains of potato starch about 15/1000 mm.

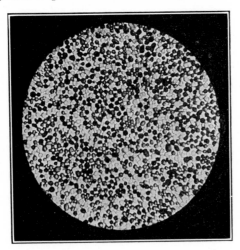

FIG. 31.1. Photomicrograph of the autochrome screen.

(.0024 inch) in diameter, colored orange, green, and blue-violet. The grains of potato starch were first passed through a sieve to obtain a uniform grain size and divided into three groups, each of which

is dyed. The grains were then mixed thoroughly (in the ratio of 4 green to 3 red and 2 blue) to secure even distribution of the different colored grains and then dusted on a glass plate which had been

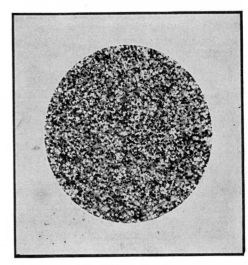

FIG. 31.2. The Agfacolor screen.

coated previously with a suitable substratum. The interstices were filled in with a fine opaque powder and the layer smoothed out by rolling under heavy pressure. The screen was next covered with a thin layer of waterproof varnish over which was coated a panchromatic emulsion. The screen is not white but a light salmon pink and transmits approximately 7.5% of the incident light.[5]

In 1932, the Autochrom screen was supplied on film under the trade name *Filmcolor*. These are no longer available.

Agfa Ultracolor Plate. This mosaic screen, now discontinued, was prepared from dyed particles of gum arabic rolled out in collodion (Fig. 32.2). The size of the color elements was about the same as in the Autochrom but more uniform, varying from 0.008 to 0.017 mm.[6] The screen

---

[4] *Brit. J. Phot.* **85**, 805 (1938).

[5] Ventujol, *Amer. Phot.* **18**, 384 (1924).

[6] Pledge, *Brit. J. Phot.* **70**, 48 (Col. Suppl.) (1923).

however, transmitted nearly twice as much light as the Autochrom because of the higher transparency of the colored grains and the absence of black filling between the grains. The color elements completely covered the plate, no filler being required. The relative transmissions of the Agfacolor and Autochrom screens are 14 and 7.5%, respectively. This material was also supplied on film base.

Dufaycolor. This process, unlike the two previously discussed, employs a geometrical type screen or *reseau* (Fig. 31.3).

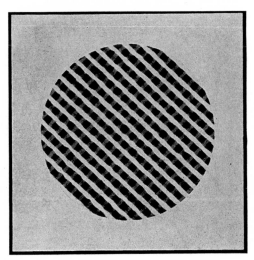

Fig. 31.3. The Dufaycolor screen.

The acetate film base is first coated with a very thin layer of collodion, dyed blue; this step is followed by printing a set of greasy ink lines with engraved rollers at an angle to the length of the roll, there being twenty lines to the millimeter and the spaces between being equal in width to the lines. In the next operation, the dye between the ink lines is bleached and a green dye colors these clear spaces. The ink is dissolved and a series of blue and green parallel lines remains, covering the entire film base.

A second set of ink lines is now printed at right angles to the first. The lines this time are broader than in the first instance and the spacing narrower, but there are the same number per millimeter as before. The second bleaching bath removes the green and blue dye where there is no protecting ink and the spaces are dyed red. The ink resist is removed, resulting in a microscopic regular pattern of green and blue squares, with red lines in absolute juxtaposition. The reason for having the red lines narrower is to equalize approximately the areas of red, green, and blue. A protective varnish is coated over the screen to prevent desensitization of the highly panchromatized emulsion used.

Dufaycolor film is supplied in both cut sheet and roll form. These normal emulsion types are slightly different as to speed and color balance so that one material will be closely adapted for the lighting conditions employed, without the use of heavily correcting color filters. Special sheet film emulsions, medium and hard, are also available when higher contrasts are desirable.[7] Because of the lack of contrast control in normal reversal processing, these special contrasts are advisable for the best reproduction of copy material, such as paintings or maps.

Exposure of Screen Materials. Color screen materials are exposed in the camera with the emulsion side away from the lens so that the exposing light will pass through the color screen before affecting the sensitive emulsion. If the screen support is glass, a focusing adjustment must be made to compensate for the lengthened light path. Screen materials range in speed from that of a medium speed black and white material (A.S.A. 8) down to one-twelfth of that value. The color sensitivity of the panchromatic emulsion and the screen transmissions determine the color temperature of the light source for which the material is balanced. Compensating

---

[7] Beale, *Phot. J.* **81**, 108 (1941).

filters are generally supplied for altering the quality of the light reaching the emulsion. If, for example, the chosen emulsion is for use in daylight, compensating filters are used for artificial light. Some processes supply two different screen emulsions, one balanced for daylight, the other for a chosen incandescent lamp. The maximum speeds are obtained by this method, since either very weak or no compensating filters are required under normal conditions.

The inseparable screen processes are generally used as positive transparencies and are, therefore, processed by reversal. The limited brightness range common to all color processes is emphasized by the reversal process. For satisfactory viewing and speed in exposure, the coating weight of the emulsion must be kept low. This factor leads to a very limited latitude. For this reason alone, it is advisable to compress the brightness range of most subjects if an accurate color reproduction is desired.[8]

Processing of Inseparable Screen Materials. Inseparable screen materials processed by reversal avoid registration difficulties since the film exposed in the camera becomes the final color positive. Special processing methods and emulsions have been developed for the reversal procedure, and the generally accepted method employs developers containing silver halide solvents.[9] In reversal processing, such substances as the thiocyanates and ammonia, included in the first developer, lead to clear highlights and an effective increase in speed. Similar solvents are also used in the negative-positive processing of screen materials but for a somewhat different purpose.

The color screen material is first developed in a developer of high activity containing the halide solvent. If the exposure is correct, time development may be em-

ployed but for unusual subjects or unknown conditions, inspection is preferable. A visual check along with a time-temperature schedule is undoubtedly the safest procedure. The material may be desensitized in Phenosafranine or Pinakryptol, if desired, and processing carried out in a fairly bright light.

After development, the film is washed in running water for one minute or a dilute acid stop bath may be used. The silver image is next bleached in an acid solution of bichromate or permanganate until all the black silver has been removed. The last stages of this operation and all the following steps may be carried out in bright light. When bleaching is complete, the film is washed briefly before clearing in an aqueous solution of sodium bisulfite. The film must then be washed and exposed fully before development. The second developer may be the same one that was used during the first development or a separate developer may be used to carry development to completion. The conversion of the positive halide image may also be carried out without re-exposure by chemical reducers such as sodium hydrosulfite or fogging agents. In any case, it is desirable to immerse the color transparency in a hardening fixing bath after the positive image is obtained. A thorough washing completes the processing. Contrast films, such as Dufaycolor Hard, are developed in a somewhat more contrasty developer than the normal emulsions, but the rest of the procedure is identical.

The color transparencies may be treated with the usual reducers and intensifiers if correction is desired. The reduction is carried out with Farmer's Reducer, while the silver or mercury intensifiers seem most suitable. Corrective work should be done with caution and in moderation.

Separable Screen Processes. The only separable screen process receiving wide-

[8] Yule, *Brit. J. Phot.* **87**, 578 (1940).

[9] Turner, *Brit. J. Phot.* **84**, 435 (1937).

spread use in the past has been the Finlay Process. It is, however, no longer available. This process, unlike those already discussed, employed a separate screen process; that is to say, the screen and the emulsion were on separate glass plates which were placed in contact in a suitable holder for the exposure.

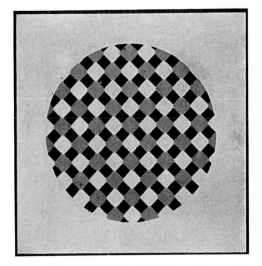

FIG. 31.4.   The Finlay screen.

The screen (Fig. 31.4) was composed of red, green, and blue color elements approximately 1/300 of an inch square. It was made by printing in dyed bichromated albumen from a black and white cross-lined screen.[10] The glass plate was first coated with collodion containing a green dye. It was then coated with bichromated albumen and exposed beneath the cross-ruled screen. The areas not protected by the insoluble albumen were bleached out and dyed with a red dye. The plate was coated with albumen a second time and exposed between a cross-lined screen so as to render the bichromated albumen insoluble over the red color areas, the unprotected areas bleached and dyed with a blue dye. A final protec-

tive layer of collodion was coated over the finished screen.

After exposure the panchromatic plate was developed in a soft negative developer and printed by contact onto a slow contrast emulsion. When dry, the positive was bound in register with a viewing screen. The color elements of this viewing screen were of the same size and orientation as in the taking screen, but of slightly different transmissions to obtain the most desirable color reproduction. The possibility of using different taking and viewing filters allows slightly higher color accuracy to be obtained with the separable screen processes. Unlimited duplication of the black and white positive allowed any number of color transparencies to be made simply and at low cost.

Copying Screen Materials. The duplication of a separable screen color transparency simply involves the production of another black and white positive to be registered with a viewing screen. The inseparable screen transparency, on the other hand, is difficult to duplicate satisfactorily. The distribution of energy from the color transparency is not the same as that from the original scene, although the visual sensation may be similar. The simple procedure of contact printing gives very degraded colors, due to the addition of black in the picture as shown in Fig. 31.5. Since the elements of the two screens will not exactly line up under normal conditions, the light from any given color element of the original may not fall on the same color elements of the screen in the new film.[11] The close combination of two geometrical screens will also cause difficulty with moiré pattern.

Another serious error is introduced by the scatter of the exposing light in the second emulsion. The emulsion below the

10 Stobart, *Phot. J.* **76**, 280 (1936).

11 Mees, *Brit. J. Phot.* **54**, 49 (Col. Suppl.) (1907).

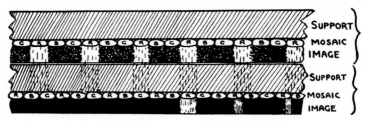

FIG. 31.5. Increase in proportion of black when copying by parallel light.
(Spencer, *Photographic Journal*, 1933.)

screen elements surrounding the color element through which the light is passing should not be exposed, but by irradiation it is exposed slightly, leading to a loss in density at those points after reversal. As the surrounding elements are of the other two primary colors, the final transmitted light will be desaturated by the addition of white.[12] (Fig. 31.6)

The first two difficulties may be overcome by the complete diffusion of the light from the color screen of the original tranparency before it strikes the screen of the film to be exposed. The necessary light spread may be obtained by separating the two films by the proper space if contact printed,[13] or, if printed by projection, by making use of

the diffraction effect of throwing the screen slightly out of focus.[14] Such procedures emphasize the third difficulty, that of irradiation in the color film emulsion. A fourth difficulty giving rise to a similar dilution of the colors is caused by the overlapping transmissions of the three-color elements making up the color screen. Thus, if light from the original transparency comes from the red screen elements, it will not only expose the emulsion behind the red elements of the copy film screen, but will also partially affect the emulsion behind the green elements of the screen. A similar effect occurs with each color. This type of color dilution may be overcome by making use of three monochromatic or narrow color bands instead of white light for exposure when copying. Each of the wave-

[12] Spencer, *Phot. J.* **73**, 19 (1933).

[13] von Hubl, *Brit. J. Phot.* **57**, 59 (1910). Harrison and Horner, *Phot. J.* **79**, 320 (1939).

[14] Tritton, *Brit. J. Phot.* **84**, 513 (1937).

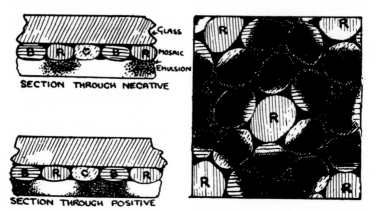

FIG. 31.6. Loss of saturation through irradiation in the emulsion. (Courtesy of Spencer, *Photographic Journal*.)

length regions chosen must be wholly within the transmission band of only one of the screen elements.

Negative-Positive Processing of Inseparable Screen Material. The logical method to employ for making a series of colored copies is to develop the original screen film to a negative and to make a number of identical positives by contact or optical printing. The same difficulties with moiré and color dilution due to the overlapping screen transmissions are encountered. Poor copies are obtained, however, even when corrective measures are applied. Harrison and Spencer found that a "color contrast effect" present in reversal processing was absent in normal negatives upon processing and made the color dilution, due to irradiation in the emulsion, a serious factor.[15] The color contrast effect, obtained with developers containing silver halide solvents, is neutralized in reversal processing by the light spreading due to irradiation. With development to a negative, the light spreading was not neutralized and serious color dilution resulted. The irradiation can be kept to a minimum by using depth developers which remove the surface halide and keep the developed image lying close to the color screen.[16]

Color Separation from Screen Materials. The color screen processes give three-color records at a single exposure and, for most color printing, these records should be separated out onto three distinct emulsions. The separable screen process is the simplest and most effective in use since a black and white block-out screen is all that is needed to allow separation negatives to be made directly from the color transparency. The block-out screen allows but one set of color elements to be observed at a time for copying. The inseparable screen processes are

somewhat more difficult in that the same problems of screen removal, color dilution, and overlapping transmissions that were considered in the last section must be taken into account. It is possible to make separation records from either a screen negative or a positive. The screen negative is preferable in that approximately double the latitude is present in such a film as compared to one processed by reversal.

A long-scale emulsion should be employed for separation since the average density range of screen transparencies is about 2.00. The transmissions of the color screen elements overlap considerably because of the necessity of short exposures for the screen film in the camera, and for a satisfactory luminosity when viewing the finished color transparency. Each of the color separations must record the densities lying behind only one of the screen colors, and for that reason the separating filters must be very sharp cutting. In Fig. 31.7 it will be seen that each of the Dufay 1_S, 2_S, and 3_S transmissions falls within the region of one of the screen filter elements. Monochromatic lights may also be employed. The filter transmissions should be kept as narrow as possible in view of exposure requirements. Separation negatives should be kept to a fairly low gamma to hold the tones of the transparency on the straight line of the emulsion's characteristic curve.

The Lenticular Process. The second basically additive method is the lenticular process. This procedure was originally developed by Berthon (1909) and Keller-Dorian (1914) and reached its greatest application in this country when the Eastman Kodak Company in 1925 acquired the rights for its use and in 1928 presented 16-mm. motion picture *Kodacolor*. The appearance of integral tripacks has sharply curtailed developments in the lenticular field, but a few firms, mainly in Europe,

---

[15] Harrison and Spencer, *Phot. J.* **77**, 250 (1937).
[16] Murray and Spencer, *Phot. J.* **77**, 330, 458 (1937).

are still experimenting on lenticular processes.

The lenticular process is essentially a screen method in which the screen is formed optically on the emulsion during exposure.

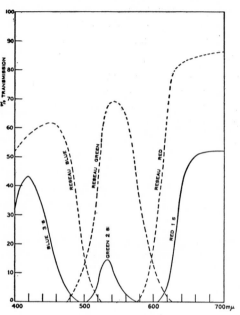

FIG. 31.7.   Reseau and analysis separation filter transmission.

The film is colorless. Berthon proposed to place a banded three-color filter over the camera objective and, by means of small lenses or lenticules on the surface of the film base, to obtain small images of the objective and its filter on the emulsion of the film. Kodacolor film contained about 600 lenticules per inch (see Fig. 31.8). From a white card, for example, a series of three small colored images is projected onto the emulsion behind each lenticule, whereas a red card will be shown by only a single image because the red light will be transmitted only by the red section of the three-color filter. The original film is processed by reversal and projected back through a similar appropriate optical system of lens and filter. As normally projected, the colors are obtained additively with the aid of the limited resolving power of the observer's eye.

The lenticular process is theoretically a most satisfactory solution to the problem of color reproduction, but in practice so many, so far insurmountable, obstacles arise that the commercial use of this method has declined sharply. Difficulties of diffusion, film shrinkage and eventual distortion, maintenance of color balance, and limited depth of field are serious problems to be overcome. Other difficulties arise in copying, such as color wedging, moiré, and low color saturation. In the motion picture field, the necessity for special projection apparatus has proved to be a serious obstacle to the commercial acceptance of lenticular processes. Because of these difficulties, the tendency in recent years has been to employ the lenticular idea for the negative part of the color process only, or to use the lenticular principle for a portion of a single color process which may later be printed subtractively.

The latest use of the lenticular method, called Pantachrome, was devised by Agfa and involved the use of parts of a number of color processes.[17] The lenticular phase of the process involves the making of two of the three-color separation records, while the printing is all done subtractively. A lenticular bipack is exposed in the camera, the front film being sensitive to blue and green, the rear emulsion to red. On the base of the front film, the usual lenticular ribbing allows the formation of an image of the objective. The lens filter is composed of three bands. In daylight, the central band is magenta and the outside two bands are yellow (colors reversed for incandescent illumination). The front film records by the normal lenticular method, the blue and green records as a line screen pattern, and the rear film records the red record in a continuous tone, since both

17 *Phot. Tech.* **1**, No. 7, 49 (1939).

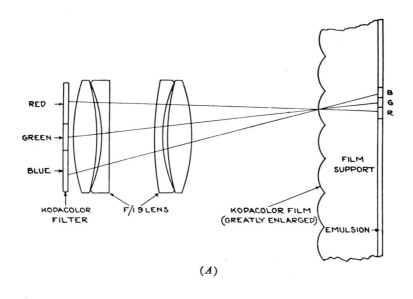

(A)

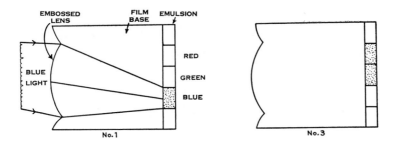

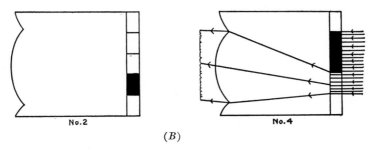

(B)

FIG. 31.8. General optical system of Kodacolor Lenticular Process, (A). Enlarged sections of film (B) show image formation in four stages: (1) exposure, (a) development, (3) bleaching and reexposure, and (4) reversal development and final projection.

filters transmit red light. The front film is developed by reversal and the rear film as a negative. The three-color separations are printed onto a single film, the cyan image being obtained from the back negative record by a standard iron toning method. The positive lenticular records from the front emulsion are printed optically onto a double layer emulsion on the reverse side of the single film, and the magenta and yellow positives are obtained by the standard dye destruction procedure as used in Gasparcolor.

CAPSTAFF, WILDER AND MILLER, *J. Soc. Mot. Pict. Eng.* **28**, 123 (1937).

FRIEDMAN, *Amer. Phot.* **34**, 689, 754, 835 (1940).

GUETENER, *J. Soc. Mot. Pict. Eng.* **28**, 447 (1937).

Chapter 32

MULTI-LAYER PROCESSES

Introduction. Whenever more than one emulsion is coated on a single support, the term "integral" is generally applied. An integral tripack consists of a single support with three light-sensitive systems on one side. Such a multi-layer material may also be called a *monopack*. The three emulsions are not separable and must be handled together during processing. There are many other methods of arranging the three light-sensitive systems such as, for example, a single support bearing two emulsions on one side and a third on the opposite side, or two emulsions coated on one support and the third on a second support. For purposes of classification [1] and discussion, various possibilities are listed in Fig. 32.1. The number of possible combinations which may be employed to obtain the three-color records is quite large but this chapter will be concerned chiefly with the methods of color formation by the most popular three-color processes when used with Integral or Two-sided Tripacks. The general term "integral tripack" will include all types unless otherwise specifically indicated.

Integral tripacks may be considered from two viewpoints: (1) the physical problems inherent in the coating of more than one emulsion on a single support, and (2) the chemical and photographic problems involved in the formation of useful color images in the appropriate emulsion layers. The growth of integral tripacks has been closely allied with the growth of those subtractive color processes that are dependent on dye coupling development, chemical dye destruction or dye bleaching, but it must be kept clearly in mind that the two are not synonymous. The development of integral tripacks has led to the commercialization of these systems of color formation, but the tripack itself may be employed with other methods of color formation. It is likewise true that the dye bleaching, dye destruction and dye coupling reactions may be carried out in media other than the integral tripack.

Historical Development. The idea of using a tripack to record a set of color separation images may be traced back, as is often the case with color processes, to du Hauron,[2] who in 1897 laid down the principles of the separable tripack and bipack. Selle,[3] in 1899, suggested the sensitization of a normal emulsion with a double dye bath of alcohol and water. One of the sensitizing dyes, soluble in water, penetrated to the lower depths of the emulsion and sensitized to green; while the other dye, soluble in alcohol, red-sensitized the upper surface only, since it was unable to reach the interior of the emulsion. In this manner, a single zone-sensitized emulsion was obtained with the upper stratum capable of recording the red record image, the lower level recording the green. Smith suggested, and produced in 1903, a coating of two or more emulsions, separated by

---

[1] Screen and lenticular processes may also be considered as tripacks where the three-color records are separated laterally instead of vertically as in the integral tripack.

[2] du Hauron, *La Triplice Photographique*, 223 (1897).

[3] Selle, B.P. 12,516.

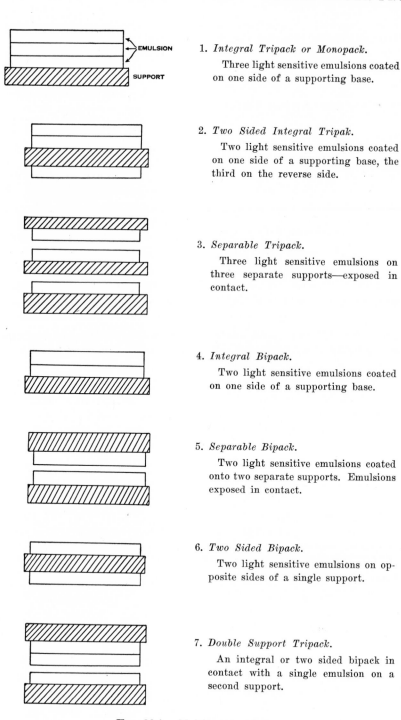

1. *Integral Tripack or Monopack.*
   Three light sensitive emulsions coated on one side of a supporting base.

2. *Two Sided Integral Tripak.*
   Two light sensitive emulsions coated on one side of a supporting base, the third on the reverse side.

3. *Separable Tripack.*
   Three light sensitive emulsions on three separate supports—exposed in contact.

4. *Integral Bipack.*
   Two light sensitive emulsions coated on one side of a supporting base.

5. *Separable Bipack.*
   Two light sensitive emulsions coated onto two separate supports. Emulsions exposed in contact.

6. *Two Sided Bipack.*
   Two light sensitive emulsions on opposite sides of a single support.

7. *Double Support Tripack.*
   An integral or two sided bipack in contact with a single emulsion on a second support.

Fig. 32.1.   Multilayer systems.

intermediate collodion layers, onto a single support. The emulsions were subsequently stripped apart for processing. K. Schinzel[4] in 1905, and Sforza in 1909, proposed integral tripacks in which the sensitized emulsions were colored with dyes which were to compose the final image. This type of integral tripack was eventually developed into the integral tripack dye destruction process, while Fischer employed dye coupling development in his monopack suggestions of 1914. This growth of multi-layered materials was paralleled by many other disclosures of bipack and tripack construction and usage, some of which are discussed in connection with the three subtractive processes to be considered.

Construction of Multi-layered Materials. Many of the features of a multi-layer material are directly concerned with the method of color formation to be employed, but the essential factors common to most such materials will be considered in this section. A typical integral tripack, shown schematically in Fig. 32.2, consists of: (1)

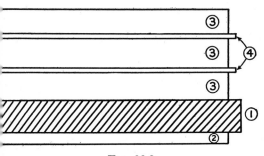

F<small>IG</small>. 32.2.

a film, paper, or glass support; (2) an antihalation coating; (3) three separate light-sensitive emulsions, usually separated from each other by (4) thin layers of gelatin. The rigid requirements for integral tripacks demand the utmost skill in emulsion manufacturing and coating. Following

[4] Schinzel, *Phot. Woch.* (1905).

are some of the characteristics of the elements in a typical monopack:

1. *Physical Characteristics of the Emulsions.* The thickness of the complete monopack is approximately 0.001 inch, so the individual coatings are extremely thin (Fig. 32.3). The thickness varies rather widely, depending upon the process for which the material is designed—negative or reversal processing—and the type of color formation to be employed. The lowest emulsion next to the support varies from 2 to 5 ten-thousandths of an inch in thickness, while the upper emulsion, or emulsions, are approximately 2 ten-thousandths inch thick. To allow adequate light transmission and to obtain sharp images in the lowest emulsion, the center and top emulsions are sometimes poor in silver salts, having been diluted with clear gelatin to preserve their transparency. On the other hand, the halides must be present in sufficient quantity to allow the formation of an adequate silver image, later to be converted to a color image. In the formation of the color image, there is sometimes an intensification factor that must be taken into account by suitably adjusting the type and density of silver image obtained. The emulsions may carry not only light-sensitive silver halides, but also sensitizing and light-filtering dyes and substances for the formation of the color images. The production of stable, nonmigrating sensitizing and filter dyes is one of the most important factors contributing to the commercial success of integral tripacks.

2. *Photographic Characteristics of the Emulsions.* The two or three light-sensitive coatings must be arranged and sensitized so that each records one of the desired spectral regions. The order of coating the various emulsions is not of fundamental importance although the red-sensitive layer is generally placed at the bottom of the

pack. The color recorded by any particular emulsion is determined by its inherent sensitivity, its sensitization, and the light-filtering action of other emulsion or filter layers through which the light must pass before it is exposed. The speed and contrast of each of the emulsions are so adjusted that with some given form of illuminant and processing, the photographic tone reproduction will be correct in each layer. The sensitizing dyes in the various emulsions must not diffuse into adjoining layers and affect their sensitivity, and the particular halides (chloride, bromide, iodide) used will be somewhat dependent on the method of color formation to be employed.

3. *Characteristics of the Separating Layers.* The intermediate layers between the light-sensitive emulsions serve one or more purposes, the most important of which are: (1) to act as color filters for the sensitive emulsions, (2) to aid in the differential processing of the various emulsions after exposure, (3) to minimize the effects of one layer on another when both are simultaneously undergoing similar chemical treatment, and (4) to aid in any possible stripping operations required to physically separate the emulsion layers after exposure. The layers may consist of gelatin or of some other substances depending on the purpose of the layer; e.g., waterproof layers may be employed. If of gelatin, the layer is about 1 ten-thousandth inch thick and may contain filter dyes or silver salts. The uses of the various types of separating layers are discussed further in connection with the formation of color images in the tripack.

Color Formation in Tripacks. Many of the problems that arise in the use of a successful integral tripack arise in the conversion of the three latent, or silver, images into usable colored images. In some cases it may only be necessary to obtain a color

negative for reseparation or printing, but at present the majority of tripack materials are processed by reversal. The conversion of the silver images into color may be carried out by almost any of the subtractive printing methods, such as chemical or dye toning, or the dye bleach, dye destruction, or coupling processes. The most important methods of color formation, however, are dye-coupling development and silver-dye destruction.

Silver-dye Destruction. This process is based upon the chemical destruction of a dye present in the emulsion layer. The destruction of the dye may be made to take place either in the presence of a developed silver image or in areas without a silver image. In either case, the silver image is the agency that controls the position of the dye image remaining in the film after chemical treatment.

Schinzel,[5] in 1905, proposed to coat an integral tripack with three silver halide emulsions which were dyed colors complementary to their light sensitivity. After development and fixation, the pack was treated with a dilute solution of hydrogen peroxide which destroyed the dye in the presence of the silver image. The removal of the silver image and "attacked" dye left an inverse dye image in each layer. Christensen discovered that finely-divided silver (in the form of the silver image) acted as a catalyst in the destruction of certain types of dye. Dyes which were attacked either slightly or not at all in the absence of silver were readily attacked in the presence of silver. Christensen [6] also proposed the use of the reducing agents themselves for attacking the dyes and suggested sodium hydrosulfite. In this way, the dye was destroyed as the silver image was developed. The same result was ob-

[5] Schinzel, *Brit. J. Phot.* **52**, 608 (1905).

[6] Christensen, *Eder's Jahrbuch* **29**, 164 (1915); *Brit. J. Phot.* **68**, 96 (1921).

tained by Luther and Holleben [7] who chemically converted the silver image into substances which directly or by treatment with another reagent destroyed the dye. They suggested vanadium ferricyanide and chromic acid among other reagents.

The Gaspar patents since 1930 are concerned with the coating and processing of tripacks in which the color formation is based on chemical dye destruction. The destruction of dye contained in an emulsion layer in areas not containing a silver image may be carried out by baths similar to the following:

Calcium hypochlorite........ 10 grams
Glacial acetic acid............ 10 cc.
Water to make.............. 1 liter

Immersion in this solution destroys the dyes wherever they are not protected by the silver image. The inverse process may be carried out by using baths which do not normally affect the dyes in the emulsion, but in the presence of silver are able to attack and bleach the dye. A typical dye destruction bleach bath is composed of:

Potassium thiocyanate........ 30 grams
Citric acid.................. 30 grams
Water to make.............. 1 liter

The reagents which may be used in the inverse process fall into several classes,[8] such as

1. Nitrogenous organic compounds
2. Compounds of thiourea
3. Special sulfur compounds
4. Certain acids indifferent to the dyes employed.

More recent applications [9] of the same principle have been concerned chiefly with:

(1) the improvement of the above method, (2) the development of procedures for the formation of the dyes in the emulsion layers after exposure rather than inclusion of the colorant in the emulsion when coated, and (3) the conversion of the silver image into other substances more useful in the subsequent dye destruction. A tripack composed of three emulsions dyed cyan, magenta, and yellow is extremely slow and rather impractical for camera exposures. The employment of dye destruction reagents which destroy dyes in the presence of silver, also necessitates the use of positives for exposure since a positive image is required. The possibility of negative materials has been improved recently by disclosure of various dye generators.

Dye Coupling Development. The formation of a dye image in conjunction with the development of a silver image may take two forms, known as primary and secondary color development. In primary color development, the oxidation product of development is a dye, whereas secondary color development involves the oxidation of the developing agent and its combination with another substance (*coupler*) to form the dye.

The growth of primary dye-coupling development goes back to Homolka,[10] who, during the course of his investigations of the latent image, desired colored, insoluble, development products. Developing agents which gave colored images had been known —such as pyrogallol—but Homolka used indoxyl and thioindoxyl to obtain blue and red-colored images of indigo and thioindigo along with the silver images. Homolka did not apply this discovery to color photography, and Fischer, in 1914, patented these primary color developers for the formation of monochrome prints. Fischer

[7] D.R.P. 396,485.

[8] *Brit. J. Phot.* **27**, 41 (1933) (Col. Suppl.).

[9] *Brit. J. Phot.* **86**, 198 (1939); **87**, 7, 419, 433, 459, 468 (1940); **88**, 220, 292 (1941).

HEYMER, Sci. Pub. Agfa Central Lab. **4**, 177 (1935).

[10] Homolka, *Phot. Korr.* **44**, 55, 115 (1907).

and Siegrist [11] laid down the foundations of secondary color development at the same time and showed how the oxidation product of developers, such as paraphenylenediamine and paraaminophenol, could couple with phenols and amines to form dyes of the indophenol, indamine, or indoanilin classes. The application of such procedures to multi-colored images was suggested at about the same time by the Neue Photographische Gesellschaft in connection with the formation of color photographs. Most of the recent applications have been concerned with the formation of indoanilin and azomethine dyes.

Primary color development is rather restricted in its application because of the limited range of colors that can be obtained. Primary color development [12] has been suggested for obtaining a yellow image of higher contrast during a normal secondary color development by having present substantive agents in the blue-sensitive emulsions so that both primary and secondary color formation together will yield a sufficiently heavy image.

Secondary color development has become the accepted method of color formation in modern dye-forming processes. The number of possible couplers for use with a few color developing agents has increased rapidly during the last ten years. A listing of the classes of dye formation may be found in the literature. For a further discussion, see Chapter 14.

The usual type of secondary color development makes use of colorless couplers which when suitably combined with the reaction products of development give the required dye image colorants. It is also possible to use colored couplers [13] in the emulsion. When color development occurs the colored coupler forms a dye of a different color than it was originally. It is therefore feasible, for example, to use a yellow-colored coupler which will form, after color development, a magenta dye. If part of the colored coupler was not used during development, both yellow and magenta colorants would be in the emulsion after processing.

The same result may be obtained by combining two different couplers in the same emulsion. The first would be colorless and form a colored dye during development. The second would be a colored coupler which formed a colorless substance during development. Colored couplers are used to obtain mask images in color negative materials such as Ektacolor.

Control of Color Formation. The localization of color formation in the various positions of an integral tripack follows two general patterns, the first of which depends on the differential processing of the various layers of emulsion, while the second method forms the colors by means of reagents already present in the proper emulsion layers.

Differential processing methods may be subdivided into those dependent on the controlled penetration of processing solutions and those dependent on some means of differential exposure of the emulsion layers. This line of demarcation is not too sharp as some suggested methods involve both—such as those employing differential re-exposure by means of the controlled penetration of light.

Controlled Penetration Methods. These methods of color formation are dependent

[11] Fischer and Siegrist, *Phot. Korr.* **51**, 18 (1914).

[12] *Brit. J. Phot.* **86**, 120 (1939).

[13] Hanson and Vittum, *J. Phot. Soc. Amer.* **13**, 94 (1947); *Brit. J. Phot.* **96**, 564 (1949).

on the fact that suitably prepared solutions penetrate into a layer of emulsion at a very slow and controllable rate.

The average developer takes only a second or two to penetrate an emulsion layer of normal thickness but, if certain "loading" reagents, such as alcohol, glycerine, or sugar are present, the penetration period is greatly extended. For example, in the reversal of an integral bipack which has been developed and subsequently bleached, it is possible by means of a loaded dye coupling developer to redevelop the top layer of halide without affecting the lower emulsion if the time of development is carefully controlled. The effectiveness and control of such penetrating solutions are greatly increased by the inclusion of gelatin-separating or filter layers between the emulsions. Whenever controlled penetration methods are to be used, the gelatin of the separating layers is chosen to give considerable swelling when wet. The employment of controlled penetration methods is not limited to developers since suitable bleaching baths or re-sensitizing solutions may be used. Controlled penetration of the bleaching solutions was used for several years in the processing of Kodachrome Film.

Differential Exposure Methods. The second type of differential processing makes use of various means of exposing, or processing, the various emulsions separately and at will. For example, if a temporary opaque screen is obtainable on both sides of the center emulsion of an integral tripack, after first development, it is a simple matter to expose the bottom emulsion through the film base, the top emulsion from the front and then to fog the center

emulsion chemically. Differential exposure methods generally depend on some feature of the monopack's separating layers, or on the emulsions themselves, to make individual exposures feasible. For example, the separating layers may contain fogged silver salts which become opaque screens during the first development and therefore protect the center layer from light until the screens are removed after the second development of the outer two emulsions, or the separating layers may be various forms of color filter (even ultraviolet) which would prevent certain spectral regions from affecting the center emulsion. The same result may be obtained by making use of color sensitizers in the emulsions that remain effective after the first development. This is the principle employed at the present time in processing Kodachrome. It is also possible to obtain the effect of differential exposure by the proper mixture of silver chloride and silver bromide emulsions since they are affected differently by a given developer, and with appropriate solutions they may be developed one at a time.

Use of Non-diffusing Substances. If the emulsions themselves can be made to hold part or all of the color-forming substances through the initial processing stages, all the differential processing methods will be unnecessary since a single stage of color formation results in the appropriate color being obtained in each layer of emulsion. The first essential for these substances is that they remain in their proper location and do not wander through the film. Such substances must be insoluble in the processing solutions and remain fixed in position. Compounds that fulfill the requirement of remaining fixed to their support without mordants are often called substantive materials. The term "nondiffusing" covers many types of color formation, such as the types of dye which are incorporated in the emulsion layers of a

TULL, *Brit. J. Phot.* **85**, 627, 647 (1938); **86**, 115 (1939); **87**, 17, 30, 39, 576, 587, 603 (1940).

FRIEDMAN, *Amer. Phot.* **34**, 914 (1940); **35**, 62, 136, 220 (1941).

dye destruction process, the couplers present in the emulsions for use in dye coupling development, dyestuff generators, and accelerators. The application of some of these special components is indicated in connection with the Anscocolor, Kodacolor, Gasparcolor, and Ektachrome processes.

Dye Bleaching. In general, dye bleaching processes are not thought of in connection with integral tripacks. However, since the usual bleach-out process (see Chapter 30) consists of three light-sensitive systems coated one above the other on a single support, it deserves mention in this section.

Bleach-out processes have been proposed in two physical forms. In the first instance, the three light-sensitive dyes or agents are coated one above the other on a single paper or transparent support. To prevent the diffusion of dye from one layer to another, dyes are generally carried in different media. Thus, one dye might be incorporated in a layer of collodion, the others in layers of gelatin. In the second type of process, the three light-sensitive agents are mixed together in one medium and then coated onto the support.

General Characteristics of Reversal Integral Tripacks. The nature of the reversal process and the critical balance required in the manufacture of integral tripack materials makes it essential that certain precautions be taken during their use to obtain the highest quality color reproductions. Not only must the film be properly exposed and processed, but the conditions under which it is stored, the duration of the exposure, and many other factors affect the resulting color transparency.

1. *Exposure.* The reversal process requires that the exposure be based on the highlight areas of the subject and it is, therefore, preferable in most cases to determine the proper exposure by measurements or calculations of the light falling on the subject (incident light). Since color reproduction errors are most apparent in the middle and lighter tones of the picture, it is essential that these portions of the subject be properly exposed. This has led to a reversal of the old adage "expose for the shadows and develop for the highlights" to "expose for the highlights and light for the shadows" where reversal processes of color photography are concerned. The latter part of this statement indicates that the lighting in the shadow portions of the subject should be sufficient for the color reproduction to be satisfactory when the camera exposure is based on the highlight illumination. Most modern color transparency materials reproduce colors well if the shadow illumination is not less than one-third to one-fourth of the intensity of the key lighting. This illumination range should not be confused with the brightness range of the subject itself, which, of course, is dependent upon the different reflectivities of various parts of the subject. Incident light measurements at the subject may be obtained by using a photoelectric type exposure meter, pointing the integrating cell toward the light source and determining the ratio between the key and shadow illumination. The same result may be obtained by using a brightness meter and reading the brightness of a standard gray card when it is alternately lighted by the key and shadow illumination (see Chapter 22).

2. *Latitude.* The range of subject brightness that can be recorded on modern integral tripacks is reasonably close to the range that may be reproduced in black-and-white photography, although certain precautions should be taken to keep this range from becoming excessive. In a subject having a wide range of reflectances, it is advisable to keep the illumination ratio low, approximately two to one. In this way, the reproduction of colors in the

darker areas will be within the limits satisfactorily reproduced by the material. If the subject has a short scale, the illumination ratio may be increased up to or over four to one and still obtain adequate color reproduction in both highlight and shadow regions of the subject. The permissible range of exposures that may be given to a reversal material and still obtain satisfactory reproduction of a given subject is very limited. In a negative-positive process, such as black-and-white print making, a number of different exposures can be given to the negative made from a normal range subject, and from any of these negatives a satisfactory print can be obtained. Generally speaking, there is only one correct exposure for a reversal color process. That is the exposure that will properly reproduce the lightest gradations in the subject at a slightly higher density than clear specular highlights. Any greater exposure will lead to a lack of detail in the highlights, and a shorter exposure, especially on long-scale subjects, will result in unsatisfactory shadow detail. It is probably because of this limited latitude that there is so little agreement among photographers regarding the actual film speed of reversal color transparency materials. Individual differences in making exposure determinations, variations among light-measuring instruments, transmission and diaphragm inaccuracies among lenses, and variations in shutter speeds are the causes of a major proportion of the disagreements regarding emulsion speed. To eliminate all these variables, the only safe procedure where high accuracy is required is the making of a test exposure on an important subject with the materials and equipment to be used for the final result.

3. *Product Tolerances.* As described earlier, the emulsions of reversal color films are extremely thin and thus require the utmost care in manufacturing to obtain a consistent product. The emulsions used in normal black-and-white photography have approximately the same thickness as the three emulsions used in a reversal integral tripack. Variations of the order of 5 to 10% in thickness of black and white emulsions will not lead to noticeable changes in the photographic result obtained. In the case of the emulsions of a reversal color film, however, changes in coating thickness of 5% or less in one emulsion lead to a significant change in the quality of the product. Such a percentage variation is only about 2/100,000th of an inch. All emulsions of a given color film cannot be considered identical and certain tolerances must be set up by the manufacturer, inside of which the film is considered satisfactory for normal use. The Eastman Kodak Company has indicated that tests on color film emulsions for still camera use are so established that emulsions are not released unless they fall within narrow limits for color balance. No sheet film is released that cannot be corrected by the use of a color compensating filter of strength no heavier than 10 (such as Kodak Color Compensating Filters CC-10M, CC-10C or CC-10Y). Similar tests hold released films within plus or minus one-half stop of their rated ASA speed for normal uses at the time of shipment by the manufacturer.

4. *Other Factors Affecting Color Films.* It can be seen that reversal color films are very sensitive to small manufacturing changes. They are also affected by a number of factors that may change the color balance, or speed, by a much larger amount than the product tolerances set up by the manufacturer. All photographic emulsions are essentially perishable and are affected by the conditions under which they are stored. This is very apparent in the case of color films since there are three sensitive emulsions involved and slight changes in relative sensitivity among the three emul-

sions lead to serious changes in color balance. Color film should be stored at temperatures below 70° F whenever possible and film not suitably sealed to be moisture-tight should be kept at relative humidities below 50%. Film sealed in moisture-tight containers will keep well at temperatures near 0° F. The deleterious effects of both high temperature and humidity tend to be more serious after the film has been exposed than before exposure. It is, therefore, advisable to have color films processed as promptly as possible after exposure to minimize the likelihood of changes in the latent image.

The reciprocity effect discussed in Chapters 8 and 11 occurs in color emulsions and it is difficult to produce three emulsions of the types required in which the reciprocity effect is the same. Thus, not only does the effective speed of the film change with the duration of the exposure, as is the case with black-and-white materials, but one of the emulsions may change relative to the other two in a color film. When this occurs, the result is a change in color balance as well as speed of the material. Variations of this type are inevitable with present materials, although their magnitude may vary from emulsion to emulsion. Such changes can readily be corrected by an adjustment in exposure and the application of color correction filters over the camera lens at the time of exposure. The manufacturer attempts to keep such variations as small as possible but the released film is tested at exposure times of normal duration for the material in question. Ektachrome Type B Film, for example, is tested at an exposure time of one second. Exposure times considerably different from those at which the manufacturer tests the film may require some filter correction.

5. *Processing.* Color films are adversely affected by slight changes in processing which would be of no importance in black-and-white work. For this reason, it is essential that the techniques and times recommended by the manufacturer of a color film should be followed explicitly. Extensive precautions are taken by the manufacturers when the film is processed by them so that variations are held to a minimum. Unsatisfactory processing such as might be obtained from improper processing times, temperatures, exhausted solutions or chemical contamination, may lead to color changes in the film much larger than the small variations inherent in the product when manufactured.

Reversal color films developed by the user may be processed in two stages so that the effects of keeping on the latent image may be minimized. Such a technique involves the processing through the first developer stage and then storing the film for subsequent re-exposure and color development. Such a procedure is advisable wherever unsatisfactory storage conditions are anticipated after exposure and before the film may be processed fully.

6. *Duplication.* It is often necessary to make duplicates from a reversal color transparency. The inherently high contrast of the original transparency and the errors in color reproduction that exist are magnified on the duplicate unless special precautions are taken. Subjects for duplication must be well exposed and not be excessively contrasty. Satisfactory duplication generally involves the use of silver or colored masks over the original transparency to obtain adequate gradation and satisfactory color reproduction (see Chapter 33).

7. *Viewing Conditions.* The reproduction of any subject by a reversal color transparency material involves certain hue and brightness changes that are typical of color reproduction processes. Such errors are not very apparent unless color matching is required. For any judgment of color

accuracy, it is essential that the transparency be viewed under the illuminant recommended by the manufacturer. The viewing conditions can considerably change the personal interpretation of the adequacy of a color reproduction (see Chapter 33). It is also true that each of the various reversal integral tripack materials available has its own characteristic color shifts due to the nature of the dyes which compose the final transparency. Each process may have colors which it reproduces extremely well and others which are not so satisfactorily recorded. These characteristics change from time to time as the manufacturer makes improvements in the materials and procedures that affect the final transparency.

Kodachrome Films and Prints. Kodachrome Film is an integral tripack in which the dye images are formed during dye coupling development in the latter stages of reversal processing. The segregation of the three subtractive colors is brought about by using sensitizers in the various emulsions which are not affected by the first development, thus making possible the differential re-exposure of the separate emulsions by colored lights.

The evolution of this widely used type of integral tripack is based on the work of Mannes and Godowsky and the Eastman Kodak Company in the construction of monopack films. The commercialization of the process in 1935 followed the application of dye coupling development to these emulsions as the most satisfactory method of color formation. A single film base is coated with three superimposed emulsions, that next to the film base being sensitive to red, the top emulsion sensitive to blue and the center emulsion sensitive to green. The two upper emulsions are separated by a layer of yellow colloidal silver to prevent the penetration of blue light to the two lower emulsions. This yellow is eliminated during processing. After exposure, the film is developed in a normal developer to give black silver negatives in each emulsion layer. The limited spectral sensitivities of the different emulsions are retained during this stage of the processing, so the remaining halides will still respond to colored light in the same manner as before development. After the first development is complete, the film is washed to remove the developer, exposed to red light through the film base and developed in a dye coupling developer containing a cyan color former or coupler to yield a positive cyan dye image along with the silver positive. Because of the lack of red sensitivity of the two upper emulsions, the red light exposure is effective only in the lower emulsion. The film is then exposed to blue light from the top and developed in a different dye coupling solution capable of yielding the proper silver and yellow dye images in the uppermost emulsion. The magenta positive image is obtained in the center emulsion by the employment of a dye coupler after fogging. A final bleaching of all the silver in the film leaves three positive dye images of the proper subtractive colorants. Kodachrome Film was previously processed by means of the controlled penetration of bleaching baths. In this system, the emulsion sensitizers did not have to remain effective after first development. The processing was more complicated, however, and has been replaced by the differential re-exposure method.

The same basic process is also available for the production of color prints. Kodachrome Prints are made from color transparencies by contact printing or enlarging. The Kodachrome Print emulsions are coated on a white pigmented acetate base instead of a transparent film support and the emulsions and processing techniques are so adjusted that low contrast dye images are obtained that are suitable for viewing by reflected light.

Another process of the same general type is Kodachrome Commercial 16 mm. motion picture film. This is a camera film processed by reversal, designed to yield a low-contrast master film from which any number of high-quality positive prints for projection may be printed.

Ansco Color Positive Film and Printon. Ansco Color Positive Film is a direct application of the early work of Fischer. The materials are integral tripacks, processed by reversal. The color formation is based on dye coupling development of emulsions which contain colorless couplers that have been made fast to diffusion. Chemical kits are supplied for processing by the photographer.

Ansco Color Positive Film contains three light-sensitive emulsions coated one above the other with separating layers between the emulsions. The order of coating is that generally employed, red-sensitive emulsion nearest to the film base, blue-recording emulsion on top. The middle, green-recording emulsion is separated from the top emulsion by a yellow separating filter layer about .001 mm. thick. An anti-halation layer of silver is coated between the film base and the red-recording emulsion. The silver in this layer is discharged during the bleaching and fixation stages of the processing. The top blue-sensitive emulsion carries a colorless yellow color former or coupler, the center green-recording emulsion carries a colorless magenta coupler, while the lower red-recording emulsion contains the cyan coupler. The coupling agents must not only be colorless, but must be of such a character that they are readily soluble in the emulsion ingredients and yet remain fast to diffusion when once coated, even during processing. This coupler characteristic is obtained by attaching long chain molecules to the basic coupler so that they become relatively immobile. Such couplers are called substantive by the manufacturer.

The processing of Ansco Color Positive Film consists of five essential steps: (1) first development to a black-and-white negative; (2) complete exposure; (3) color development; (4) bleaching of silver; and (5) fixation. Altogether six solutions are used as the film must be hardened to prevent excessive softening of the emulsions, cleared to prevent stain from oxidized color developer and carried through a stop bath after first development. Water washes are also included at several stages during processing. Total processing time is about an hour and a quarter. Other films of a similar type available in Europe are Agfa Color Reversible, Gevacolor and Ferrania Reversible Color Film.

Ansco Printon is similar to Ansco Color Positive Film in its construction and processing. Printon emulsions are coated on a white pigmented film base with the necessary adjustments of photographic characteristics so that the density and contrast are suitable for viewing by reflected light. Prints may be made from positive color transparencies either by contact or projection. A suitable light source must be carefully balanced by means of color compensating filters to yield light of the proper quality for the Printon emulsion. Printon is fast enough for normal projection equipment and the processing time is approximately one and one-half hours.

Ansco Color Duplicating Film is used for making duplicates from positive color transparencies. This film is processed by reversal and gives lower contrast than Ansco Color Positive Film so that duplicates of reasonable contrast and color fidelity may be obtained. Printon processing solutions may be used.

Ektachrome Films. Ektachrome Film is a typical integral tripack, processed by reversal color development. The color formation is based on treatment of the single film by a color developer and its reaction with the colorless coupling agents present in each of the three emulsions. Chemical kits are available for the processing of this film by the photographer.

Ektachrome Film contains three light-sensitive emulsions coated one above the other. The coating order is the same as generally employed, with the red-recording emulsion being coated next to the film base, the green-recording emulsion in the center and the blue-sensitive emulsion on top. The top two emulsions are separated by a blue-absorbing layer containing silver. An anti-halation layer of dye in gelatin is coated on the back side of the film base. The coupling agents in Ektachrome Film are protected from the other ingredients in the emulsion by oily globules in which they are suspended. The finely divided globules carrying the coupling agent are dispersed throughout the emulsion before coating. The purpose of these oily globules is to prevent coupler interaction with other components of the emulsions and to prevent wandering throughout the material. The emulsions are of normal thickness for reversible integral tripacks.

Processing of Ektachrome Film consists of the usual five steps for reversal color film processing. There are only five solutions required: first developer, hardener, color developer, bleach, and the clearing and fixing solution. This last solution is used twice during the processing sequence. There are water rinses between each stage of processing. Total elapsed time is approximately one hour.

Ektachrome Aero Film, formerly available for the armed forces as Kodacolor Aero Film, is similar to Ektachrome Film except for processing differences. Designed for aerial photography, this material gives somewhat higher contrast than

Ektachrome Film and is of higher speed. This speed increase is obtained by development to the higher contrast required in aerial photographs. Requirements of color balance and grain structure are somewhat less strict for such uses. Filters are suggested for this material for use at various elevations to give satisfactory color balance.

Gasparcolor. Gasparcolor is the only commercial example of the dye destruction process in color photography. This type process, now used as a printing material from reversal color transparencies, was formerly used in Great Britain as a release printing stock for color motion pictures. This cine material was followed by a tripack coated on a white film support that was manufactured in the United States during the war for the use of the armed forces in printing color transparencies. Both materials yielded a positive color image from a positive original.

Gasparcolor cine film was a two-sided integral tripack and was printed by exposure to three suitable black-and-white separation positives. One side of the tripack carried a yellow-dyed red sensitive emulsion over which was coated a magenta-dyed blue sensitive emulsion. The third emulsion, on the other side of the base, was dyed cyan and was blue sensitive. The colors of the dyed emulsions were the normal subtractive printing colors with the emulsion sensitivities being arranged so that each might be exposed to the proper separation positive without having any effect on the other two coatings (see Fig. 32.4). The yellow-dyed red sensitive emulsion, for example, was exposed by red light from the black-and-white positive obtained from the blue separation negative. The exposure

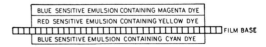

Fig. 32.4. Color illustration of processes.

was made through the magenta-dyed emulsion which passed red light freely and yet was insensitive to red. In a similar manner, the other emulsions were exposed to the proper separation positives by blue light from opposite sides of the tripack.

Gasparcolor printing material for use with positive color transparencies is a normal integral tripack with the three emulsions coated one above the other on one side of a white film support. The coating and sensitizing order is that usually employed, the red sensitive emulsion next to the white support with the blue recording emulsion above the middle green recording emulsion. Each emulsion is dyed a color complementary to the recording of that emulsion, the lowest emulsion cyan, the center emulsion magenta, and the upper emulsion yellow. The unexposed material therefore appears black before processing.

After exposure to a positive color transparency, the Gasparcolor emulsions are developed in a normal black-and-white developer, fixed and washed. The dyes in the three emulsions in contact with the silver images are then destroyed by treatment in a dye bleaching bath. Removal of the silver in the three emulsions and washing complete the processing. The finished tripack thus contains three positive dye images.

General Characteristics of Integral Color Negatives. A color negative is like a black-and-white negative in that the brighter parts of the subject are recorded after development as the darker portions of the negative, whereas a very low brightness subject area may be reproduced as almost clear film. A color negative, as its name implies, is also colored and the colors are obtained from the same types of cyan, magenta and yellow dyes that are used in reversal processes. Since the color negative is developed only once, however, to yield the colored images in the three layers,

the colors are essentially complementary to those of the original subject. A bright magenta, for example, would be recorded as a dark green in a color negative. There are certain other factors, such as masks and product techniques, that may shift the colors from being exact complements of the original but a color negative does have these general characteristics.

1. Exposure and Latitude. The exposure of color negatives should follow the same techniques as those recommended for reversal integral tripacks. Although they are negative processes rather than reversal processes, it is still essential that the highlight and middle-tone regions of the subject be recorded properly. Color errors in the reproduction of these areas of the subject are more obvious than they are in the shadow areas so that exposure should still be based on the brightness of the highlights of the subject.

As is usually true with negative-positive processes, the exposure latitude is somewhat greater than with reversal processes. With short-scale subjects, some variation in exposure is permissible without suffering from color degradation in the reproduction. The latitude is, however, much smaller than in present black and white negative materials and the same precautions should be taken that are necessary with reversal processes.

2. Product Tolerances. The permissible variations in manufacturing of a color negative material are somewhat greater than those existing for reversal processes. Although the manufacturing tolerances are much smaller than they are in black-and-white films, the possibility of making adjustments in the printing processes for small variations in the color negative makes it unnecessary to limit released film to such close standards of color balance.

3. Photographic and Color Quality. Because of the elimination of the reversal process and the somewhat extended range of color negative materials, it is possible to obtain from a color negative somewhat improved photographic gradation in a color print. In general, the improvement is of the same order of magnitude that would be expected when making black-and-white prints on paper from a reversal black and white material compared to making a paper print from a regular black-and-white negative. It is also possible to have somewhat higher color accuracy because of the possibility of incorporating masks into the color negative which are used when printing. Masks cannot be incorporated in a reversal integral tripack unless it is intended only for subsequent printing. Since most reversal integral tripacks are judged by their appearance on an illuminator, such masks would alter the color and gradation of the color positive. In a color negative, however, the appearance of the negative is of no consequence since it is only an intermediate step in obtaining a positive color reproduction. The colors may all be shifted from true complements and the gradation may be distorted in any manner which will yield a satisfactory final reproduction by the printing process to be employed. Several techniques have been developed for the inclusion of masks in an integral color negative and two are discussed in the following section.

Kodacolor. Kodacolor Film, introduced in 1942 by the Eastman Kodak Company, is an integral tripack roll film material employing dye coupling development to obtain a color negative. After development by the manufacturer, the negative is printed to obtain a color positive on a paper base. The emulsion order is that generally employed, red-recording emulsion next to the film base, blue-recording emulsion on top. The coupling agents are of the protected type, discussed under

Ektachrome, and after development yield cyan, magenta, and yellow negative dye images in their respective emulsion layers.

About three years after its introduction, Kodacolor Film was improved by the addition of a separate blue sensitive emulsion between the yellow filtering layer and the green recording emulsion. This emulsion, used to make a mask, was not affected by the original camera exposure since it was under the yellow filter layer. The exposed film was first developed to obtain the three negative dye images. The silver halides remaining in these three emulsions were then removed by exposing the film from the top by blue light and from the base side by yellow light and developing in a normal black and white developer. All the silver was then removed, leaving the three negative dye images and the unaffected layer of silver halide in the mask layer. Exposure of this emulsion was then made by blue or white light from the base side of the film and developed to give a silver image. Since this emulsion was blue sensitive and was exposed through the cyan and magenta dye images, it produced a silver mask whose densities corrected for the undesirable blue absorptions of the cyan and magenta dyes (see Chapter 33). The addition of this silver mask led to considerably improved color reproduction in the final color print made from the Kodacolor negative. In 1949 this masking system was discarded and two colored dye images substituted as masks. These dye masks were obtained by using colored couplers in two of the emulsion layers as discussed under Ektacolor. Present Kodacolor films, both Daylight and Type A, contain five dye images. Three are negative images—cyan, magenta, and yellow. The two mask images are red and yellow positive images located in the red and green recording emulsion layers.

Product	Type	Image Formation
Kodachrome	Reversal Transparency	Dye Coupling—Differential re-exposure
Ansco Color Positive	Reversal Transparency	Dye Coupling—Incorporated couplers
Ektachrome	Reversal Transparency	Dye Coupling—Protected incorporated couplers
Agfa Color	Reversal Transparency	Dye Coupling—Incorporated couplers
Ilford Color	Reversal Transparency	Dye Coupling—Differential re-exposure
Ferrania Color	Reversal Transparency	Dye Coupling—Incorporated couplers
Gevacolor	Reversal Transparency	Dye Coupling—Incorporated couplers
Kodachrome Print	Reversal Print	Dye Coupling—Differential re-exposure
Printon	Reversal Print	Dye Coupling—Incorporated couplers
Gasparcolor	Reversal Print	Dye Destruction
Kodacolor	Color Negative	Dye Coupling—Protected incorporated couplers —colored coupler masks
Ansco Color Negative	Color Negative	Dye Coupling—Incorporated couplers
Ektacolor	Color Negative	Dye Coupling—Protected incorporated couplers —colored coupler masks
Agfa Color Negative	Color Negative	Dye Coupling—Incorporated couplers
Ektacolor Print Film	Color Transparency from Color Negative	Dye Coupling—Protected incorporated couplers

Ektacolor. Kodak Ektacolor Film, introduced in 1949, is a typical sheet film integral tripack in that the order and sensitizing of the emulsion coatings is that generally employed. The emulsion next to the base is red sensitive and contains a protected coupler which forms the cyan dye. The green sensitive emulsion yields the magenta and the top blue-recording emulsion the yellow dye image. A single color development forms these three negative dye images simultaneously. The developed film is also bleached and fixed to remove silver and halides. Processing may be carried out by the photographer in less than 45 minutes in Ektacolor processing chemicals. The color developer is non-allergenic.

Ektacolor Film was the first material announced that contained colored couplers or color formers. In Ektachrome a *colorless* protected coupler is used that gives a cyan dye image when color developed. In Ektacolor, the usual cyan-forming colorless coupler is replaced with a red *colored* coupler. When color developed this protected coupler forms a cyan dye image.

Whatever unused colored coupler remains in the emulsion is a red dye image, its strength being dependent on the amount of cyan dye formed—the more cyan dye formed the less red remaining. In a color negative the cyan dye is a negative image. The residual colored coupler will therefore be a red positive image. The same effect may be obtained by using a colorless coupler to form the cyan negative and a red colored coupler that forms a colorless image on development. In either case, the red-recording emulsion layer of the film contains two dye images after color development, a cyan negative image and a red positive image. The red positive acts as a mask when the color negative is printed (Chapter 33).

The green-recording emulsion of Ektacolor Film contains a yellow colored coupler. After color development this emulsion layer contains a negative magenta dye image and a positive yellow dye image. The blue-recording emulsion contains the usual colorless coupler used in forming the negative yellow dye image. The processed Ektacolor negative thus contains three negative and two positive dye images. The positive dye images act as masks when the Ektacolor negative is printed, allowing a complete color separation of the three negative images to be obtained. A processed Ektacolor negative may be printed directly onto Ektacolor Print Film to obtain a positive transparency or onto three sheets of Kodak Pan Matrix Film for imbibition dye printing. It may also be used in the preparation of photomechanical plates or positives for other types of color printing. The color fidelity obtainable from such a negative material is quite high and the photographic tone gradation is generally superior to that obtained when printing from reversal color transparencies.

Ektacolor Print Film. This film, introduced by Eastman Kodak in 1950, is designed for making transparency positives from Ektacolor negatives. The emulsion order is normal for multilayer films, the red sensitive emulsion being next to the film base. The emulsions contain colorless protected couplers which yield cyan, magenta, and yellow dye images after color development. The same four processing solutions are used as for Ektacolor negative film.

Ektacolor Print Film has somewhat sharper sensitivity bands than is usual in multilayer films designed for camera exposure. The exposure may be made by white light or by separate red, green and blue exposures. The exposure latitude is quite small and the image contrast high. Ektacolor Print Film is especially valuable whenever it is necessary to obtain a number of identical transparencies of the same subject. When printing from Ektacolor negatives high color fidelity is assured because of the two colored masks in the negative material (see Chapter 33).

Ansco Color Negative Film (Plenacolor). This roll film material is returned to the manufacturer for processing to a color negative and printing on an integral tripack paper. The film structure is normal, the lowest emulsion containing a colorless coupler which forms the cyan negative dye image upon color development. The middle emulsion contains a colorless magenta coupler and the top emulsion a colorless yellow color former. A colloidal silver yellow filter layer under the top blue-recording emulsion prevents blue light from affecting the lower emulsions.

When first introduced masks were formed in the center and bottom emulsions after color development. This was accomplished by converting the silver formed during color development back to silver bromide and re-exposing through the back of the film using colored light. The effectiveness of this exposure was controlled by the absorptions of the already formed cyan and magenta dye negative images. Positive silver masks were then developed in these layers. After the removal of the residual silver halides, washing and drying, the color negative was printed on a multilayer paper, processed by dye coupling development. Plenacolor film does not now contain silver masks.

Dupont Color Release Positive Film. This is a multi-layer film intended for obtaining a color positive from three color separation negatives. The light sensitive silver halides in the three layers of the film are suspended in three synthetic polymers which act as color formers as well as carriers of the light-sensitive halides. The dyes are thus formed during color development from the synthetic polymers.[14]

Since this film is a color positive material to be used in printing from three separation negatives, the color sensitivity of the dye-forming layers does not have to correspond to the usual system of red-recording layer giving the cyan image, green-

[14] Jennings, Stanton, and Weiss, *J. Soc. Mot. Pict. Eng.* **55**, 455 (1950).

recording layer giving the magenta image and blue-recording layer giving the yellow image. In this film the blue-recording layer is on top and contains the magenta color-forming chemicals. The middle layer is red sensitive and contains the polymer necessary to form the cyan dye image. The bottom layer contains the polymer that will form the yellow dye image on development and this layer is green sensitive. The processed film thus contains the magenta dye positive in the top layer, the yellow dye image in the bottom layer.

Printing is done by using colored light to expose each layer to the proper separation negative. Red light is used in expos-

ing the red record negative, blue light in exposing the green record negative, and green light when exposing the blue record negative. Processing time is about forty-five minutes and requires color development, bleaching, and fixation with the usual washes and rinses.

At the present time this film is available only for 35 mm. motion picture color printing.

Film Layer	Sensi- tivity	Separation Record	Exposed By	Dye Formed
Top	Blue	Green	Blue light	Magenta
Center	Red	Red	Red light	Cyan
Bottom	Green	Blue	Green light	Yellow

Chapter 33

ACCURACY OF COLOR REPRODUCTION

Introduction. It would seem evident that a color photograph should reproduce as accurately as possible all the colors of the original subject. In order to reach maximum usefulness, such accuracy is particularly essential in the color reproduction of scientific subjects, such as, for example, a clinical specimen. In the general field of photography, however, facsimile reproduction is not necessarily desirable. The artistic requirements of a given subject may make it advisable to distort the colors in the reproduction purposely. Such factors as color contrast and eye fatigue, the surroundings, and the nature of the viewing conditions may seriously affect the visual impression received by an observer. It is common knowledge, for example, that the eye soon accustoms itself to illuminants of such varying color distribution as outdoor sunlight and indoor incandescent lamps, so that after a short period of adaptation, the colors of objects seen under either of these illuminants appear perfectly normal.

Since practical color processes achieve their reproduction by means of a three-color analysis, the following discussion is concerned with the accuracy with which colors can be reproduced by existing processes. A color process capable of accurate reproduction is essential, at least theoretically, before intentional color alterations can be introduced. In general, the color processes available today, particularly the separable color print processes, have not been utilized to their fullest capabilities from the standpoint of color accuracy, the majority of unsatisfactory reproductions being due to faulty manipulation or temporary product difficulties rather than to any limitations imposed by the process itself.

The improvement in the quality of color reproduction during the last thirty years has been chiefly due to improved techniques and the introduction of superior materials for carrying out the necessary operations. The basic methods of analysis and synthesis have seen very few innovations since 1900. There was a lack of accuracy of reproduction in the early processes, largely attributable to the inadequacy of available materials. As the quality of color reproduction has been raised, the foundations of three-color photography are being re-examined in an effort to improve present results and to indicate further lines of attack on the problem of obtaining accurate color reproduction.

Colorimetry. Any investigation into the accuracy of color reproduction must of necessity make use of some standard to which the results may be referred. The methods involved in the measurement and specification of color constitute the science of colorimetry.[1] The fundamental basis of colorimetry is that natural colors may be matched visually by certain mixtures of three properly chosen primary colors. The primary colors chosen may be either narrow—essentially monochromatic—re-

---

[1] For an excellent discussion of Colorimetry and Spectrophotometry, subjects of growing importance in color photography, the reader is referred to Hardy, *Handbook of Colorimetry*, Technology Press, Cambridge, 1936.

gions of the spectrum, or rather wide transmission areas; in either case, some combination can be found to match the unknown color. The amounts of three specific primary colors necessary to match an unknown color are called its *tristimulus values*. The tristimulus values for a typical tricolor red filter, for example, are $X = 635$, $Y = 315$, $Z = 0$. A set of tristimulus values may readily be converted mathematically into trichromatic coefficients, or coordinates, which are useful in showing graphically the characteristics of all colors. Two of the trichromatic coordinates serve to determine the location of any color on a chromaticity diagram. These two coordinates, along with one of the tristimulus values, serve to specify the three attributes of any one color in relation to all other colors. In the chromaticity diagram of Fig. 33-1, the trichromatic coordinates of a set of tricolor separation filters have been plotted as examples. The curved solid line represents the locus of

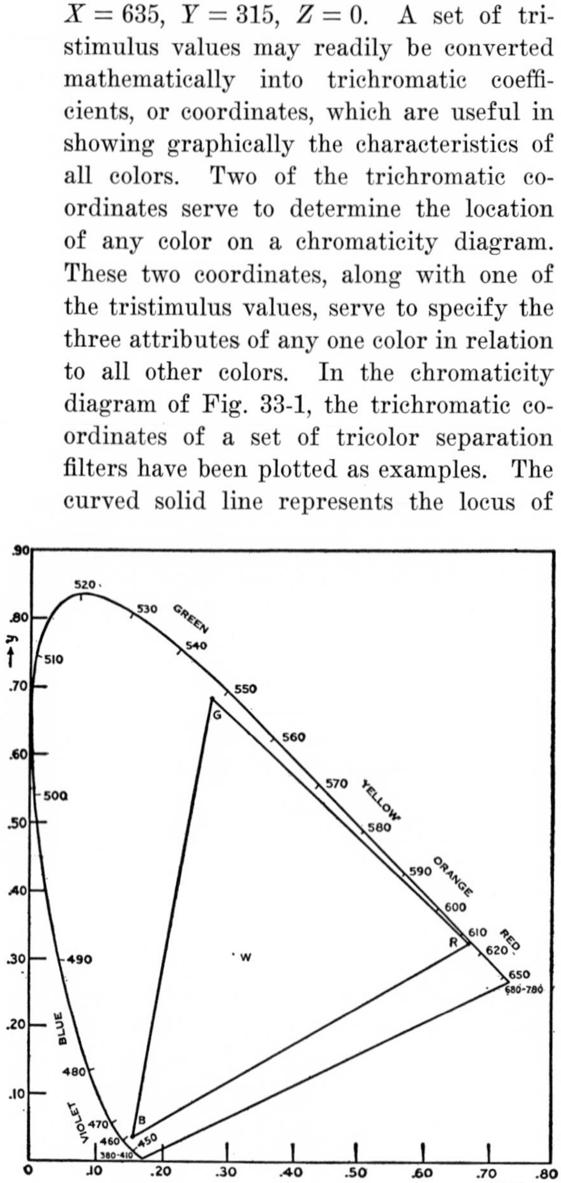

the spectrum colors and W is the location of the white point on the diagram. As the position in the chromaticity diagram of any color moves from the vicinity of the spectrum locus toward the white point, the color tends to become less saturated. Complementary colors are on opposite sides of the white point. Trichromatic coordinates may be obtained by calculation from the results of color matches made in a colorimeter or by calculation from spectrophotometric curves.[2]

Additive and Subtractive Reproduction. It is perhaps unfortunate that additive and subtractive color processes have been treated as two separate methods for the reproduction of color. Optically, these two ways of synthesizing a color analysis are identical. There is no difference between the visual appearance on the screen of a black-and-white positive projected through the red filter of a projection lantern and a cyan positive projected through the same red filter. In both cases the screen is black, red or some value of red, depending on the opacity to red light of the two positives. An additive synthesis is performed by projecting simultaneously the three appropriate black-and-white transparencies through red, green and blue filters with three projectors. The subtractive synthesis can be performed by the projection of cyan, magenta and yellow positives in one projector at the same time, by means of red, green, and blue lights which together form white. If the positives were made from the same analysis set of separation negatives and the subtractive colorants, cyan, magenta, and yellow, were ideal, the results of these two syntheses

Fɪɢ. 33.1.

[2] Southall, *Introduction to Physiological Optics*, Oxford, 1937. MacAdam, *J. Soc. Mot. Pict. Eng.* **31**, 343 (1938). Murray and Spencer, *Colour in Theory and Practice*, Vol. I, 1940. Wright, *Phot. J.* **80**, 25 (1940). Evans, *An Introduction to Color*, John Wiley and Sons, Inc., 1948.

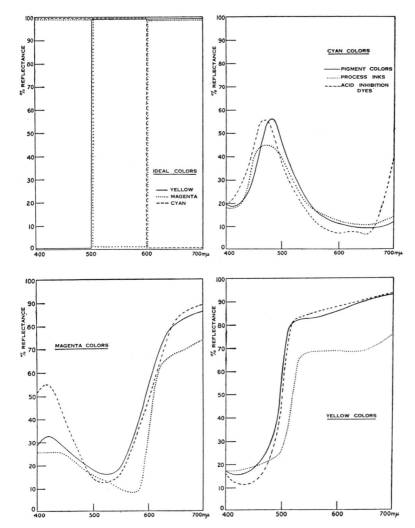

Fig. 33.2. Ideal and real reflectance values for subtractive printing colors.

(using identical projection primaries) would be the same.

If the three filters shown in Fig. 33.1 were used for an additive synthesis, the colors that could be reproduced would be those lying within the triangle formed by the filters when plotted on a chromaticity diagram. Although this triangle does not include all colors, the range is sufficiently great to include the colors of almost every naturally occurring object.

Subtractive Color Correction. By far the largest quantity of color reproductions are obtained by means of subtractive color synthesis and this method must be employed to obtain a color reproduction to be viewed by reflected light. It is natural, therefore, that the greatest efforts have been expended in trying to overcome, or minimize, the color errors found in subtractive reproductions. All the early investigations were empirical in that attempts at correction of the observed deficiencies were made chiefly by trial and error. Since the greatest commercial interest was in color printing by means of inks (letterpress, lithography, and gravure), it was natural that the first corrective measures were developed for application in mechanical color printing processes rather than in purely photographic methods of color reproduction.

Need for Correction. The necessity for correcting the colors of a reproduction arises from the fact that the three printing colorants, cyan, magenta, and yellow, do not reflect and absorb light in the manner required to make them optically equivalent to the additive red, green, and blue colors. For example, the cyan image, when printed onto paper, should produce the same effect visually in red light as would a black-and-white slide projected by red light onto a screen, and the cyan image should disappear completely when viewed with green or blue light. The only purpose of the image in each case is to act as a control valve for the red reflectances. The cyan image should absorb red light completely and reflect or transmit the remainder of the spectrum for accurate reproduction and the maximum color gamut. An examination of the reflectance curve of the "ideal" cyan shows a complete absorption of red and complete reflectance of blue and green. Practical cyan colorants, however (Fig. 33.2), depart from the ideal in that they do not absorb red completely, and, of more importance, they do absorb a very large portion of the blue and green they are supposed to reflect. The "ideal" magenta colorant should be a perfect absorber of green and should reflect the remainder of the spectrum, namely, red and blue. Obtainable magentas do not absorb green completely and are far from satisfactory reflectors of blue. Most yellow colorants, on the other hand, are satisfactory for

practical purposes. The inefficient red absorption of the cyan and the inefficient green absorption of the magenta are secondary defects and may be ignored in a first approximation, but the poor green and blue reflectances of the cyan and the poor blue reflectance of the magenta are sufficient to cause noticeable reproduction errors. It is evident from the character of these typical printing inks why printers have used the terms blue, red, and yellow in naming their printing colors. In fulfilling the necessary press and light fastness requirements, the available inks do not approach the desired cyan and magenta hues.

Effect of Normal Printing Colors. The result of using the printing inks available leads to a darkening of the "cold" colors and a desaturation of the "warm" colors. In Fig. 33.3, where five colors and their reproductions have been plotted on a chro-

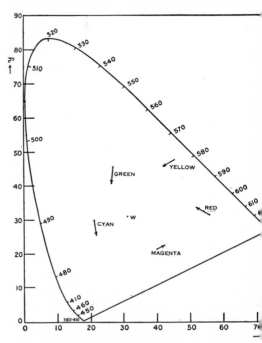

FIG. 33.3. Five colors (dots) and their reproductions, (arrow heads) plotted on a chromaticity diagram.

maticity diagram, the color shifts may be readily observed. Examination of the defective blue reflection of a typical cyan shows that when this ink is printed to deposit red densities on the paper support (absorption of red light), it also deposits a certain percentage of blue density (absorption of blue light). The same situation exists with the magenta where the printing of green densities involves, because of the deficient spectral reflection, the printing of blue densities. Since it is the yellow ink that is *supposed* to print all the blue densities in the reproduction, the amount of yellow required to produce a neutral gray scale (composed of equal parts of red, green and blue densities) is considerably decreased. The quantity of yellow printing in all areas of the picture is of course dependent on the amount of yellow required by the gray scale. This situation leads, therefore, to lesser deposits of yellow ink than are required for accurate reproduction of all yellow and colors containing yellow in the chromatic [3] areas of the picture—a desaturation or dilution with white. The same situation with the magenta is brought about by the undesirable green densities deposited by the cyan ink. All colors containing magenta and yellow are therefore less saturated than desired. On the other hand, the poor reflection of the blue region of the spectrum by both the cyan and magenta and the poor reflection of the green by the cyan ink lead to a rather limited brightness for blues, greens and their mixtures in a color print.

Corrective Measures. The deficiencies noted cannot be corrected by the simple expedient of changing the contrast of one or more of the printing colors since any slight improvement brought about for some particular color would be offset by a fur-

ther loss of color accuracy in some other colors. An empirical approach to correction may be made in two directions. In the first place, a study of the spectrophotometric curves of the printing inks indicates that improved color reproduction will be obtained by a decrease in the amounts of yellow and magenta in all areas of the print where cyan is required. In this manner, the unwanted extra blue and green densities deposited by the cyan ink are partially corrected. The second method of approach to the problem is to consider the reproduction of a picture made from the three printing inks. If a correct reproduction of such a picture can be made, i.e., if each of the three printers deposits the same amount of ink as was present in the original reproduction, it is reasonable to suppose that other reproductions made under the same conditions of other types of original would be fairly accurate.

The employment of corrective measures will lead to a very considerable improvement in the accuracy of color reproduction. In photomechanical processes, the corrective measures may be applied by hand. After the metal plates have been proofed, the magenta and yellow images are locally etched to decrease the amounts of magenta and yellow inks printing in areas where cyan is deposited in the picture. Successive proofs and local etchings are carried out until the desired correction is obtained. Since the extent of the corrections necessary is *not* dependent on the subject matter but only on the characteristics of the printing colors employed, the correction for any given density of a particular color will always be the same. It is therefore possible to employ photographic means to obtain the desired corrections. Photographic color correction, or *masking*, involves the alteration of the density distribution of a given negative, or positive, by binding in contact with it another positive, or nega-

---

[3] Chromatic colors are those distinguished by *hue* (red, yelow, blue, etc.). Achromatic colors are those without *hue* (grays, white, black).

tive. A mask of this type may be used to alter the contrast only, or the contrast and the color separation values. Photographic color correction as normally carried out will not lead to perfect color reproduction because only the larger defects can be satisfactorily corrected. To be commercially feasible, the number of corrective operations must be kept to a minimum. However, since the color errors it is desirable to correct are not of equal magnitude, simple masking will not lead to facsimile reproduction but it will give considerably improved results.

A system of photographic color correction described by Murray is typical of the procedure followed.[4] A normal red-separation negative is exposed and developed. The green and blue separations are made having density ranges 1.6 and 1.4 times that of the red negative. From the red-record negative, two positives are made having density ranges 40% of the green record and 30% of the blue record.[5] These positives are bound with the green and blue separations to form the color-corrected negatives. The positive masks on the green and blue record negatives prevent some magenta and yellow from printing in those regions where cyan is present, thus decreasing the degradation of cyans, blues and greens. At the same time, the increased contrast of the magenta and yellow images (neutralized by their masks for all neutral or achromatic tones) leads to a higher

saturation (increased printing strength) of all reds, yellows and magentas.[6]

Black-Printers. The superimposition of three normal process inks leads to very poor reproduction of detail in the dark neutral areas of the picture. The maximum neutral density obtainable is about 1.3. Wherever higher densities are required, the tendency is for the neutral tones to become colored, generally reddish. For this reason, printers have been led to use four-color processes for quality reproduction, making use of the three standard subtractive colors and a fourth, black, impression. There are two uses to which the black-printer can be put. In the first case, it can be used to print only on the dark neutral areas of the print, so supplying the necessary additional deposits to make possible achromatic detail in densities greater than about 1.3. In the second place, the black-printer can be used to supply *all* the neutral tones of the picture, whatever their density, as well as the gray component for all chromatic areas requiring it.

The first suggestion for a black-printer seems to have come in 1897 from Albert,[7] who suggested the removal of the achromatic components from each color impression in the final print so that the three color printings supplied only the chromatic portions of the picture. A fourth printing supplied all the black to the reproduction. A black-printer of this type, supplying all the achromatic portions of the picture, greatly improves the photograph because of the absence of any difficulty in properly balancing the three chromatic colors at all densities which in ordinary practice is somewhat difficult to accomplish. This use

---

[4] *The Modern Masking Method for Correct Color Reproduction*, Eastman Kodak Co., Rochester, N. Y.

[5] Since this procedure was proposed in 1937, it has been shown that somewhat superior results could be obtained by preparing the mask for the blue separation negative from the green rather than the red separation negative. An alternate procedure is to obtain the mask for the blue separation negative from a special negative exposed from the subject with a yelow filter.

[6] An excellent review of photographic masking methods, mostly for use with printing inks, was given by Tritton, *Phot. J.* **78**, 732 (1938). See also F. Preucil, *Nat. Lithographer* **56**, June–July 1949.

[7] D.R.P. 101, 379.

for a black-printer is sometimes helpful in three-color photographic printing as well as for printing inks. The second type of black-printer involves the printing in of achromatic areas of densities greater than can be satisfactorily reproduced by the three printing colors alone. The negative for such a printer is generally exposed to the copy through a yellow filter on panchromatic material. If a print of normal density is made from this negative, the black will degrade all the color areas of the picture. To avoid this difficulty, the black-printer positive is only lightly exposed, thus limiting its deposits to the shadows. Considerable hand corrective work is generally necessary even with such an expedient. Murray suggested an improvement (for certain specified types of copy) by recommending an infrared separation negative for making the black-printer.[8] The applicability of the infrared method is dependent on the fact that most coloring materials reflect infrared strongly while many achromatic materials absorb infrared radiation. Thus, a black printer made from an infrared record will not deposit black on any but achromatic areas. Yule [9] has shown that the densities of the black-printer should be related to the lowest equivalent density of the three color components when suitably color corrected and, for the most accurate reproduction, a mask from such a black-printer should further correct each of the color corrected separation negatives.[10] Black-printers are rarely used in strictly photographic reproduction methods since the combined dyes, or pigments, yield satisfactory neutral images of adequate density—the improvement in color accuracy does not generally justify the extra operations.

Other Photographic Color Correction Methods. The amount of color correction required for most photographic color printing methods is not so great as that needed for printing inks because of the somewhat superior spectral absorptions of the colorants used. As shown in Fig. 33.2, the deficiencies of the various magentas, for example, vary somewhat, and for the fullest color correction the extent of the masking required should be determined for the process employed.[11]

It is possible to increase the color saturation of certain areas of the picture by the use of weak positives obtained from negatives made with "minus color" filters (cyan, magenta, and yellow) as masks in contact with the normal separation negatives. In this manner, the areas printed by any given color are restricted by the mask. This method is not so widely used as some of the other masking procedures discussed.

In general, it may be stated that some correction is desirable in almost every case. The extent to which masking should be carried is dependent on the presence of colors that would be poorly reproduced without corrective measures, and the necessity for high color accuracy. It is better to undercorrect than to carry the masking to extremes, both from the standpoint of color accuracy and the "photographic quality" of the reproduction. The physical combination of negatives and positives of fairly high contrast leads to difficulties with image spread at the outlines of objects and a general destruction of the proper gradation. Optical means for carrying out the masking operations have been suggested [12] to overcome these difficulties, but they are expensive and hard to operate.

---

[8] Murray, *Nat. Lithographer* **41**, 19 (1934); *Photo-Engravers Bull.* **23**, 13 (1934); **24**, 208 (1935).

[9] Yule, *J. Opt. Soc. Am.* **30**, 322 (1940).

[10] Yule, *Brit. J. Phot.* **87**, 99, 112 (1940).

[11] *Photo-Technique* **1**, No. 3, 19 (1939).

[12] *Klimsch's Jahrbuch* **29**, 67 (1936).

Corrections may also be made electrically [13] or by means of special photographic emulsions or copy coloring materials,[14] which automatically give the desired masking effect.

It is also possible to employ colored images as masks. The density of the colored image to the light-emulsion combination employed determines the extent of the correction obtainable with a given mask. A method suggested by Eastman Kodak Company [15] for use with the Wash-Off Relief process involves the making of a relief film from the red-separation negative and dyeing it to the proper contrast in the cyan dye. This relief film is combined with the green-separation negative or its projected image, and the combination is used in exposing the relief film to be dyed magenta. The density of the cyan dye to blue light gives considerable color correction for the magenta image. After dyeing this image magenta, the combination of blue-separation negative and cyan and magenta dyed positive relief images is used in exposing the relief film to be dyed yellow. This method does not give full color correction and is rather difficult to use except for contact printing, but because of its low cost (no extra material necessary for use as masks) and worth-while correction, it has found considerable use. A similar use

for colored masks has been adapted for photomechanical reproduction.[16] A red light exposure is color developed to yield a magenta negative image. This mask is used during the exposure of the green and blue separation negatives, its density to green and blue light giving the desired masking effect.

The theoretical color corrections required for a set of acid imbibition dyes has been calculated and various simplified approximations proposed that cover the larger errors of reproduction.[17] For example, it has been shown that the red-filter negative should be masked by a positive from the green-filter negative; the green-filter negative should be masked by a positive from the red-filter negative; the blue-filter negative should be masked by a positive from the green filter negative. Various two-mask methods have been calculated since the most important masks are the red-filter masking positive on the green-record negative and the green-filter masking positive on the blue-filter negative. Selman [18] has published details of three distinct procedures for obtaining satisfactory correction for Wash-Off Relief dyes, two using the silver relief images as masks and a third using standard positive images.

Accuracy of Color Transparencies. Color transparencies of the screen or integral tripack types are used for direct printing, projection, or as a means for obtaining three color-separation negatives for subtractive color printing. The accuracy of reproduction of screen materials was discussed in Chapter 31 and this section will deal more specifically with subtractive integral tripacks.

---

[13] *Brit. J. Phot.* **86**, 259 (1939); **87**, 112 (1940). *Modern Lithography* **18**, 28, 105 (1950).

[14] Automatic color correction may be obtained optically by exposing the color-separation negatives through, or subduing the copy by means of, negative masks. If copy is being colored for subsequent photographic separation, special paints, such as the Kodak Fluorescent Water Colors that fluoresce under ultraviolet illumination, may be employed. After the color-separations have been exposed in the normal manner, supplementary exposures by means of ultraviolet light fluorescence add density in certain areas of the negatives requiring color correction.

[15] *Color Printing with Eastman Wash-Off Relief Film*, Eastman Kodak Company, Rochester, N. Y.

[16] *Bulletin for the Graphic Arts*, No. 10, Eastman Kodak Co. (1947).

[17] MacAdam, *J. Opt. Soc. Amer.* **28**, 466 (1938). Marriage, *Phot. J.* **80**, 364 (1940); **88B**, 75 (1948). Brewer, Hanson, and Horton, *J. Opt. Soc. Amer.* **39**, 924 (1949).

[18] Selman, *Phot. J.* **80**, 375 (1940).

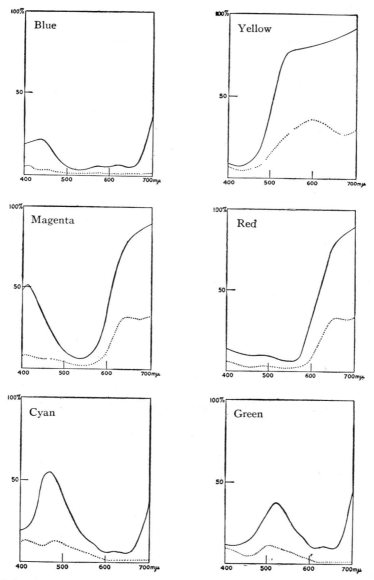

FIG. 33.4. Original (solid lines) and positive color transparency reproduction (dotted lines). Spectrophotometric curves of six bright colors.

A color transparency considered by itself, thereby disregarding errors due to improper exposure and processing, may not be an accurate reproduction of the original scene because (1) the limited latitude of the reversal process involves inac-curate reproduction of all but a fairly short range of subject luminosities, and (2) the spectral absorptions of the dyes composing the three positive color images are not ideal. The extreme brilliance of the average color transparency leads to its visual acceptance as an accurate reproduction of the original scene. Colorimetric measurements, however, show very definite inaccuracies in the transparency. In Fig. 33.4, for example, the spectrophotometric curves of the original colors and their reproduction in a transparency are considerably different, yet the eye will accept such a transparency as a good match.[19] The acceptance of such color errors is not of importance until it is necessary to make a color reproduction from the transparency.

Roles of the Color Transparency. Printing from positive color transparencies involves the preparation of a set of three separation negatives, to be printed in the usual manner. It is also possible to print by contact or projection onto reversal materials of the dye bleach, dye destruction or dye coupling types. The positive color transparency may be considered either as an original color picture to be photographed, or as a set of physically inseparable colored separation positives. One desired goal is the accurate reproduction of the positive color transparency. Such a result requires similar colorants in similar amounts at each point of the reproduction as was present in the color transparency. A second method seeks to obtain a reproduction of the original scene from which the transparency was made.

---

[19] These curves, incidentally, show the vital importance of proper exposure for the color it is necessary to reproduce accurately. All six colors received equal illumination, but for the best reproduction of the violet and green a greater exposure would be advisable. Such an increase would have decreased the accuracy of reproduction of the lighter red, yellow, and magenta color patches. The colors shown are special cases and should not be interpreted as a general case. Most, less saturated, colors would be reproduced considerably better. The differences between original and reproduction would not be quite so marked if plotted on a chromaticity diagram.

Hunt, *Phot. J.* **91B**, 107 (1951).

Inaccuracies of a Color Print. If a set of color separation negatives is made from a color transparency, as discussed in Chapter 29, and printed by any of the subtractive printing processes, the color reproduction usually proves to be somewhat disappointing because of one or more of the following factors:

1. The differences in the reproduction of the transparency as a print.
2. The unsatisfactory spectral absorptions of the printing colors employed.
3. The transparency is not the same as the original subject (colorimetric view of equality).

The inherent limitations of a paper print as compared with a transparency, whether in black and white or in color, cannot be too strongly emphasized. Because of the limited brightness range which a print viewed by reflected light is able to reproduce satisfactorily, the gradation of a considerable portion of all but very short scale subjects is incorrectly recorded. For example, by means of color correction, it is possible to reproduce the original color transparency quite accurately as a set of dyed imbibition matrices to be examined by transmitted light. If these same matrices are lowered in contrast to make them suitable for viewing by reflected light, the reproduction will not appear to be as satisfactory. It is important to note that approximate color accuracy is in the matrix images but simply cannot be seen by reflected light.

The previous discussion of the inefficient spectral absorptions of printing colors applies to the reproduction of color transparencies, and to obtain color accuracy, some of the masking correctives must be employed. The color correction should be as complete as possible because other errors, which cannot be eliminated, will cause some color degradation.

FIG. 33-5. Viewing illustration with Wratten No. 29, 61 and 49 filters shows necessity of masking in order to adequately separate the color records of the processed transparency.

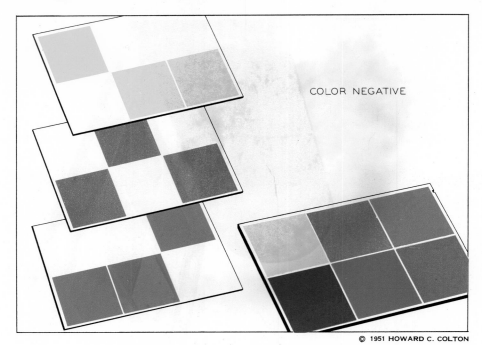

FIG. 33-9. Color plate of regular color negative.

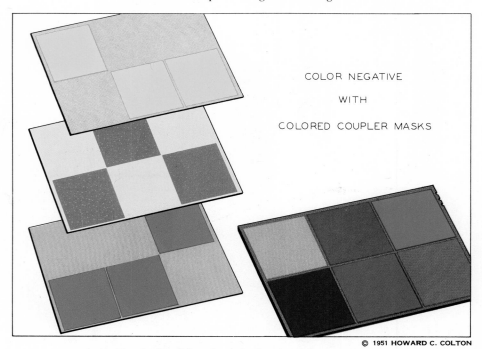

FIG. 33-10. Color plate of colored coupler negative.

Comparison viewing through analysis tricolor filters shows elimination of undesirable dye images by use of colored couplers in a color negative.

The third difficulty is dependent on the memory of the observer for the original scene as compared with the color print. The color transparency is not an accurate reproduction of the original scene, since it suffers from all the defects of inefficient spectral absorptions of the dyes composing the three positive images in the transparency. A reproduction of the transparency in the form of a paper print has had removed the psychological acceptance of the colors due to the extreme brightness range of the transparency, and, therefore, the color errors are more apparent. It is not surprising, therefore, if a straight reproduction from a color transparency bears little resemblance to the original copy. It is in reality an inaccurate reproduction (print) of an inaccurate reproduction (integral tripack) printed within the limitations imposed by the brightness range of a paper print. Masking, as usually employed, will minimize but not eliminate the color errors of the processes involved.

Recording Integral Color Records. An improvement can be made by attempting to record the color analysis performed by the tripack film itself. If the layers of the film are properly sensitized so that each layer records one of the color-separations, it would be desirable to take the separations apart physically. If this could be done with a knife, for example, three separation negatives or positives equivalent to those that might have been exposed in the normal manner by successive exposures in a view camera would be obtained. Three such color records would eliminate the difficulties that would be encountered in trying to reproduce the color transparency by photographic means. Since such a procedure is physically impractical, it is attempted optically. The green separation record of the original subject, for example, exists in a positive color transparency as the positive magenta dye image. If this image could be recorded on a single separation negative without including either of the other two dyes of the transparency, a separation negative would be available equivalent in all important respects to one made directly from the original subject. The proper procedure to record the green record (magenta dye image) from the transparency would be to photograph the film by means of green light to which the magenta dye appears opaque. This is illustrated in Fig. 33.5 which shows a single frame of a color transparency on which is recorded a color chart containing patches of red, green, blue, cyan, magenta, and yellow colorants. In the left-hand frame is shown the composition of the three dye layers which together make the complete transparency. Photographing the color transparency with green light, however, records not only the magenta dye image but also the cyan dye image, which is not wanted. This can readily be observed by examining Fig. 33.5 through a green tricolor filter (Wratten No. 61). Not only is the central magenta image visible, but the lower cyan image appears almost half as dense. This cyan dye is a record of the red light present in the original subject and therefore should not appear in the green separation negative. In a similar manner, when it is desired to make a blue-separation from the transparency, the separation-negative made through the blue filter records not only the upper yellow dye image but also the lower cyan and magenta images. A satisfactory red record may be obtained by photographing the transparency with a red filter. These undesirable contaminations of the green and blue separation negatives are due to the unwanted absorption of blue light by the magenta and cyan dyes and the unwanted absorption of green light by the cyan dye. These are illustrated in Fig. 33.6. The problem of obtaining a satisfactory set of color separations, or making a duplicate transparency from an integral tripack resolves itself into the problem of attempting to record each of the dye images separately without interference from the other two.

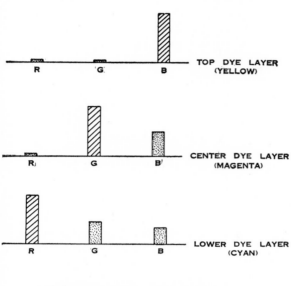

FIG. 33.6. Proper and undesirable light absorptions by typical integral tri-pack dye images.

Negative Color Masks. The recording of undesirable *positive* transparency images can be prevented by neutralizing the offending images with *negatives* of like color and contrast.[20] A red filter negative exposed in contact with a transparency will, for example, record the cyan dye layer. If this black-and-white negative is converted by toning into a negative cyan

---

[20] Strictly speaking, there are, of course, improper densities recorded on the negatives to be used as masks and the corrective measures necessary for the two undesirable dye layers in any given case will not be identical. These errors are of a second order in importance and may be ignored in practice.

image with a contrast equal to that of the tripack positive cyan image, the effect of the latter may be neutralized. When the tripack and the cyan negative (mask) are bound together, both green and blue separation negatives can be made without the cyan image of the tripack being recorded on the separation negatives. This can readily be seen by observing the effect of placing a cyan negative beside the cyan positive in the bottom layer of the tripack film (Fig. 33.5). Under these circumstances the entire bottom layer would be cyan so that no cyan positive image could be photographed. In a similar manner, a magenta negative mask can be prepared that will neutralize the magenta image of the tripack. If both cyan and magenta negative masks are attached to the transparency, the blue separation negative obtainable from the combination will be approximately equivalent to a color separation negative exposed to the original copy through the blue filter. If such procedures were practical it would be possible to obtain the same result as by stripping the layers apart and photographing them separately. Such procedures have not been commercially feasible. Similar results have been obtained by the use of negative silver masks rather than dye masks, even though they do not have the advantage of being able to use several masks simultaneously when making a single exposure.

Silver Negative Masks. A somewhat more practical procedure leading to similar corrected separation negatives makes use of negative silver images as masks on the color transparency. A contact negative made from the transparency using a magenta filter, for example, records the cyan and yellow images (the red and blue-separation records) of the tripack. If such a negative mask of the correct contrast is bound in register with the color transparency while the green separation negative is being exposed, only the magenta dye layer will be recorded for the green color separation negative. In a similar manner, negative masks exposed through cyan and yellow filters may be used in the preparation of corrected red and blue separation negatives.

The contrast of negative silver masks cannot be as high as the dye masks considered in the previous section since a neutral negative mask with a contrast as high as the transparency would cancel the achromatic components of the picture. Negative silver masks are, therefore, prepared with density ranges from 25 to 40% of the range of the transparency from which they were made.

The use of negative silver masks of any type over a color transparency has the additional advantage that the density range of the transparency is reduced before the color separation negatives are prepared. Such a masked transparency with its reduced density range can readily be recorded on the straight-line portion of the characteristic curves of suitable color-separation negative emulsions. Photographic tone reproduction is thus maintained and losses of quality due to halation are minimized.

Single Negative Masks. With any correcting masks applied to a color transparency, some loss of photographic quality may be expected due to misregister and slight errors in tone reproduction. To maintain the photographic quality of the original as well as to simplify the procedures involved, general photographic practice at present is to limit the number of color correcting masks to one or two.

The simplest procedure, leading to worthwhile color correction, makes use of a single negative silver mask bound in register with the transparency while each of the color separation negatives is being exposed. Since the cyan dye image is the worst of-

fender in obtaining a set of satisfactory color-separation negatives without masking, a red filter is generally used in exposing the mask. The exact color of the filter used in the preparation of this mask is dependent on the particular dyes in the transparency material and various processing and product characteristics. These may change, and it is advisable to obtain the latest recommendations from the manufacturer of the transparency material.[21]

The negative silver mask is exposed onto any panchromatic material and processed to a gamma of approximately 0.3 in a developer producing an image which is as nearly neutral as obtainable. The exposure should be adjusted so that the shadow portions of the color transparency are recorded on the toe portion of the mask's characteristic curve. Silver masks on film are generally diffused slightly during exposure so that no difficulty will be encountered with register when binding the mask and transparency together.[22]

Two Negative Masks. The use of a single mask over a color transparency allows correction of brightness and saturation errors but will not correct for hue shifts in the reproduction. To obtain both corrections, it is necessary to use two masks obtained from the transparency by exposures with different color filters. Two masks may therefore be obtained by printing from the color transparency using red light for the first mask and green or yellow light for the second. The particular color filters used during exposure should be chosen from the manufacturer's instructions for the type of integral tripack film being printed.

The first (red light exposure) mask is registered with the color transparency dur-

---

[21] Color Separation and Masking—Kodak Color Data Book (1951). Masking Color Transparencies—Kodak Graphic Arts Data Book (1951).

[22] Yule, *Phot. J.* **84**, 321 (1944).

(a)

(b)

FIG. 33.7. Photo of original (a) and highlight mask (b).

ing the exposure of the red and green separations. This mask is then removed and replaced by the second mask (green or yellow light exposure) for the exposure of the blue color separation negative.

Tone Correction Masks. Like other photographic materials, color transparencies show the same form of reproduction curve with the usual toe, straight line, and shoulder regions. Areas of the subject recorded on the toe portion of the transparency will be reproduced at lower contrast than darker parts of the original subject. This leads to a softer reproduction and less "sparkle" than would be obtained with perfect tone reproduction when technically correct (all of the transparency recorded on the straight-line portion of the $D \log E$ curve of the separation negative) separation negatives are made from such a transparency. This contrast reduction in the highlight portions of the subject is carried over to the printing stage of the reproduction process. Since printing processes also generally have a softer reproduction in their highlight areas, the over-all loss of contrast in the lower densities may become objectionable. A typical example of such a subject would be a color transparency made of a bride in a white satin wedding dress where the photographic quality of the resultant reproduction is dependent mainly on the maintenance of proper contrast relationships in the highlight portions of the picture. A straight color reproduction of such a subject is generally too flat and lacking in tonal separation.

Such a tonal reproduction error may be eliminated or minimized by the proper use of a tone corrective mask. A mask of this type is often termed a highlight mask as the tone correction is generally applied only to the highlight portions of the reproduction. A highlight mask can be prepared by making a very high contrast underex-

posed negative from the color transparency. Its appearance is that of an underexposed and overdeveloped negative (Fig. 33.7). The highlight mask is applied to the color transparency and used during the exposure of the color correcting masks. The additional density applied to the color transparency in the highlight portions decreases or eliminates the contrast reduction in those areas that would take place when the color mask is applied to the transparency. The net result on the separation negatives is the same as if the color transparency did not show lower contrast in the toe region in its reproduction curve. Highlight masks are generally used in contact with color transparencies only when color correcting masks are being exposed (Fig. 33.8). The same principle may be applied to separation negatives or color negatives.[23]

Color Negatives. An integral tripack in which negative dye images are formed in the color development is called a color negative. There are several advantages to working with color negatives rather than positive color transparencies for reproduction purposes. While they are useless for viewing purposes, they do not suffer from the limited exposure latitude inherent in all reversal processes and supplementary masks can be incorporated in a color negative material that could not be used with a positive color transparency designed for viewing or projection.

Reproduction from a color negative involves exactly the same difficulties of optical separation discussed earlier (Fig. 33.9). In a color negative, however, silver or dye masks can be incorporated in a material itself so that further corrective steps in printing may be unnecessary. Shortly after the introduction of Kodacolor Film, a silver mask layer was incorporated in the emulsion. This positive mask was exposed during processing and recorded the

[23] Speck, *J. Phot. Soc. Amer.* **11**, 9 (1945).

(a)

(b)

Fig. 33.8. (a) Regular color correction mask made from color transparency,
(b) Color correction mask made from transparency with highlight mask.

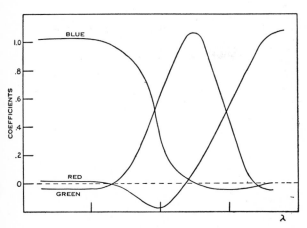

FIG. 33.11. Typical color mixture curves.

of colored couplers in the emulsion layers themselves.[24]

As discussed in Chapter 32, Ektacolor and Kodacolor films contain five dye images after color development. Three of these images, one in each layer, are the usual cyan, magenta, and yellow dye images required in a color negative. The center emulsion contains, besides the magenta negative image, a yellow positive dye image obtained from the residual yellow colored coupler of this emulsion layer. The yellow positive image supplies the proper amount of blue absorption at each density in the picture to bring the total blue absorption at any point to a constant value. If there is a large quantity of magenta dye formed

blue densities of the cyan and magenta dye images. A more complete solution to this problem has recently been announced by Eastman Kodak Company in the use

[24] Hanson and Vittum, *P.S.A. Journal* **13**, 94 (1947). Hanson, *J. Opt. Soc. Amer.* **40**, 166 (1950).

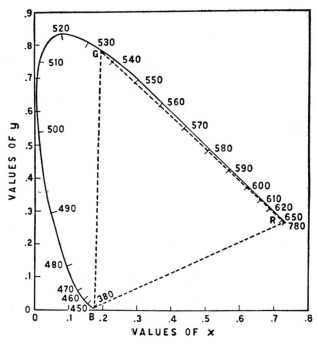

FIG. 33.12.A. Color gamut obtainable with positive amounts of the indicated homogeneous primaries shown inside dashed triangle. (Hardy, *J. Opt. Soc. Am.* **27**, 227 (1937).)

in a given area, there will be a small quantity of residual yellow dye. If very little magenta dye is formed, there will be a

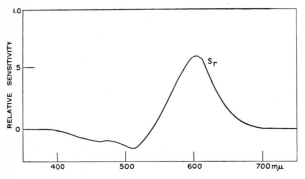

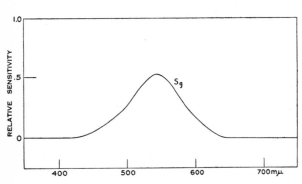

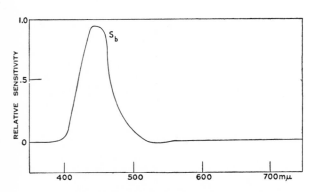

FIG. 33.12.B. Functions S_r, S_g and S_b represent the effective spectral sensitivities of the emulsions used in making separation negatives to control the homogeneous primaries of Fig. 33.12.A. (Hardy, *J. Opt. Soc. Am.* **27**, 227 (1937).)

large quantity of yellow colored coupler remaining in the emulsion layer. Since both magenta dyes and yellow dyes absorb blue, there will be a constant blue absorption throughout the center emulsion layer. This layer will therefore not show any image when examined by blue light (Fig. 33.10). This is exactly what is wanted when printing from a multi-layer film. The *effect* is the same as if the magenta dye were perfect (did not absorb blue light).

The same scheme is carried out to make the cyan dye effectively perfect when using Ektacolor or Kodacolor for color printing. The red positive dye image from the red colored coupler of the bottom emulsion supplies the required amount of blue and green absorption to make the cyan negative invisible when printing from the color negative with blue or green light. With colored couplers it is thus possible to obtain a reproduction from a color negative as good as would be obtained if the three dyes of the color negative were theoretically perfect. Colored couplers are only applicable to processes intended for printing rather than direct viewing or projection.

Developments in Color Theory. The foundation on which Maxwell based his original work on color reproduction was the three-color visual mechanism proposed by Young. The experimental visual color mixture curves presented by Maxwell and other workers were, for a time, thought to supply the clue as to the proper type of color analysis and synthesis necessary for satisfactory color reproduction. The mixture curves were obtained from experiments on the visual matching of spectral colors by means of three essentially monochromatic primary lights, colored red, green and blue. The exact colors chosen as primaries were not of vital importance because most colors could be matched by several suitable sets of primaries. Maxwell

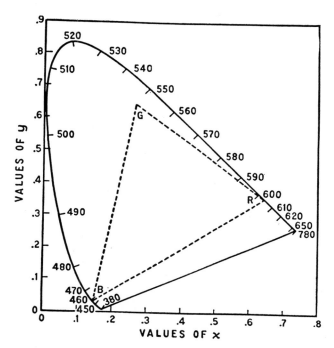

FIG. 33.12.C. Color gamut obtainable with positive amounts of nonhomogeneous primaries. (Hardy, *J. Opt. Soc. Am.* **27**, 227 (1937).)

assumed that the photographic emulsion integrated, by means of its sensitivity and the transmission of the filter employed, all the energy falling on it so that its color record was that shown by the positive portion of the appropriate color mixture curve. This viewpoint was strongly supported by Ives[25] among others, but was soon displaced by a purely objective view of color photography.

The subjective viewpoint, i.e., that the observer's visual system was of basic importance, was discarded because of the belief that spectral color mixture data were not applicable to color photography. Serious questions were raised as to the exposure summation by the photographic emulsion and it was proposed that, if the color records were to follow the color mixture

curves, the final synthesis should be made with monochromatic lights—a situation impractical in most cases. To be visually practical as to brilliance, the additive synthesis colors would have to cover the spectrum, each color being roughly one-third of the visible region. When such colors are used for color vision experiments, the mixture curves exhibit much larger negative portions than those in Fig. 33.11, which were obtained from monochromatic mixtures. Since the problem in color photography is to reproduce natural colors of wide spectral reflectances instead of spectral colors, it was considered advisable to base color reproduction on the practical color analysis filters which would merely determine the regions where the complementary colors were to print. A set of wide overlapping color curves were presented by Bull as the ideal requirements

[25] Ives, *J. Frank. Inst.* **125**, 345 (1888); **127**, 54 (1889).

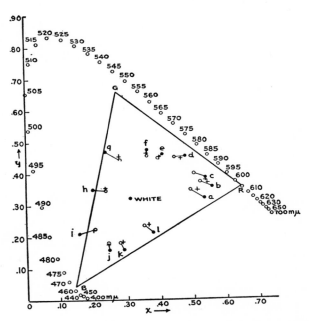

FIG. 33.13. Calculated chromaticity reproductions of : (*a*) Circled points, an additive process using spectral sensitivities proportional to the positive portions of the color mixture curves; (*b*) Crosses, an additive process in which masking is used to introduce first approximations to the effect of negative spectral sensitivities (MacAdam, *J. Opt. Soc. Am.* **28**, 399 (1938).)

for color analysis filters.[26] This objective viewpoint gained wide acceptance and directed most color work until 1930. The errors that were apparent in color reproduction[27] were readily explained as due to the unsatisfactory spectral absorptions of the subtractive printing colors and improvements in this direction were regarded as being of greater importance than further attempts at perfecting the analysis filters.

In 1935, Spencer[28] carried out an exhaustive series of experiments on the effect of various types of analysis color filters on the accuracy of subtractive color reproduction, and observed that the more closely the color filters came to corresponding with the "ideals" demanded by the objective

theory, the less satisfactory the reproduction of color. Spencer pointed out that the commercial filters in common usage (which were designed to approximate the ideals as closely as possible) gave better reproduction in that they did *not* fulfill the ideal requirements. Indeed, the commercial filters were somewhat closer to the positive portions of the color mixture curves. At about the same time an investigation by van Kreveld[29] established the additivity law for photographic exposures[30] as demanded by the original concept of Maxwell. Such discoveries, along with the rapid improvement in color materials, naturally led to a new series of investigations into the theoretical basis of color photography.

[26] Bull, *Phot. J.* **51**, 148 (1904) ; **52**, 448 (1905) ; **75**, 71, 258 (1935).

[27] *Phot. J.* **63**, 403 (1923).

[28] Spencer, *Phot. J.* **75**, 377 (1935).

[29] van Kreveld, *Z. wiss. Phot.* **32**, 222 (1934).

[30] Webb, *J. Opt. Soc. Amer.* **26**, 12 (1936). MacAdam, SMPTE **56**, 487 (1951).

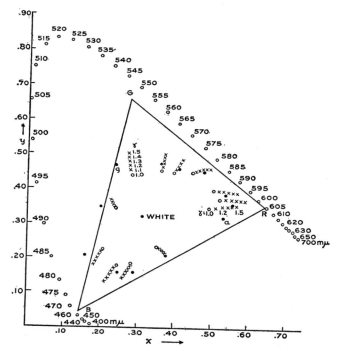

Fig. 33.14. Calculated chromaticity reproductions of additive process in which spectral sensitivities are proportional to the positive portions of the spectral sensitivity curves. Result of gamma changes from 10 to 1.5. (MacAdam, *J. Opt. Soc. Am.* **28**, 399 (1938).)

Theory of Additive Three-Color Photography. The theory of three-color photography has recently been under investigation by a number of workers, among them Schaefer and Ackermann, Neugebauer, Hardy and Wurzburg, Harrison and Horner, MacAdam, and Yule. These investigations emphasize the subjective theory of color photography in that they are based on the color-mixture data of the average human observer.

The goal of color reproduction is to obtain a visual match between the print and the original subject. This does not imply that the spectrophotometric energy distributions will be the same but merely that the visual appearance of the subject and reproduction will be identical. The visual identity of two colors occurs when they have proportional tristimulus values. Hardy [31] has shown that the effective spectral sensitivities (sensitivity of emulsions and filter transmissions) of the analysis system are directly related to the color mixture curves of the observer and the colors to be used in the synthesis. This follows from Hardy's equations.

$$X = X_r S_r + X_g S_g + X_b S_b,$$
$$Y = Y_r S_r + Y_g S_g + Y_b S_b,$$
$$Z = Z_r S_r + Z_g S_g + Z_b S_b,$$

where x, y, and z are the distribution functions of the standard observer adopted by the International Commission on Illumination, S_r, S_g, S_b are the effective spectral

[31] Hardy and Wurzburg, *J. Opt. Soc. Amer.* **27**, 227 (1937).

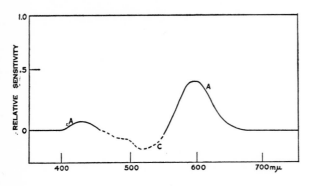

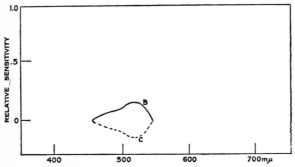

Fig. 33.15. Combination of negative and mask may yield an effective spectral sensitivity identical with S_r function of Fig. 33.14. (Hardy, *J. Opt. Soc. Am.* **27**, 227 (1937).)

sensitivities of the emulsion filter combinations employed, and x_r, y_r, z_r are dependent on the chromaticity of the synthesis colors. It is evident from these equations that the choice of a given set of additive synthesis colors pre-determines the effective spectral sensitivities to be employed when making the color analysis. This fact is clearly evident from calculations by Hardy showing the analysis characteristics required for different synthesis primaries. Fig. 33.12 shows the effective spectral sensitivity functions required for the widely different synthesis primaries shown in their respective chromaticity diagrams.

For additive processes, the choice of synthesis colors is based [32] on (1) the widest

possible gamut of colors that can be reproduced (taking into account the colors that are apt to be required), (2) the colors that will lead to the smallest practical negative regions for the analysis spectral sensitivities, and (3) the necessity in some cases (nonseparable screen plates, for example) of using the same colors for analysis and synthesis. The effective spectral sensitivity curves shown in Fig. 33.12 are typical of those generally obtained but are not of fundamental importance except for their own special synthesis colors. While the negative regions of such curves vary widely with the synthesis colors employed, the positive portions of the curves are always quite similar. The use of effective spectral sensitivities proportional to the positive portions of the color mixture curves [33] leads to quite accurate reproduction as shown in Fig. 33.13 (after MacAdam) where the reproductions of the various colors have been displaced towards the center of the chromaticity diagram. A slight increase in the reproduction gamma leads to some improvement of the color accuracy,[34] Fig. 33.14. The negative portions of the spectral sensitivity curves should be taken into account for the most accurate color reproduction. Hardy (*loc. cit.*) discussed several photographic methods that may be employed, one of them being a form of masking similar to that already discussed, although exposures and not log exposures (densities) should be subtracted by the mask.[35] In Fig. 33.15, for example, the positive and negative portions of the curve may be recorded on separate emulsions and a positive mask from the one recording the negative region registered in contact with the standard negative. The mask will subtract exposures. Special toe recording

[32] Harrison and Horner, *Phot. J.* **77**, 706 (1937). Schaefer and Ackermann, *Z. Physik* **8**, 55 (1927).

[33] MacAdam, *J. Opt. Soc. Amer.* **28**, 399 (1938).
[34] Wright, *Phot. J.* **80**, 25 (1940).
[35] Hardy and Wurzburg, *J. Opt. Soc. Amer.* **27**, 227 (1937).

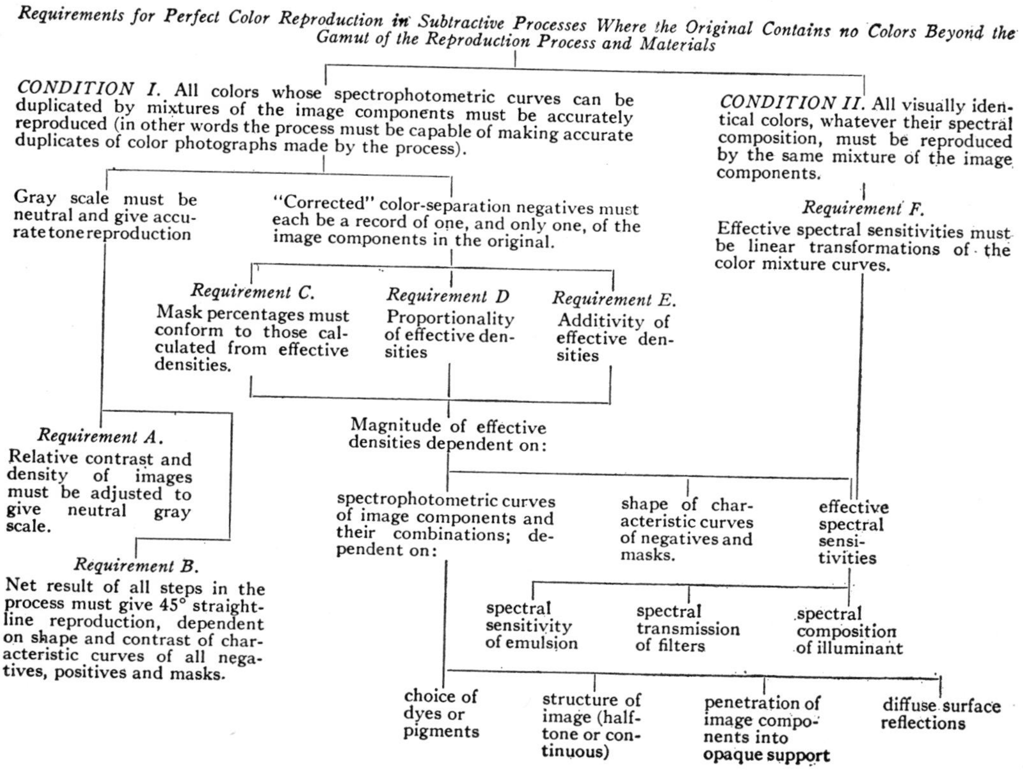

Requirements for Perfect Color Reproduction in Subtractive Processes Where the Original Contains no Colors Beyond the Gamut of the Reproduction Process and Materials

CONDITION I. All colors whose spectrophotometric curves can be duplicated by mixtures of the image components must be accurately reproduced (in other words the process must be capable of making accurate duplicates of color photographs made by the process).

CONDITION II. All visually identical colors, whatever their spectral composition, must be reproduced by the same mixture of the image components.

Requirement F.
Effective spectral sensitivities must be linear transformations of the color mixture curves.

Gray scale must be neutral and give accurate tone reproduction

"Corrected" color-separation negatives must each be a record of one, and only one, of the image components in the original.

Requirement C.
Mask percentages must conform to those calculated from effective densities.

Requirement D
Proportionality of effective densities

Requirement E.
Additivity of effective densities

Requirement A.
Relative contrast and density of images must be adjusted to give neutral gray scale.

Magnitude of effective densities dependent on:

Requirement B.
Net result of all steps in the process must give 45° straight-line reproduction, dependent on shape and contrast of characteristic curves of all negatives, positives and masks.

spectrophotometric curves of image components and their combinations; dependent on:

shape of characteristic curves of negatives and masks.

effective spectral sensitivities

spectral sensitivity of emulsion

spectral transmission of filters

spectral composition of illuminant

choice of dyes or pigments

structure of image (half-tone or continuous)

penetration of image components into opaque support

diffuse surface reflections

FIG. 33.16. Yule, *J. Opt. Soc. Am.* **28**, 419 (1938).

emulsions are necessary to allow exposures rather than densities to be subtracted. Other photographic and electrical means of recording the negative spectral sensitivities have been discussed elsewhere.[36]

Application to Subtractive Color Photography. An extension of the above theory to subtractive color reproduction is of the greatest importance because of the widespread commercial use of such processes. Subtractive printing colors offer special problems since they do not conform to the simple laws of additive color mixture. With a given cyan dye, for example, two deposits printed one above the other will not necessarily lead to a density equal to the sum of the two original densities and,

furthermore, the dominant wave length may shift with the dye concentration. Subtractive printing colors reacting in this manner are called "unstable" because their spectral characteristics are not constant. Since the effective spectral sensitivities to be employed in the color analysis are determined by the printing colors, the indicated sensitivities vary with changes in the printing color conditions and, therefore, cannot be established permanently. MacAdam[37] formulated an approximate law for subtractive color mixtures which made it possible to determine the effective spectral sensitivities necessary for a given set of subtractive colors. In the case of a

[36] *Brit. J. Phot.* **80**, 125, 141, 155 (1940).

[37] MacAdam, *J. Opt. Soc. Amer.* **28**, 466 (1938); **39**, 22 (1948). Clarkson and Vickerstaff, *Phot. J.* **88B**, 26 (1948).

particular set of acid imbibition dyes the negative regions of the effective spectral sensitivities were insignificant enough to be ignored (see Fig. 33.17). This is not always so, however, and appropriate addi-

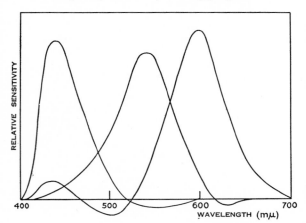

Fɪɢ. 33.17.   Relative spectral sensitivity curves. (MacAdam, *J. Opt. Soc. Am.* **28,** 466 (1938).)

tional masking might be required if the negative sensitivities are any greater than in this particular example.

MacAdam (*loc. cit.*) and Yule,[38] in an analysis of the factors affecting color reproduction (Fig. 33.16), showed that masking was essential in subtractive color reproduction to counteract the deficient spectral absorptions of the printing colors. The application of the sensitivities shown in Fig. 33.17, and the employment of three masks on the separation negatives resulted in excellent color reproduction. The masks for the red and blue separation negatives were obtained from the green separation negative, while the mask for the green record was obtained from the red separation negative.

It is evident that photographic color correction, or masking, discussed earlier in this chapter on the basis of its empirical use, really serves two purposes, both of which are based on sound theoretical considerations. In subtractive color reproduction masking is not only a corrective for the non-ideal spectral characteristics of the printing colors but it enables the reproduction to be based on imaginary primaries whose color mixture curves do not have appreciable negative portions.[39]

[38] Yule, *J. Opt. Soc. Amer.* **28,** 419, 481 (1938).

[39] Miller, *J. Opt. Soc. Amer.* **31,** 477 (1941).

AUTHOR INDEX